McGraw Hill Education

connectED.mcgraw-hill.com

STEM McGraw-Hill is committed to providing instructional materials in Science, Technology, Engineering, and Mathematics (STEM) that give all students a solid foundation, one that prepares them for college and careers in the 21st century.

Send all inquiries to:
McGraw-Hill Education
STEM Learning Solutions Center
8787 Orion Place
Columbus, OH 43240

ISBN: 978-0-07-665692-9
MHID: 0-07-665692-6

Printed in the United States of America.

6 7 8 9 RMN 18 17 16

CONTENTS IN BRIEF

Organized by Focal Areas

TEKS Focal Area

Mathematical Processes

7.1 Mathematical Process Handbook

TEKS Focal Area

Number and Operations

7.2, 7.3 **1** Rational Numbers

TEKS Focal Area

Proportionality

7.4 **2** Proportional Relationships

7.4 **3** Apply Proportionality to Percent

7.5 **4** Apply Proportionality to Geometry

7.6 **5** Apply Proportionality to Probability

TEKS Focal Area

Expressions, Equations, and Relationships

7.7 **6** Multiple Representations of Linear Relationships

7.10, 7.11 **7** Equations and Inequalities

7.8, 7.9 **8** Develop Geometry with Algebra

TEKS Focal Area

Measurement and Data

7.12 **9** Statistics and Sampling

TEKS Focal Area

Personal Financial Literacy

7.13 **10** Personal Financial Literacy

Problem-Solving Projects

Your assignment's due tomorrow...

but your book is in your locker!

NOW WHAT?

Even in crunch time, with ConnectED, we've got you covered!

With ConnectED, you have instant access to all of your study materials—anytime, anywhere. From homework materials to study guides—it's all in one place and just a click away. ConnectED even allows you to collaborate with your classmates and use mobile apps to make studying easy.

Resources built for you—available 24/7:

- Your eBook available wherever you are
- Personal Tutors and Self-Check Quizzes whenever you need them
- An Online Calendar with all of your due dates
- eFlashcard App to make studying easy
- A message center to stay in touch

Reimagine Learning

Go Online!

connectED.mcgraw-hill.com

Vocab

Learn about new vocabulary words.

Watch

Watch animations and videos.

Tutor

See and hear a teacher explain how to solve problems.

Tools

Explore concepts with virtual manipulatives.

Check

Check your progress.

eHelp

Get targeted homework help.

Worksheets

Access practice worksheets.

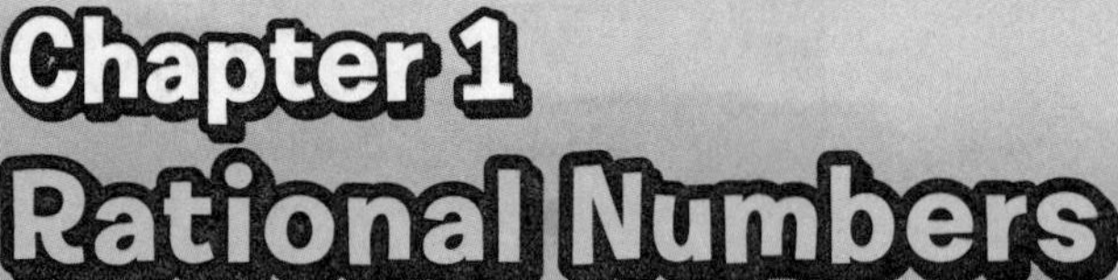

Chapter 1 Rational Numbers

What Tools Do You Need?	20		
When Will You Use This?	21		
Are You Ready?	22		
Foldable	23		
	25	**Hands-On Lab 1-a:** Model Rational Numbers	7.2
	27	**Lesson 1** Terminating and Repeating Decimals	7.2
	35	**Hands-On Lab 2-a:** Sets of Rational Numbers	7.2
	37	**Lesson 2** Relationships Between Sets of Rational Numbers	7.2
	45	**Lesson 3** Add and Subtract Integers	7.3(A), 7.3(B)
	53	**Lesson 4** Multiply and Divide Integers	7.3(A), 7.3(B)
	61	**Focus on Mathematical Processes:** The Four-Step Plan	7.1(B), 7.3(A)
Mid-Chapter Check	64		
	65	**Hands-On Lab 5-a:** Use Models to Add and Subtract Rational Numbers	7.3(A)
	69	**Lesson 5** Fluently Add and Subtract Rational Numbers: Like Fractions	7.3(A), 7.3(B)
	77	**Lesson 6** Fluently Add and Subtract Rational Numbers: Unlike Fractions	7.3(A), 7.3(B)
	85	**Lesson 7** Fluently Add and Subtract Rational Numbers: Mixed Numbers	7.3(A), 7.3(B)
	93	**Lesson 8** Fluently Multiply Rational Numbers	7.3(A), 7.3(B)
	101	**Lesson 9** Fluently Divide Rational Numbers	7.3(A), 7.3(B)
	109	**21st Century Career** Fashion Designer	7.1(A), 7.3(A), 7.3(B)
Chapter Review	111		
Chapter Reflect	114		

TEKS

Go to page 109 to learn about a 21st Century Career in **Fashion Design!**

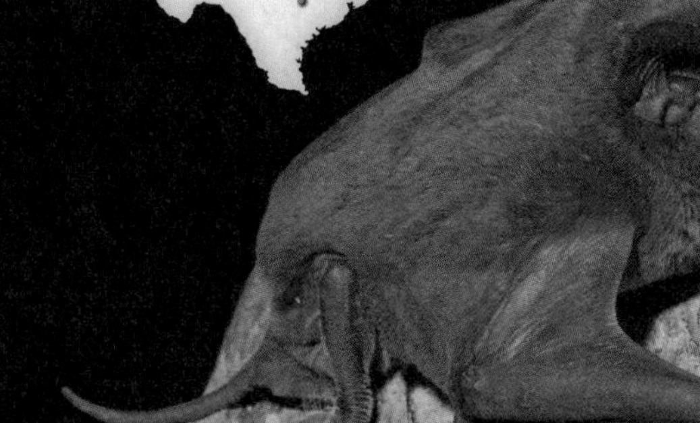

Chapter 2 Proportional Relationships

What Tools Do You Need? 116
When Will You Use This? 117
Are You Ready? 118
Foldable 119

Page	Title	TEKS
121	**Hands-On Lab 1-a:** Ratios and Rates	7.4(B), 7.4(D)
123	**Lesson 1** Unit Rates	7.4(B), 7.4(D)
131	**Lesson 2** Complex Fractions and Unit Rates	7.4(B), 7.4(D)
139	**Lesson 3** Convert Unit Rates	7.4(B), 7.4(D)
147	**Lesson 4** Proportional and Nonproportional Relationships	7.4(D)
155	**Focus on Mathematical Processes:** Draw a Diagram	7.1(B), 7.4(B), 7.4(D)
158	**Mid-Chapter Check**	
159	**Lesson 5** Graph Proportional Relationships	7.4(D), 7.4(A)
167	**Hands-On Lab 5-b:** Model Proportional Relationships	7.4(D)
169	**Lesson 6** Solve Proportional Relationships	7.4(D)
177	**Lesson 7** Convert Between Systems	7.4(E), 7.3(A)
185	**Hands-On Lab 8-a:** Rate of Change	7.4(A), 7.4(D)
187	**Lesson 8** Constant Rate of Change	7.4(A), 7.4(D)
195	**Lesson 9** Constant of Proportionality	7.4(C), 7.4(A)
203	**21st Century Career** Biomechanical Engineering	7.1(A), 7.4(A), 7.4(D)

Chapter Review 205
Chapter Reflect 208

Go to page 203 to learn about a 21st Century Career in **Biomechanical Engineering!**

Chapter 3
Apply Proportionality to Percent

What Tools Do You Need? 210
When Will You Use This? 211
Are You Ready? 212
Foldable 213

Page		TEKS
215	**Hands-On Lab 1-a:** Percent Diagrams	7.4(D)
219	**Lesson 1** Percent of a Number	7.4(D)
227	**Lesson 2** Percent and Estimation	7.4(D)
235	**Hands-On Lab 3-a:** Find Percents	7.4(D)
237	**Lesson 3** The Percent Proportion	7.4(D)
245	**Lesson 4** The Percent Equation	7.4(D)
253	**Focus on Mathematical Processes:** Determine Reasonable Answers	7.1(B), 7.4(D)
256	**Mid-Chapter Check**	
257	**Hands-On Lab 5-a:** Model Percent of Change	7.4(D)
259	**Lesson 5** Percent of Change	7.4(D)
267	**Lesson 6** Financial Literacy: Sales Tax, Tips, and Markup	7.4(D)
275	**Lesson 7** Discount	7.4(D)
283	**Lesson 8** Financial Literacy: Simple Interest	7.4(D), 7.13(E)
291	**Spreadsheet Lab 8-b:** Compound Interest	7.4(D), 7.13(E)
293	**21st Century Career** Video Game Design	7.1(A), 7.4(D)

Chapter Review 295
Chapter Reflect 298

Go to page 293 to learn about a 21st Century Career in **Video Game Design!**

Chapter 4
Apply Proportionality to Geometry

What Tools Do You Need? 300
When Will You Use This? 301
Are You Ready? 302
Foldable 303

Page		TEKS
305	**Hands-On Lab 1-a:** Investigate Online Maps and Scale Drawings	7.5(C)
309	**Lesson 1** Scale Drawings	7.5(C)
317	**Hands-On Lab 2-a:** Similar Triangles	7.5(A), 7.5(C)
321	**Lesson 2** Critical Attributes of Similar Figures	7.5(A), 7.5(C)
329	**Focus on Mathematical Processes:** Make a Model	7.1(B), 7.5(C)
332	**Mid-Chapter Check**	
333	**Hands-On Lab 3-a:** Changes in Perimeter and Area	7.5(A), 7.5(C)
335	**Lesson 3** Changes in Dimension	7.5(C), 7.5(A)
343	**Hands-On Lab 4-a:** Model Circumference	7.8(C), 7.5(B)
345	**Lesson 4** Circumference	7.5(B), 7.9(B)
353	**21st Century Career** Roller Coaster Design	7.1(A), 7.5(C)

Chapter Review 355
Chapter Reflect 358

Go to page 353 to learn about a 21st Century Career in
Roller Coaster Design!

Chapter 5
Apply Proportionality to Probability

What Tools Do You Need? 360
When Will You Use This? 361
Are You Ready? 362
Foldable 363

Page	Title	TEKS
365	**Hands-On Lab 1-a:** Sample Spaces	7.6(A)
367	**Lesson 1** Probability of Simple Events	7.6(E), 7.6(A)
375	**Hands-On Lab 2-a:** Make Predictions	7.6(H), 7.6(C)
379	**Lesson 2** Theoretical and Experimental Probability	7.6(I), 7.6(D)
387	**Hands-On Lab 2-b:** Experimental Data	7.6(C), 7.6(I)
391	**Lesson 3** Probability of Compound Events	7.6(I), 7.6(D)
399	**Focus on Mathematical Processes:** Act It Out	7.1(B), 7.6(H)

Mid-Chapter Check 402

Page	Title	TEKS
403	**Virtual Manipulative Lab 4-a:** Simulate Simple Events	7.6(B)
405	**Lesson 4** Simulations	7.6(B)
413	**Hands-On Lab 4-b:** Simulate Compound Events	7.6(B)
417	**Hands-On Lab 5-a:** Independent and Dependent Events	7.6(B), 7.6(I)
419	**Lesson 5** Independent and Dependent Events	7.6(D), 7.6(A)
427	**21st Century Career** Pediatricians	7.1(A), 7.6(I)

Chapter Review 429
Chapter Reflect 432

Go to page 427 to learn about a 21st Century Career in **Medicine!**

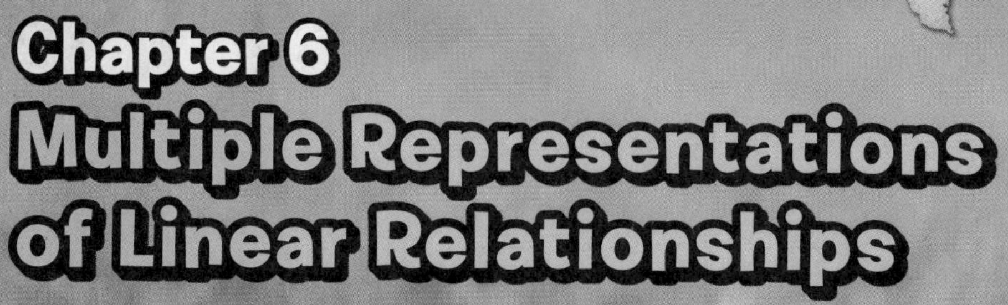

Chapter 6 Multiple Representations of Linear Relationships

What Tools Do You Need? 434
When Will You Use This? 435
Are You Ready? 436
Foldable 437

Page		TEKS
439	**Hands-On Lab 1-a:** Linear Relationships	7.7
441	**Lesson 1** Identify Linear Relationships	7.7
449	**Lesson 2** Equations of Linear Relationships	7.7
457	**Focus on Mathematical Processes:** Make a Table	7.1(B), 7.7
460	**Mid-Chapter Check**	
461	**Lesson 3** Slope	7.7
469	**Graphing Technology Lab 4-a:** Nonproportional Linear Relationships	7.7
473	**Lesson 4** Slope-Intercept Form	7.7
481	**Lesson 5** Write Equations from Tables and Graphs	7.7
489	**Graphing Technology Lab 5-b:** Family of Linear Relationships	7.7
491	**21st Century Career** Shark Scientist	7.1(A), 7.7

Chapter Review 493
Chapter Reflect 496

Go to page 491 to learn about a 21st Century Career in **Animal Conservation!**

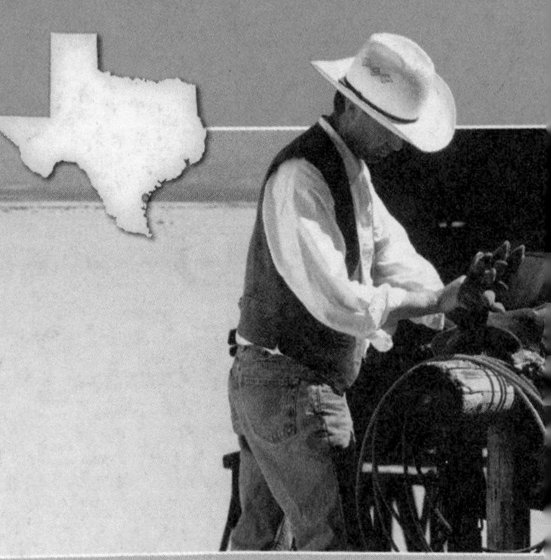

Chapter 7 Equations and Inequalities

What Tools Do You Need? 498
When Will You Use This? 499
Are You Ready? 500
Foldable 501

Page	Title	TEKS
503	**Lesson 1** Equations and Inequalities	7.11(B)
511	**Lesson 2** Solve One-Step Equations	7.10(A)
519	**Hands-On Lab 3-a:** Model and Solve Equations with Rational Coefficients	7.11(A)
521	**Lesson 3** Solve Equations with Rational Coefficients	7.10(A)
529	**Hands-On Lab 4-a:** Model and Solve Two-Step Equations	7.11(A), 7.10(A)
533	**Lesson 4** Solve and Write Two-Step Equations	7.11(A), 7.10(B)
541	**Focus on Mathematical Processes:** Work Backward	7.1(B), 7.10(A)
544	**Mid-Chapter Check**	
545	**Hands-On Lab 5-a:** Model Two-Step Equations using the Distributive Property	7.11(A), 7.10(C)
549	**Lesson 5** Solve Two-Step Equations using the Distributive Property	7.11(A), 7.10(C)
557	**Lesson 6** Solve One-Step Inequalities	7.10(A)
565	**Hands-On Lab 7-a:** Model and Solve Two-Step Inequalities	7.11(A), 7.10(C)
569	**Lesson 7** Solve and Write Two-Step Inequalities	7.11(A), 7.10(A)
577	**21st Century Career** Veterinary Technician	7.1(A), 7.11(A)

Chapter Review 579
Chapter Reflect 582

Go to page 577 to learn about a 21st Century Career in
Veterinary Medicine!

Chapter 8 Develop Geometry with Algebra

What Tools Do You Need? 584
When Will You Use This? 585
Are You Ready? 586
Foldable 587

TEKS

589 **Lesson 1** Angle Relationships 7.11(C)

597 **Lesson 2** Complementary and Supplementary Angles 7.11(C)

605 **Geometry Software Lab 3-a:** Angles in Triangles 7.11(C)
609 **Lesson 3** Sum of Angles in Triangles 7.11(C)

617 **Hands-On Lab 4-a:** Model Area of Circles 7.8(C), 7.9(B)
619 **Lesson 4** Area of Circles 7.8(C), 7.9(B)

627 **Lesson 5** Area of Composite Figures 7.9(C)

635 **Focus on Mathematical Processes:** Solve a Simpler Problem 7.1(B), 7.9(C)

Mid-Chapter Check 638

639 **Lesson 6** Volume of Prisms 7.9(A)

647 **Hands-On Lab 7-a:** Volume Relationships of Prisms and Pyramids 7.8(A), 7.9(A)
651 **Lesson 7** Volume of Pyramids 7.9(A), 7.8(B)

659 **Hands-On Lab 8-a:** Nets of Rectangular Prisms 7.9(D)
663 **Lesson 8** Surface Area of Rectangular Prisms 7.9(D)

671 **Hands-On Lab 9-a:** Nets of Triangular Prism 7.9(D)
673 **Lesson 9** Surface Area of Triangular Prisms 7.9(D)
681 **Hands-On Lab 9-b:** Relate Surface Area and Volume 7.9(D), 7.9(A)

685 **Lesson 10** Surface Area of Pyramids 7.9(D)

693 **21st Century Career** Landscape Architect 7.1(A), 7.9(B)

Chapter Review 695
Chapter Reflect 698

Go to page 693 to learn about a 21st Century Career in **Landscape Architecture!**

Chapter 9 Statistics and Sampling

What Tools Do You Need? 700
When Will You Use This? 701
Are You Ready? 702
Foldable 703

Page	Title	TEKS
705	**Lesson 1** Bar Graphs and Dot Plots	7.6(G)
713	**Hands-On Lab 2-a:** Connect Bar Graphs to Circle Graphs	7.6(G)
715	**Lesson 2** Circle Graphs	7.6(G)
723	**Lesson 3** Make Predictions about a Population	7.6(F), 7.6(G)
731	**Lesson 4** Unbiased and Biased Samples	7.6(F), 7.12(B)
739	**Hands-On Lab 4-b:** Multiple Samples of Data	7.6(F), 7.12(B)
743	**Focus on Mathematical Processes:** Use a Graph	7.1(B), 7.6(G)
746	**Mid-Chapter Check**	
747	**Lesson 5** Misleading Graphs and Statistics	7.6(G)
755	**Hands-On Lab 6-a:** Collect Data	7.12(A), 7.12(C)
757	**Lesson 6** Compare Populations	7.12(A), 7.12(C)
767	**Hands-On Lab 6-b:** Visual Overlap of Data Distributions	7.12(A), 712(C)
769	**Lesson 7** Select an Appropriate Display	7.6(G)
777	**21st Century Career** Market Research Analyst	7.1(A), 7.6(F)

Chapter Review 779
Chapter Reflect 782

Go to page 777 to learn about a 21st Century Career in **Market Research!**

Chapter 10 Personal Financial Literacy

What Tools Do You Need? 784
When Will You Use This? 785
Are You Ready? 786

TEKS

787 **Lesson 1** Sales and Income Tax 7.13(A)

791 **Lesson 2** Personal and Family Budgets 7.13(B), 7.13(D)

795 **Lesson 3** Assets and Liabilities 7.13(C)

799 **Lesson 4** Simple and Compound Interest 7.13(E)

803 **Lesson 5** Shopping: Monetary Incentives 7.13(F)

Chapter Review 807
Chapter Reflect 810

Texas Essential Knowledge and Skills, Grade 7

Track Your TEKS Progress

The knowledge and skills that you will learn this year are listed on these pages. Throughout the year, your teacher will ask you to rate how confident you feel about your knowledge of each one. Don't worry if you have no clue **before** you learn about them. Your will rate your knowledge before and after you learn them. Your teacher will provide you with more instructions. Watch how your knowledge and skills grow as the year progresses!

☹ I have no clue. 😐 I've heard of it. ☺ I know it!

7.1 Mathematical Process Standards		Before ☹	Before 😐	Before ☺	After ☹	After 😐	After ☺
The student uses mathematical processes to acquire and demonstrate mathematical understanding. The student is expected to:							
7.1(A)	Apply mathematics to problems arising in everyday life, society, and the workplace;						
7.1(B)	Use a problem-solving model that incorporates analyzing given information, formulating a plan or strategy, determining a solution, justifying the solution, and evaluating the problem-solving process and the reasonableness of the solution;						
7.1(C)	Select tools, including real objects, manipulatives, paper and pencil, and technology as appropriate, and techniques, including mental math, estimation, and number sense as appropriate, to solve problems;						
7.1(D)	Communicate mathematical ideas, reasoning, and their implications using multiple representations, including symbols, diagrams, graphs, and language as appropriate;						
7.1(E)	Create and use representations to organize, record, and communicate mathematical ideas;						
7.1(F)	Analyze mathematical relationships to connect and communicate mathematical ideas; and						
7.1(G)	Display, explain, and justify mathematical ideas and arguments using precise mathematical language in written or oral communication.						

7.2 Number and Operations	Before ☹	Before 😐	Before ☺	After ☹	After 😐	After ☺
The student applies mathematical process standards to represent and use rational numbers in a variety of forms. The student is expected to:						
Extend previous knowledge of sets and subsets using a visual representation to describe relationships between sets of rational numbers.						

7.3 Number and Operations		☹	😐	☺	☹	😐	☺
The student applies mathematical process standards to add, subtract, multiply, and divide while solving problems and justifying solutions. The student is expected to:							
7.3(A)	Add, subtract, multiply, and divide rational numbers fluently; and						
7.3(B)	Apply and extend previous understandings of operations to solve problems using addition, subtraction, multiplication, and division of rational numbers;						

7.4 Proportionality		☹	😐	☺	☹	😐	☺
The student applies mathematical process standards to represent and solve problems involving proportional relationships. The student is expected to:							
7.4(A)	Represent constant rates of change in mathematical and real-world problems given pictorial, tabular, verbal, numeric, graphical, and algebraic representations, including $d = rt$;						
7.4(B)	Calculate unit rates from rates in mathematical and real-world problems;						
7.4(C)	Determine the constant of proportionality. $\left(k = \frac{y}{x}\right)$ within mathematical and real-world problems;						
7.4(D)	Solve problems involving ratios, rates, and percents, including multi-step problems involving percent increase and percent decrease, and financial literacy problems; and						
7.4(E)	Convert between measurement systems, including the use of proportions and the use of unit rates.						

7.5 Proportionality	Before ☹	Before 😐	Before ☺	After ☹	After 😐	After ☺
The student applies mathematical process standards to use geometry to describe or solve problems involving proportional relationships. The student is expected to:						
7.5(A) Generalize the critical attributes of similarity, including ratios within and between similar shapes;						
7.5(B) Describe π as the ratio of the circumference of a circle to its diameter; and						
7.5(C) Solve mathematical and real-world problems involving similar shapes and scale drawings.						

7.6 Proportionality	Before ☹	Before 😐	Before ☺	After ☹	After 😐	After ☺
The student applies mathematical process standards to use probability and statistics to describe or solve problems involving proportional relationships. The student is expected to:						
7.6(A) Represent sample spaces for simple and compound events using lists and tree diagrams; and						
7.6(B) Select and use different simulations to represent simple and compound events with and without technology.						
7.6(C) Make predictions and determine solutions using experimental data for simple and compound events;						
7.6(D) Make predictions and determine solutions using theoretical probability for simple and compound events;						
7.6(E) Find the probabilities of a simple event and its complement and describe the relationship between the two;						
7.6(F) Use data from a random sample to make inferences about a population;						
7.6(G) Solve problems using data represented in bar graphs, dot plots, and circle graphs, including part-to-whole and part-to-part comparisons and equivalents;						
7.6(H) Solve problems using qualitative and quantitative predictions and comparisons from simple experiments; and						
7.6(I) Determine experimental and theoretical probabilities related to simple and compound events using data and sample spaces.						

7.7 Expressions, Equations, and Relationships		Before			After	
The student applies mathematical process standards to represent linear relationships using multiple representations. The student is expected to:						
Represent linear relationships using verbal descriptions, tables, graphs, and equations that simplify to the form $y = mx + b$.						

7.8 Expressions, Equations, and Relationships							
The student applies mathematical process standards to develop geometric relationships with volume. The student is expected to:							
7.8(A)	Model the relationship between the volume of a rectangular prism and a rectangular pyramid having both congruent bases and heights and connect that relationship to the formulas;						
7.8(B)	Explain verbally and symbolically the relationship between the volume of a triangular prism and a triangular pyramid having both congruent bases and heights and connect that relationship to the formulas; and						
7.8(C)	Use models to determine the approximate formulas for the circumference and area of a circle and connect the models to the actual formulas.						

7.9 Expressions, Equations, and Relationships		Before 🙁	Before 😐	Before 🙂	After 🙁	After 😐	After 🙂
The student applies mathematical process standards to solve geometric problems. The student is expected to:							
7.9(A)	Solve problems involving the volume of rectangular prisms, triangular prisms, rectangular pyramids, and triangular pyramids;						
7.9(B)	Determine the circumference and area of circles;						
7.9(C)	Determine the area of composite figures containing combinations of rectangles, squares, parallelograms, trapezoids, triangles, semicircles, and quarter circles; and						
7.9(D)	Solve problems involving the lateral and total surface area of a rectangular prism, rectangular pyramid, triangular prism, and triangular pyramid by determining the area of the shape's net.						

7.10 Expressions, Equations, and Relationships		Before 🙁	Before 😐	Before 🙂	After 🙁	After 😐	After 🙂
The student applies mathematical process standards to use one-variable equations and inequalities to represent situations. The student is expected to:							
7.10(A)	Write one-variable, two-step equations and inequalities to represent constraints or conditions within problems;						
7.10(B)	Represent solutions for one-variable, two-step equations and inequalities on number lines; and						
7.10(C)	Write a corresponding real-world problem given a one-variable, two-step equation or inequality.						

7.11 Expressions, Equations, and Relationships		Before ☹	Before 😐	Before ☺	After ☹	After 😐	After ☺
The student applies mathematical process standards to solve one-variable equations and inequalities. The student is expected to:							
7.11(A)	Model and solve one-variable, two-step equations and inequalities;						
7.11(B)	Determine if the given value(s) make(s) one-variable, two-step equations and inequalities true; and						
7.11(C)	Write and solve equations using geometry concepts, including the sum of the angles in a triangle, and angle relationships.						

7.12 Measurement and Data		☹	😐	☺	☹	😐	☺
The student applies mathematical process standards to use statistical representations to analyze data. The student is expected to:							
7.12(A)	Compare two groups of numeric data using comparative dot plots or box plots by comparing their shapes, centers, and spreads;						
7.12(B)	Use data from a random sample to make inferences about a population; and						
7.12(C)	Compare two populations based on data in random samples from these populations, including informal comparative inferences about differences between the two populations.						

7.13 Personal Financial Literacy		Before			After		
		☹	😐	☺	☹	😐	☺
The student applies mathematical process standards to develop an economic way of thinking and problem solving useful in one's life as a knowledgeable consumer and investor. The student is expected to:							
7.13(A)	Calculate the sales tax for a given purchase and calculate income tax for earned wages;						
7.13(B)	Identify the components of a personal budget, including income, planned savings for college, retirement, and emergencies, taxes, and fixed and variable expenses, and calculate what percentage of each category comprises of the total budget;						
7.13(C)	Create and organize a financial assets and liabilities record and construct a net worth statement;						
7.13(D)	Use a family budget estimator to determine the minimum household budget and average hourly wage needed for a family to meet its basic needs in the student's city or another large city nearby;						
7.13(E)	Calculate and compare simple interest and compound interest earnings; and						
7.13(F)	Analyze and compare monetary incentives, including sales, rebates, and coupons.						

Mathematical Processes Handbook

Texas Essential Knowledge and Skills

Targeted TEKS

7.1 The student uses mathematical processes to acquire and demonstrate mathematical understanding.

Mathematical Processes

7.1, 7.1(A), 7.1(B), 7.1(C), 7.1(D), 7.1(E), 7.1(F), 7.1(G)

Essential Question

WHAT processes help me explore and explain mathematics?

What You'll Learn

MP The mathematical process standards listed below will help you to become a successful problem solver and to use math effectively in your daily life. Throughout this handbook, you will learn about each of these mathematical processes and how they are integrated in the chapters and lessons of this book.

Focus on Mathematical Process A 3

MP **Apply Math to the Real World** Apply mathematics to problems arising in everyday life, society, and the workplace.

Focus on Mathematical Process B 5

MP **Use a Problem-Solving Model** Use a problem-solving model that incorporates analyzing given information, formulating a plan or strategy, determining a solution, justifying the solution, and evaluating the problem-solving process and the reasonableness of the solution.

Focus on Mathematical Process C 7

MP **Select Tools and Techniques** Select tools, including real objects, manipulatives, paper and pencil, and technology as appropriate, and techniques, including mental math, estimation, and number sense as appropriate, to solve problems.

Focus on Mathematical Process D 9

MP **Use Multiple Representations** Communicate mathematical ideas, reasoning, and their implications using multiple representations, including symbols, diagrams, graphs, and language as appropriate.

Focus on Mathematical Process E 11

MP **Organize Ideas** Create and use representations to organize, record, and communicate mathematical ideas.

Focus on Mathematical Process F 13

MP **Analyze Relationships** Analyze mathematical relationships to connect and communicate mathematical ideas.

Focus on Mathematical Process G 15

MP **Justify Arguments** Display, explain, and justify mathematical ideas and arguments using precise mathematical language in written or oral communication.

Apply the Mathematical Processes to Every Lesson

Use the chart at the beginning of each lesson throughout this text to select which processes you used to solve a particular problem.

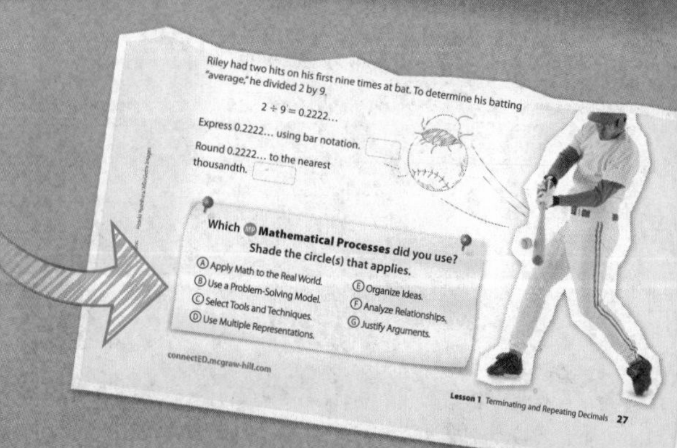

Apply Math to the Real World

I need to double this recipe. How much flour do I need?

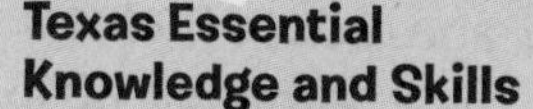
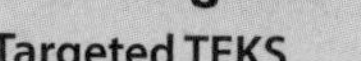

Texas Essential Knowledge and Skills

Targeted TEKS

7.1(A) Apply mathematics to problems arising in everyday life, society, and the workplace.

It may not always seem like it, but the concepts you will learn this year in class can be used in everyday life. Suppose you want to double the ingredients from the recipe below. Well, NOW you are going to use some of what you learned in class.

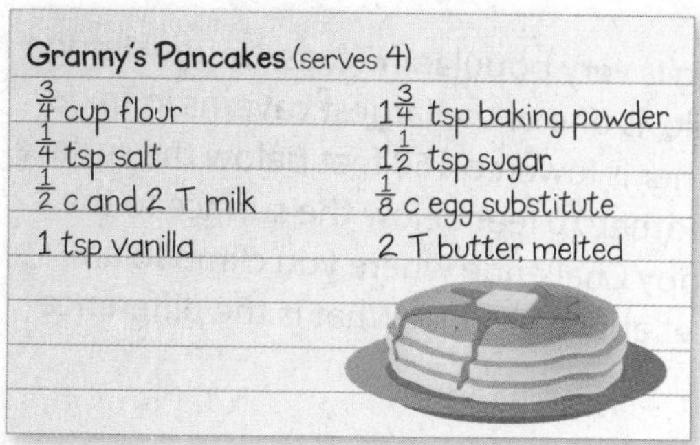

1. What skill(s) will you use to see how much of each ingredient you would use if you were to double the recipe?

2. You planned for eight people to come for a pancake breakfast, but just found out that 10 people are coming! The recipe serves 4. What will you need to do to determine the amount of each ingredient to serve 10 people?

3. Complete the recipe card so that it serves 10 people. Is it appropriate to round any of the ingredients? Explain.

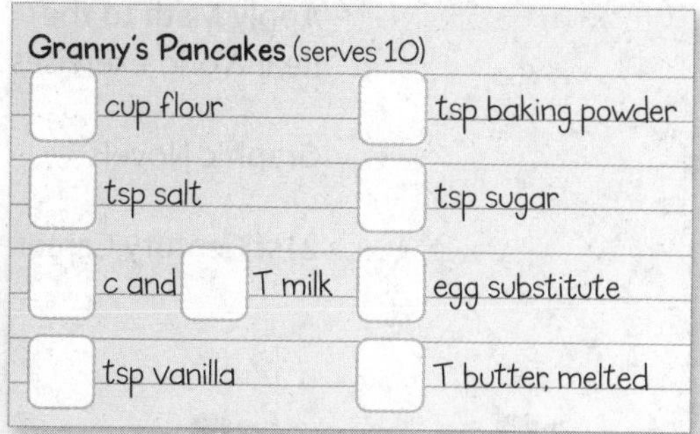

It's Your Turn!

List the skills needed to solve each exercise. Then solve.

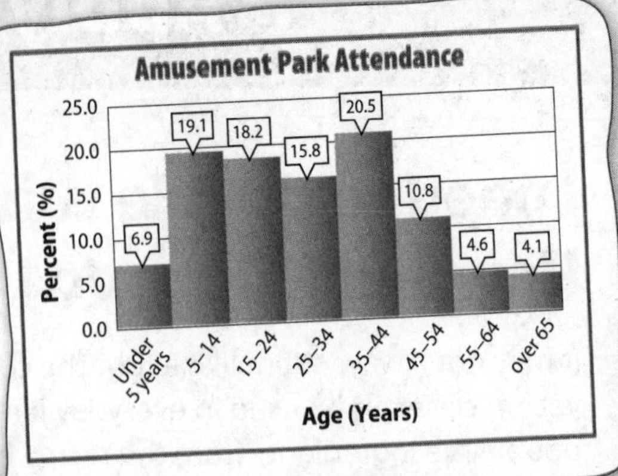

4. The histogram shows the percent of people in different age groups that recently attended an amusement park. A total of 1.045 million people attended. How many of them were less than 25 years of age?

____

____

5. Cave exploration or spelunking is very popular in Texas. Natural Bridge Caverns, outside of San Antonio, is one of the largest caverns in Texas. On one of the tours, your brother is lowered 160 feet below the surface by rope. Then he continues another 70 feet below the surface to the Fault Room. You take the Canopy Challenge where you climb to an adventure course that is 60 feet above ground. What is the difference between the elevations?

____

____

6. You and your family are traveling to a football game. You and your mother leave at 8:00 A.M. Your dad needs to wait for your sister to get home from dance practice, so he leaves at 9:30 A.M. If your mother drives at an average rate of 50 miles per hour, and your dad drives at an average rate of 65 miles per hour, will he pass her before they get to the game or not? Suppose the game is 205 miles away. Who will get there first?

____

____

Find it in Your Book!

MP Apply Math to the Real World

Look at Chapter 1. Write the page number(s) where you find these examples of Mathematical Process A.

__________ Apply Math to the Real World exercises

__________ Graphic Novels

__________ 21st Century Career

Use a Problem-Solving Model

How do I begin solving this problem?

Jared will paint a large wall in his house. The wall is 32 feet long and 12 foot high. There are two windows, each with dimensions 6 feet by 5 feet. A gallon of paint covers about 350 square feet. How many gallons of paint will he need to paint two coats of paint on the wall?

You can use the four-step problem-solving plan. Let's study each step.

Texas Essential Knowledge and Skills

Targeted TEKS

7.1(B) Use a problem-solving model that incorporates analyzing given information, formulating a plan or strategy, determining a solution, justifying the solution, and evaluating the problem-solving process and the reasonableness of the solution.

1. **Analyze** Read the problem. Circle the information that you are given and underline what you are trying to determine.

2. **Plan** Decide on an appropriate strategy to use. Some strategies are listed below.

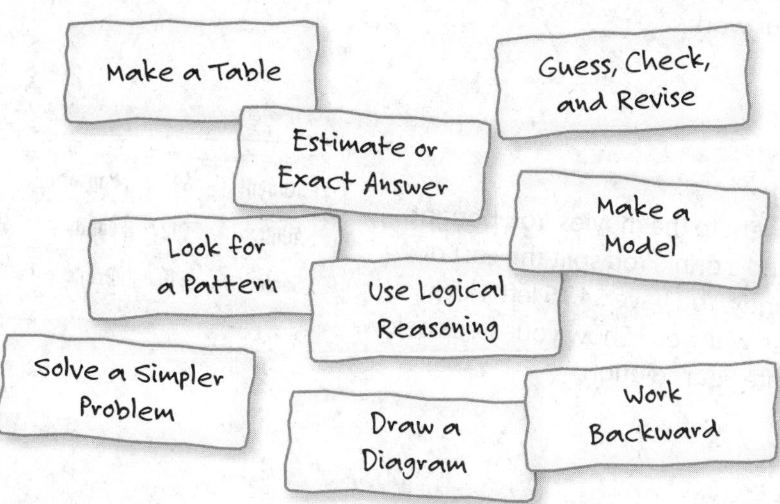

What strategy will you use to solve the problem above?

3. **Solve** Apply your strategy to solve the problem.

4. **Justify and Evaluate** Determine if your solution is accurate and makes sense. Explain.

It's Your Turn!

Solve each problem by using the four-step problem-solving model.

5. Texas ranks #1 for the number of farms in the country. There are 247,500 farms that take up 130,400,000 acres which is about $\frac{3}{4}$ of the area of the entire state. About how many acres are not made up of farmland? Round your answer to the nearest thousand.

Analyze Circle the information you know and underline what you are trying to determine. Is there any information you will not use?

Plan What strategy will you use to solve this problem?

Solve Solve the problem. Show your steps below. What is the solution?

Justify and Evaluate Does your answer make sense? Can you solve the problem another way to check your work?

Student	$9	Popcorn	$6.50
Adult	$12	Candy	$5
Senior	$10	Drink	$4.50

6. You and a friend went to the movies. You bought a student ticket and a drink. You split the cost of popcorn and a candy. You have $4.75 left. How much did you take with you? Show your steps below. Justify and evaluate your solution.

Find it in Your Book!

MP Use a Problem-Solving Model

Look at Chapter 1. Write the page number(s) where you find these examples of Mathematical Process B.

_____ Use a Problem-Solving Model exercises

_____ Multi-Step Problem-Solving exercises

_____ Focus on Mathematical Processes lesson

Select Tools and Techniques

Which tools would you use to finish this piece of artwork?

You might need paints, a brush, or maybe charcoal or colored pencils. You might also need some art training! So, let's investigate how to choose and use the proper tools and techniques to solve math problems.

Texas Essential Knowledge and Skills

Targeted TEKS

7.1(C) Select tools, including real objects, manipulatives, paper and pencil, and technology as appropriate, and techniques, including mental math, estimation, and number sense as appropriate, to solve problems.

1. Math tools are objects like paper and pencil, calculators, algebra tiles, and rulers. List three more math tools that are helpful in solving problems.

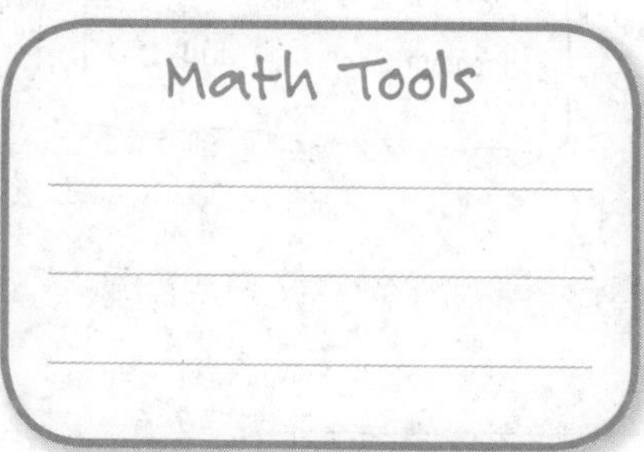

2. Math techniques are strategies like estimation, drawing a diagram, using mental math, etc. List three more math techniques that are helpful in solving problems.

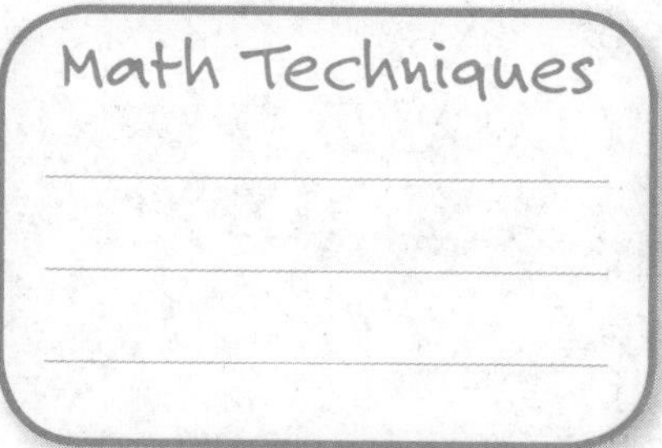

3. Describe a situation in which you would use a protractor.

____

It's Your Turn!

List the tools or techniques you would use to solve each problem. Then solve the problem.

4. You need to make a scale model of your room for your art class. The scale is $\frac{3}{4}$ inch represents 1 foot. What are the dimensions of your model?

5. Your family wants to go to a Dallas Cowboy's football game. The prices at Cowboys Stadium are the highest of all the teams. About how much would it cost a family of four to go to a game, park, buy 2 programs, and each have a soda and a hot dog?

Dallas Cowboys Football	
Average Ticket Price	$110.20
Parking	$75.00
Soda	$6.00
Hot Dog	$5.50
Program	$10

6. Your dance group spent $679.35 on props, hall space, and programs for a recital. The ticket prices for the recital are shown in the table. If you sold a total of 46 adult tickets and 59 student tickets, how much did the group make after paying for the supplies?

Recital Tickets	
Adult	$15.00
Student	$8.00

Find it in Your Book!

MP Select Tools and Techniques

Look at Chapter 1. Write the page number(s) where you find these examples of Mathematical Process C.

_______ Select Tools and Techniques exercises

_______ Hands-On Labs

Use Multiple Representations

Are you a visual person or do you prefer to use words?

You might prefer to use diagrams or drawings when explaining ideas. Or you might prefer to use words. In math, we also use different ways to represent the same idea. We can use words, graphs, tables, numbers, symbols, or diagrams.

Texas Essential Knowledge and Skills TEKS

Targeted TEKS

7.1(D) Communicate mathematical ideas, reasoning, and their implications using multiple representations, including symbols, diagrams, graphs, and language as appropriate.

1. Suppose you are selling T-shirts as a fundraiser for Key Club. The club makes a \$6.30 profit for every T-shirt sold. Complete each representation shown.

Words

_______ per T-shirt

Numbers

Profit (\$)	Number of shirts
6.30	1
12.60	
18.90	

Symbols

Let $p =$ profit
$t =$ number of T-shirts sold

$p = \square\, t$

Graph

y: 30, 25, 20, 15, 10, 5
O, x: 1, 2, 3, 4, 5, 6

All of these model the same relationship between profit and number of T-shirts sold, just in different ways.

2. Which relationship would you prefer to use to determine the profit if 100 T-shirts were sold? Explain.

____

____

____

It's Your Turn!

Use the multiple representations shown to solve each problem.

3. The waterpark Schlitterbahn West in New Braufels, Texas cycles about 24,000 gallons per minute through the Comal River.

a. Tables Complete the table to show the number of gallons used in 1, 2, 3, 4, and 5 minutes.

Time, *m* (minutes)	Gallons, *w* (thousand gallons)

b. Graph Graph the ordered pairs on the coordinate plane.

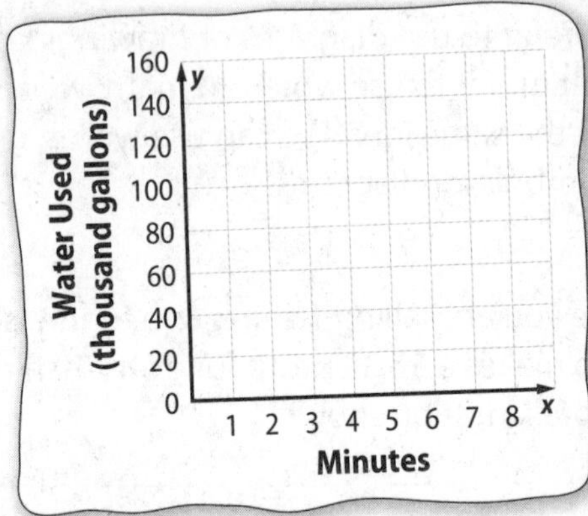

c. Symbols Write an equation to show the number of gallons of water *w* used in *m* minutes.

____

4. Kitra is creating a treasure hunt for the school carnival. The scale on the map is 0.5 inch = 0.25 mile.

a. Tables Complete the table to determine the actual distance for 0.5, 1, 1.5, 2, and 2.5 inches on the map.

b. Symbols Write an equation to determine the actual distance *d* for *m* inches on the map. ____________

Map Length *m* (in.)	Distance *d* (mi)

Find it in Your Book!

MP Use Multiple Representations

Look at Chapter 6. Write the page number(s) where you find these examples of Mathematical Process D.

____________ Use Multiple Representations exercises

Organize Ideas

How can I organize what I learn in math class to help me understand it better?

Texas Essential Knowledge and Skills

Targeted TEKS

7.1(E) Create and use representations to organize, record, and communicate mathematical ideas.

Throughout this text, you will complete tables and graphic organizers to help you organize and record what you are learning. Once you do this, it can be easier to draw a conclusion, write a formula or equation, or see a pattern.

1. A *compare and contrast* graphic organizer is shown below. Research two different Texas universities and compare and contrast them using any aspect(s) of the university. Complete the graphic organizer.

University 1	University 2
__________	__________

How are they alike?

1. __________
2. __________
3. __________

How are they different?

1. __________
2. __________
3. __________

It's Your Turn!

2. The chart shows some graphic organizers you may have learned before. Circle the ones that you have used before in other classes.

Types of Graphic Organizers		
concept map	timeline	flowchart
spider map	Venn diagram	Web
fishbone map	compare and contrast map	K-W-L chart

3. Another kind of graphic organizer is a Foldable. Foldables are three-dimensional graphic organizers that help you create study guides. Look through Chapter 1 in your text. Describe the Foldable you will create for this chapter. How do you think it will help you organize the information you will learn in Chapter 1?

____

____

____

4. Turn to page 35 in your text. Find the terms *integers, rational numbers* and *whole numbers*. Complete the graphic organizer for those words. Place an X in the appropriate column for each word. Then find a definition or an example.

Term	Know it well	Have heard it	No clue	Definition or Example

Find it in Your Book!

Organize Ideas

Look at Chapter 1. Write the page number(s) where you find these examples of Mathematical Process E.

__________ Organize Ideas exercises

__________ Foldables

__________ Graphic Organizers

Justify Arguments

Have you ever questioned something that someone else said?

Texas Essential Knowledge and Skills

Targeted TEKS

7.1(G) Display, explain, and justify mathematical ideas and arguments using precise mathematical language in written or oral communication.

If your friend told you that his dog could run 45 miles per hour, would you believe him? What would your friend need to do to justify his comment? You might want to see the dog run and use a stopwatch to time him. In math, we often need to justify our conclusions as well. We can use *inductive* or *deductive* reasoning.

1. Use the Internet or another source to look up the meanings of the terms *inductive reasoning* and *deductive reasoning*. Write the meanings in your own words.

____

____

____

2. Label each example below as either using inductive or deductive reasoning.

_______ Reasoning

Every dog that Elijah met has fleas, so he believes that all dogs have fleas.

_______ Reasoning

Equilateral triangles have 3 congruent sides. Elena has a triangle with 3 congruent sides, so she has an equilateral triangle.

Throughout this text, you may be asked to evaluate an argument that someone else made. If you determine that the argument is false, you may be asked to provide a counterexample. A *counterexample* is just one example that shows a statement is not true.

3. Determine if the following statement is true. If it is not true, provide a counterexample:

All prime numbers are odd.

____

It's Your Turn!

Complete each step in the solution shown. Use the Properties of Equality (Addition, Subtraction, Multiplication, or Division).

4. $a - 15 = 36$ Write the equation.

$+15 = +15$ ________________

$a = 51$ Simplify.

5. $5p = 35$ Write the equation.

$\frac{5p}{5} = \frac{35}{5}$ ________________

$p = 7$ Simplify.

For each of the following statements, determine if the statement is *true* or *false*. If false, provide a counterexample.

6. All four-legged pieces of furniture are tables.

____

7. All rectangles have 4 right angles.

____

8. The population of Texas is about 8% of the total population of the United States. Daniel claims that since the population of the United States is about 312 million, the population of Texas must be around 35 million. Is his claim reasonable? Explain.

____

____

____

Find it in Your Book!

MP Justify Arguments

Look at Chapter 1. Write the page number(s) where you find these examples of Mathematical Process G.

________ Justify Arguments exercises

________ Evaluate exercises in H.O.T. problems

Review

Use the Mathematical Processes

Solve.

The courtyard at Eastmoor Middle School is shaped like a rectangle that is 40.3 feet long. The width of the courtyard is 14.6 feet less than the length.

a. Draw and label a diagram of the school courtyard. What is the perimeter of the courtyard? ______

b. Student council wants to plant 14 trees so they are equally spaced around the courtyard. Draw a diagram showing where the trees should be planted. About how far apart are the trees? ______

Look Ahead

Determine which mathematical processes you used to determine the solution. Shade the circles that apply.

Which MP Mathematical Processes did you use?
Shade the circle(s) that applies.

Ⓐ Apply Math to the Real World.
Ⓑ Use a Problem-Solving Model.
Ⓒ Select Tools and Techniques.
Ⓓ Use Multiple Representations.
Ⓔ Organize Ideas.
Ⓕ Analyze Relationships.
Ⓖ Justify Arguments.

Reflect

Answering the Essential Question

Use what you learned about the mathematical processes to complete the graphic organizer. Write two different processes that you use for each category. Then describe how each process helps you explore and explain mathematics.

Explore

Process

Process

Essential Question

WHAT processes help me explore and explain mathematics?

Process

Process

Explain

Answer the Essential Question. WHAT processes help me explore and explain mathematics?

Chapter 1
Rational Numbers

Texas Essential Knowledge and Skills

Targeted TEKS

7.3 The student applies mathematical process standards to add, subtract, multiply, and divide while solving problems and justifying solutions. *Also addresses 7.2.*

Mathematical Processes

7.1, 7.1(A), 7.1(B), 7.1(C), 7.1(D), 7.1(E), 7.1(F), 7.1(G)

Essential Question

WHAT happens when you add, subtract, multiply, and divide rational numbers?

Math in the Real World

Wakeboarding Hydrous Wakepark at Allen Station offers an after school wakeboarding program for students. For $150, students get 12 hours of sessions. Express a fraction in simplest form that compares the number of hours to the total cost for this program.

Go Online!
www.connectED.mcgraw-hill.com

Watch   Worksheets  Vocab  Tutor   Tools  Check 

What Tools Do You Need?

Vocabulary

bar notation
common denominator
least common denominator
like fractions
rational numbers
repeating decimal
terminating decimal
unlike fractions

Review Vocabulary

An *improper fraction* is a fraction in which the numerator is greater than or equal to the denominator, such as $\frac{21}{4}$. A *mixed number* is a number composed of a whole number and a fraction, such as $5\frac{1}{4}$.

In the organizer below, express each mixed number as an improper fraction and each improper fraction as a mixed number. The first one in each column is done for you.

Mixed Numbers and Improper Fractions

Change Mixed Numbers	Change Improper Fractions
$3\frac{1}{2} = \frac{7}{2}$	$\frac{41}{4} = 10\frac{1}{4}$
$5\frac{1}{3} =$	$\frac{16}{3} =$
$8\frac{2}{5} =$	$\frac{23}{5} =$
$6\frac{4}{9} =$	$\frac{90}{11} =$
$10\frac{3}{8} =$	$\frac{66}{7} =$
$7\frac{3}{4} =$	$\frac{101}{2} =$
$15\frac{5}{6} =$	$\frac{87}{20} =$

When Will You Use This?

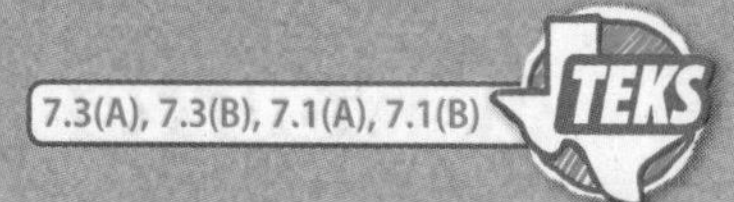

Caitlyn, Theresa, and Aisha in

Get Organized

Thanks for coming over to help organize my closet!

Sure.

No problem. I live to organize.

I bought a really great new closet organizer! I can't wait to install it!

Uh oh.

I'm not sure this will fit in your closet. It seems a bit big.

CLOSET ORGANIZERS

It says that the size of the storage cube is $18\frac{3}{4}$" and there are three of them.

I'll measure the space, then we can figure it out.

I just measured the closet rod, and it is $12\frac{7}{8}$". I wrote it all down.

$18\frac{3}{4} + 18\frac{3}{4} + 18\frac{3}{4} + 12\frac{7}{8}$

We are doomed!!

YIKES!! Fractions! How are we going to add them up??

Theresa, just breathe! We can figure it out!

Your Turn! **You will solve this problem in the chapter.**

Are You Ready?

Quick Review

Review 4.3(C), 4.3(G) TEKS

Example 1

Express $\frac{25}{100}$ in simplest form.

$$\frac{25}{100} \overset{\div 25}{=} \frac{1}{4}$$

Divide the numerator and denominator by the GCF, 25.

Since the GCF of 1 and 4 is 1, the fraction $\frac{1}{4}$ is in simplest form.

Example 2

Represent $3\frac{2}{3}$ on a number line.

Determine the two whole numbers between which $3\frac{2}{3}$ lies.

$3 < 3\frac{2}{3} < 4$

Since the denominator is 3, divide each space into 3 sections.

Draw a dot at $3\frac{2}{3}$.

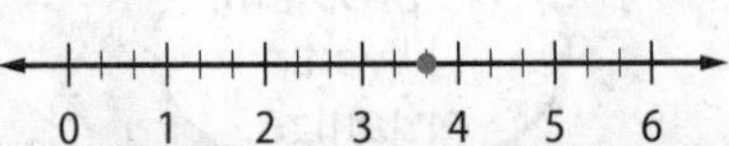

Quick Check

Fractions **Express each fraction in simplest form.**

1. $\frac{24}{36} =$ ______
2. $\frac{45}{50} =$ ______
3. $\frac{88}{121} =$ ______

Show your work.

Graphing **Represent each fraction or mixed number on the number line below.**

4. $\frac{1}{2}$
5. $\frac{3}{4}$
6. $1\frac{1}{4}$
7. $2\frac{1}{2}$

Which problems did you answer correctly in the Quick Check? Shade those exercise numbers below.

① ② ③ ④ ⑤ ⑥ ⑦

Use the Foldable throughout this chapter to help you learn about rational numbers.

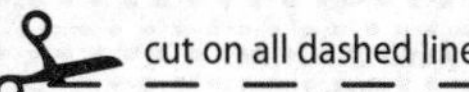

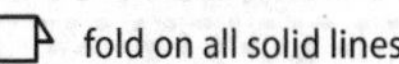

tape to page 112

Operations with Rational Numbers

+ or −
like fractions

÷
fractions

×
fractions

+ or −
unlike fractions

Use the Foldable throughout this chapter to help you learn about rational numbers.

cut on all dashed lines fold on all solid lines tape to page 112

page 112

Examples

Examples

page 112

Examples

Examples

Tab 2

Tab 1

Hands-On Lab 1-a

Model Rational Numbers

INQUIRY HOW can I use multiple representations to model negative rational numbers?

Water evaporates from Earth at an average of about $-\frac{3}{4}$ inch per week.

Texas Essential Knowledge and Skills

Targeted TEKS

7.2 Extend previous knowledge of sets and subsets using a visual representation to describe relationships between sets of rational numbers.

Mathematical Processes

7.1(C), 7.1(E), 7.1(F)

Hands-On Activity

Graph $-\frac{3}{4}$ on a number line.

Step 1 Use the fraction strip below that is divided in fourths above a number line.

Mark a 0 on the right side and a −1 on the left side.

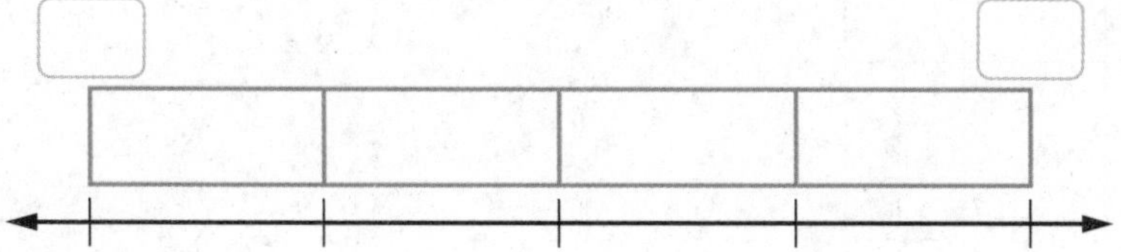

Step 2 Starting from the right, shade three fourths. Label the number line with $-\frac{1}{4}$, $-\frac{2}{4}$, and $-\frac{3}{4}$.

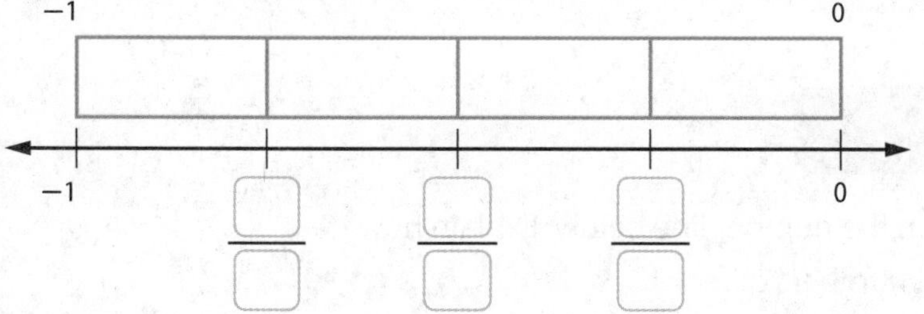

Step 3 Draw the number line portion of the model in Step 2.

Place a dot on the number line to represent $-\frac{3}{4}$.

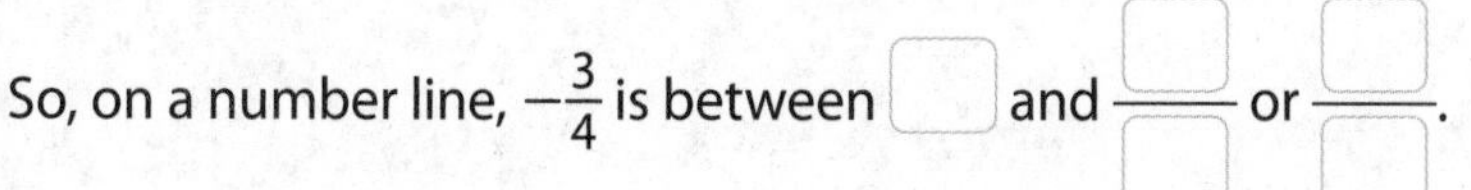

So, on a number line, $-\frac{3}{4}$ is between ☐ and $\frac{☐}{☐}$ or $\frac{☐}{☐}$.

Investigate

MP Select Tools and Techniques Work with a partner. Graph each rational number on a number line. Use a fraction strip if needed.

1. $-\frac{3}{8}$

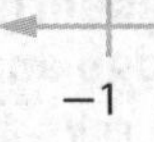

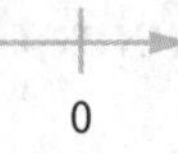

2. $-1\frac{2}{5}$

Analyze and Reflect

Work with a partner to complete each table. Use a number line if needed.

		< or >	
3.	$\frac{9}{8}$		$\frac{5}{8}$
4.	$\frac{13}{8}$		$\frac{3}{8}$
5.	$\frac{15}{8}$		$\frac{13}{8}$

		< or >	
6.	$-\frac{9}{8}$		$-\frac{5}{8}$
7.	$-\frac{13}{8}$		$-\frac{3}{8}$
8.	$-\frac{15}{8}$		$-\frac{13}{8}$

9. **MP Analyze Relationships** Compare and contrast the information in the tables.

Create

10. **MP Organize Ideas** Graph $-\frac{3}{4}$ and $\frac{3}{4}$ on the number line below. Explain how the representations of the two rational numbers differ.

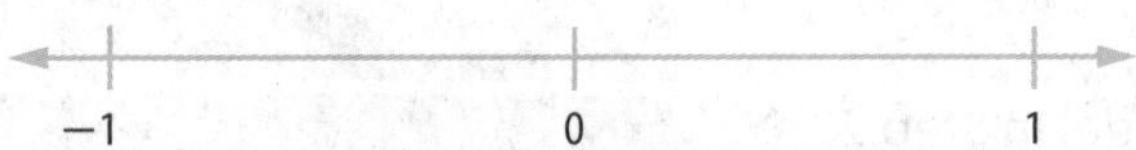

11. **INQUIRY** HOW can I use multiple representations to model negative rational numbers?

Lesson 1

Terminating and Repeating Decimals

Launch the Lesson: Vocabulary

Any fraction can be expressed as a decimal by dividing the numerator by the denominator.

A decimal whose digits repeat in groups of one or more is called a **repeating decimal**. Repeating decimals can be represented using **bar notation**. In bar notation, a bar is drawn only over the digit(s) that repeat.

$0.3333... = 0.\overline{3}$ $0.1212... = 0.\overline{12}$ $11.38585... = 11.3\overline{85}$

If the repeating digit is zero, the decimal is a **terminating decimal**. The terminating decimal $0.25\overline{0}$ is typically written as 0.25.

Match each repeating decimal to the correct bar notation.

0.1111...	$0.6\overline{1}$
0.61111...	$0.\overline{1}$
0.616161...	$0.\overline{61}$

Texas Essential Knowledge and Skills

Targeted TEKS

7.2 Extend previous knowledge of sets and subsets using a visual representation to describe relationships between sets of rational numbers.

Mathematical Processes

7.1(A), 7.1(B)

Vocabulary

repeating decimal

bar notation

terminating decimal

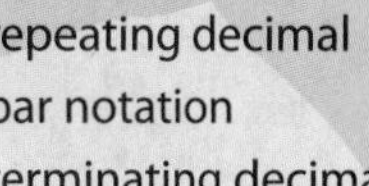

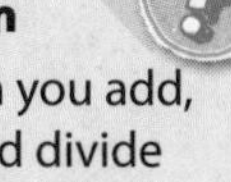

Essential Question

WHAT happens when you add, subtract, multiply, and divide rational numbers?

Real-World Link

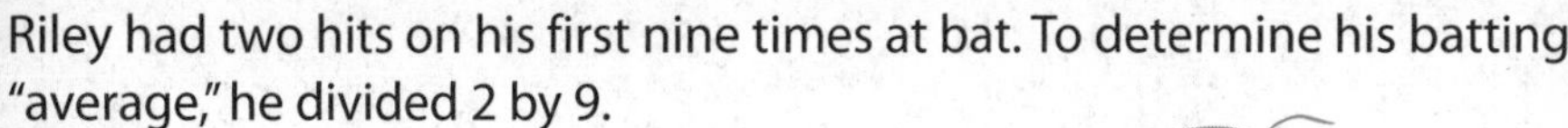

Riley had two hits on his first nine times at bat. To determine his batting "average," he divided 2 by 9.

$2 \div 9 = 0.2222...$

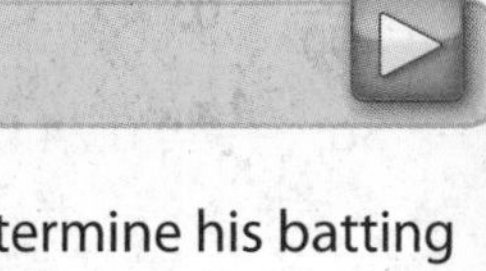

Express 0.2222... using bar notation. ______

Round 0.2222... to the nearest thousandth. ______

Which MP Mathematical Processes did you use? Shade the circle(s) that applies.

Ⓐ Apply Math to the Real World.

Ⓑ Use a Problem-Solving Model.

Ⓒ Select Tools and Techniques.

Ⓓ Use Multiple Representations.

Ⓔ Organize Ideas.

Ⓕ Analyze Relationships.

Ⓖ Justify Arguments.

Work Zone

Express Fractions as Decimals

Our decimal system is based on powers of 10 such as 10, 100, and 1,000. If the denominator of a fraction is a power of 10, you can use place value to express the fraction as a decimal.

Words	Fraction	Decimal
seven tenths	$\frac{7}{10}$	0.7
nineteen hundredths		
one-hundred five thousandths		

If the denominator of a fraction is a factor of 10, 100, 1,000, or any greater power of ten, you can use mental math and place value.

Tutor

Examples

Express each fraction or mixed number as a decimal.

1. $\frac{74}{100}$

Use place value to express the equivalent decimal.

$\frac{74}{100} = 0.74$ Read $\frac{74}{100}$ as *seventy-four hundredths.*

So, $\frac{74}{100} = 0.74$.

2. $\frac{7}{20}$

Think $\frac{7}{20} = \frac{35}{100}$ (×5 numerator and denominator)

So, $\frac{7}{20} = 0.35$.

3. $5\frac{3}{4}$

$5\frac{3}{4} = 5 + \frac{3}{4}$ Think of it as a sum.

$= 5 + 0.75$ You know that $\frac{3}{4} = 0.75$.

$= 5.75$ Add mentally.

So, $5\frac{3}{4} = 5.75$.

Got It? Do these problems to find out.

a. $\frac{3}{10}$ **b.** $\frac{3}{25}$ **c.** $-6\frac{1}{2}$

Show your work.

a. ________

b. ________

c. ________

Tutor

Examples

4. Express $\frac{3}{8}$ as a decimal.

$$\begin{array}{r} 0.375 \\ 8\overline{)3.000} \\ -24 \\ \hline 60 \\ -56 \\ \hline 40 \\ -40 \\ \hline 0 \end{array}$$

Divide 3 by 8.

Division ends when the remainder is 0.

So, $\frac{3}{8} = 0.375$.

5. Express $-\frac{1}{40}$ as a decimal.

$$\begin{array}{r} 0.025 \\ 40\overline{)1.000} \\ -80 \\ \hline 200 \\ -200 \\ \hline 0 \end{array}$$

Divide 1 by 40.

So, $-\frac{1}{40} = -0.025$.

6. Express $\frac{7}{9}$ as a decimal.

$$\begin{array}{r} 0.777\ldots \\ 9\overline{)7.000} \\ -63 \\ \hline 70 \\ -63 \\ \hline 70 \\ -63 \\ \hline 7 \end{array}$$

Divide 7 by 9.

Notice that the division will never terminate in zero.

So, $\frac{7}{9} = 0.777\ldots$ or $0.\overline{7}$.

Bar Notation
Remember that you can use bar notation to indicate a number pattern that repeats indefinitely.
$0.333\ldots = 0.\overline{3}$.

Got It? Do these problems to find out.

Express each fraction or mixed number as a decimal. Use bar notation if needed.

d. $-\frac{7}{8}$ **e.** $2\frac{1}{8}$

f. $-\frac{3}{11}$ **g.** $8\frac{1}{3}$

d. ____________

e. ____________

f. ____________

g. ____________

STOP and Reflect

Suppose 0.6 of the fish are goldfish. Write this decimal as a fraction in the space below.

h. ____________

i. ____________

j. ____________

Express Decimals as Fractions

Every terminating decimal can be expressed as a fraction with a denominator of 10, 100, 1,000, or a greater power of ten. Use the place value of the final digit as the denominator.

Example

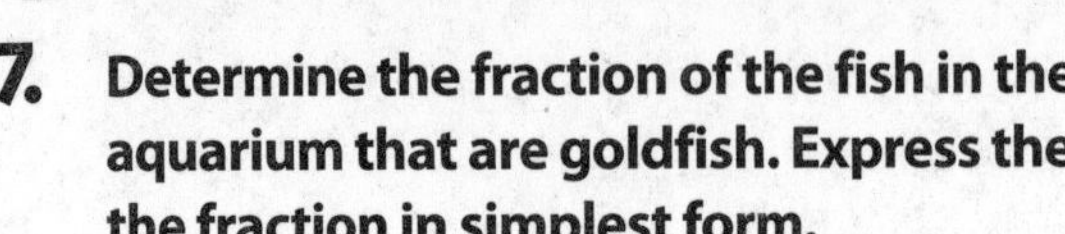

Watch Tutor

7. Determine the fraction of the fish in the aquarium that are goldfish. Express the the fraction in simplest form.

Fish	Amount
Guppy	0.25
Angelfish	0.4
Goldfish	0.15
Molly	0.2

$0.15 = \frac{15}{100}$ The digit 5 is in the hundredths place.

$= \frac{3}{20}$ Simplify.

So, $\frac{3}{20}$ of the fish are goldfish.

Got It? Do these problems to find out.

Determine the fraction of the aquarium made up by each fish. Express the fraction in simplest form.

h. molly **i.** guppy **j.** angelfish

Guided Practice

Express each fraction or mixed number as a decimal. Use bar notation if needed. (Examples 1–6)

1. $\frac{2}{5} =$ ________ Show your work.

2. $-\frac{9}{10} =$ ________

3. $\frac{5}{9} =$ ________

4. During a hockey game, an ice resurfacer travels 0.75 mile. What fraction represents this distance? (Example 7)

____

5. **Building on the Essential Question** How can you express a fraction as a decimal?

____

____

____

Rate Yourself!

Are you ready to move on? Shade the section that applies.

YES ? NO

Find out online. Use the Self-Check Quiz.

Name ________________ My Homework ________________

Independent Practice

7.2, 7.1(B) TEKS

Express each fraction or mixed number as a decimal. Use bar notation if needed. (Examples 1–6)

1. $\frac{1}{2}$ = ________

2. $-4\frac{4}{25}$ = ________

3. $\frac{1}{8}$ = ________

4. $\frac{3}{16}$ = ________

5. $-\frac{33}{50}$ = ________

6. $-\frac{17}{40}$ = ________

7. $5\frac{7}{8}$ = ________

8. $9\frac{3}{8}$ = ________

9. $-\frac{8}{9}$ = ________

10. $-\frac{1}{6}$ = ________

11. $-\frac{8}{11}$ = ________

12. $2\frac{6}{11}$ = ________

Express each decimal as a fraction or mixed number in simplest form. (Example 7)

13. −0.2 = ________

14. 0.55 = ________

15. 5.96 = ________

16. The screen on Brianna's new phone is 2.85 centimeters long. What mixed number represents the length of the phone screen? (Example 7)

____

17. **STEM** A praying mantis is an interesting insect that can rotate its head 180 degrees. Suppose the praying mantis at the right is 10.5 centimeters long. What mixed number represents this length? (Example 7)

____

18. MP **Use a Problem-Solving Model** Suppose you buy a 1.25-pound package of ham at $5.20 per pound.

a. What fraction of a pound did you buy?

b. How much money did you spend?

H.O.T. Problems Higher Order Thinking

19. **Analyze** Express a fraction that is equivalent to a terminating decimal between 0.5 and 0.75.

20. **Evaluate** Fractions in simplest form that have denominators of 2, 4, 8, 16, and 32 produce terminating decimals. Fractions with denominators of 6, 12, 18, and 24 produce repeating decimals. What causes the difference? Explain.

21. **Analyze** The value of pi (π) is 3.1415926… . The mathematician Archimedes believed that π was between $3\frac{1}{7}$ and $3\frac{10}{71}$. Was Archimedes correct? Explain your reasoning.

22. **Evaluate** A *unit fraction* is a fraction that has 1 as its numerator. Write the four greatest unit fractions that are repeating decimals. Then express each fraction as a decimal.

23. **Create** Write a real-world scenario in which it would be appropriate to express a value in fractional form.

Name ______________________________

Multi-Step Problem Solving

24. Thirty-six 7th graders were asked to choose their favorite color. The table shows the fraction of students that chose each color. What decimal shows the difference between the most and least popular colors?
N P MP

Color	Fraction
Red	$\frac{5}{18}$
Yellow	$\frac{1}{6}$
Blue	$\frac{4}{9}$
Green	$\frac{1}{9}$

Ⓐ $0.1\overline{6}$ Ⓒ $0.\overline{3}$

Ⓑ $0.\overline{1}$ Ⓓ $0.\overline{5}$

Use a problem-solving model to solve this problem.

1 Analyze

Read the problem. Circle the information you know.
Underline what the problem is asking you to find.

2 Plan

What will you need to do to solve the problem? Write your plan in steps.

Step 1 Express each fraction as a ____________.

Step 2 Determine which decimal is the ____________ and which is the ____________. Then subtract.

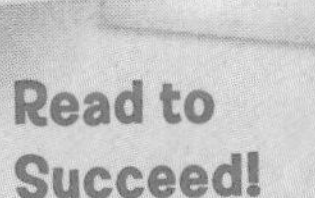

Read to Succeed!
Read the question carefully. Since it asks for the difference, you will need to subtract.

3 Solve

Use your plan to solve the problem. Show your steps.

Express each fraction as a decimal. Subtract the least from the greatest.

$\frac{5}{18}$ = ______ $\frac{1}{6}$ = ______ $\frac{4}{9}$ = ______ $\frac{1}{9}$ = ______

______ − ______ or ______ Subtract.

There were ______ more of the students chose ______ as their favorite color over ______. So, the correct answer is ______. Fill in that answer choice.

4 Justify and Evaluate

How do you know your solution is accurate?

____

____

____

N = Number and Operations P = Proportionality MP = Mathematical Processes

More Multi-Step Problem Solving

Use a problem-solving model to solve each problem.

25. The table shows the lengths of straws, in centimeters, that Jessica has available for an art project.

Straw	Length (cm)
Striped	12.5
White	10.75
Clear	13.35
Blue	11.3

She cut the white straw into two equal-size pieces. What mixed number represents the length of each piece of white straw after cutting? N P MP

Ⓐ $6\frac{1}{4}$

Ⓑ $5\frac{13}{20}$

Ⓒ $5\frac{3}{8}$

Ⓓ $5\frac{1}{8}$

26. Roger made a square sign to place on his bedroom door shown below in the sketch. What is the decimal equivalent of the perimeter, in inches, of his sign? N P MP

27. Destiny read $\frac{1}{4}$ of a book on the day she received it. The next day, she read $\frac{5}{8}$ of the book. On the third day, she finished reading the book. What decimal represents the fraction of the book Destiny read on the third day? N P MP

28. Graph and label the fractions $-\frac{2}{3}$, $-\frac{3}{5}$, and $-\frac{5}{8}$ on the number line shown using their equivalent decimal value. Explain how you determined where to place each fraction.

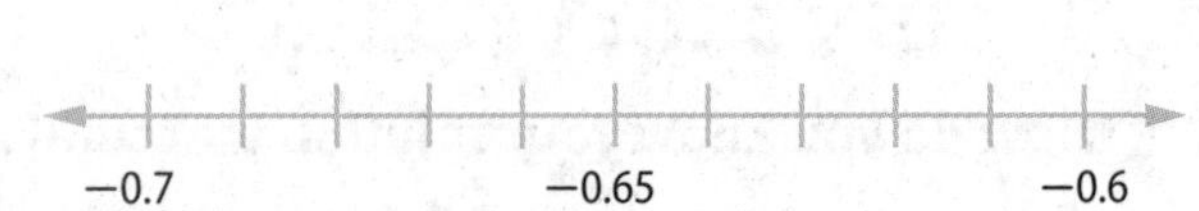

N = Number and Operations P = Proportionality MP = Mathematical Processes

Hands-On Lab 2-a

Sets of Rational Numbers

INQUIRY **HOW can you use a visual representation to describe relationships between sets of rational numbers?**

Mrs. Porter's family drove 39 miles to Corpus Christi, Texas, for a nice relaxing day at the beach. The height of the low tide at the beach was −1 feet, while the height of the high tide was 1.78 feet.

Texas Essential Knowledge and Skills TEKS

Targeted TEKS

7.2 Extend previous knowledge of sets and subsets using a visual representation to describe relationships between sets of rational numbers.

Mathematical Processes

7.1(C), 7.1(D), 7.1(E), 7.1(F)

Hands-On Activity

The set of whole numbers and their opposites are called **integers**. **Rational numbers** are the set of numbers that can be written in the form $\frac{a}{b}$, where a and b are integers and $b \neq 0$.

Step 1 Write the numbers 39, −1, and 1.78 on a small self-stick note. Write one number per self-stick note.

Step 2 Label three note cards **Whole Numbers**, **Integers**, and **Rational Numbers**. Place these note cards across your desk.

Step 3 Sort the self-stick notes by placing them on the appropriate note card(s). Use the definitions above, if needed, to help make your decisions. Note if there are any self-stick notes that belong to more than one category.

Whole Numbers

Integers

Rational Numbers

Investigate

1. Which number(s) could be placed into more than one category? Justify your response.

2. **MP** **Organize Ideas** Explain how you determined the placement of the number 1.78.

3. Write a number that only belongs to the category Rational Numbers. Justify your response.

Work with a partner.

MP **Analyze Relationships** Circle whether the statement is *true* or *false*. If *true*, explain your reasoning. If *false*, provide a counterexample.

4. A rational number is always an integer. True False

5. All integers are whole numbers. True False

6. **Find the Error** A Venn diagram uses overlapping circles to show relationships. A classmate drew the Venn diagram to show the relationship between whole numbers, integers, and rational numbers. Evaluate the Venn diagram and describe the error. Justify your response.

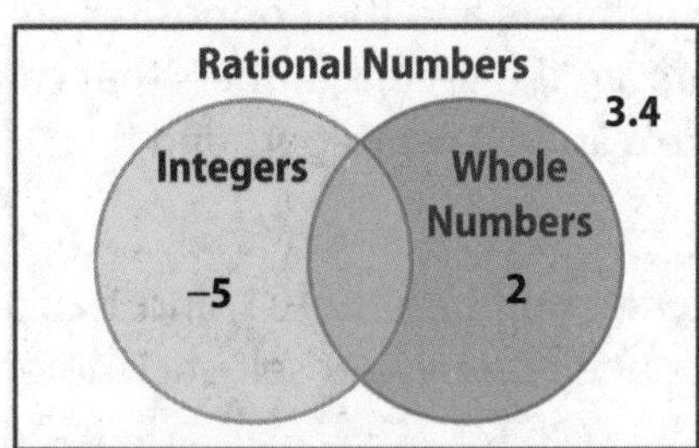

Create

On Your Own

7. MP **Use Multiple Representations** Create a Venn diagram to show the correct relationship between the sets of whole numbers, integers, and rational numbers. Explain how you created the diagram.

8. INQUIRY HOW can you use a visual representation to describe relationships between sets of rational numbers?

Lesson 2

Relationships Between Sets of Rational Numbers

Launch the Lesson: Vocabulary

A **rational number** is a number that can be expressed as a ratio of two integers written as a fraction, in which the denominator is not zero. The Venn diagram below shows that the number 2 can be called many things. It is a whole number, integer, and rational number. The number −1.4444... is only a rational number.

Common fractions, terminating and repeating decimals, percents, and integers are all rational numbers.

Write the numbers from the number bank on the diagram.

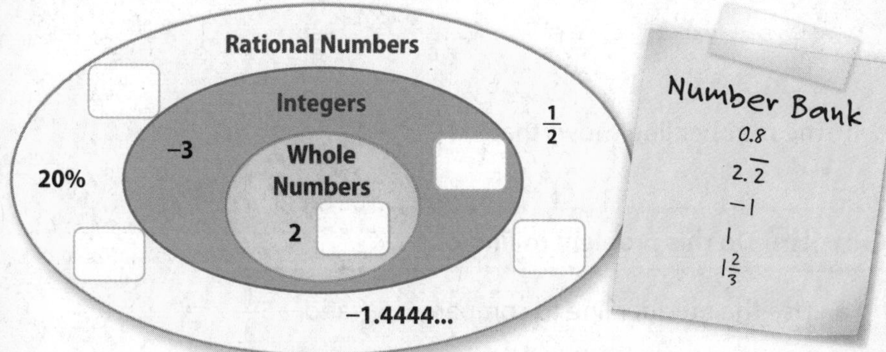

Texas Essential Knowledge and Skills

Targeted TEKS

7.2 Extend previous knowledge of sets and subsets using a visual representation to describe relationships between sets of rational numbers.

Mathematical Processes

7.1(A), 7.1(B), 7.1(C)

Vocabulary

rational number

common denominator

least common denominator

Essential Question

WHAT happens when you add, subtract, multiply, and divide rational numbers?

Real-World Investigation

Not all numbers are rational numbers. The Greek letter π (pi) represents the nonterminating and nonrepeating number whose first few digits are 3.14.... This number is an *irrational number*.

Use the Internet to search for the digits of pi. Describe what you find.

Which MP Mathematical Processes did you use? Shade the circle(s) that applies.

Ⓐ Apply Math to the Real World.
Ⓑ Use a Problem-Solving Model.
Ⓒ Select Tools and Techniques.
Ⓓ Use Multiple Representations.
Ⓔ Organize Ideas.
Ⓕ Analyze Relationships.
Ⓖ Justify Arguments.

Work Zone

Compare Rational Numbers

A **common denominator** is a common multiple of the denominators of two or more fractions. The **least common denominator** or **LCD** is the LCM or least common multiple of the denominators. You can use the LCD to compare fractions. You can also use a number line.

Example

1. Fill in the ◯ with <, >, or = to make $-1\frac{5}{6}$ ◯ $-1\frac{1}{6}$ a true sentence.

Graph each rational number on a number line.

Mark off equal-size increments of $\frac{1}{6}$ between −2 and −1.

$-2 \quad -1\frac{5}{6} \quad -1\frac{4}{6} \quad -1\frac{3}{6} \quad -1\frac{2}{6} \quad -1\frac{1}{6} \quad -1$

The number line shows that $-1\frac{5}{6} < -1\frac{1}{6}$.

Show your work.

a. ______

Got It? Do this problem to find out.

a. Use the number line to compare $-5\frac{5}{9}$ and $-5\frac{1}{9}$.

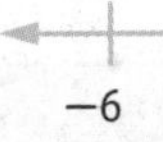

−6 −5

LCD

To find the least common denominator for $\frac{7}{12}$ and $\frac{8}{18}$, find the LCM of 12 and 18.

$12 = 2 \times 2 \times 3$

$18 = 2 \times 3 \times 3$

$LCM = 2 \times 2 \times 3 \times 3$

$= 36$

Example

2. Fill in the ◯ with <, >, or = to make $\frac{7}{12}$ ◯ $\frac{8}{18}$ a true sentence.

The LCD of the denominators 12 and 18 is 36.

$$\frac{7}{12} = \frac{7 \times 3}{12 \times 3} = \frac{21}{36} \qquad \frac{8}{18} = \frac{8 \times 2}{18 \times 2} = \frac{16}{36}$$

Since $\frac{21}{36} > \frac{16}{36}$, $\frac{7}{12} > \frac{8}{18}$.

Got It? Do these problems to find out.

b. $\frac{5}{6}$ ◯ $\frac{7}{9}$ **c.** $\frac{1}{5}$ ◯ $\frac{7}{50}$ **d.** $-\frac{9}{16}$ ◯ $-\frac{7}{10}$

Example

3. In Mr. Huang's class, 20% of students own roller shoes. In Mrs. Trevino's class, 5 out of 29 students own roller shoes. In which class does a greater fraction of students own roller shoes?

Express each number as a decimal and then compare.

$20\% = 0.2$ $\qquad \frac{5}{29} = 5 \div 29 \approx 0.1724$

Since $0.2 > 0.1724$, $20\% > \frac{5}{29}$.

More students in Mr. Huang's class own roller shoes.

Percents as Decimals

To write a percent as a decimal, remove the percent sign and then move the decimal point two places to the left. Add zeros if necessary.

20% = 0.20

Got It? **Do this problem to find out.**

e. In a second period class, 37.5% of students like to bowl. In a fifth period class, 12 out of 29 students like to bowl. In which class does a greater fraction of the students like to bowl?

e. ________

Order Rational Numbers

You can order rational numbers using place value. First, express each number using the same form. Then order the numbers.

Example

4. Order the set {3.44, π, 3.14, $3.\overline{4}$} from least to greatest.

Express π as a decimal. Then line up the decimal points and compare using place value.

3.140	Annex a zero.	3.440	Annex a zero.
3.1415926...	$\pi \approx 3.1415926...$	3.444...	$3.\overline{4} = 3.444...$
Since $0 < 1$, $3.14 < \pi$.		Since $0 < 4$, $3.44 < 3.\overline{4}$.	

So, the order of the numbers from least to greatest is 3.14, π, 3.44, and $3.\overline{4}$.

Got It? **Do this problem to find out.**

f. Order the set {23%, 0.21, $\frac{1}{4}$, $\frac{1}{5}$} from least to greatest.

f. ________

Example

5. Nolan is the quarterback on the football team. He completed 67% of his passes in the first game. He completed 0.64, $\frac{3}{5}$, and 69% of his passes in the next three games. List Nolan's completed passing numbers from least to greatest.

Express each number as a decimal and then compare.

$67\% = 0.67$ $\quad 0.64 = 0.64$ $\quad \frac{3}{5} = 0.6$ $\quad 69\% = 0.69$

Nolan's completed passing numbers from least to greatest are $\frac{3}{5}$, 0.64, 67%, and 69%.

Guided Practice

Fill in each ◯ with <, >, or = to make a true sentence. Use a number line if necessary. (Examples 1 and 2)

1. $-\frac{4}{5}$ ◯ $-\frac{1}{5}$

2. $1\frac{3}{4}$ ◯ $1\frac{5}{8}$

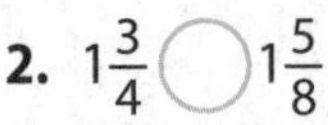

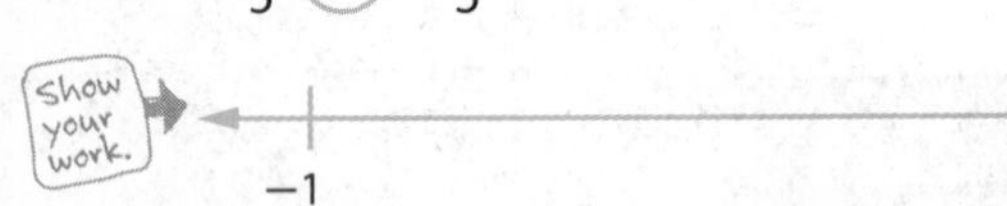

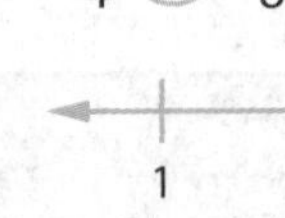

3. Elliot and Shanna are both soccer goalies. Elliot saves 3 goals out of 4. Shanna saves 7 goals out of 11. Who has the better average, Elliot or Shanna? Explain. (Example 3)

4. The lengths of four insects are 0.02 inch, $\frac{1}{8}$ inch, 0.1 inch, and $\frac{2}{3}$ inch. List the lengths in inches from least to greatest. (Examples 4 and 5)

5. **Building on the Essential Question** How can you compare two rational numbers, expressed as fractions?

Rate Yourself!

☐ I understand how to compare and order rational numbers.

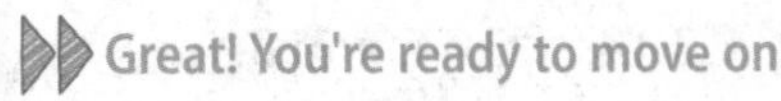

☐ I still have some questions about comparing and ordering rational numbers.

No problem! Go online to access a Personal Tutor.

Name ______________________ My Homework ______________________

Independent Practice

Fill in each ◯ with <, >, or = to make a true sentence. Use a number line if necessary. (Examples 1 and 2)

1. $-\frac{3}{5}$ ◯ $-\frac{4}{5}$

2. $-7\frac{5}{8}$ ◯ $-7\frac{1}{8}$

3. $6\frac{2}{3}$ ◯ $6\frac{1}{2}$

4. $-\frac{17}{24}$ ◯ $-\frac{11}{12}$

5. On her first quiz in social studies, Meg answered 92% of the questions correctly. On her second quiz, she answered 27 out of 30 questions correctly. On which quiz did Meg have the better score? (Example 3)

____

Order each set of numbers from least to greatest. (Example 4)

6. $\{0.23, 19\%, \frac{1}{5}\}$

____

7. $\{-0.615, -\frac{5}{8}, -0.62\}$

____

8. Liberty Middle School is holding a fundraiser. The sixth-graders have raised 52% of their goal amount. The seventh- and eighth-graders have raised 0.57 and $\frac{2}{5}$ of their goal amounts, respectively. List the classes in order from least to greatest of their goal amounts. (Example 5)

____

Fill in each ◯ with <, >, or = to make a true sentence.

9. $1\frac{7}{12}$ gallons ◯ $1\frac{5}{8}$ gallons

10. $2\frac{5}{6}$ hours ◯ 2.8 hours

11. **MP Apply Math to the Real World** Refer to the graphic novel frame below. If the closet organizer has a total width of $69\frac{1}{8}$ inches and the closet is $69\frac{3}{4}$ inches wide, will the organizer fit? Explain.

H.O.T. Problems Higher-Order Thinking

12. **Evaluate** Identify the ratio that does not have the same value as the other three. Justify your reasoning.

12 out of 15	0.08	80%	$\frac{4}{5}$

13. **Analyze** Justify how you know which number, $1\frac{15}{16}$, $\frac{17}{8}$, or $\frac{63}{32}$, is closest to 2.

14. **Create** Write a real-world problem in which you would compare and order rational numbers. Then solve the problem.

15. **Analyze** Are the fractions $\frac{5}{6}$, $\frac{5}{7}$, $\frac{5}{8}$, and $\frac{5}{9}$ arranged in order from least to greatest or from greatest to least? Explain.

Name ______________________________

Multi-Step Problem Solving

16. The table shows the change in value for four stocks over one day. What is the difference between the greatest value change and the least value change expressed as a decimal? N P MP

Stock	Value
MCD	+1.75%
THC	+0.65
BIG	$+\frac{7}{8}$
GES	$+1\frac{1}{4}$

Ⓐ 1.25

Ⓑ 1.2325

Ⓒ 1.1

Ⓓ 0.6

Use a problem-solving model to solve this problem.

1 Analyze

Read the problem. Circle the information you know. Underline what the problem is asking you to find.

2 Plan

What will you need to do to solve the problem? Write your plan in steps.

Step 1 Express each number as a __________. Then compare.

Step 2 Determine which decimal is the __________ and which is the __________. Then subtract.

3 Solve

Use your plan to solve the problem. Show your steps.
Write each percent or fraction as a decimal. Then subtract.

1.75% = ________ 0.65 = ________ $\frac{7}{8}$ = ________ $1\frac{1}{4}$ = ________

________ − ________ = ________ Subtract.

The difference between the greatest value change and least value change is ________.

The correct answer is ________. Fill in that answer choice.

Read to Succeed!

Remember to move the decimal point two places to the left when changing the percent 1.75% to a decimal.

4 Justify and Evaluate

How do you know your solution is accurate?

____

____

____

N = Number and Operations P = Proportionality MP = Mathematical Processes

More Multi-Step Problem Solving

Use a problem-solving model to solve each problem.

17. In Mr. Amir's class, 24 out of 30 students have a pet. In Ms. Hala's class, 55% of students have a pet. Which statement below correctly compares the fraction of students who have a pet in Mr. Amir's class to the fraction of students who have a pet in Ms. Hala's class?

Ⓐ $\frac{4}{5} = \frac{11}{20}$

Ⓑ $\frac{4}{5} < \frac{11}{30}$

Ⓒ $\frac{4}{5} > \frac{4}{55}$

Ⓓ $\frac{4}{5} > \frac{11}{20}$

18. The circle graph below shows the favorite subjects of seventh-grade students in a gym class. There are 32 students in the class. How many more students chose Math than Social Studies and Language Arts? N P MP

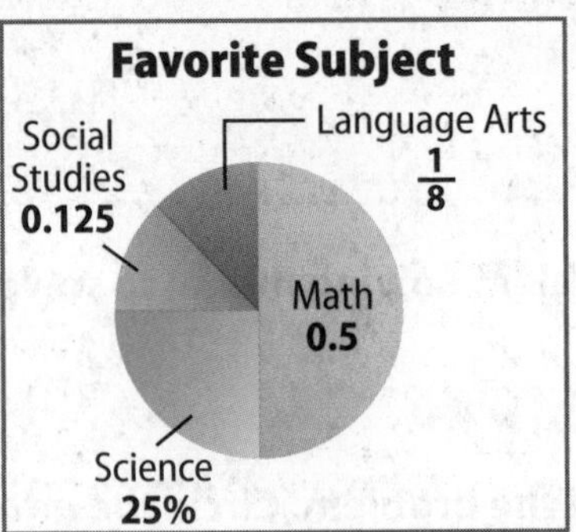

19. The table shows the amount of time Pablo practiced his saxophone over three days. Pablo realized he made an error by writing the reciprocal for the time spent on Monday. Once he corrects the error, what is the decimal equivalent of the number that would come first if the times were ordered from greatest to least? N P MP

Day	Time (hr)
Monday	$\frac{4}{3}$
Tuesday	$\frac{7}{8}$
Wednesday	$\frac{5}{6}$

20. Which of the following numbers is closest to 88% on the number line?

$\frac{4}{5}, \frac{8}{9}, \frac{21}{25}$

Write both the decimal and fraction form of the number. N P MP

N = Number and Operations P = Proportionality MP = Mathematical Processes

Lesson 3

Add and Subtract Integers

Launch the Lesson: Real World

Texas Essential Knowledge and Skills

Targeted TEKS

7.3(A) Add, subtract, multiply, and divide rational numbers fluently. *Also addresses 7.3(B).*

Mathematical Processes

7.1(A), 7.1(B)

Essential Question

WHAT happens when you add, subtract, multiply, and divide rational numbers?

Vincente and his family spent the weekend hiking trails at Big Bend National Park in Texas. They hike to the top of Emery Peak with an elevation of about 2,500 meters above sea level. They descend 1,000 meters to their camp site. Write an addition expression to determine the height of the camp site above sea level. Then determine the sum and explain its meaning.

1. Write an integer to represent each situation.

   Emery Peak is about 2,500 meters above sea level. ☐

   They descend 1,000 meters to their camp site. ☐

2. Write an addition expression to represent this situation.

3. Select a math tool to determine the sum.

4. Explain the meaning of the sum.

5. Write and solve an addition expression to determine the total distance hiked to their camp site.

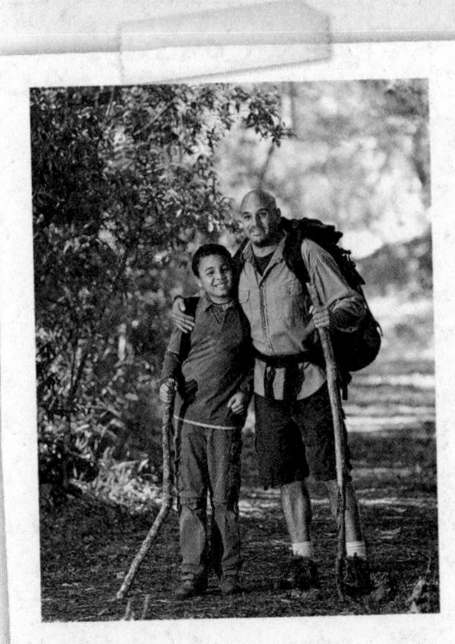

Which MP Mathematical Processes did you use? Shade the circle(s) that applies.

Ⓐ Apply Math to the Real World.
Ⓑ Use a Problem-Solving Model.
Ⓒ Select Tools and Techniques.
Ⓓ Use Multiple Representations.
Ⓔ Organize Ideas.
Ⓕ Analyze Relationships.
Ⓖ Justify Arguments.

Key Concept

Add Integers

Words To add integers with the same sign, add their absolute values. To add integers with different signs, subtract their absolute values and use the sign of the greater absolute value.

Examples $-3 + (-4) = -7$ $3 + (-4) = -1$

Work Zone

Tutor

Examples

1. Determine $-14 + (-8)$.

$-14 + (-8) = -22$ Add the absolute values; $14 + 8 = 22$. Since both signs are negative, the sum is also negative.

2. Determine $-7 + 18$.

$-7 + 18 = 11$ Subtract the absolute values; $18 - 7 = 11$. Since 18 has the greater absolute value, the sum is positive.

Got It? **Do these problems to find out.**

a. $-5 + (-7)$ **b.** $10 + (-4)$ **c.** $-37 + 25$

a. ________

b. ________

c. ________

Key Concept

Subtract Integers

Words To subtract an integer, add its additive inverse.

Symbols $p - q = p + (-q)$

Examples $4 - 9 = 4 + (-9) = -5$ $7 - (-10) = 7 + (10) = 17$

The number line below shows $4 - 9 = -5$.

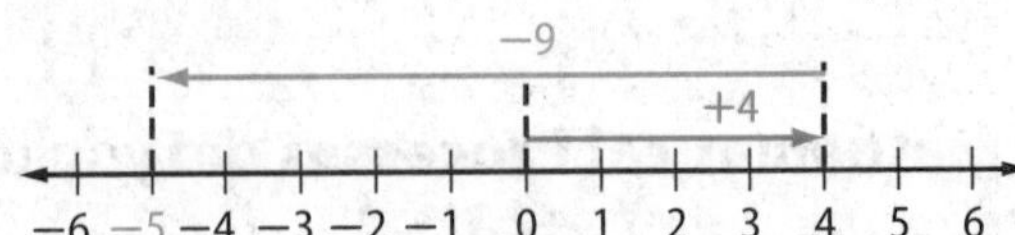

When you subtract 9 on the number line, the result is the same as adding −9.

9 and −9 are additive inverses

$4 - 9 = -5$

$4 + (-9) = -5$

same result

Examples

Tutor

3. Determine 7 − 11.

$7 - 11 = 7 + (-11)$ To subtract 11, add −11.

$= -4$ Simplify.

4. Determine −21 − 13.

$-21 - 13 = -21 + (-13)$ To subtract 13, add −13.

$= -34$ Simplify.

Got It? Do these problems to find out.

d. $8 - 14$ **e.** $-15 - 31$ **f.** $-27 - (-19)$

Show your work.

d. ______

e. ______

f. ______

Add and Subtract More than Two Integers

Examples

Tutor

5. Determine −13 + 15 + (−8).

$-13 + 15 + (-8) = 15 + (-13) + (-8)$ Commutative Property (+)

$= 15 + (-21)$ Add absolute values with the same signs; 13 + 8 = 21.

$= -6$ Subtract absolute values; 21 − 15 = 6. Since −21 has the greater absolute value, the sum is negative.

6. Determine 21 − 35 + (−17).

$21 - 35 + (-17) = 21 + (-35) + (-17)$ Additive Inverse

$= 21 + (-52)$ Add absolute values with the same signs; 35 + 17 = 52.

$= -31$ Subtract absolute values; 52 − 21 = 31. Since −52 has the greater absolute value, the sum is negative.

Show your work.

g. ______

Got It? Do these problems to find out.

g. $-7 + 16 + (-12)$ **h.** $-14 + (-25) - 16$

h. ______

Tutor

Example

7. **Financial Literacy A bank account has a starting balance of $156. What is the balance after sending electronic checks for $42 and $36, then depositing $83?**

Sending an electronic check decreases the account balance, so integers for this situation are −42 and −36. Depositing increases the account balance. Add these integers to the starting balance to determine the new balance.

$156 + (-42) + (-36) + 83$

$= 156 + 83 + (-42 + -36)$ — Associative Property (+)

$= 239 + (-78)$ — Add absolute values with the same signs.

$= 161$ — Subtract absolute values; $239 - 78 = 161$. Since 239 has the greater absolute value, the sum is positive.

So, the account balance is now $161.

Got It? **Do this problem to find out.**

j. Britta played in a golf tournament and scored −3, +1, −2, and +2 in four rounds. What was her final score?

j. ________

Guided Practice

Add or subtract. (Examples 1–4)

1. $18 + (-4) =$ ________

2. $17 - (-6) =$ ________

3. $-24 + (-7) =$ ________

4. The outside temperature is −13°F. The temperature drops by 9°F, but then increases by 16°F. Write an addition expression to describe the change in temperatures. Then determine the final outside temperature. (Examples 5–7)

____

5. **Building on the Essential Question** How are adding and subtracting integers similar? ________

____

____

Rate Yourself!

How well do you understand adding and subtracting integers? Circle the image that applies.

Clear

Somewhat Clear

Not So Clear

Find out online. Use the Self-Check Quiz.

Check

Name ______________________ My Homework ______________________

Independent Practice

7.3(A), 7.3(B), 7.1(A) TEKS

Add or subtract. (Examples 1–6)

1. $8 + (-19) =$ ______

2. $27 - 31 =$ ______

3. $-58 - (-72) =$ ______

4. $-22 + (-34) =$ ______

5. $-21 - 40 =$ ______

6. $-35 + 67 =$ ______

7. $71 + (-43) - 13 =$ ______

8. $-47 - 33 + 25 =$ ______

9. $-39 - (-51) - 21 =$ ______

10. A football team gained 4 yards on a play, lost 8 yards on the next play, then gained 2 yards on the third play. Write an addition expression to describe the total change of yardage. Then determine the sum and explain its meaning. (Example 7)

____

____

11. Sally begins hiking at an elevation of 224 feet. Then, she descends 131 feet and climbs 67 feet higher than her current position. She then descends 163 feet. Write an addition sentence to describe the situation. Then determine and interpret the sum. (Example 7)

____

____

12. A helicopter is flying at an altitude of 785 feet. It descends 570 feet, and then ascends 595 feet. Write an expression to represent this situation. Then determine and interpret the sum. (Example 7)

____

____

13. Use the information below to answer the following question.

City	Amarillo	Dallas	Lubbock	San Antonio
Record High Temperature (°F)	111	113	114	110
Record Low Temperature (°F)	−14	−1	−17	0

Which city has the greatest range of temperatures? What is the range of temperatures?

14. Find the Error Hiroshi is determining $-42 - (-37)$. Find his mistake and correct it.

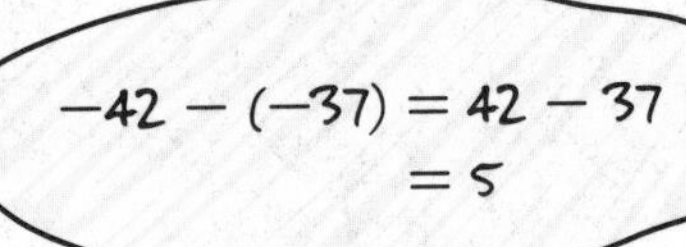

H.O.T. Problems Higher Order Thinking

15. Create Write a real-world problem that can be solved by modeling integer operations on the number line.

16. Evaluate Determine whether the following statement is *true* or *false*. A subtraction expression with a positive integer and a negative integer can have a difference of zero. If *true*, provide three examples. If *false*, give a counterexample.

17. Create Write two different subtraction expressions, each of which has a difference of −10. Then write an equivalent addition expression for each. Explain how you know the expressions are equivalent.

18. Evaluate For which integer values of x is the expression $|x| + (-3)$ greater than zero? Justify your response.

Name ______________________________

Multi-Step Problem Solving

19. The table shows the change in temperature over the course of one week. If the starting temperature on Sunday was 45°F, what was the temperature range between the warmest temperature and the coldest temperature? N MP

Ⓐ 3°F
Ⓑ 4°F
Ⓒ 5°F
Ⓓ 6°F

Day	Monday	Tuesday	Wednesday	Thursday	Friday	Saturday	Sunday
Change from Previous Day (°F)	+1	−3	+4	−2	+3	−2	0

Use a problem-solving model to solve this problem.

1 Analyze

Read the problem. Circle the information you know. Underline what the problem is asking you to find.

2 Plan

What will you need to do to solve the problem? Write your plan in steps.

Step 1 Determine the temperature for each ____________.

Step 2 Compare the temperatures. Then ____________.

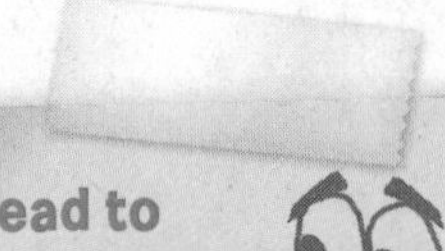

When adding integers with different signs, subtract their absolute values and use the sign of the greater absolute value.

3 Solve

Use your plan to solve the problem. Show your steps.

Determine the temperature for each day by adding the integers. Then subtract.

$45 + 1 = 46$ $46 + (-3) = 43$ $43 + 4 = 47$ $47 + (-2) = 45$

$45 + 3 = 48$ $48 + (-2) = 46$ $46 + 0 =$ ______

______ − ______ = ______ Subtract.

The temperature range for the week is ______°F.

The correct answer is ______. Fill in that answer choice.

4 Justify and Evaluate

How do you know your solution is accurate?

____

____

____

N = Number and Operations MP = Mathematical Processes

More Multi-Step Problem Solving

Use a problem-solving model to solve each problem.

20. An airplane is flying at an altitude of 823 feet. It descends 335 feet and then ascends to 741 feet. What is the average altitude of the three heights in which the plane is flying? N MP

Ⓐ 684 feet

Ⓑ 847 feet

Ⓒ 1,230 feet

Ⓓ 1,900 feet

21. The line graph below shows the balance in a checking account over the past four weeks. What is the overall net change, in dollars, of the balance in the checking account?

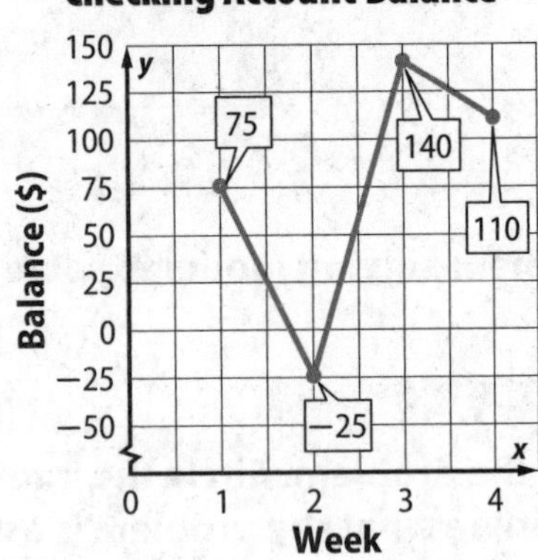

22. The table shows the elevations of two different volcanoes. What is one-half of the difference in elevation between Aconcagua and the average depth of an ocean, which is 4,267 meters below sea level? N MP

Volcano	Elevation (m)
Llullaillaco	6,739
Aconcagua	7,021

23. Diego and Cai are playing a trivia game. They earn 5 points for correctly answering an easy question and 10 points for correctly answering a hard question. They lose 5 points for incorrectly answering an easy question and 10 points for incorrectly answering a hard question. What are their final scores? N MP

	Diego	Cai
# of Correct Easy Questions	4	2
# of Incorrect Easy Questions	2	4
# of Correct Hard Questions	3	4
# of Incorrect Hard Questions	1	0

N = Number and Operations MD = Measurement and Data MP = Mathematical Processes FL = Personal Financial Literacy

Lesson 4

Multiply and Divide Integers

Launch the Lesson: Real World

Texas Essential Knowledge and Skills

Targeted TEKS

7.3(A) Add, subtract, multiply, and divide rational numbers fluently. *Also addresses 7.3(B).*

Mathematical Processes

7.1(A), 7.1(B)

Essential Question

WHAT happens when you add, subtract, multiply, and divide rational numbers?

A hot air balloon pilot is flying his balloon 560 meters above the ground. When landing, he descends the balloon at a rate of about 8 meters per second. How long will it take for the balloon to land?

1. Would you use a positive or negative integer to represent the balloon's rate of change? Explain your reasoning.

2. Complete the table to show how far the balloon will descend after 5 seconds.

Time (s)	Distance (m)	Height (m)
1	−8	552
2		
3		
4		
5		

3. Graph the data on the coordinate plane below.

4. **Create** Write a multiplication equation that describes how long it will take to descend 560 feet.

5. How long will it take for the balloon to land? Explain how you solved the problem.

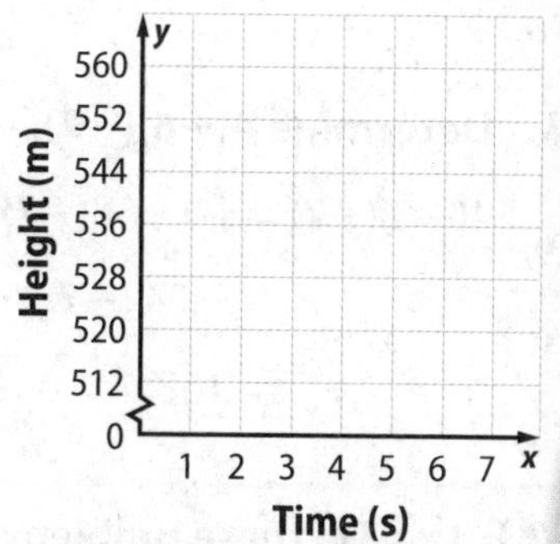

Which MP Mathematical Processes did you use? Shade the circle(s) that applies.

Ⓐ Apply Math to the Real World.
Ⓑ Use a Problem-Solving Model.
Ⓒ Select Tools and Techniques.
Ⓓ Use Multiple Representations.
Ⓔ Organize Ideas.
Ⓕ Analyze Relationships.
Ⓖ Justify Arguments.

Key Concept

Multiply Integers

Words The product of two integers with different signs is negative.

The product of two integers with the same sign is positive.

Examples $3(-2) = -6$ $-3(-2) = 6$

Tutor

Examples

1. Determine 7(−8).

$7(-8) = -56$ The integers have different signs.
The product is negative.

2. Determine −6(−9).

$-6(-9) = 54$ The integers have the same sign.
The product is positive.

3. Determine −2(−5)(−4).

$-2(-5)(-4) = [-2(-5)](-4)$ Associative Property

$= 10(-4)$ $-2(-5) = 10$

$= -40$ $10(-4) = -40$

4. Determine 4(−6)(−7).

$4(-6)(-7) = [4(-6)](-7)$ Associative Property

$= -24(-7)$ $4(-6) = -24$

$= 168$ $-24(-7) = 168$

Got It? Do these problems to find out.

a. $-5(12)$ **b.** $9(-13)$ **c.** $-2(12)(-5)$

d. $4(-17)$ **e.** $-6(-29)$ **f.** $3(-33)(-16)$

Show your work.

a. ______

b. ______

c. ______

d. ______

e. ______

f. ______

Divide Integers

Key Concept

Words The quotient of two integers with the different signs is negative.

The quotient of two integers with the same sign is positive.

Examples $12 \div (-3) = -4$ $-12 \div (-3) = 4$

Tutor

Examples

5. Determine $-24 \div 3$.

$-24 \div 3 = -8$ The integers have different signs. The quotient is negative.

6. Determine $\frac{60}{-10}$.

$\frac{60}{-10} = -6$ The integers have different signs. The quotient is negative.

7. Determine $\frac{3 + (-12)}{-3}$.

$\frac{3 + (-12)}{-3} = \frac{-9}{-3}$ The numerator acts like a grouping symbol. Add first. Then divide.

$= 3$ The integers have the same signs. The quotient is positive.

8. Determine $\frac{49 - (-14)}{7}$.

$\frac{49 - (-14)}{7} = \frac{63}{7}$ Subtract first. Then divide.

$= 9$ The integers have the same signs. The quotient is positive.

Got It? Do these problems to find out.

g. $45 \div -5$ **h.** $\frac{-116}{4}$ **i.** $\frac{-37 - 15}{-2}$

j. $-63 \div -7$ **k.** $\frac{-225}{15}$ **l.** $\frac{6 - (-42)}{-12}$

g. ________

h. ________

i. ________

j. ________

k. ________

l. ________

Multi-Step Example

9. **STEM** **The record low temperature in Wichita Falls, Texas, is −24°C. Use the expression $\frac{9C + 160}{5}$ to determine this temperature in degrees Fahrenheit. Round to the nearest degree. The record high temperature is 117°F. Determine the range in degrees Fahrenheit.**

Step 1

$$\frac{9C + 160}{5} = \frac{9(-24) + 160}{5}$$ Replace C with −24.

$$= \frac{-216 + 160}{5}$$ Multiply.

$$= \frac{-56}{5}$$ Add.

$$= -11.2$$ Divide.

So, −24°C is about −11°F.

Step 2 Subtract to determine the temperature range.
$117 - (-11) = 128$

The temperature range is 128°F.

Guided Practice

Determine the value of each expression. (Examples 1–8)

1. $-8(-14)$ ______

2. $-54 \div 3$ ______

3. $\frac{29 + (-44)}{5}$ ______

4. An atmospheric research aircraft began descending from an altitude of 36,000 feet above its base, at a rate of 125 feet per minute. How long did it take for the aircraft to land at its base? (Example 9) ______

5. **Building on the Essential Question** How is dividing integers similar to multiplying integers? ______

Rate Yourself!

Are you ready to move on? Shade the section that applies.

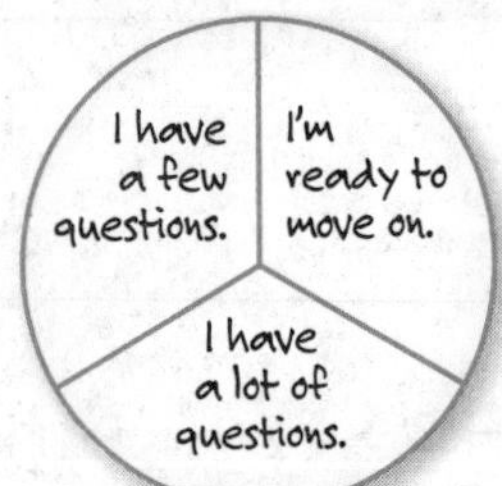

Find out online. Use the Self-Check Quiz.

Name ______________________ My Homework ______________________

Independent Practice

7.3(A), 7.3(B), 7.1(A) TEKS

Determine the value of each expression. (Examples 1–8)

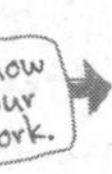

1. $-7(-6)$ ______

2. $4(-12)$ ______

3. $65 \div (-5)$ ______

4. $-6(20)$ ______

5. $\frac{-13 - 27}{8}$ ______

6. $\frac{-180}{15}$ ______

7. $-3(6)(-4)$ ______

8. $-8(-2)(-5)$ ______

9. $\frac{-36 + 58}{-11}$ ______

10. During a seven-day period, the level of an irrigation pond receded 28 centimeters. Write a division expression to represent the change. Then determine the average daily change in the level of the pond. (Example 9)

____

11. A glacier receded at a rate of 350 feet per day for two consecutive weeks.

How much did the glacier's position change in all? (Example 9) ______

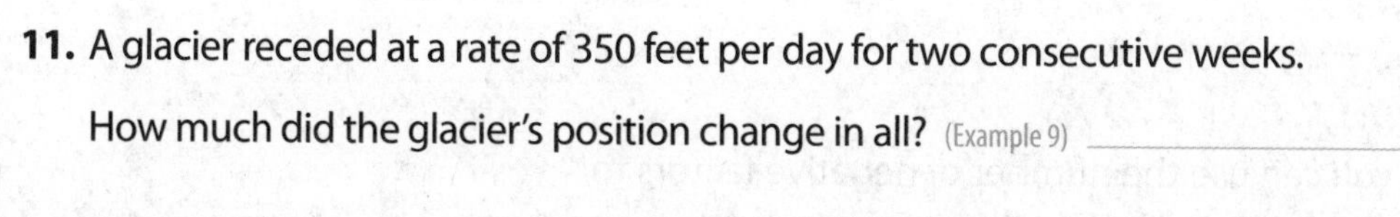

12. Financial Literacy Marcus purchases 75 shares of stock. A year after purchasing the stocks, the value of the stock is $2 less per share. Write a multiplication expression to determine the change in Marcus's investment.

Explain your answer. (Example 9) ______________________

____

13. The distance remaining for a half-marathon race over several minutes is shown in the table. Use the information to determine the constant rate of change in minutes per mile. (Example 9)

____

Time (min)	Distance Remaining (mi)
40	8
56	6
72	4
88	2

14. During a scoring drive, a football team gained or lost yards on each play as shown at the right. What was the average number of yards per play for this drive? ______

Yards Gained or Lost					
+6	−2	+8	0	+23	−4
+5	+12	−4	−3	+18	+1

15. **Financial Literacy** During the past week, Mrs. Washer monitored her online bank account activity. She recorded the following transactions: \$157, −\$85, −\$38, and −\$18. Write and evaluate an expression to determine the average transaction amount. ______

H.O.T. Problems Higher-Order Thinking

16. **Create** Name two integers whose quotient is −7.

______

17. **Evaluate** Determine the sign of each of the following if n is a negative number. Justify your reasoning.

a. n^2 ______

b. n^3 ______

c. n^4 ______

d. n^5 ______

18. **Analyze** Justify how you can use the number of negative factors to determine the sign of the product of more than two integers.

______

19. **Evaluate** The sum of any two whole numbers is always a whole number. So, the set of whole numbers (0, 1, 2, 3, ...) is said to be *closed* under addition. This is an example of the *Closure Property*. State whether each statement is *true* or *false*. If false, give a counterexample.

a. The set of whole numbers is closed under subtraction. ______

b. The set of integers is closed under multiplication. ______

Name ______________________________

Multi-Step Problem Solving

20. On a wildlife reserve, scientists have noticed that the population of a turtle has decreased. The table shows the population for two different years. Use the data to determine the average rate of change per year of the turtle population between 2007 and 2012. N MP

Year	Number of Turtles
2007	842
2012	602

Ⓐ −240 turtles per year
Ⓑ −20 turtles per year
Ⓒ −48 turtles per year
Ⓓ −34 turtles per year

Use a problem-solving model to solve this problem.

1 Analyze

Read the problem. Circle the information you know.
Underline what the problem is asking you to find.

2 Plan

What will you need to do to solve the problem? Write your plan in steps.

Step 1 Determine the __________ in years and number of turtles.

Step 2 __________ the __________ in the number of turtles by the __________ in years.

3 Solve

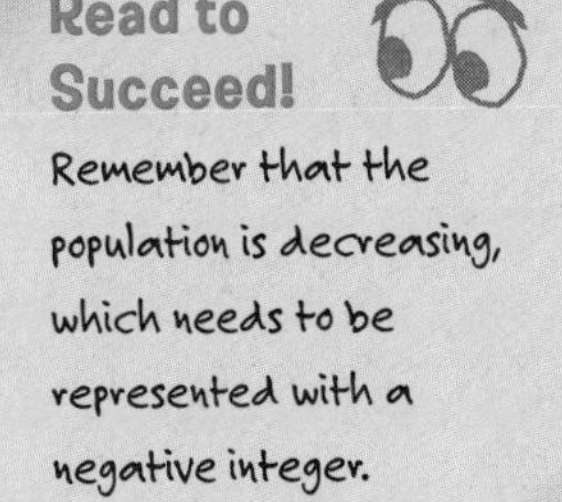

Use your plan to solve the problem. Show your steps.
Determine the difference in years and the number of turtles.

2012 − 2007 = ______ 602 − 842 = ______

Determine the average rate of decrease of the turtle population.

______ ÷ ______ = ______. Divide.

The average rate of change of the turtle population is ______ turtles per year.

The correct answer is ______. Fill in that answer choice.

4 Justify and Evaluate

How do you know your solution is accurate?

____

____

____

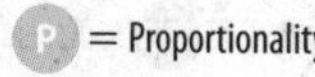 N = Number and Operations 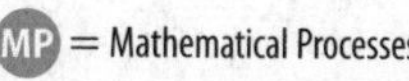 P = Proportionality MP = Mathematical Processes

More Multi-Step Problem Solving

Use a problem-solving model to solve each problem.

21. Calvin has a hot dog stand in the city. The table below shows his daily profits for five days. Determine the average gain over the five-day period. N MP

Day	Profit
1	$123 gain
2	$55 loss
3	$77 gain
4	$101 gain
5	$26 loss

Ⓐ $44

Ⓑ $77

Ⓒ $55

Ⓓ $66

22. A submarine is descending from the surface of the water. The table below shows the position of the submarine relative to the surface of the water for specific time periods. Use the information to determine the position of the submarine relative to the surface after 8 minutes. Assume the rate remains constant. N MP

Depth (ft)	Time (min)
−240	2
−600	5
−840	7

23. Morgan records the temperature for five consecutive days as seen in the table below. Use the expression $F = \frac{9C + 160}{5}$ to determine the average temperature in degrees Fahrenheit. N P MP

Day	Temperature
1	−5°C
2	0°C
3	3°C
4	−1°C
5	−3°C

24. Create a new triangle by multiplying the *x*- and *y*-coordinates of each vertex by −2. Display the new coordinates in the table. Describe how the new triangle compares to the original triangle. N MD MP

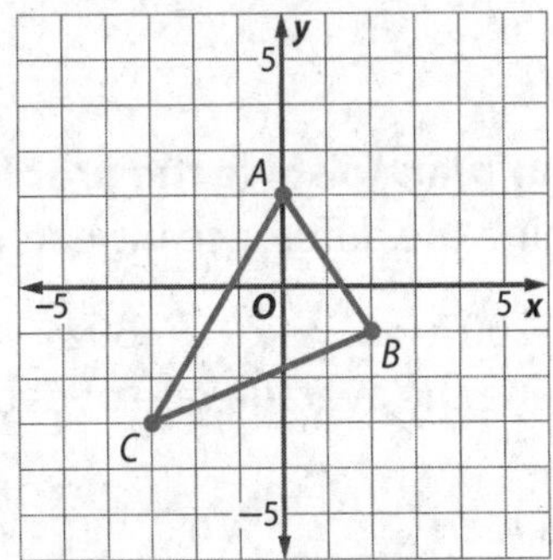

Vertex	Original Coordinates	New Coordinates
A		
B		
C		

N = Number and Operations P = Proportionality MD = Measurement and Data MP = Mathematical Processes

The Four-Step Plan

'Round and 'Round

The Forte family visited the Mall of America in Minneapolis. The Ferris wheel in the mall's amusement park is about 25 yards tall. Another thrill ride is about 60 feet tall.

How much taller in feet is the Ferris wheel compared to the thrill ride?

Mathematical Process
7.1(B) Use a problem-solving model that incorporates analyzing given information, formulating a plan or strategy, determining a solution, justifying the solution, and evaluating the problem-solving process and the reasonableness of the solution.

Targeted TEKS 7.3(A)

Analyze *What are the facts?*

- The height of the Ferris wheel is 25 yards.
- A thrill ride is 60 feet tall.

Plan *What is your strategy to solve this problem?*

I will ______________________________.

Solve *How can you apply the strategy?*

One yard is equal to 3 feet. Write the ratio $\frac{3 \text{ feet}}{1 \text{ yard}}$.

Convert 25 yards to feet.

$25 \text{ yards} \cdot \frac{3 \text{ feet}}{1 \text{ yard}} = \square$ feet

Subtract.

$\square - 60 = \square$ feet

So, the Ferris wheel is about $\square$ feet taller than the thrill ride.

Justify and Evaluate *How do you know your solution is accurate?*

____

____

____

Cool Treats

Mr. Martino's class learned the average American consumes about 23 quarts of ice cream every year. The class also learned the average American in the north-central United States consumes about 38 pints more than the average.

How much ice cream in gallons is consumed every year by the average American in the north-central United States?

1 Analyze

Read the problem. Circle the information you know. Underline what the problem is asking you to find.

2 Plan

What is your strategy to solve this problem?

I will ______________________________

____

3 Solve

How can you apply the strategy?

Justify and Evaluate

How do you know your solution is accurate?

____

____

____

Multi-Step Problem Solving

Work with a small group to solve the following problems. Show your work on a separate piece of paper.

1. Financial Literacy

Terry opened a savings account in December with $150 and deposited $30 each month beginning in January. Terry also received a 4% bonus from her bank that was added to her balance at the end of July.

What is the value of Terry's account at the end of July?

2. STEM

The average height for a male over the age of 20 years old is 69.4 inches.

What percent of the average male height is the femur bone? Round to the nearest tenth of a percent.

Bones in an Adult Male

Bone	Length (in.)
Femur (upper leg)	19.88
Tibia (inner lower leg)	16.94
Fibula (outer lower leg)	15.94

3. Patterns

Numbers that can be represented by a triangular arrangement of dots are called *triangular numbers*. The first four triangular numbers are shown.

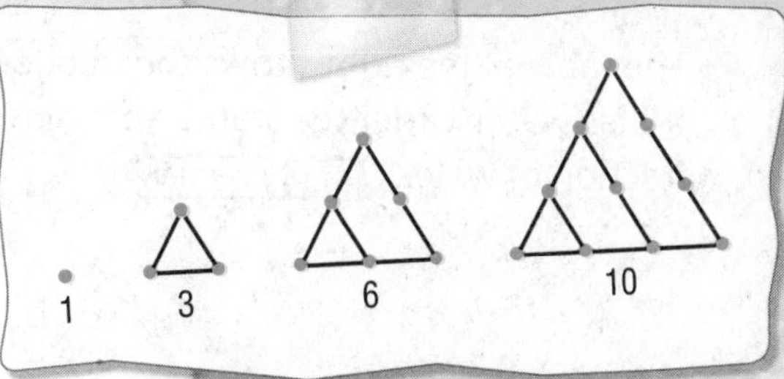

Describe the pattern in the first four numbers. Then list the next three triangular numbers.

4. Transportation

Mr. Norman has agreed to drive 4 students to their gymnastics practice.

If one student rides in the front seat and three students ride in the back, in how many ways can the 4 students be arranged in the car?

Mid-Chapter Check

Vocabulary Check

Vocab

1. Define *rational number*. Give some examples of rational numbers written in different forms. TEKS 7.2, 7.1(D)

Key Concept Check

2. Complete the Venn diagram to show the correct relationship between the sets of whole numbers, integers, and rational numbers. Then give a real-world example for each type of number. TEKS 7.2, 7.1(E)

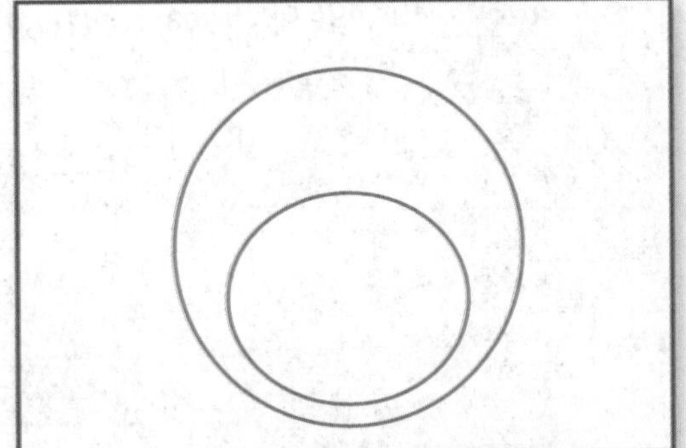

3. The maximum height of an Asian elephant is 9.8 feet. What mixed number represents this height? TEKS 7.2, 7.1(A)

4. The table at the right shows the fraction of each state that is water. Order the states from *least* to *greatest* fraction of water. TEKS 7.2, 7.1(A)

What Part is Water?	
Alaska	$\frac{3}{41}$
Michigan	$\frac{40}{97}$
Wisconsin	$\frac{1}{6}$

Multi-Step Problem Solving

5. STEM The air temperature is affected by changes in elevation. Use the expression $\frac{-3.5A}{1{,}000}$, where A represents the altitude in feet, to determine the number of degrees Fahrenheit by which the temperature changes at an altitude of 6,000 feet. N EE MP

Ⓐ 2.1°F

Ⓑ −2.1°F

Ⓒ −21°F

Ⓓ −210°F

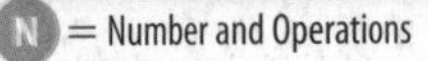 N = Number and Operations 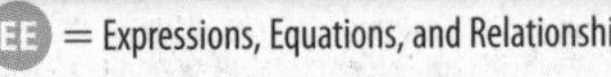 EE = Expressions, Equations, and Relationships 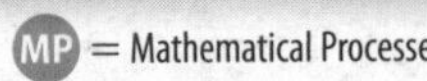 MP = Mathematical Processes

Hands-On Lab 5-a

Use Models to Add and Subtract Rational Numbers

INQUIRY HOW can you use multiple representations to add and subtract positive and negative like fractions?

In eight times at bat, Max hit 2 doubles, 5 singles, and struck out 1 time. Find the fraction of the times that Max hit either a single or a double.

Texas Essential Knowledge and Skills

Targeted TEKS

7.3(A) Add, subtract, multiply, and divide rational numbers fluently.

Mathematical Processes

7.1(C), 7.1(D), 7.1(E), 7.1(F)

Hands-On Activity 1

Step 1 Since there were 8 times at bat, create a vertical number line that is divided into eighths.

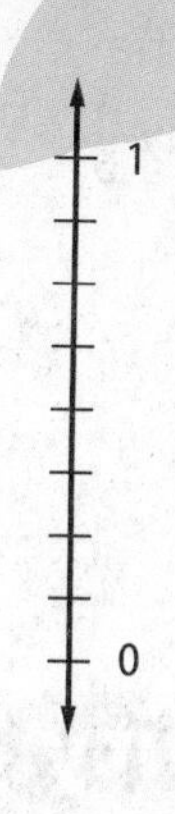

Step 2 Graph the fraction of doubles, $\frac{2}{8}$, on the number line.

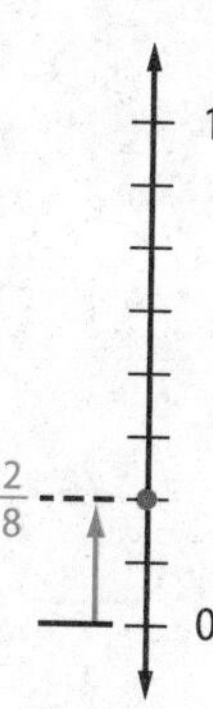

Step 3 From the $\frac{2}{8}$ point, count $\frac{5}{8}$ more on the number line.

So, $\frac{2}{8} + \frac{5}{8} = \frac{\square}{\square}$.

Max got a hit $\frac{\square}{\square}$ of the times he was at bat.

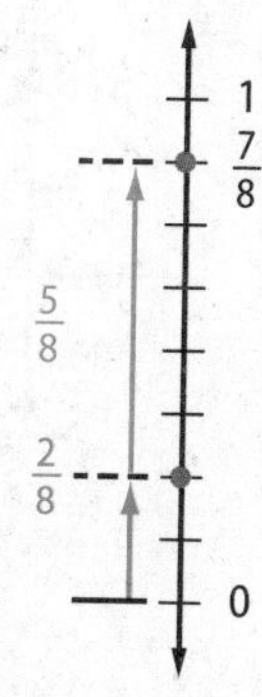

Hands-On Activity 2

Determine $\frac{3}{6} - \frac{4}{6}$.

Step 1 Divide a number line into sixths. Since we do not know if our answer is negative or positive, include fractions to the left and to the right of zero.

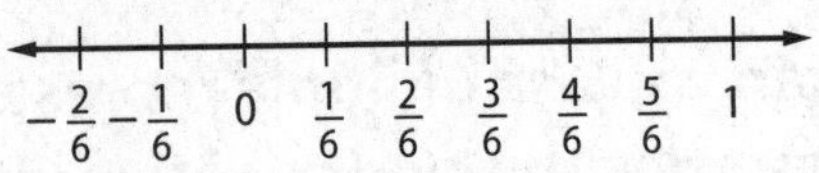

Step 2 Graph $\frac{3}{6}$ on the number line.

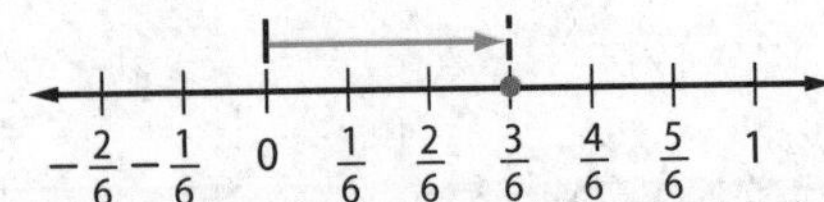

Step 3 Move 4 units to the ________ to show taking away $\frac{4}{6}$.

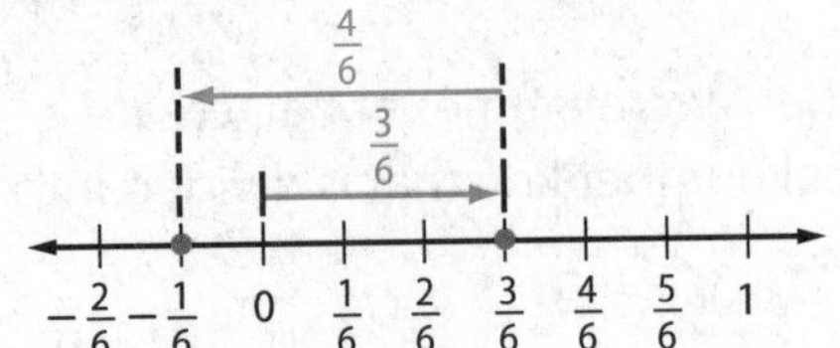

So, $\frac{3}{6} - \frac{4}{6} = \frac{\square}{\square}$.

Hands-On Activity 3

Determine $-\frac{4}{7} - \frac{2}{7}$. Fill in the missing numbers in the diagram below.

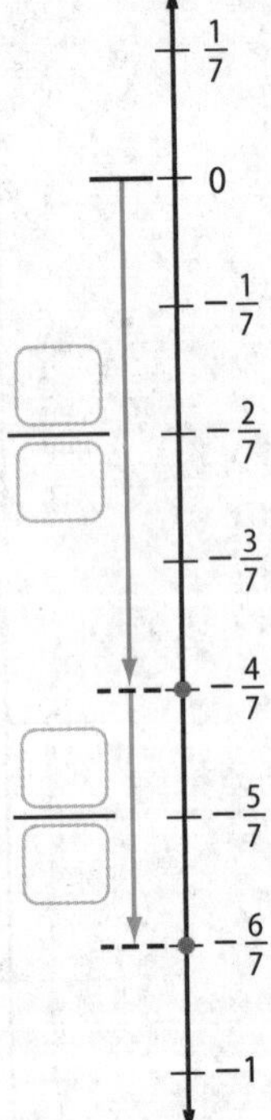

$-\frac{4}{7} - \frac{2}{7} = \frac{\square}{\square}$.

Investigate

Work with a partner. Use a number line to add or subtract. Express in simplest form.

1. $\frac{1}{5} + \frac{2}{5} =$ ______

2. $-\frac{3}{7} + \left(-\frac{1}{7}\right) =$ ______

3. $-\frac{3}{8} + \frac{5}{8} =$ ______

4. $\frac{8}{12} - \frac{4}{12} =$ ______

5. $-\frac{4}{9} + \frac{5}{9} =$ ______

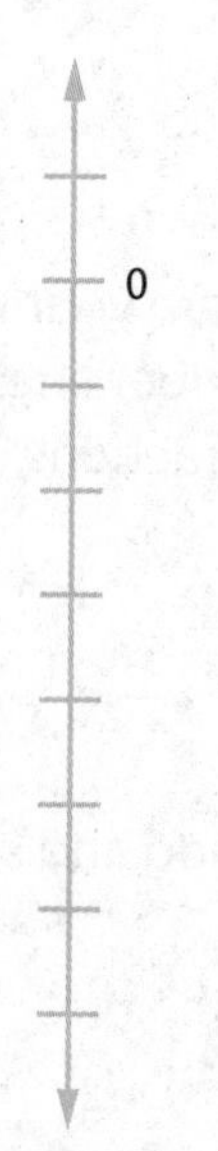

6. $\frac{4}{7} - \frac{6}{7} =$ ______

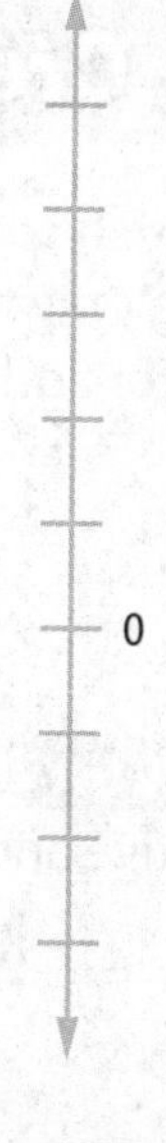

Analyze and Reflect

MP Select Tools and Techniques Work with a partner to complete the table. The first one is done for you.

	Expression	Use only the Numerators	Use a number line to add or subtract the fractions.
	$-\frac{5}{6}-\left(-\frac{1}{6}\right)$	$-5-(-1)$ $=-4$	$\frac{1}{6}$, $-\frac{5}{6}$; -1, $-\frac{5}{6}$, $-\frac{4}{6}$, $-\frac{3}{6}$, $-\frac{2}{6}$, $-\frac{1}{6}$, 0, $\frac{1}{6}$, $\frac{2}{6}$
7.	$-\frac{5}{6}-\frac{1}{6}$	$-5-1=-6$	0
8.	$\frac{5}{6}-\frac{1}{6}$	$5-1=4$	0
9.	$-\frac{5}{6}+\frac{1}{6}$	$-5+1+-4$	0

Create

10. **MP Analyze Relationships** Refer to the table above. Compare your results for using only the numerators with your results for using a number line. Write a rule for adding and subtracting positive and negative like fractions.

11. **INQUIRY** HOW can you use multiple representations to add and subtract positive and negative like fractions?

Lesson 5

Fluently Add and Subtract Rational Numbers: Like Fractions

Launch the Lesson: Real World

Sean surveyed his classmates to determine which type of tennis shoe they own. The results are shown in the Venn diagram below. What fraction of the students surveyed own either cross trainers or high tops? What fraction more own cross trainers than high tops?

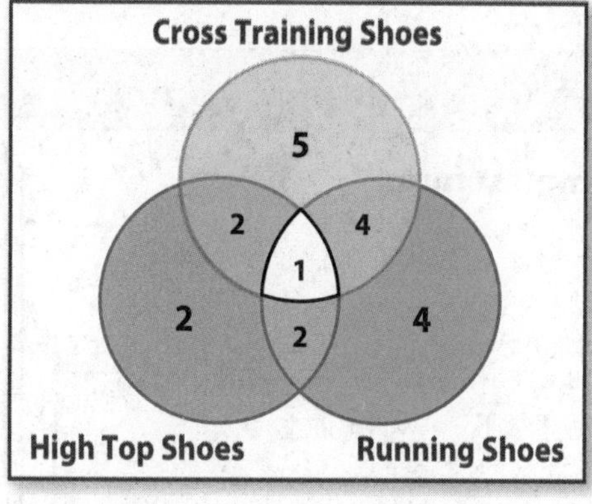

1. What fraction of students own cross trainers?

2. What fraction of students own high tops?

3. What fraction of the students surveyed own either cross trainers or high tops?

4. What fraction more of the students surveyed own cross trainers than high tops?

Texas Essential Knowledge and Skills

Targeted TEKS

7.3(A) Add, subtract, multiply, and divide rational numbers fluently. *Also addresses 7.3(B).*

Mathematical Processes

7.1(A), 7.1(B), 7.1(C)

Vocabulary

like fractions

Essential Question

WHAT happens when you add, subtract, multiply, and divide rational numbers?

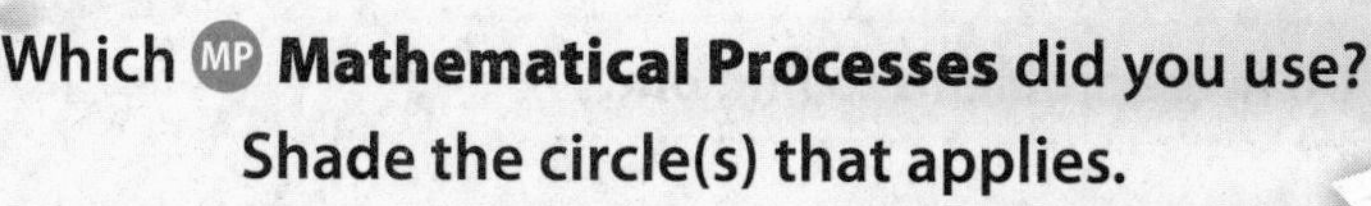

Which MP **Mathematical Processes** did you use? Shade the circle(s) that applies.

Ⓐ Apply Math to the Real World.
Ⓑ Use a Problem-Solving Model.
Ⓒ Select Tools and Techniques.
Ⓓ Use Multiple Representations.
Ⓔ Organize Ideas.
Ⓕ Analyze Relationships.
Ⓖ Justify Arguments.

Key Concept

Add and Subtract Like Fractions

Words To add or subtract like fractions, add or subtract the numerators and write the result over the denominator.

Examples

Numbers	Algebra
$\frac{5}{10} + \frac{2}{10} = \frac{5+2}{10}$ or $\frac{7}{10}$	$\frac{a}{c} + \frac{b}{c} = \frac{a+b}{c}$, where $c \neq 0$
$\frac{11}{12} - \frac{4}{12} = \frac{11-4}{12}$ or $\frac{7}{12}$	$\frac{a}{c} - \frac{b}{c} = \frac{a-b}{c}$, where $c \neq 0$

Work Zone

Fractions that have the same denominators are called **like fractions**.

Tutor

Examples

Add. Express in simplest form.

1. $\frac{5}{9} + \frac{2}{9}$

$\frac{5}{9} + \frac{2}{9} = \frac{5+2}{9}$ Add the numerators.

$= \frac{7}{9}$ Simplify.

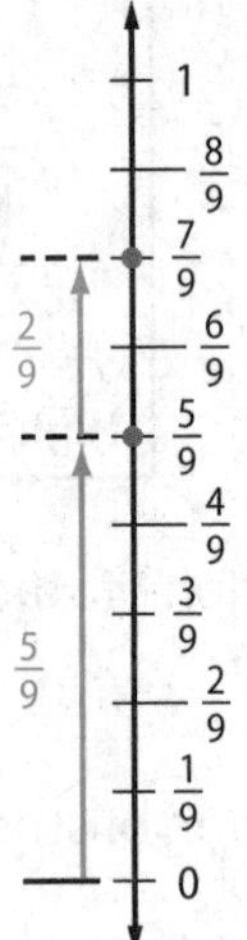

Negative Fractions

Remember $-\frac{1}{2} = \frac{-1}{2} = \frac{1}{-2}$. Typically, the form $\frac{-1}{2}$ is used when performing computations.

2. $-\frac{3}{5} + \left(\frac{-1}{5}\right)$

$-\frac{3}{5} + \left(\frac{-1}{5}\right) = \frac{-3}{5} + \left(\frac{-1}{5}\right)$

$= \frac{-3+(-1)}{5}$ Add the numerators.

$= \frac{-4}{5}$ or $-\frac{4}{5}$ Use the rules for adding integers.

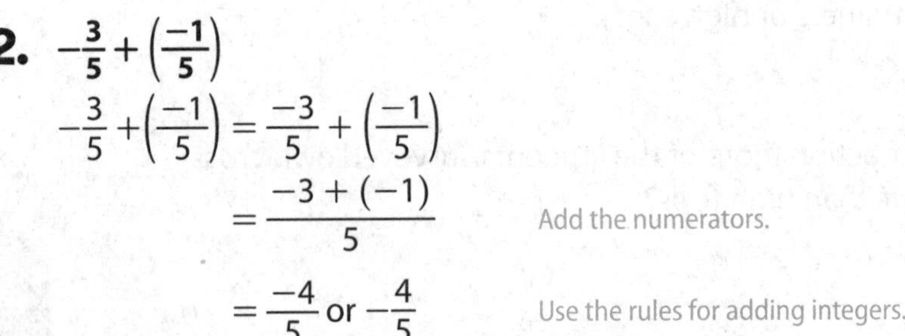

Got It? Do these problems to find out.

a. $\frac{1}{3} + \frac{2}{3}$

b. $-\frac{3}{7} + \frac{1}{7}$

c. $-\frac{2}{5} + \left(-\frac{2}{5}\right)$

d. $-\frac{1}{4} + \frac{1}{4}$

a. ______

b. ______

c. ______

d. ______

Example

3. Sofia ate $\frac{3}{5}$ of a cheese pizza. Jack ate $\frac{1}{5}$ of a cheese pizza and $\frac{2}{5}$ of a pepperoni pizza. How much pizza did Sofia and Jack eat altogether?

$\frac{3}{5}+\left(\frac{1}{5}+\frac{2}{5}\right)=\frac{3}{5}+\left(\frac{2}{5}+\frac{1}{5}\right)$ Commutative Property of Addition

$=\left(\frac{3}{5}+\frac{2}{5}\right)+\frac{1}{5}$ Associative Property of Addition

$=1+\frac{1}{5}$ or $1\frac{1}{5}$ Simplify.

So, Sofia and Jack ate $1\frac{1}{5}$ pizzas altogether.

Got It? Do this problem to find out.

e. Eduardo used fabric to make three costumes. He used $\frac{1}{4}$ yard for the first, $\frac{2}{4}$ yard for the second, and $\frac{3}{4}$ yard for the third costume. How much fabric did Eduardo use altogether?

e. ______

Examples

4. Determine $-\frac{5}{8}-\frac{3}{8}$.

$-\frac{5}{8}-\frac{3}{8}=-\frac{5}{8}+\left(-\frac{3}{8}\right)$ Add $-\frac{3}{8}$.

$=\frac{-5+(-3)}{8}$ Add the numerators.

$=-\frac{8}{8}$ or -1 Simplify.

Subtracting Integers

To subtract an integer, add its opposite.

$-9-(-4)=-9+4$

$=-5$

5. Determine $\frac{5}{8}-\frac{7}{8}$.

$\frac{5}{8}-\frac{7}{8}=\frac{5-7}{8}$ Subtract the numerators.

$=-\frac{2}{8}$ or $-\frac{1}{4}$ Simplify.

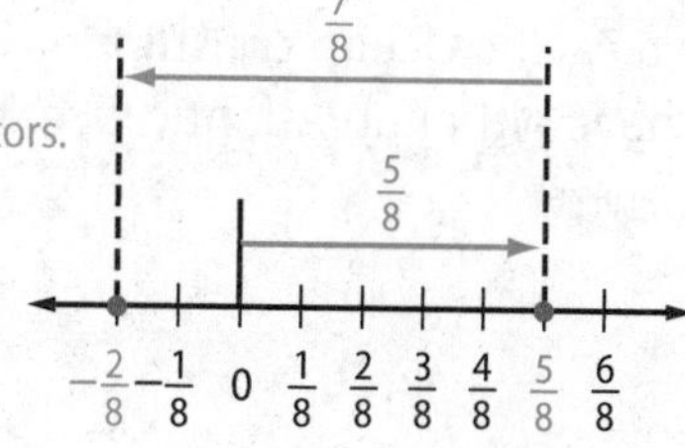

Got It? Do these problems to find out.

f. $\frac{5}{9}-\frac{2}{9}$

g. $-\frac{5}{9}-\frac{2}{9}$

h. $-\frac{11}{12}-\left(-\frac{5}{12}\right)$

f. ______

g. ______

h. ______

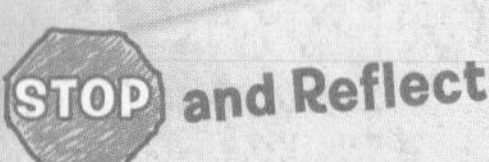

In Example 6, what word or words indicate that you should subtract to solve the problem? Write your answer below.

Choose an Operation

You can add or subtract like fractions to solve real-world problems.

Example

6. About $\frac{8}{100}$ of the population of the United States lives in Texas. Another $\frac{4}{100}$ lives in Ohio. About what fraction more of the U.S. population lives in Texas than in Ohio?

$\frac{8}{100} - \frac{4}{100} = \frac{8-4}{100}$ Subtract the numerators.

$= \frac{4}{100}$ or $\frac{1}{25}$ Simplify.

About $\frac{1}{25}$ more of the U.S. population lives in Texas than in Ohio.

Guided Practice

Add or subtract. Express in simplest form. (Examples 1–5)

1. $\frac{3}{5} + \frac{1}{5} =$ ______

2. $\frac{2}{7} + \frac{1}{7} =$ ______

3. $\left(\frac{5}{8} + \frac{1}{8}\right) + \frac{3}{8} =$ ______

4. $-\frac{4}{5} - \left(-\frac{1}{5}\right) =$ ______

5. $\frac{5}{14} - \left(-\frac{1}{14}\right) =$ ______

6. $\frac{2}{7} - \frac{6}{7} =$ ______

7. Of the 50 states in the United States, 14 have an Atlantic Ocean coastline and 5 have a Pacific Ocean coastline. What fraction of U.S. states have either an Atlantic Ocean or Pacific Ocean coastline? (Example 6)

8. **Building on the Essential Question** What is a simple rule for adding and subtracting like fractions?

Rate Yourself!

How confident are you about adding and subtracting like fractions? Check the box that applies.

Check

Find out online. Use the Self-Check Quiz.

FOLDABLES Time to update your Foldable!

Name ______ My Homework ______

Independent Practice

7.3(A), 7.1(C) TEKS

Add or subtract. Express in simplest form. (Examples 1, 2, 4 and 5)

1. $\frac{5}{7}+\frac{6}{7}=$ ______

2. $\frac{3}{8}+\left(-\frac{7}{8}\right)=$ ______

3. $-\frac{1}{9}+\left(-\frac{5}{9}\right)=$ ______

4. $\frac{9}{10}-\frac{3}{10}=$ ______

5. $-\frac{3}{4}+\left(-\frac{3}{4}\right)=$ ______

6. $-\frac{5}{9}-\frac{2}{9}=$ ______

7. In Mr. Navarro's first period class, $\frac{17}{28}$ of the students got an A on their math test. In his second period class, $\frac{11}{28}$ of the students got an A. What fraction more of the students got an A in Mr. Navarro's first period class than in his second period class? Express in simplest form. (Example 6)

______

8. To make a greeting card, Bryce used $\frac{1}{8}$ sheet of red paper, $\frac{3}{8}$ sheet of green paper, and $\frac{7}{8}$ sheet of white paper. How many sheets of paper did Bryce use? (Example 3) ______

9. The table shows the Instant Messenger abbreviations students at Hillside Middle School use the most.

Instant Messenger Abbreviations	
L8R (Later)	$\frac{48}{100}$
LOL (Laughing out loud)	$\frac{26}{100}$
BRB (Be right back)	$\frac{19}{100}$
CUL8R (See you later)	$\frac{7}{100}$

   a. What fraction of these students uses LOL or CUL8R when using Instant Messenger? ______

   b. What fraction of these students uses L8R or BRB when using Instant Messenger? ______

   c. What fraction more of these students write L8R than CUL8R when using Instant Messenger? ______

10. **Select Tools and Techniques** Cross out the expression that does not belong. Explain your reasoning.

$\frac{2}{7}+\frac{3}{7}$	$\frac{4}{7}-(-\frac{1}{7})$
$\frac{8}{7}-\frac{3}{7}$	$\frac{10}{7}+(-\frac{3}{7})$

11. **Find the Error** Kylie is adding $\frac{2}{7}$ and $-\frac{3}{7}$. Find her mistake and correct it.

$$\frac{2}{7}+(\frac{-3}{7})=\frac{2+(-3)}{7+7}$$
$$=-\frac{1}{14}$$

H.O.T. Problems Higher-Order Thinking

12. **Analyze** Select two like fractions with a difference of $\frac{1}{3}$ and with denominators that are not 3. Justify your selection.

13. **Evaluate** Simplify the following expression.

$$\frac{14}{15}+\frac{13}{15}-\frac{12}{15}+\frac{11}{15}-\frac{10}{15}+\ldots-\frac{4}{15}+\frac{3}{15}-\frac{2}{15}+\frac{1}{15}$$

14. **Create** Write a real-world problem that can be solved by adding or subtracting like fractions. Then solve the problem.

15. **Analyze** Is the difference between a positive like fraction and a negative like fraction *always*, *sometimes*, or *never* positive? Justify your answer with an example.

Name ______

Multi-Step Problem Solving

16. Moki asked his classmates where they would like to take a vacation. The bar graph shows the fraction of the class that chose each option. What fraction more of the class prefer the beach than the other three vacations combined? N MD MP

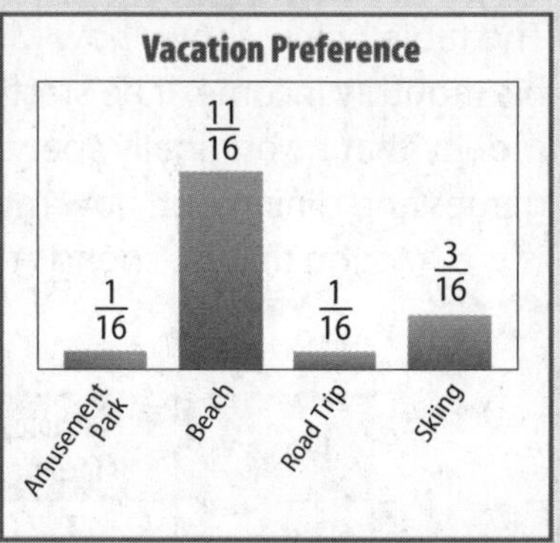

Ⓐ $\frac{3}{8}$

Ⓑ $\frac{9}{16}$

Ⓒ $\frac{5}{8}$

Ⓓ $\frac{5}{16}$

Use a problem-solving model to solve this problem.

1 Analyze

Read the problem. Circle the information you know.
Underline what the problem is asking you to find.

2 Plan

What will you need to do to solve the problem? Write your plan in steps.

Step 1 ______ the fractions for amusement park, road trip, and skiing.

Step 2 ______ the sum from the classmates that prefer the beach.

3 Solve

Use your plan to solve the problem. Show your steps.

$\frac{1}{16} + \frac{1}{16} + \frac{3}{16} =$ ____ Determine the sum.

____ − ____ = ____ or ____ Subtract to determine the difference.

There are ____ more of the class that prefer a beach vacation.

The correct answer is ____. Fill in that answer choice.

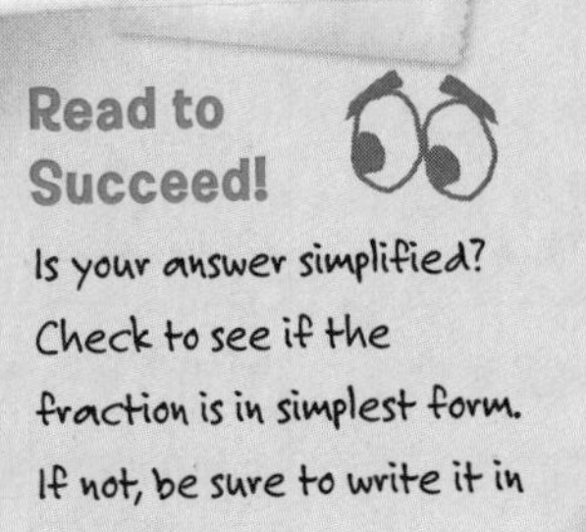

4 Justify and Evaluate

How do you know your solution is accurate?

______

______

______

N = Number and Operations MD = Measurement and Data MP = Mathematical Processes

More Multi-Step Problem Solving

Use a problem-solving model to solve each problem.

17. The table below shows how Mason spends his monthly income. If he starts saving the money that he originally spent on video games and dining out, how much greater is the fraction that he spends than saves? N MP

Category	Fraction of Income
Clothing	$\frac{7}{15}$
Music	$\frac{2}{15}$
Video Games	$\frac{4}{15}$
Dining Out	$\frac{2}{15}$

Ⓐ $\frac{1}{5}$ Ⓑ $\frac{3}{2}$ Ⓒ $\frac{3}{5}$ Ⓓ $\frac{2}{5}$

18. The table shows two types of music notes and how many beats they represent. How many total beats are represented by an augmented eighth followed by two sixteenth notes and another augmented eighth note? N MP

Note	Symbol	Beats
Sixteenth Note		$\frac{1}{4}$
Augmented Eighth Note		$\frac{3}{4}$

19. The table shows the time Jira spends as she gets ready for school. The tasks are listed in order of when she completes them. How many minutes does she spend getting ready before she brushes her teeth? N MP

Task	Time Spent (hours)
Shower	$\frac{2}{12}$
Get dressed	$\frac{1}{12}$
Eat breakfast	$\frac{3}{12}$
Brush teeth	$\frac{1}{12}$
Fix hair	$\frac{5}{12}$

20. The table shows two data sets. Which set has a greater average? By how much greater?

Data Set 1	$-\frac{10}{11}$	$-\frac{2}{11}$	$\frac{7}{11}$	$\frac{5}{11}$
Data Set 2	$-\frac{9}{31}$	$-\frac{1}{31}$	$\frac{3}{31}$	$\frac{1}{31}$

N = Number and Operations MP = Mathematical Processes

Fluently Add and Subtract Rational Numbers: Unlike Fractions

Launch the Lesson: Real World

Brianna practiced softball for 15 minutes and basketball for 20 minutes. What fraction of one hour did she practice?

1. Complete the table to show the fractions of one hour for certain minutes.

Number of Minutes	Fraction of One Hour	Simplified Fraction
5	$\frac{5}{60}$	$\frac{1}{12}$
10		
15		
20		
30		

2. Explain why $\frac{1}{6}$ hour + $\frac{1}{3}$ hour = $\frac{1}{2}$ hour.

3. Explain why $\frac{7}{12}$ hour − $\frac{1}{2}$ hour = $\frac{1}{12}$ hour.

Which MP Mathematical Processes did you use? Shade the circle(s) that applies.

Ⓐ Apply Math to the Real World.
Ⓑ Use a Problem-Solving Model.
Ⓒ Select Tools and Techniques.
Ⓓ Use Multiple Representations.
Ⓔ Organize Ideas.
Ⓕ Analyze Relationships.
Ⓖ Justify Arguments.

Texas Essential Knowledge and Skills

Targeted TEKS

7.3(A) Add, subtract, multiply, and divide rational numbers fluently. *Also addresses 7.3(B).*

Mathematical Processes

7.1(A), 7.1(B), 7.1(G)

Vocabulary

unlike fractions

Essential Question

WHAT happens when you add, subtract, multiply, and divide rational numbers?

Key Concept

Add or Subtract Unlike Fractions

To add or subtract fractions with different denominators,

- Rename the fractions using the least common denominator (LCD).
- Add or subtract as with like fractions.
- If necessary, simplify the sum or difference.

Work Zone

Before you can add two **unlike fractions**, or fractions with different denominators, rename one or both of the fractions so that they have a common denominator.

Watch Tutor

Example

1. Determine $\frac{1}{2} + \frac{1}{4}$.

Method 1 **Use a number line.**

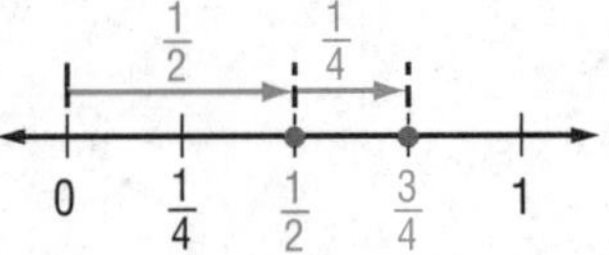

Divide the number line into fourths since the LCD is 4.

Method 2 **Use the LCD.**

The least common denominator of $\frac{1}{2}$ and $\frac{1}{4}$ is 4.

$\frac{1}{2} + \frac{1}{4} = \frac{1 \times 2}{2 \times 2} + \frac{1 \times 1}{4 \times 1}$ Rename using the LCD, 4.

$= \frac{2}{4} + \frac{1}{4}$ Add the fractions.

$= \frac{3}{4}$ Simplify.

Using either method, $\frac{1}{2} + \frac{1}{4} = \frac{3}{4}$.

STOP and Reflect

Circle the pairs of fractions that are unlike fractions.

$\frac{1}{3}$ and $\frac{5}{3}$ $\frac{1}{7}$ and $\frac{1}{5}$ $\frac{5}{9}$ and $\frac{4}{11}$

Got It? **Do these problems to find out.**

Add. Express in simplest form.

a. $\frac{1}{6} + \frac{2}{3}$

b. $\frac{9}{10} + \left(-\frac{1}{2}\right)$

c. $\frac{1}{4} + \frac{3}{8}$

d. $-\frac{1}{3} + \left(-\frac{1}{4}\right)$

a. ________

b. ________

c. ________

d. ________

Example

2. **Determine** $\left(-\frac{3}{4}+\frac{5}{9}\right)+\frac{7}{4}$.

$\left(-\frac{3}{4}+\frac{5}{9}\right)+\frac{7}{4}=\left(\frac{5}{9}+\left(-\frac{3}{4}\right)\right)+\frac{7}{4}$ Commutative Property of Addition

$=\frac{5}{9}+\left(-\frac{3}{4}+\frac{7}{4}\right)$ Associative Property of Addition

$=\frac{5}{9}+1$ or $1\frac{5}{9}$ Simplify.

Show your work.

Got It? Do these problems to find out.

e. $\frac{2}{5}+\left(\frac{4}{7}+\frac{3}{5}\right)$

f. $\left(-\frac{3}{10}+\frac{5}{8}\right)+\frac{23}{10}$

e. ______

f. ______

Example

3. **Determine** $-\frac{2}{3}-\frac{1}{2}$.

Method 1 **Use a number line.**

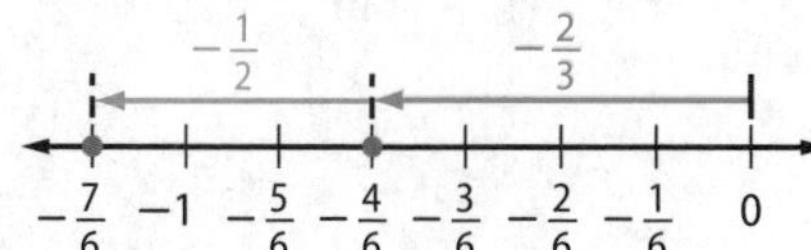

Divide the number line into sixths since the LCD is 6.

Method 2 **Use the LCD.**

$-\frac{2}{3}-\frac{1}{2}=-\frac{2\times 2}{3\times 2}-\frac{1\times 3}{2\times 3}$ Rename using the LCD, 6.

$=-\frac{4}{6}-\frac{3}{6}$ Simplify.

$=\frac{-4}{6}-\frac{3}{6}$ Rewrite $-\frac{4}{6}$ as $\frac{-4}{6}$.

$=\frac{-4-3}{6}$ or $\frac{-7}{6}$ Subtract the numerators. Simplify.

Check by adding $-\frac{7}{6}+\frac{1}{2}=-\frac{7}{6}+\frac{3}{6}=-\frac{4}{6}$ or $-\frac{2}{3}$ ✔

Using either method, $-\frac{2}{3}-\frac{1}{2}=-\frac{7}{6}$ or $-1\frac{1}{6}$.

Check for Reasonableness

Estimate the difference.

$-\frac{2}{3}-\frac{1}{2}\approx-\frac{1}{2}-\frac{1}{2}$ or -1

Compare $-\frac{7}{6}$ to the estimate. $-\frac{7}{6}\approx-1$. So, the answer is reasonable.

Got It? Do these problems to find out.

Subtract. Express in simplest form.

g. $\frac{5}{8}-\frac{1}{4}$

h. $\frac{3}{4}-\frac{1}{3}$

i. $\frac{1}{2}-\left(-\frac{2}{5}\right)$

g. ______

h. ______

i. ______

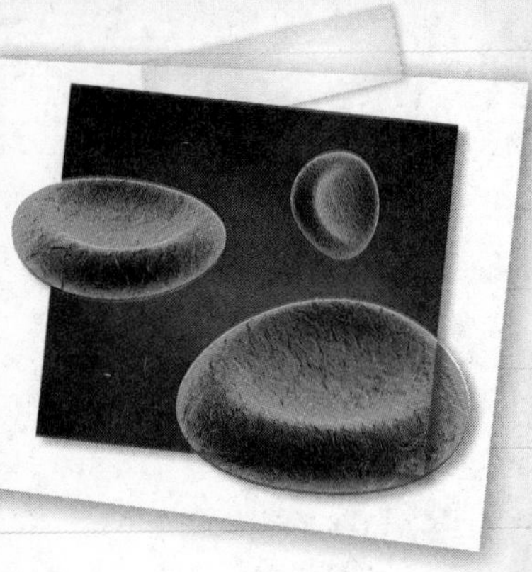

Choose an Operation

Add or subtract unlike fractions to solve real-world problems.

Example

4. STEM Use the table to determine the fraction of the total population that has type A or type B blood.

Blood Type Frequencies	
ABO Type	**Fraction**
O	$\frac{11}{25}$
A	$\frac{21}{50}$
B	$\frac{1}{10}$
AB	$\frac{1}{25}$

To determine the fraction of the total population, add $\frac{21}{50}$ and $\frac{1}{10}$.

$\frac{21}{50} + \frac{1}{10} = \frac{21 \times 1}{50 \times 1} + \frac{1 \times 5}{10 \times 5}$ Rename using the LCD, 50.

$= \frac{21}{50} + \frac{5}{50}$ Add the fractions.

$= \frac{26}{50}$ or $\frac{13}{25}$ Simplify.

So, $\frac{13}{25}$ of the population has type A or type B blood.

Guided Practice

Add or subtract. Express in simplest form. (Examples 1–3)

1. $\frac{3}{5} + \frac{1}{10} =$ ______

2. $-\frac{5}{6} + \left(-\frac{4}{9}\right) =$ ______

3. $\left(\frac{7}{8} + \frac{3}{11}\right) + \frac{1}{8} =$ ______

4. $\frac{4}{5} - \frac{3}{10} =$ ______

5. $\frac{3}{8} - \left(-\frac{1}{4}\right) =$ ______

6. $\frac{3}{4} - \frac{1}{3} =$ ______

7. Cassandra cuts $\frac{5}{16}$ inch off the top of a photo and $\frac{3}{8}$ inch off the bottom. How much shorter is the total height of the photo now? Explain. (Example 4)

8. **Building on the Essential Question** Compare adding unlike fractions and adding like fractions.

Rate Yourself!

Are you ready to move on? Shade the section that applies.

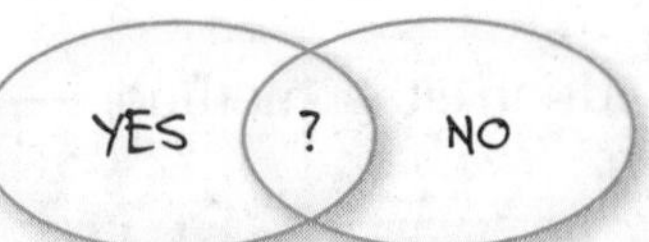

Find out online. Use the Self-Check Quiz.

FOLDABLES Time to update your Foldable!

Name ______ My Homework ______

Independent Practice

7.3(A), 7.3(B), 7.1(G) TEKS

Add or subtract. Express in simplest form. (Examples 1–3)

1. $\frac{1}{6} + \frac{3}{8} =$ ______

2. $-\frac{1}{15} + \left(-\frac{3}{5}\right) =$ ______

3. $\left(\frac{15}{8} + \frac{2}{5}\right) + \left(-\frac{7}{8}\right) =$ ______

4. $\left(-\frac{7}{10}\right) - \frac{2}{5} =$ ______

5. $\frac{7}{9} - \frac{1}{3} =$ ______

6. $-\frac{7}{12} + \frac{7}{10} =$ ______

7. $-\frac{4}{9} - \frac{2}{15} =$ ______

8. $\frac{5}{8} + \frac{11}{12} =$ ______

9. $\frac{7}{9} + \frac{5}{6} =$ ______

MP **Justify Arguments Choose an operation to solve each problem. Explain your reasoning. Then solve the problem. Express in simplest form.** (Example 4)

10. Mrs. Escalante was riding a bicycle on a bike path. After riding $\frac{2}{3}$ of a mile, she discovered that she still needed to travel $\frac{3}{4}$ of a mile to reach the end of the path. How long is the bike path?

______

______

11. Four students were scheduled to give book reports in 1 hour. After the first report, $\frac{2}{3}$ hour remained. The next two reports took $\frac{1}{6}$ hour and $\frac{1}{4}$ hour. What fraction of the hour remained?

______

______

12. One hundred sixty cell phone owners were surveyed.

    a. What fraction of owners prefers using their cell phone for text messaging or playing games? Explain.

    ______

    b. What fraction of owners prefers using their phone to take pictures or text message?

    ______

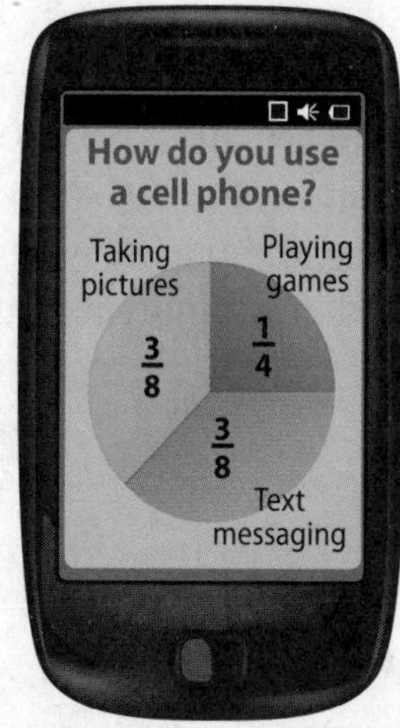

13. Pepita and Francisco each spend an equal amount of time on homework. The table shows the fraction of time they spend on each subject. Complete the table by determining the missing fraction for each student.

Homework	Fraction of Time	
	Pepita	Francisco
Math		$\frac{1}{2}$
English	$\frac{2}{3}$	
Science	$\frac{1}{6}$	$\frac{3}{8}$

14. Find the Error Theresa is determining $\frac{1}{4} + \frac{3}{5}$. Find her mistake and correct it. Explain your answer.

H.O.T. Problems Higher-Order Thinking

15. Analyze Fractions whose numerators are 1, such as $\frac{1}{2}$ or $\frac{1}{3}$, are called *unit fractions*. Devise a method you can use to add two unit fractions mentally.

16. Analyze Provide a counterexample to the following statement.

The sum of three fractions with odd numerators is never $\frac{1}{2}$.

17. Analyze Suppose a bucket is placed under two faucets. If one faucet is turned on alone, the bucket will be filled in 6 minutes. If the other faucet is turned on alone, the bucket will be filled in 4 minutes. What fraction of the bucket will be filled in 1 minute if both faucets are turned on at the same time? Explain.

Name ____________________

Multi-Step Problem Solving

18. Rashan has a reading assignment to complete this week. He completes some of the assignment each day. By Wednesday night, he has completed two-thirds of his assignment. What fraction more of his assignment does Rashan complete on Wednesday than on Tuesday? N MP

Day	Total Fraction Completed
Monday	$\frac{1}{6}$
Tuesday	$\frac{1}{4}$
Wednesday	$\frac{2}{3}$

Ⓐ $\frac{5}{12}$

Ⓑ $\frac{1}{12}$

Ⓒ $\frac{1}{3}$

Ⓓ $\frac{1}{4}$

Use a problem-solving model to solve this problem.

1 Analyze

Read the problem. Circle the information you know.
Underline what the problem is asking you to find.

2 Plan

What will you need to do to solve the problem? Write your plan in steps.

Step 1 Determine the __________ completed on Wednesday and Tuesday.

Step 2 Determine how much more he completed __________.

3 Solve

Use your plan to solve the problem. Show your steps.

$\frac{2}{3} - \frac{1}{4} =$ ____ $\frac{1}{4} - \frac{1}{6} =$ ____

Determine how much more was completed on Wednesday.

____ − ____ = ________ Subtract.

He completed ____ more of the assignment on Wednesday.

The correct answer is ______. Fill in that answer choice.

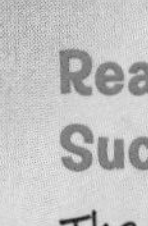

Read to Succeed!

The fractions in the table are cumulative, meaning they are the total fraction he has completed. It is not the fraction he completes each day.

4 Justify and Evaluate

How do you know your solution is accurate?

____

____

____

N = Number and Operations MP = Mathematical Processes

More Multi-Step Problem Solving

Use a problem-solving model to solve each problem.

19. Over three days, a veterinarian measures the difference between a cat's weight and the weight on its first visit. What is the net weight change of the cat's weight, in pounds, from the second visit to the fourth? N MP

Visit	Difference from Original Weight (lb)
Second	$-\frac{1}{2}$
Third	$-\frac{1}{5}$
Fourth	$-\frac{3}{10}$

Ⓐ $\frac{1}{5}$

Ⓑ $\frac{1}{10}$

Ⓒ $-\frac{1}{5}$

Ⓓ $-\frac{1}{10}$

20. How many units greater is the perimeter of Triangle *B* than the perimeter of Triangle *A*? N EE MP

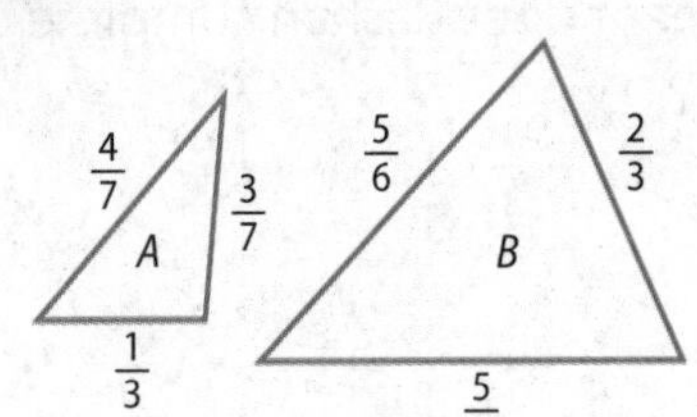

21. The table shows the fraction of each soccer game that Zoe spent playing goalie. On average, how much of one game did Zoe spend playing goalie? Express your answer as a decimal. N MP MD

Game	Fraction of Game as Goalie
1	$\frac{1}{4}$
2	$\frac{5}{8}$
3	$\frac{1}{2}$
4	$\frac{5}{8}$

22. The circle graph shows how Ramiro handles his monthly income. What fraction more does he spend or give to charity than he saves? N P MP

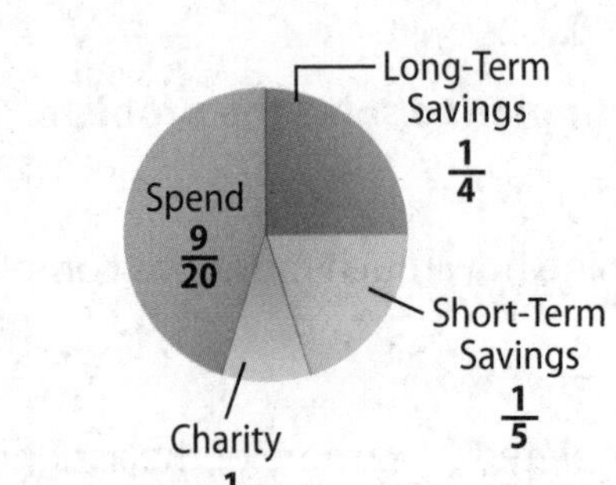

N = Number and Operations P = Proportionality EE = Expressions, Equations, and Relationships MD = Measurement and Data MP = Mathematical Processes

Fluently Add and Subtract Rational Numbers: Mixed Numbers

Launch the Lesson: Real World

Texas Essential Knowledge and Skills

Targeted TEKS

7.3(A) Add, subtract, multiply, and divide rational numbers fluently. *Also addresses 7.3(B).*

Mathematical Processes

7.1(A), 7.1(B), 7.1(G)

Essential Question

WHAT happens when you add, subtract, multiply, and divide rational numbers?

Junior and adult hockey sticks are shown below. What is the difference between the length of the two hockey sticks?

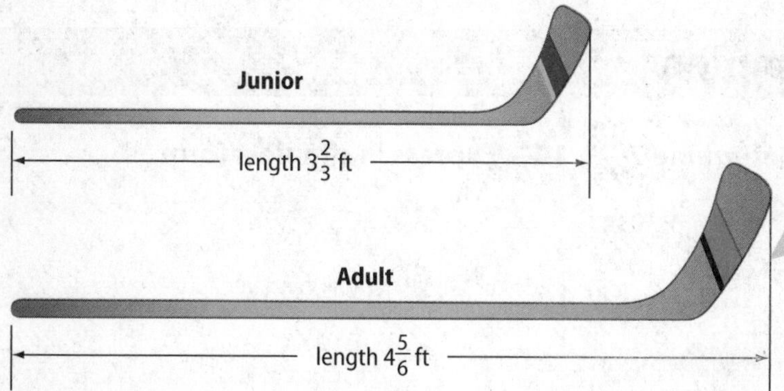

1. Write an expression to determine how much longer the adult hockey stick is than the junior hockey stick.

Rename the fractions using the LCD, 6.

Subtract the fractions. Then subtract the whole numbers.

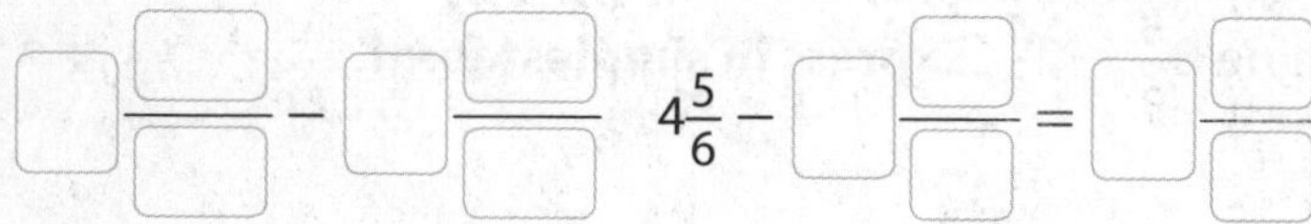

2. Explain how to determine $3\frac{7}{10} - 2\frac{2}{5}$. Then use your conjecture to determine the difference. ______

Which MP Mathematical Processes did you use? Shade the circle(s) that applies.

Ⓐ Apply Math to the Real World.
Ⓑ Use a Problem-Solving Model.
Ⓒ Select Tools and Techniques.
Ⓓ Use Multiple Representations.
Ⓔ Organize Ideas.
Ⓕ Analyze Relationships.
Ⓖ Justify Arguments.

Work Zone

Add and Subtract Mixed Numbers

To add or subtract mixed numbers, first add or subtract the fractions. If necessary, rename them using the LCD. Then add or subtract the whole numbers and simplify if necessary.

Sometimes when you subtract mixed numbers, the fraction in the first mixed number is less than the fraction in the second mixed number. In this case, rename one or both fractions in order to subtract.

Properties

$120\frac{1}{2} + 40\frac{1}{3}$ can be written as $(120 + \frac{1}{2}) + (40 + \frac{1}{3})$. Then the Commutative and Associative Properties can be used to reorder and regroup the numbers to determine the sum.

Tutor

Examples

1. Determine $7\frac{4}{9} + 10\frac{2}{9}$. Express in simplest form.

Estimate $7 + 10 = 17$

$$\begin{array}{r} 7\frac{4}{9} \\ +10\frac{2}{9} \\ \hline 17\frac{6}{9} \text{ or } 17\frac{2}{3} \end{array}$$

Add the whole numbers and fractions separately.

Simplify.

Check for Reasonableness $17\frac{2}{3} \approx 17$ ✓

2. Determine $8\frac{5}{6} - 2\frac{1}{3}$. Express in simplest form.

Estimate $9 - 2 = 7$

$$\begin{array}{r} 8\frac{5}{6} \\ -2\frac{1}{3} \\ \hline \end{array} \rightarrow \begin{array}{r} 8\frac{5}{6} \\ -2\frac{2}{6} \\ \hline 6\frac{3}{6} \text{ or } 6\frac{1}{2} \end{array}$$

Rename the fraction using the LCD. Then subtract.

Simplify.

Check for Reasonableness $6\frac{1}{2} \approx 7$ ✓

Got It? Do these problems to find out.

Add or subtract. Express in simplest form.

a. $6\frac{1}{8} + 2\frac{5}{8}$ **b.** $5\frac{1}{5} + 2\frac{3}{10}$ **c.** $1\frac{5}{9} + 4\frac{1}{6}$

d. $5\frac{4}{5} - 1\frac{3}{10}$ **e.** $13\frac{7}{8} - 9\frac{3}{4}$ **f.** $8\frac{2}{3} - 2\frac{1}{2}$

a. ______

b. ______

c. ______

d. ______

e. ______

f. ______

Example

3. **Determine $2\frac{1}{3} - 1\frac{2}{3}$.**

Method 1 **Rename Mixed Numbers**

Estimate $2 - 1\frac{1}{2} = \frac{1}{2}$

Since $\frac{1}{3}$ is less than $\frac{2}{3}$, rename $2\frac{1}{3}$ before subtracting.

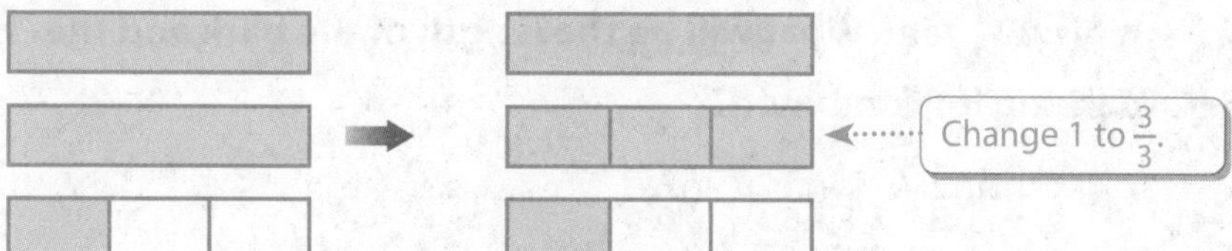

$2\frac{1}{3} = 1\frac{3}{3} + \frac{1}{3}$ or $1\frac{4}{3}$

$2\frac{1}{3} \rightarrow 1\frac{4}{3}$ Rename $2\frac{1}{3}$ as $1\frac{4}{3}$.

$-1\frac{2}{3} \rightarrow -1\frac{2}{3}$ Subtract the whole numbers and then the fractions.

$\frac{2}{3}$

Check for Reasonableness $\frac{2}{3} \approx \frac{1}{2}$ ✓

Method 2 **Express as Improper Fractions**

$2\frac{1}{3} \rightarrow \frac{7}{3}$ Write $2\frac{1}{3}$ as $\frac{7}{3}$.

$-1\frac{2}{3} \rightarrow -\frac{5}{3}$ Write $1\frac{2}{3}$ as $\frac{5}{3}$.

$\frac{2}{3}$ Simplify.

So, $2\frac{1}{3} - 1\frac{2}{3} = \frac{2}{3}$.

Using either method, the answer is $\frac{2}{3}$.

Fractions Greater Than One

An improper fraction has a numerator that is greater than or equal to the denominator. Examples of improper fractions are $\frac{5}{4}$ and $2\frac{6}{5}$.

Got It? Do these problems to find out.

Subtract. Express in simplest form.

g. $7 - 1\frac{1}{2}$

h. $5\frac{3}{8} - 4\frac{11}{12}$

i. $11\frac{2}{5} - 2\frac{3}{5}$

j. $8 - 3\frac{3}{4}$

k. $3\frac{1}{4} - 1\frac{3}{4}$

l. $16 - 5\frac{5}{6}$

g. ________

h. ________

i. ________

j. ________

k. ________

l. ________

Choose an Operation

Add or subtract unlike fractions to solve real-world problems.

Example

4. An urban planner is designing a skateboard park. The length of the skateboard park is $120\frac{1}{2}$ feet. The length of the parking lot is $40\frac{1}{3}$ feet. What will be the length of the park and the parking lot combined?

$120\frac{1}{2} + 40\frac{1}{3} = 120\frac{3}{6} + 40\frac{2}{6}$ — Rename $\frac{1}{2}$ as $\frac{3}{6}$ and $\frac{1}{3}$ as $\frac{2}{6}$.

$= 160 + \frac{5}{6}$ — Add the whole numbers and fractions separately.

$= 160\frac{5}{6}$ — Simplify.

The total length is $160\frac{5}{6}$ feet.

Guided Practice

Add or subtract. Express in simplest form. (Examples 1–3)

1. $8\frac{1}{2} + 3\frac{4}{5} =$ ______

2. $7\frac{5}{6} - 3\frac{1}{6} =$ ______

3. $11 - 6\frac{3}{8} =$ ______

4. A hybrid car's gas tank can hold $11\frac{9}{10}$ gallons of gasoline. It contains $8\frac{3}{4}$ gallons of gasoline right now. How much more gasoline is needed to fill the tank? (Example 4) ______

5. **Building on the Essential Question** How can you subtract mixed numbers when the fraction in the first mixed number is less than the fraction in the second mixed number? ______

Rate Yourself!

How confident are you about adding and subtracting mixed numbers? Shade the ring on the target.

Find out online. Use the Self-Check Quiz.

Name ____________________ My Homework ____________________

Independent Practice

7.3(A), 7.3(B), 7.1(C) TEKS

Add or subtract. Express in simplest form. (Examples 1–3)

1. $2\frac{1}{9} + 7\frac{4}{9} =$ ______

2. $8\frac{5}{12} + 11\frac{1}{4} =$ ______

3. $10\frac{4}{5} - 2\frac{1}{5} =$ ______

4. $9\frac{4}{5} - 2\frac{3}{10} =$ ______

5. $11\frac{3}{4} - 4\frac{1}{3} =$ ______

6. $9\frac{1}{5} - 2\frac{3}{5} =$ ______

7. $6\frac{3}{5} - 1\frac{2}{3} =$ ______

8. $14\frac{1}{6} - 7\frac{1}{3} =$ ______

9. $8 - 3\frac{2}{3} =$ ______

MP Justify Arguments For Exercises 10 and 11, choose an operation to solve. Explain your reasoning. Then solve the problem. Express your answer in simplest form. (Example 4)

10. If Juliana and Brody hiked both of the trails listed in the table, how far did they hike?

Trail	Length (mi)
Woodland Park	$3\frac{2}{3}$
Mill Creek Way	$2\frac{5}{6}$

____

11. The length of Kasey's garden is $4\frac{5}{8}$ feet. Determine the width of Kasey's garden if it is $2\frac{7}{8}$ feet shorter than the length.

____

12. Karen wakes up at 6:00 A.M. It takes her $1\frac{1}{4}$ hours to shower, get dressed, and comb her hair. It takes her $\frac{1}{2}$ hour to eat breakfast, brush her teeth, and make her bed. At what time will she be ready for school? ______________________________

Add or subtract. Express in simplest form.

13. $-3\frac{1}{4} + (-1\frac{3}{4}) =$ ______

14. $-3\frac{1}{2} + (-4\frac{2}{3}) =$ ______

15. $6\frac{1}{3} + 1\frac{2}{3} + 5\frac{5}{9} =$ ______

16. $3\frac{1}{4} + 2\frac{5}{6} - 4\frac{1}{3} =$ ______

H.O.T. Problems Higher Order Thinking

17. **Create** Write a real-world problem that could be represented by the expression $5\frac{1}{2} - 3\frac{7}{8}$. Then solve your problem.

18. **Evaluate** A string is cut in half. One of the halves is thrown away. One fifth of the remaining half is cut away and the piece left is 8 feet long. How long was the string initially? Justify your answer.

19. **Create** Using three mixed numbers as sides lengths, draw an equilateral triangle with a perimeter of $8\frac{1}{4}$ feet.

20. **Analyze** Explain how you could use mental math to determine the following sum. Then solve. Justify your answer.

$$1\frac{1}{4} + 2\frac{2}{3} + 3\frac{1}{3} + 4\frac{3}{4}$$

Name ______________________________

Multi-Step Problem Solving

21. The table shows the makeup of the cheese tray at the DeSilva family reunion. If the family eats $6\frac{5}{6}$ pounds of the cheese, how many pounds of cheese remain on the tray? N MP

Type of Cheese	Amount (lb)
Cheddar	$3\frac{1}{2}$
Provolone	$2\frac{1}{2}$
Swiss	$2\frac{1}{4}$

Ⓐ 1 pound
Ⓑ $1\frac{5}{12}$ pound
Ⓒ $1\frac{1}{2}$ pound
Ⓓ $2\frac{7}{12}$ pound

Use a problem-solving model to solve this problem.

1 Analyze

Read the problem. Circle the information you know.
Underline what the problem is asking you to find.

2 Plan

What will you need to do to solve the problem? Write your plan in steps.

Step 1 Determine the amount of cheese on the tray by __________ the mixed numbers.

Step 2 __________ the weight of cheese that was eaten from the original amount on the cheese tray.

3 Solve

Use your plan to solve the problem. Show your steps.
Determine the amount of cheese on the tray. Then subtract.

$3\frac{1}{2} + 2\frac{1}{2} + 2\frac{1}{4} =$ _____ Add.

_____ − _____ = _____ Subtract.

There were _____ pounds remaining on the cheese tray.

The correct answer is _____. Fill in that answer choice.

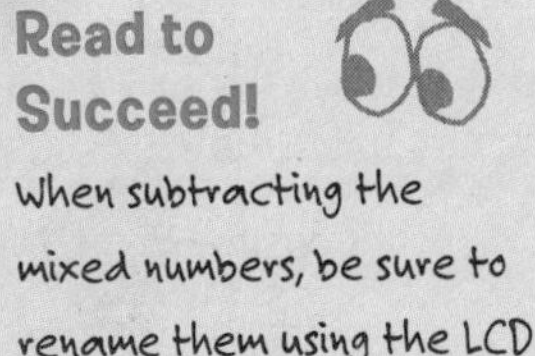

Read to Succeed!
When subtracting the mixed numbers, be sure to rename them using the LCD before trying to subtract.

4 Justify and Evaluate

How do you know your solution is accurate?

____

____

____

N = Number and Operations MP = Mathematical Processes

More Multi-Step Problem Solving

Use a problem-solving model to solve each problem.

22. The table shows Lily's length from the time she was born. How many more inches did she grow during the first month than during her second month? N MP

Age	Length (in.)
Birth	$19\frac{3}{4}$
1 Month	$22\frac{1}{4}$
2 Month	$23\frac{1}{4}$

Ⓐ $\frac{3}{4}$ inch

Ⓑ $1\frac{1}{4}$ inches

Ⓒ $1\frac{1}{2}$ inches

Ⓓ $3\frac{1}{2}$ inches

23. The side measures for two sides of a triangle are shown. What is the measure, in inches, of side *A* if the perimeter of the triangle is 180 inches? N EE MP

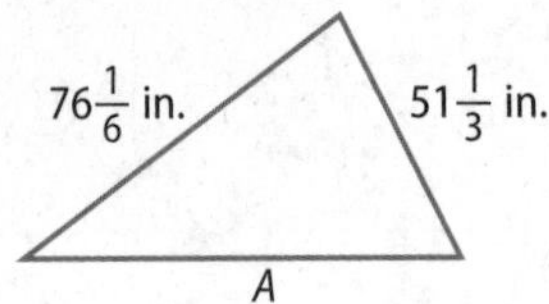

24. Farid's family took a road trip. The circle graph shows the part of an hour that each family member drove. What fraction more of an hour did his parents drive than the rest of the family combined? N MD MP

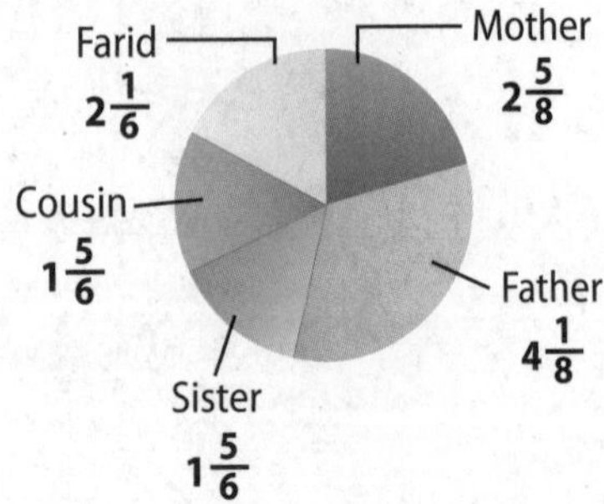

25. A point is plotted on a coordinate grid at $-7\frac{2}{3}, -11\frac{1}{2}$. A second point is plotted 9 units to the right and $2\frac{2}{3}$ units down. What are the coordinates of the second point? Is it in a different quadrant than the first point? Explain your reasoning. N MD MP

N = Number and Operations EE = Expressions, Equations, and Relationships MD = Measurement and Data MP = Mathematical Processes

Lesson 8

Fluently Multiply Rational Numbers

Launch the Lesson: Real World

There are 12 students at the lunch table. Two thirds of the students ordered a hamburger for lunch. One half of those students that ordered a hamburger put cheese on it. What fraction of the students at the lunch tables ordered a cheeseburger?

Step 1 Draw an X through the students that did not order a hamburger.

Step 2 Draw a C on the students that ordered cheese on their hamburger.

1. What fraction of the students at the lunch table ordered a cheeseburger? Express in simplest form. ______

2. What is $\frac{1}{2}$ of $\frac{2}{3}$? Express in simplest form. ______

3. Write your own word problem that involves fractions that can be solved using a diagram like the one above.

______

______

______

Which MP Mathematical Processes did you use? Shade the circle(s) that applies.

Ⓐ Apply Math to the Real World.
Ⓑ Use a Problem-Solving Model.
Ⓒ Select Tools and Techniques.
Ⓓ Use Multiple Representations.
Ⓔ Organize Ideas.
Ⓕ Analyze Relationships.
Ⓖ Justify Arguments.

Texas Essential Knowledge and Skills

Targeted TEKS
7.3(A) Add, subtract, multiply, and divide rational numbers fluently. *Also addresses 7.3(B).*

Mathematical Processes
7.1(A), 7.1(B), 7.1(C)

Essential Question
WHAT happens when you add, subtract, multiply, and divide rational numbers?

Key Concept

Multiply Fractions

Words To multiply fractions, multiply the numerators and multiply the denominators.

Examples

Numbers: $\frac{1}{2} \times \frac{2}{3} = \frac{1 \times 2}{2 \times 3}$ or $\frac{2}{6}$

Algebra: $\frac{a}{b} \cdot \frac{c}{d} = \frac{a \cdot c}{b \cdot d}$ or $\frac{ac}{bd}$, where $b, d \neq 0$

Work Zone

When multiplying two fractions, express the product in simplest form. The numerator and denominator of either fraction may have common factors. If this is the case, you can simplify before multiplying.

Examples

Multiply. Express in simplest form.

1. $\frac{1}{2} \times \frac{1}{3}$

$\frac{1}{2} \times \frac{1}{3} = \frac{1 \times 1}{2 \times 3}$ ← Multiply the numerators. ← Multiply the denominators.

$= \frac{1}{6}$ Simplify.

2. $2 \times \left(-\frac{3}{4}\right)$

$2 \times \left(-\frac{3}{4}\right) = \frac{2}{1} \times \left(\frac{-3}{4}\right)$ Write 2 as $\frac{2}{1}$ and $-\frac{3}{4}$ as $\frac{-3}{4}$.

$= \frac{2 \times (-3)}{1 \times 4}$ ← Multiply the numerators. ← Multiply the denominators.

$= \frac{-6}{4}$ or $-1\frac{1}{2}$ Simplify.

GCF

In Example 3, GCF stands for the greatest of the common factors of two or more numbers.

Example: The GCF of 8 and 2 is 2.

3. $\frac{2}{7} \times \left(-\frac{3}{8}\right)$

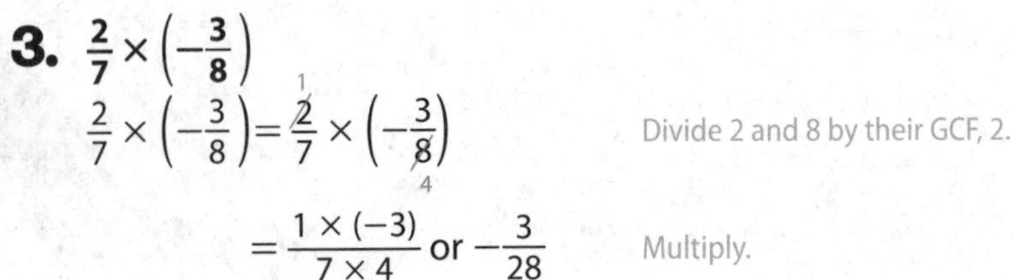

$\frac{2}{7} \times \left(-\frac{3}{8}\right) = \frac{\overset{1}{\cancel{2}}}{7} \times \left(-\frac{3}{\underset{4}{\cancel{8}}}\right)$ Divide 2 and 8 by their GCF, 2.

$= \frac{1 \times (-3)}{7 \times 4}$ or $-\frac{3}{28}$ Multiply.

Got It? Do these problems to find out.

Multiply. Express in simplest form.

a. $\frac{3}{5} \times \frac{1}{2}$ **b.** $\frac{2}{3} \times (-4)$ **c.** $-\frac{1}{3} \times \left(-\frac{3}{7}\right)$

a. ______

b. ______

c. ______

Multiply Mixed Numbers

When multiplying by a mixed number, you can rename the mixed number as an improper fraction. You can also multiply mixed numbers using the Distributive Property and mental math.

Watch Tutor

Example

4. Determine $\frac{1}{2} \times 4\frac{2}{5}$. Express in simplest form.

Estimate $\frac{1}{2} \times 4 = 2$

Method 1 **Rename the mixed number.**

$\frac{1}{2} \times 4\frac{2}{5} = \frac{1}{\cancel{2}_1} \times \frac{\cancel{22}^{11}}{5}$ — Rename $4\frac{2}{5}$ as an improper fraction, $\frac{22}{5}$. Divide 2 and 22 by their GCF, 2.

$= \frac{1 \times 11}{1 \times 5}$ — Multiply.

$= \frac{11}{5}$ — Simplify.

$= 2\frac{1}{5}$ — Simplify.

Method 2 **Use mental math.**

The mixed number $4\frac{2}{5}$ is equal to $4 + \frac{2}{5}$.

So, $\frac{1}{2} \times 4\frac{2}{5} = \frac{1}{2}\left(4 + \frac{2}{5}\right)$. Use the Distributive Property to multiply, then add mentally.

$\frac{1}{2}\left(4 + \frac{2}{5}\right) = 2 + \frac{1}{5}$ — Think half of 4 is 2 and half of 2 fifths is 1 fifth.

$= 2\frac{1}{5}$ — Rewrite the sum as a mixed number.

Check for Reasonableness $2\frac{1}{5} \approx 2$ ✔

So, $\frac{1}{2} \times 4\frac{2}{5} = 2\frac{1}{5}$.

Using either method, the answer is $2\frac{1}{5}$.

Simplifying

If you forget to simplify before multiplying, you can always simplify the final answer. However, it is usually easier to simplify before multiplying.

Got It? Do these problems to find out.

Multiply. Express in simplest form.

d. $\frac{1}{4} \times 8\frac{4}{9}$

e. $5\frac{1}{3} \times 3$

f. $-1\frac{7}{8} \times \left(-2\frac{2}{5}\right)$

d. ______

e. ______

f. ______

Example

Tutor

5. Humans sleep about $\frac{1}{3}$ of each day. Let each year equal $365\frac{1}{4}$ days. Determine the number of days in a year the average human sleeps.

Determine $\frac{1}{3} \times 365\frac{1}{4}$.

Estimate $\frac{1}{3} \times 360 = 120$

$\frac{1}{3} \times 365\frac{1}{4} = \frac{1}{3} \times \frac{1,461}{4}$ Rename the mixed number as an improper fraction.

$= \frac{1}{\cancel{3}_1} \times \frac{\cancel{1,461}^{487}}{4}$ Divide 3 and 1,461 by their GCF, 3.

$= \frac{487}{4}$ or $121\frac{3}{4}$ Multiply. Then rename as a mixed number.

Check for Reasonableness $121\frac{3}{4} \approx 120$ ✔

The average human sleeps $121\frac{3}{4}$ days each year.

Meaning of Multiplication

Recall that one meaning of 3×4 is three groups with 4 in each group. In Example 5, there are $365\frac{1}{4}$ groups with $\frac{1}{3}$ in each group.

Guided Practice

Multiply. Express in simplest form. (Examples 1–4)

1. $\frac{2}{3} \times \frac{1}{3} =$ ______

2. $-\frac{1}{4} \times \left(-\frac{8}{9}\right) =$ ______

3. $2\frac{1}{4} \times \frac{2}{3} =$ ______

4. **STEM** The weight of an object on Mars is about $\frac{2}{5}$ its weight on Earth. How much would an $80\frac{1}{2}$-pound dog weigh on Mars? (Example 5) ______

5. **Building on the Essential Question** How is the process of multiplying fractions different from the process of adding fractions?

______

______

______

______

Rate Yourself!

How well do you understand multiplying fractions? Circle the image that applies.

Clear

Somewhat Clear

Not So Clear

Find out online. Use the Self-Check Quiz.

Check

FOLDABLES Time to update your Foldable!

Independent Practice

7.3(A), 7.3(B), 7.1(C) TEKS

Multiply. Express in simplest form. (Examples 1–4)

1. $\frac{3}{4} \times \frac{1}{8} =$ ______

2. $\frac{2}{5} \times \frac{2}{3} =$ ______

3. $-9 \times \frac{1}{2} =$ ______

4. $-\frac{1}{5} \times \left(-\frac{5}{6}\right) =$ ______

5. $\frac{2}{3} \times \frac{1}{4} =$ ______

6. $-\frac{1}{12} \times \frac{2}{5} =$ ______

7. $\frac{2}{5} \times \frac{15}{16} =$ ______

8. $\frac{4}{7} \times \frac{7}{8} =$ ______

9. $\left(-1\frac{1}{2}\right) \times \frac{2}{3} =$ ______

10. The width of a vegetable garden is $\frac{1}{3}$ times its length. If the length of the garden is $7\frac{3}{4}$ feet, what is the width in simplest form? (Example 5)

______

11. One evening, $\frac{2}{3}$ of the students in Rick's class watched television. Of those students, $\frac{3}{8}$ watched a reality show. Of the students that watched the show, $\frac{1}{4}$ of them recorded the show. What fraction of the students in Rick's class watched and recorded a reality TV show?

______

Write each numerical expression. Then evaluate the expression.

12. one half of negative five eighths

______

______

13. one third of eleven sixteenths

______

______

14. **Apply Math to the Real World** Refer to the graphic novel frame below.

a. The height of the closet is 96 inches, and Aisha would like to have 4 rows of cube organizers. What is the most the height of each cube organizer can be?

b. Aisha would like to stack 3 shoe boxes on top of each other at the bottom of the closet. The height of each shoe box is $4\frac{1}{2}$ inches. What is the total height of the 3 boxes?

H.O.T. Problems Higher-Order Thinking

15. **Create** Write a real-world problem that involves determining the product of $\frac{3}{4}$ and $\frac{1}{8}$.

16. **Analyze** Two positive improper fractions are multiplied. Is the product *sometimes*, *always*, or *never* less than 1? Explain.

17. **Evaluate** Determine two fractions that are each greater than $\frac{2}{5}$ whose product is less than $\frac{2}{5}$.

18. **Evaluate** Determine the missing fraction in the following multiplication sentence. $\frac{5}{8} \times \frac{a}{b} = -\frac{1}{4}$

Name ___

Multi-Step Problem Solving

19. The thermometer shows the temperature in Badger, Minnesota, at 10 P.M. The temperature decreased by $\frac{1}{3}$ of its absolute value by 4 A.M. What is the final temperature, to the nearest degree Fahrenheit? N MP

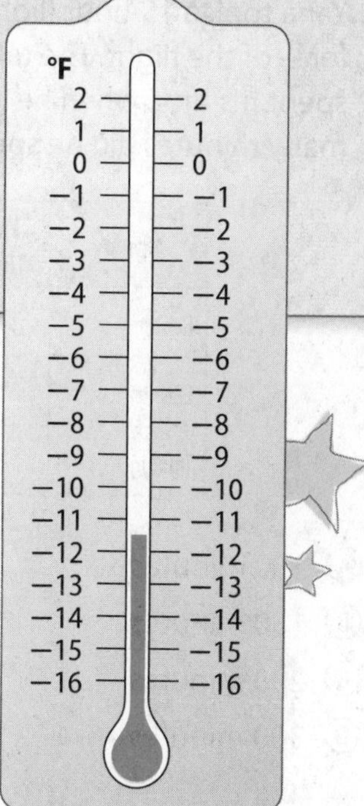

Ⓐ −4
Ⓑ −8
Ⓒ −15
Ⓓ −19

Use a problem-solving model to solve this problem.

1 Analyze

Read the problem. Circle the information you know. Underline what the problem is asking you to find.

2 Plan

What will you need to do to solve the problem? Write your plan in steps.

Step 1 Determine ______ of the absolute value of ______.

Step 2 Then ______ the product from the current temperature.

3 Solve

Use your plan to solve the problem. Show your steps.

Determine the product. Then subtract from the current temperature.

$11\frac{1}{2} \times \frac{1}{3} =$ ______

______ − ______ = ______ Subtract.

The final temperature was about ______ degrees Fahrenheit.

The correct answer is ______. Fill in that answer choice.

Read to Succeed!
The final temperature decreased, which means the absolute value of the final temperature will be greater than the absolute value of the original temperature.

4 Justify and Evaluate

How do you know your solution is accurate?

___

___

___

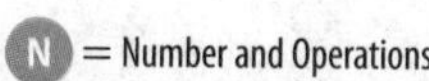

More Multi-Step Problem Solving

Use a problem-solving model to solve each problem.

20. Yana took a 15-hour flight to Korea. He slept for $\frac{1}{3}$ of the flight. The table shows how Yana spent his time when he was awake. How many minutes did he spend talking? N MP

Activity	Fraction of Time Awake
Reading	$\frac{1}{2}$
Eating	$\frac{1}{6}$
Talking	$\frac{1}{3}$

Ⓐ 100 minutes
Ⓑ 180 minutes
Ⓒ 200 minutes
Ⓓ 300 minutes

21. The table shows the number of miles for each segment of a triathlon. Laleh trained on a team of 5 people. Each person completed each segment of the race. How many total yards did her team swim? N P MP

Activity	Distance (miles)
Swim	$2\frac{2}{5}$
Bike ride	112
Run	$26\frac{1}{5}$

22. Rectangle 1 has a length of $2\frac{1}{2}$ inches and a width of $\frac{1}{3}$ inch. Rectangle 2 is created by multiplying each side by a factor of $1\frac{1}{2}$. Determine how many more square inches the new area is than the original area. N EE MP

23. The circle graph shows the breakdown of Seth's math grade. His quiz grade consists of 6 quizzes, each worth equal amounts. He missed $\frac{1}{10}$ of the possible points on his first quiz. What fraction of his overall grade do the missed points represent? Which is worth a greater fraction of his grade, Quizzes and Homework or Quizzes and Tests? Explain. N P MD MP

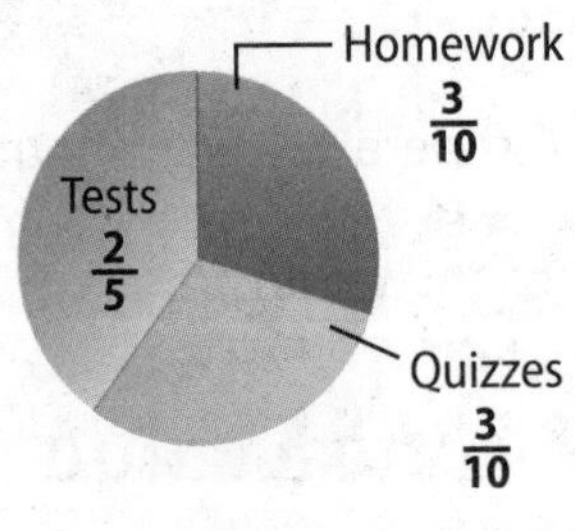

Fluently Divide Rational Numbers

Launch the Lesson: Real World

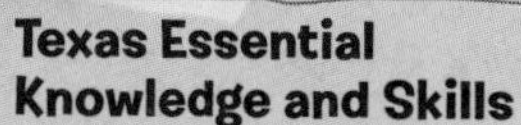

Texas Essential Knowledge and Skills

Targeted TEKS
7.3(A) Add, subtract, multiply, and divide rational numbers fluently. *Also addresses 7.3(B).*

Mathematical Processes
7.1(A), 7.1(B), 7.1(C), 7.1(E)

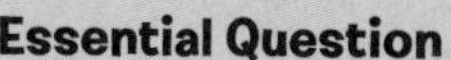

Essential Question
WHAT happens when you add, subtract, multiply, and divide rational numbers?

Deandre has three oranges and each orange is divided evenly into fourths. Determine $3 \div \frac{1}{4}$.

Step 1 Draw three oranges. The first one is drawn for you.

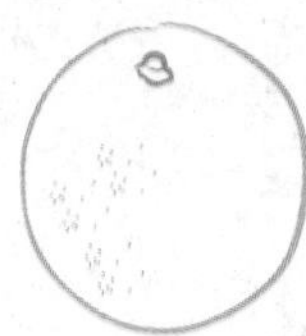

Step 2 Imagine you cut each orange into fourths. Draw the slices for each orange.

So, $3 \div \frac{1}{4} = 12$. Deandre will have ☐ orange slices.

1. Determine $3 \div \frac{1}{2}$. Use a diagram. ______

2. What is true about $3 \div \frac{1}{2}$ and 3×2? ______

Which MP **Mathematical Processes** did you use? Shade the circle(s) that applies.

Ⓐ Apply Math to the Real World.
Ⓑ Use a Problem-Solving Model.
Ⓒ Select Tools and Techniques.
Ⓓ Use Multiple Representations.
Ⓔ Organize Ideas.
Ⓕ Analyze Relationships.
Ⓖ Justify Arguments.

Key Concept

Divide Fractions

Watch

Words To divide by a fraction, multiply by its multiplicative inverse, or reciprocal.

Examples

Numbers: $\frac{7}{8} \div \frac{3}{4} = \frac{7}{8} \cdot \frac{4}{3}$

Algebra: $\frac{a}{b} \div \frac{c}{d} = \frac{a}{b} \cdot \frac{d}{c}$, where $b, c, d \neq 0$

Work Zone

Dividing 3 by $\frac{1}{4}$ is the same as multiplying 3 by the reciprocal of $\frac{1}{4}$, which is 4.

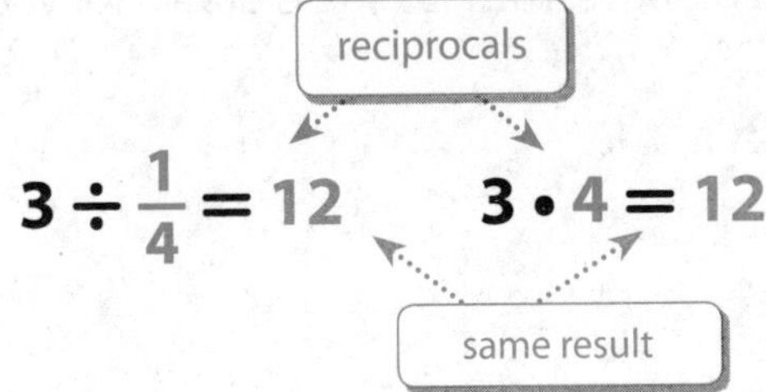

Is this pattern true for any division expression?

Consider $\frac{7}{8} \div \frac{3}{4}$, which can be rewritten as $\frac{\frac{7}{8}}{\frac{3}{4}}$.

$\frac{\frac{7}{8}}{\frac{3}{4}} = \frac{\frac{7}{8} \times \frac{4}{3}}{\frac{3}{4} \times \frac{4}{3}}$ Multiply the numerator and denominator by the reciprocal of $\frac{3}{4}$, which is $\frac{4}{3}$.

$= \frac{\frac{7}{8} \times \frac{4}{3}}{1}$ $\frac{3}{4} \times \frac{4}{3} = 1$

$= \frac{7}{8} \times \frac{4}{3}$

So, $\frac{7}{8} \div \frac{3}{4} = \frac{7}{8} \times \frac{4}{3}$. The pattern is true in this case.

STOP and Reflect

What is the reciprocal of $\frac{2}{3}$? of 15? of $-\frac{4}{9}$? Write your answers below

Examples

Tutor

1. Determine $\frac{1}{3} \div 5$.

$\frac{1}{3} \div 5 = \frac{1}{3} \div \frac{5}{1}$ A whole number can be written as a fraction over 1.

$= \frac{1}{3} \times \frac{1}{5}$ Multiply by the reciprocal of $\frac{5}{1}$, which is $\frac{1}{5}$.

$= \frac{1}{15}$ Multiply.

2. Determine $\frac{3}{4} \div \left(-\frac{1}{2}\right)$. Express in simplest form.

Estimate $1 \div \left(\frac{1}{2}\right) = \square$

$\frac{3}{4} \div \left(-\frac{1}{2}\right) = \frac{3}{4} \cdot \left(-\frac{2}{1}\right)$ Multiply by the reciprocal of $-\frac{1}{2}$, which is $-\frac{2}{1}$.

$= \frac{3}{\cancelto{2}{4}} \cdot \left(-\frac{\cancelto{1}{2}}{1}\right)$ Divide 4 and 2 by their GCF, 2.

$= -\frac{3}{2}$ or $-1\frac{1}{2}$ Multiply.

Check for Reasonableness $-1\frac{1}{2} \approx -2$ ✓

Got It? **Do these problems to find out.**

Divide. Express in simplest form.

a. $\frac{3}{4} \div \frac{1}{4}$ **b.** $-\frac{4}{5} \div \frac{8}{9}$ **c.** $-\frac{5}{6} \div \left(-\frac{2}{3}\right)$

a. ________

b. ________

c. ________

Divide Mixed Numbers

To divide by a mixed number, first rename the mixed number as a fraction greater than one. Then multiply the first fraction by the reciprocal, or multiplicative inverse, of the second fraction.

Example

Tutor

3. Determine $\frac{2}{3} \div 3\frac{1}{3}$. Express in simplest form.

$\frac{2}{3} \div 3\frac{1}{3} = \frac{2}{3} \div \frac{10}{3}$ Rename $3\frac{1}{3}$ a fraction greater than one.

$= \frac{2}{3} \cdot \frac{3}{10}$ Multiply by the reciprocal of $\frac{10}{3}$, which is $\frac{3}{10}$.

$= \frac{\cancelto{1}{2}}{\cancelto{1}{3}} \cdot \frac{\cancelto{1}{3}}{\cancelto{5}{10}}$ Divide out common factors.

$= \frac{1}{5}$ Multiply.

Got It? **Do these problems to find out.**

Divide. Express in simplest form.

d. $5 \div 1\frac{1}{3}$ **e.** $-\frac{3}{4} \div 1\frac{1}{2}$ **f.** $2\frac{1}{3} \div 5$

d. ________

e. ________

f. ________

Example

4. The side pieces of a butterfly house are $8\frac{1}{4}$ inches long. How many side pieces can be cut from a board measuring $49\frac{1}{2}$ inches long?

To determine how many side pieces can be cut, divide $49\frac{1}{2}$ by $8\frac{1}{4}$.

Estimate Use compatible numbers. $48 \div 8 = 6$

$49\frac{1}{2} \div 8\frac{1}{4} = \frac{99}{2} \div \frac{33}{4}$ Rename the mixed numbers as fractions greater than one.

$= \frac{99}{2} \cdot \frac{4}{33}$ Multiply by the reciprocal of $\frac{33}{4}$, which is $\frac{4}{33}$.

$= \frac{\overset{3}{\cancel{99}}}{\underset{1}{\cancel{2}}} \cdot \frac{\overset{2}{\cancel{4}}}{\underset{1}{\cancel{33}}}$ Divide out common factors.

$= \frac{6}{1}$ or 6 Multiply.

So, 6 side pieces can be cut.

Check for Reasonableness Compare to the estimate. $6 = 6$ ✓

Guided Practice

Divide. Express in simplest form. (Examples 1 – 3)

1. $\frac{1}{8} \div \frac{1}{3} =$ ______

Show your work.

2. $-3 \div \left(-\frac{6}{7}\right) =$ ______

3. $-\frac{7}{8} \div \frac{3}{4} =$ ______

4. On Saturday, Lindsay walked $3\frac{1}{2}$ miles in $1\frac{2}{5}$ hours. What was her walking pace in miles per hour? Express in simplest form. (Example 4) ______

5. **Building on the Essential Question** How is dividing fractions related to multiplying?

______
______
______
______

Rate Yourself!

Are you ready to move on? Shade the section that applies.

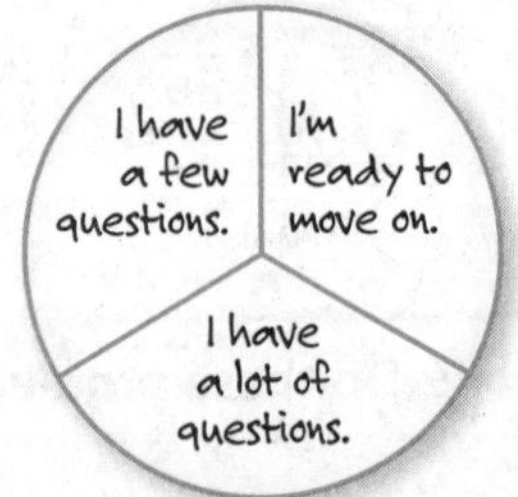

Find out online. Use the Self-Check Quiz.

FOLDABLES Time to update your Foldable!

Name ______________________ My Homework ______________________

Independent Practice

7.3(A), 7.3(B), 7.1(C), 7.1(D) TEKS

Divide. Express in simplest form. (Examples 1 – 3)

1. $\frac{3}{8} \div \frac{6}{7} =$ ______

2. $-\frac{2}{3} \div \left(-\frac{1}{2}\right) =$ ______

3. $\frac{1}{2} \div 7\frac{1}{2} =$ ______

4. $6 \div \left(-\frac{1}{2}\right) =$ ______

5. $-\frac{4}{9} \div (-2) =$ ______

6. $\frac{2}{3} \div 2\frac{1}{2} =$ ______

7. Cheryl is organizing her movie collection. If each movie case is $\frac{3}{4}$ inch wide, how many movies can fit on a shelf $5\frac{1}{4}$ feet wide? (Example 4)

____

8. Use the table to solve. Express your answers in simplest form.

a. How many times as heavy is the Golden Eagle as the Red-Tailed Hawk? ______

b. How many times as heavy is the Golden Eagle as the Northern Bald Eagle? ______

Bird	Maximum Weight (lb)
Golden Eagle	$13\frac{9}{10}$
Northern Bald Eagle	$9\frac{9}{10}$
Red-Tailed Hawk	$3\frac{1}{2}$

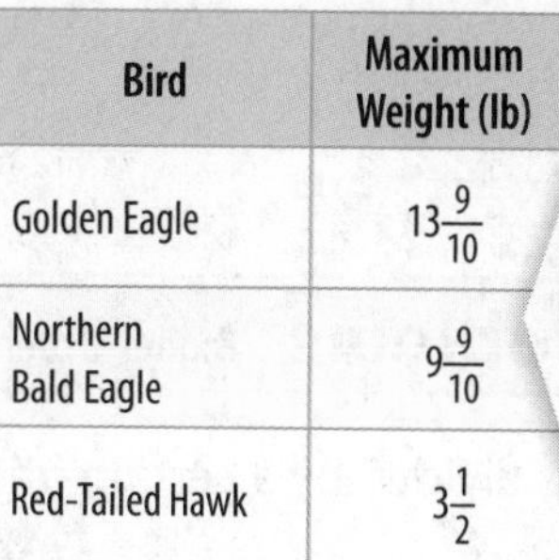

9. MP **Select Tools and Techniques** Draw a model of the verbal expression below and then evaluate the expression. Explain how the model shows the division process.

one half divided by two fifths ______

____

____

____

____

Copy and Solve **For Exercises 10 and 11, show your work on a separate piece of paper.**

10. MP **Use Multiple Representations** Jorge recorded the distance that five of his friends live from his house in the table shown.

Student	Miles
Lucia	$5\frac{1}{2}$
Lon	$8\frac{2}{3}$
Sam	$12\frac{5}{6}$
Jamal	$2\frac{7}{9}$
Tye	$17\frac{13}{18}$

a. **Numbers** Tye lives about how many times farther away than Jamal? ____

b. **Algebra** The mean is the sum of the data divided by the number of items in the data set. Write and solve an equation to determine the mean number of miles that Jorge's friends live from his house. Express your answer in simplest form.

c. **Model** Draw a bar diagram that can be used to determine how many more miles Lon travels than Lucia to get to Jorge's house.

11. Tara bought a dozen folders. She took $\frac{1}{3}$ of the dozen and then divided the remaining folders equally among her four friends. What fraction of the dozen did each of her four friends receive? How many folders was this per person?

12. Find the Error Blake is determining $\frac{4}{5} \div \frac{6}{7}$. Find his mistake and correct it.

H.O.T. Problems Higher Order Thinking

13. Evaluate If $\frac{5}{6}$ is divided by a certain fraction $\frac{a}{b}$, the result is $\frac{1}{4}$. What is the fraction $\frac{a}{b}$? ____

14. Analyze So far, the Rabun family has traveled 30 miles in $\frac{1}{2}$ hour. If it is currently 3:00 P.M. and their destination is 75 miles away from them, at what time will the Rabun family reach their destination? Explain how you solved the problem.

15. Create Write and solve a real-world problem that can be solved by dividing fractions.

Name ______________________________

Multi-Step Problem Solving

16. William has $15\frac{3}{5}$ quarts of paint. He equally divided the paint into 3 gallon-sized containers. If he has already used 2 containers, how many gallons of paint does he have left? Express your answer as a decimal. N P MP

Use a problem-solving model to solve this problem.

1 Analyze

Read the problem. Circle the information you know.
Underline what the problem is asking you to find.

Read to Succeed!

Use a pencil to write your answer in the boxes at the top of the grid and to fill in the correct bubble of the number below.

2 Plan

What will you need to do to solve the problem? Write your plan in steps.

Step 1 Convert quarts to __________ by dividing by 4.

Step 2 Then divide the quotient by _____ to determine how many gallons is in each container.

3 Solve

Use your plan to solve the problem. Show your steps.
Convert quarts to gallons.

$15\frac{3}{5} \div 4 =$ ______

Divide by 3 to determine the amount in each container.

______ $\div 3 =$ ______

Each container holds ______ gallons of paint. Complete the grid.

					.		
⊕	0	0	0	0		0	0
⊖	1	1	1	1		1	1
	2	2	2	2		2	2
	3	3	3	3		3	3
	4	4	4	4		4	4
	5	5	5	5		5	5
	6	6	6	6		6	6
	7	7	7	7		7	7
	8	8	8	8		8	8
	9	9	9	9		9	9

4 Justify and Evaluate

How do you know your solution is accurate?

____

____

____

N = Number and Operations P = Proportionality MP = Mathematical Processes

More Multi-Step Problem Solving

Use a problem-solving model to solve each problem.

17. The table shows how much Caleb paid for beans at the local market. How much more per pound will it cost to buy the most expensive beans per pound than the cheapest beans per pound? N P MP

Type	Weight (lb)	Cost ($)
Black beans	4	6
Lentil beans	$3\frac{1}{8}$	4
Kidney beans	$6\frac{1}{4}$	11

18. The side length of Cube 1 is $2\frac{1}{2}$ inches. Cube 2 has a side length of 5 inches. How many times larger is the volume of Cube 2? N EE MP

19. A family-sized container of macaroni holds sixteen $\frac{3}{4}$-cup servings. A chef prepares meals using $1\frac{1}{3}$ cups in each bowl. How many bowls can the chef prepare from one family-sized container? N P MP

20. Compare the mean of the data below with and without the outlier, which is the extremely high data value. Which mean represents the majority of the data more closely? Explain. N MD MP

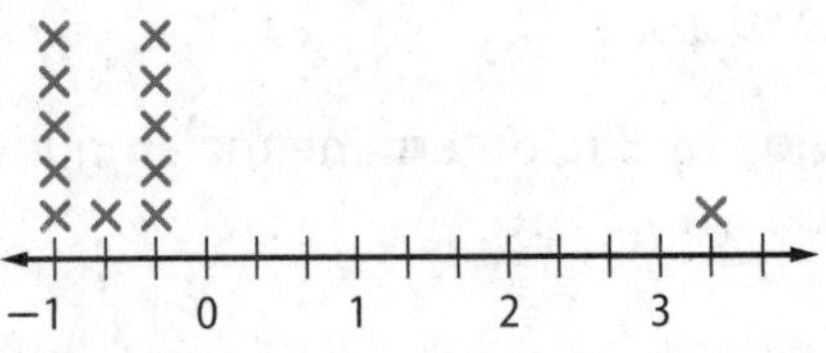

N = Number and Operations   P = Proportionality   EE = Expressions, Equations, and Relationships   MD = Measurement and Data   MP = Mathematical Processes

21ST CENTURY CAREER

Fashion Designer

Do you enjoy reading fashion magazines, keeping up with the latest trends, and creating your own unique sense of style? You might want to consider a career in fashion design. Fashion designers create new designs for clothing, accessories, and shoes. In addition to being creative and knowledgeable about current fashion trends, fashion designers need to be able to take accurate measurements and calculate fit by adding, subtracting, and dividing measurements.

Mathematical Process
7.1(A) Apply mathematics to problems arising in everyday life, society, and the workplace.

Targeted TEKS 7.3(A), 7.3(B)

Is This the Career for You?

Are you interested in a career as a fashion designer? Take some of the following courses in high school.

- Algebra
- Art
- Digital Design
- Geometry

Explore college and careers at ccr.mcgraw-hill.com

A Flair for Fashion!

Use the information in the table to solve each problem. Express in simplest form.

1. For size 8, does Dress Style A or B require more fabric? Explain. ______

2. How many yards of fabric are needed to make Style A in sizes 8 and 14? ______

3. Estimate how many yards of fabric are needed to make Style B in each of the sizes shown. Then determine the actual amount of fabric.

4. For Style B, how much more fabric is required for size 14 than for size 12? ______

5. A designer has half the amount of fabric needed to make Style A in size 10. How much fabric does she have? ______

6. A bolt has $12\frac{1}{8}$ yards of fabric left on it. How many dresses in Style B size 12 could be made? How much fabric is left over?

Amount of Fabric Needed (yards)				
Dress Style	Size 8	Size 10	Size 12	Size 14
A	$3\frac{3}{8}$	$3\frac{1}{2}$	$3\frac{3}{4}$	$3\frac{7}{8}$
B	$3\frac{1}{4}$	$3\frac{1}{2}$	$3\frac{7}{8}$	4

TEKS Career Project

It's time to update your career portfolio! Prepare a list of questions that you would ask a fashion designer if you were going to hire them. Work with a partner and perform a mock interview using the questions you wrote. Listen carefully to their questions, then answer the questions as you would if you were a fashion designer.

Suppose you are an employer hiring a fashion designer. What question would you ask a potential employee?

-
-

Vocabulary Check

Work with a partner to unscramble each of the clue words. After unscrambling each of the terms, use the numbered letters to determine a vocabulary term that relates to all of the other terms. Ask for help for each vocabulary term as needed.

RAB TONNOTIA ☐☐☐ ☐☐☐☐☐☐☐☐ (1, 7)

TAMTINRINGE ☐☐☐☐☐☐☐☐☐☐☐ (3)

GIEPEATNR ☐☐☐☐☐☐☐☐☐ (4)

KIEL STAFCOIRN ☐☐☐☐ ☐☐☐☐☐☐☐☐☐ (5)

LUKIEN ☐☐☐☐☐☐ (6, 8)

NOMMOC NIOAREOMNDT ☐☐☐☐☐☐ ☐☐☐☐☐☐☐☐☐☐☐ (2)

☐☐☐☐☐☐☐☐

1 2 3 4 5 6 7 8

Complete each sentence using one of the unscrambled words above.

1. The process of using a line over the repeating digits of a decimal is called ______________.
2. Fractions with different denominators are called ______________ fractions.
3. The decimal form of a rational number is a(n) ______________ decimal.
4. A ______________ decimal is a decimal in which the repeating digit is zero.
5. Fractions with the same denominator are called ______________.

Check

Key Concept Check

Use Your FOLDABLES

Use your Foldable to help review the chapter. Share your Foldable with a partner and take turns summarizing what you learned in this chapter, while the other partner listens carefully. Ask for and give help of any concepts, as needed. TEKS 7.1(D), 7.1(E)

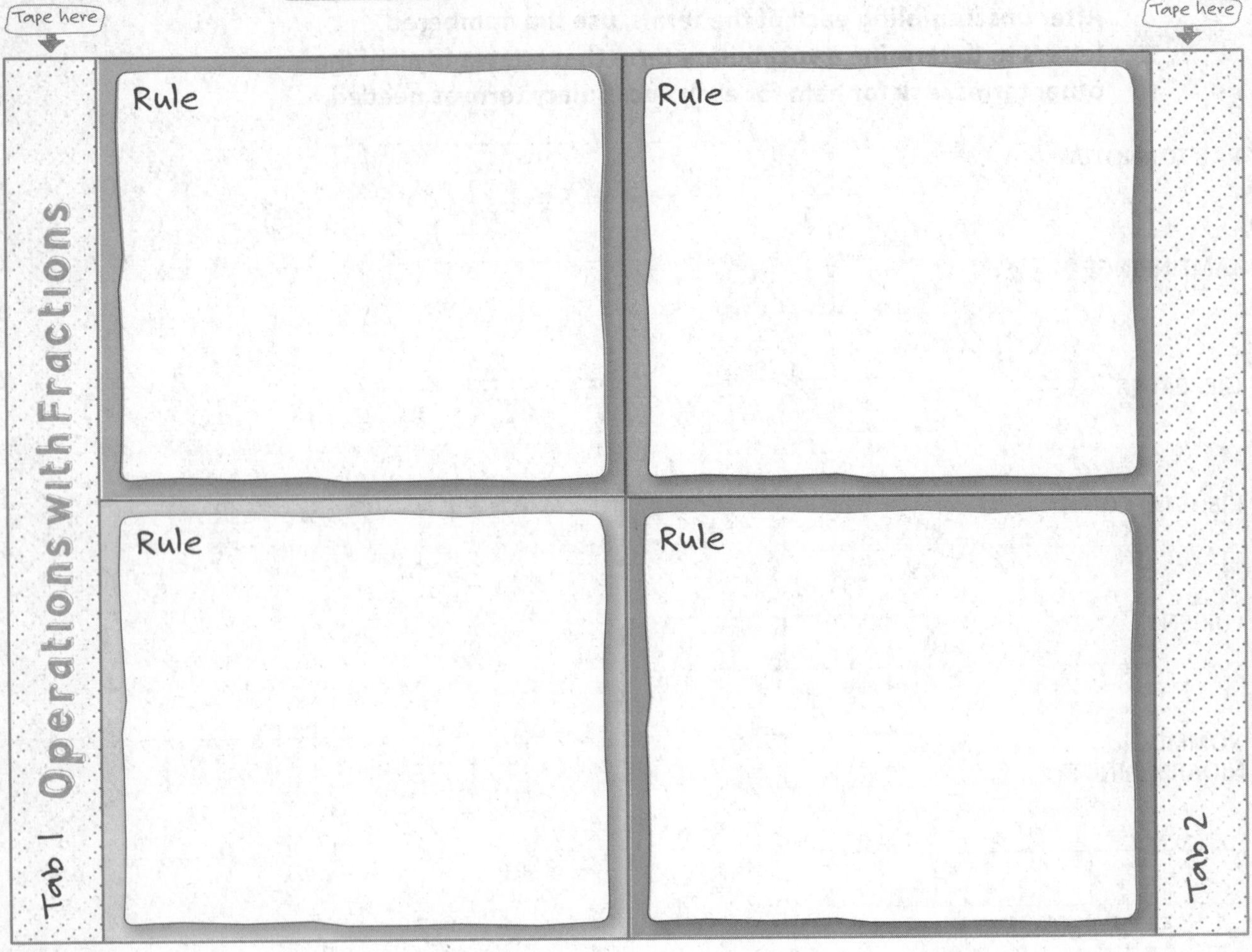

Tape here

Tape here

Tab 1 Operations with Fractions

Rule	Rule
Rule	Rule

Tab 2

Got it?

Circle the correct term or number to complete each sentence. TEKS 7.3(A), 7.3(B)

1. $\frac{1}{5}$ and $\left(\frac{1}{3}, \frac{3}{5}\right)$ are like fractions.

2. To add like fractions, add the (numerators, denominators).

3. To add unlike fractions, rename the fractions using the least common (numerator, denominator).

4. To divide by a fraction, (multiply, divide) by its reciprocal.

Multi-Step Problem Solving

Use a problem-solving model to solve the problem.

5. The table shows the results of the field day finals of the air plane toss. The winner is the student who had the greater average for the three tosses. Which student won the airplane toss? Justify your solution. N MP

Student	Toss 1 (ft)	Toss 2 (ft)	Toss 3 (ft)
Trinity	$54\frac{1}{4}$	$57\frac{3}{16}$	59
Bradley	$56\frac{13}{16}$	$60\frac{1}{2}$	53

1 Analyze

2 Plan

3 Solve

4 Justify and Evaluate

Got it?

6. The recipe shown makes 5 dozen chocolate chip cookies. Mrs. Henderson wants to make 90 chocolate chips cookies using this recipe. How much flour does she need to make the 90 chocolate chip cookies? Justify your solution. N MP

Chocolate Chip Cookie Recipe			
flour	$2\frac{1}{4}$ c	sugar	$\frac{3}{4}$ c
baking soda	1 tsp	brown sugar	$\frac{3}{4}$ c
butter	1 c	eggs	2
chocolate chips	2 c	vanilla	1 tsp

N = Number and Operations MP = Mathematical Processes

Reflect

Answering the Essential Question

Use what you learned about operations with rational numbers to complete the graphic organizer. Describe a process to perform each operation. TEKS 7.1(D), 7.1(E), 7.1(G)

Add

Subtract

Essential Question

WHAT happens when you add, subtract, multiply, and divide rational numbers?

Multiply

Divide

Answer the Essential Question. WHAT happens when you add, subtract, multipy, and divide rational numbers? Verbally share your response with a partner, asking for and giving help if needed.

When Will You Use This?

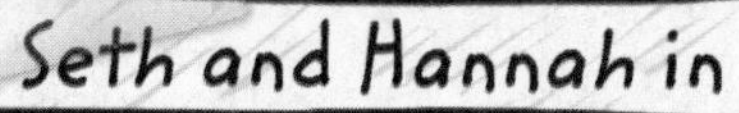

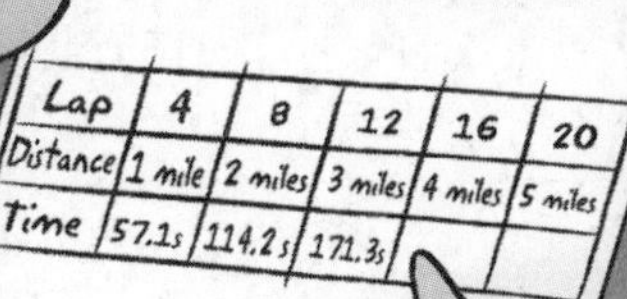

Lap	4	8	12	16	20
Distance	1 mile	2 miles	3 miles	4 miles	5 miles
Time	57.1s	114.2s	171.3s		

Your Turn! **You will solve this problem in the chapter.**

Are You Ready?

Quick Review

Example 1

Express the ratio of wins to losses as a fraction in simplest form.

Madison Mavericks	
Team Statistics	
Wins	10
Losses	12
Ties	8

wins ⋯⋯➤ losses ⋯⋯➤ $\frac{10}{12} = \frac{5}{6}$

The ratio of wins to losses is $\frac{5}{6}$.

Example 2

Determine whether the ratios 250 miles in 4 hours and 500 miles in 8 hours are equivalent.

Compare the ratios by writing them in simplest form.

250 miles : 4 hours = $\frac{250}{4}$ or $\frac{125}{2}$

500 miles : 8 hours = $\frac{500}{8}$ or $\frac{125}{2}$

The ratios are equivalent because they simplify to the same fraction.

Quick Check

Ratios **Express each ratio as a fraction in simplest form.**

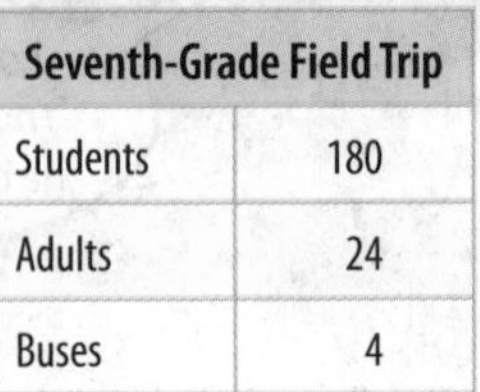

Seventh-Grade Field Trip	
Students	180
Adults	24
Buses	4

1. adults : students ______

2. students : buses ______

3. buses : people ______

Equivalent Ratios **Determine whether the ratios are equivalent. Explain.**

4. 20 nails for every 5 shingles
   12 nails for every 3 shingles

5. 12 out of 20 doctors agree
   15 out of 30 doctors agree

How Did You Do?

Which problems did you answer correctly in the Quick Check? Shade those exercise numbers below.

① ② ③ ④ ⑤

Use the Foldable throughout this chapter to help you learn about proportional relationships.

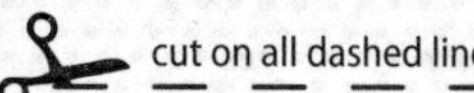

cut on all dashed lines

fold on all solid lines

tape to page 206

proportional

nonproportional

page 206

Tab 1

Write About It

Write About It

page 206

Tab 2

Hands-On Lab 1-a

Ratios and Rates

INQUIRY **HOW can I use multiple representations to solve problems involving ratios and rates?**

When Jeremy gets his allowance, he agrees to save part of it. His savings and expenses are in the ratio 7:5. If his daily allowance is \$3, determine how much he saves each day.

Texas Essential Knowledge and Skills TEKS

Targeted TEKS

7.4(B) Calculate unit rates from rates in mathematical and real-world problems. *Also addresses 7.4(D).*

Mathematical Processes

7.1(A), 7.1(C), 7.1(D), 7.1(E)

Hands-On Activity

You can use a bar diagram to represent the ratio 7:5. A bar diagram is also called a *strip diagram*.

Step 1 Complete the bar diagram below by writing *savings, expenses,* and *\$3* in the correct boxes.

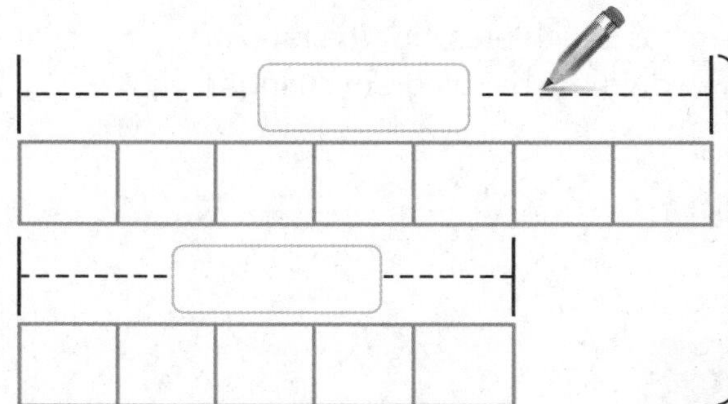

Total amount = ☐

(Daily Allowance)

Step 2 Let x represent each part of a bar. Write and solve an equation to find the amount of money each bar represents.

$7x + \square x = 3$ Write the equation.

$12x = 3$ There are 12 parts in all.

$\frac{12x}{12} = \frac{3}{12}$ Division Property of Equality

$x = \frac{\square}{\square}$ or 0.25 Simplify.

Step 3 Determine the amount Jeremy saves each day. Since each part of the bar represents \$0.25, Jeremy's savings are represented by

$7 \times \$\square$ or \$1.75.

So, Jeremy saves \$☐ each day.

Investigate

Work with a partner to answer the following question.

1. The ratio of the number of boys to the number of girls on the swim team is 4:2. If there are 24 athletes on the swim team, how many more boys than girls are there? Use a bar diagram to solve. ______

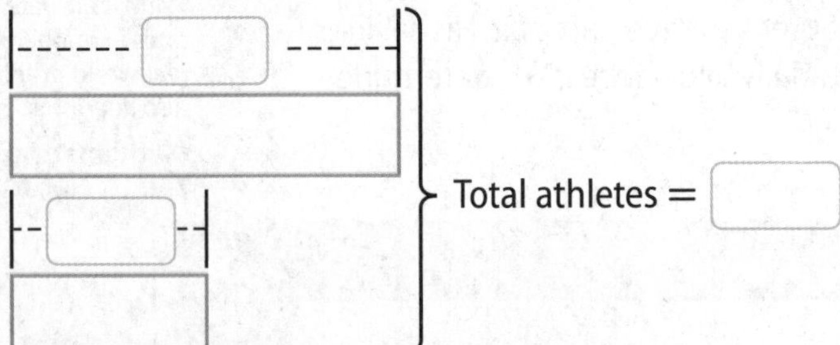

Analyze and Reflect

Work with a partner to answer the following question.

2. **MP Organize Ideas** Suppose the swim team has 24 athletes, but the ratio of boys to girls on the swim team is 3 : 5. How would the bar diagram change?

Create

3. **MP Apply Math to the Real World** Write a real-world problem that could be represented by the bar diagram shown below. Then solve your problem.

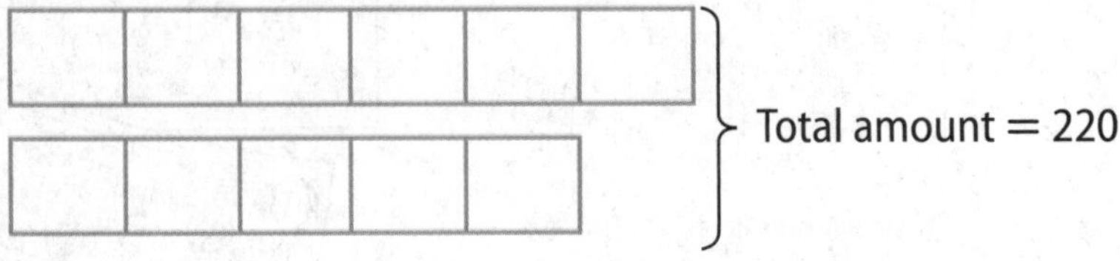

4. **INQUIRY** HOW can I use multiple representations to solve problems involving ratios and rates?

Lesson 1
Unit Rates

Launch the Lesson: Real World

Watch

You can take a person's pulse by placing your middle and index finger on the underside of their wrist. Choose a partner and take their pulse for two minutes. How can we determine the number of beats per minute? per $\frac{1}{2}$ minute?

Texas Essential Knowledge and Skills

Targeted TEKS

7.4(B) Calculate unit rates from rates in mathematical and real-world problems.
Also addresses 7.4(D).

Mathematical Processes

7.1(A), 7.1(B), 7.1(C), 7.1(G)

Vocab

Vocabulary

rate

unit rate

Essential Question

HOW can you show that two objects are proportional?

1. Record the results for 2 minutes in the diagram below.

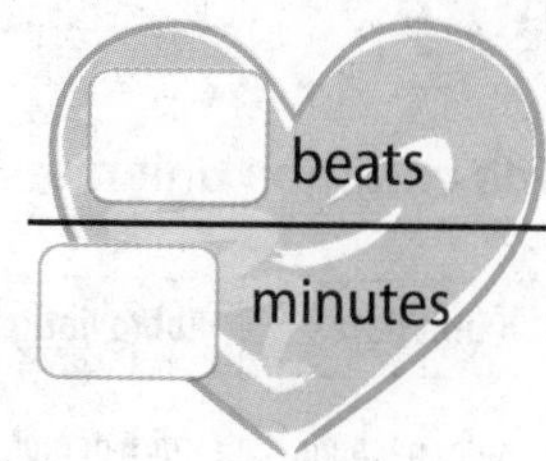

2. Use the results from Exercise 1 to complete the bar diagram and determine the number of beats per minute for your partner.

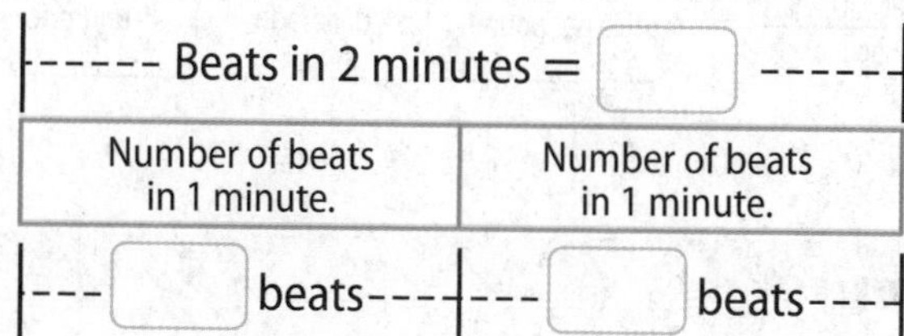

So, your partner's heart beats ______ times per minute.

3. Use the results from Exercise 1 to determine the number of beats for $\frac{1}{2}$ minute for your partner.

______

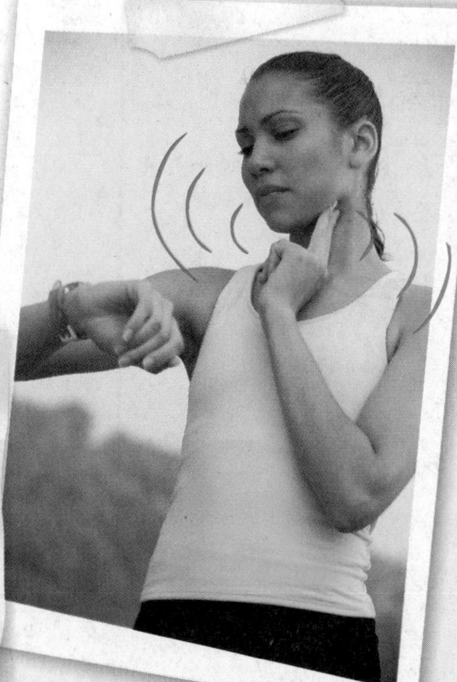

Which MP Mathematical Processes did you use? Shade the circle(s) that applies.

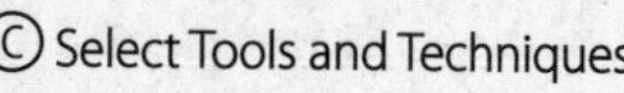

Ⓐ Apply Math to the Real World.
Ⓑ Use a Problem-Solving Model.
Ⓒ Select Tools and Techniques.
Ⓓ Use Multiple Representations.
Ⓔ Organize Ideas.
Ⓕ Analyze Relationships.
Ⓖ Justify Arguments.

Work Zone

Calculate a Unit Rate

A ratio that compares two quantities with different kinds of units is called a **rate**. When you found each other's pulse, you were actually determining the heart *rate*.

$$\frac{160 \text{ beats}}{2 \text{ minutes}}$$

The units *beats* and *minutes* are different.

When a rate is simplified so that it has a denominator of 1 unit, it is called a **unit rate**.

$$\frac{80 \text{ beats}}{1 \text{ minute}}$$

The denominator is 1 unit.

The table below shows some common unit rates.

Rate	Unit Rate	Abbreviation	Name
$\frac{\text{number of miles}}{1 \text{ hour}}$	miles per hour	mi/h or mph	average speed
$\frac{\text{number of miles}}{1 \text{ gallon}}$	miles per gallon	mi/gal or mpg	gas mileage
$\frac{\text{number of dollars}}{1 \text{ pound}}$	price per pound	dollars/lb	unit price

Real World

Example

Tutor

1. Adrienne biked 24 miles in 4 hours. If she biked at a constant speed, how many miles did she ride in one hour?

$$24 \text{ miles in 4 hours} = \frac{24 \text{ mi}}{4 \text{ h}}$$ Write the rate as a fraction.

$$= \frac{24 \text{ mi} \div 4}{4 \text{ h} \div 4}$$ Divide the numerator and the denominator by 4.

$$= \frac{6 \text{ mi}}{1 \text{ h}}$$ Simplify.

Adrienne biked 6 miles in one hour.

STOP and Reflect

Circle the unit rate below that represents 18 cans for $6.

$\frac{9 \text{ cans}}{\$3}$ $\frac{3 \text{ cans}}{\$1}$ $\frac{4 \text{ cans}}{\$1}$

Got It? Do these problems to find out.

Show your work.

Calculate each unit rate. Round to the nearest hundredth if necessary.

a. $300 for 6 hours

b. 220 miles on 8 gallons

a. ______

b. ______

Example

Tutor

2. Calculate the unit price if it costs $2 for eight juice boxes.

$2 for eight boxes $= \frac{\$2}{8 \text{ boxes}}$ — Write the rate as a fraction.

$= \frac{\$2 \div 8}{8 \text{ boxes} \div 8}$ — Divide the numerator and the denominator by 8.

$= \frac{\$0.25}{1 \text{ box}}$ — Simplify.

The unit price is $0.25 per juice box.

Got It? Do this problem to find out.

c. Calculate the unit price if a 4-pack of mixed fruit sells for $2.12.

c. ________

Multi-Step Example

Tutor

3. The prices of 3 different sizes of bags of dog food are given in the table. Which size bag has the lowest price per pound rounded to the nearest cent?

Dog Food Prices	
Bag Size (lb)	**Price ($)**
40	49.00
20	23.44
8	9.88

Step 1 40-pound bag
$49.00 ÷ 40 pounds ≈ $1.23 per pound

Step 2 20-pound bag
$23.44 ÷ 20 pounds ≈ $1.17 per pound

Step 3 8-pound bag
$9.88 ÷ 8 pounds ≈ $1.24 per pound

The 20-pound bag sells for the lowest price per pound.

Alternate Method

One 40-lb bag is equivalent to two 20-lb bags or five 8-lb bags. The cost for one 40-lb bag is $49, the cost for two 20-lb bags is about 2 × $23 or $46, and the cost for five 8-lb bags is about 5 × $10 or $50. So, the 20-lb bag has the lowest price per pound.

Got It? Do this problem to find out.

d. Tito wants to buy some peanut butter to donate to the local food pantry. Tito wants to buy as much peanut butter as possible for the best price. Which brand should he buy?

Peanut Butter Sales	
Brand	**Sale Price**
Nutty	12 ounces for $2.19
Grandma's	18 ounces for $2.79
Bee's	28 ounces for $4.69
Save-A-Lot	40 ounces for $6.60

d. ________

Multi-Step Example

4. Lexi painted 2 faces in 8 minutes at the Crafts Fair. At this rate, how many faces can she paint in 40 minutes?

Method 1 **Calculate a Unit Rate**

Step 1 2 faces in 8 minutes $= \frac{2 \text{ faces} \div 8}{8 \text{ min} \div 8} = \frac{0.25 \text{ face}}{1 \text{ min}}$ Find the unit rate.

Step 2 Multiply the unit rate by 40 minutes.

$\frac{0.25 \text{ face}}{1 \text{ min}} \cdot 40 \text{ min} = 10 \text{ faces}$ Divide out the common units.

Method 2 **Draw a Bar Diagram**

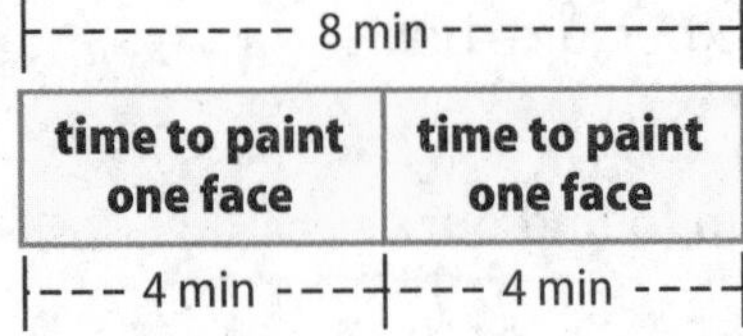

It takes 4 minutes to paint one face. In 40 minutes, Lexi can paint 40 ÷ 4 or 10 faces.

Using either method, Lexi can paint 10 faces in 40 minutes.

Guided Practice

1. CD Express offers 4 CDs for $60. Music Place offers 6 CDs for $75. Which store offers the better buy? (Examples 1–3)

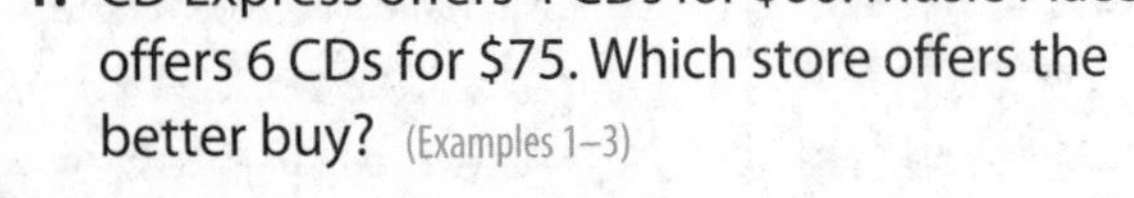

2. After 3.5 hours, Pasha had traveled 217 miles. If she travels at a constant speed, how far will she have traveled after 4 hours? (Example 4) ______

3. Write 5 pounds for $2.49 as a unit rate. Round to the nearest hundredth. (Example 2)

______

4. **Building on the Essential Question** Use an example to describe how a *rate* is a measure of one quantity per unit of another quantity.

______

______

Rate Yourself!

Are you ready to move on? Shade the section that applies.

YES ? NO

Find out online. Use the Self-Check Quiz.

Check

Name ______________________ My Homework ______________________

Independent Practice

7.4(D), 7.4(B), 7.1(G) TEKS

Calculate each unit rate. Round to the nearest hundredth if necessary. (Examples 1 and 2)

1. 360 miles in 6 hours ______

2. 6,840 customers in 45 days ______

3. 45.5 meters in 13 seconds ______

4. $7.40 for 5 pounds ______

5. Estimate the unit rate if 12 pairs of socks sell for $5.79. (Examples 1 and 2)

______

6. MP **Justify Arguments** The results of a swim meet are shown. Who swam the fastest? Explain your reasoning. (Example 3)

Name	Event	Time (s)
Tawni	50-m Freestyle	40.8
Pepita	100-m Butterfly	60.2
Susana	200-m Medley	112.4

______

7. Ben can type 153 words in 3 minutes. At this rate, how many words can he type in 10 minutes? (Example 4)

______

8. Kenji buys 3 yards of fabric for $7.47. Then he realizes that he needs 2 more yards. How much will the extra fabric cost? (Example 4)

______

9. The record for the Boston Marathon's wheelchair division is 1 hour, 18 minutes, and 27 seconds.

a. The Boston Marathon is 26.2 miles long. What was the average speed of the record winner of the wheelchair division?

Round to the nearest hundredth. ______

b. At this rate, about how long would it take this competitor to complete a 30-mile race? ______

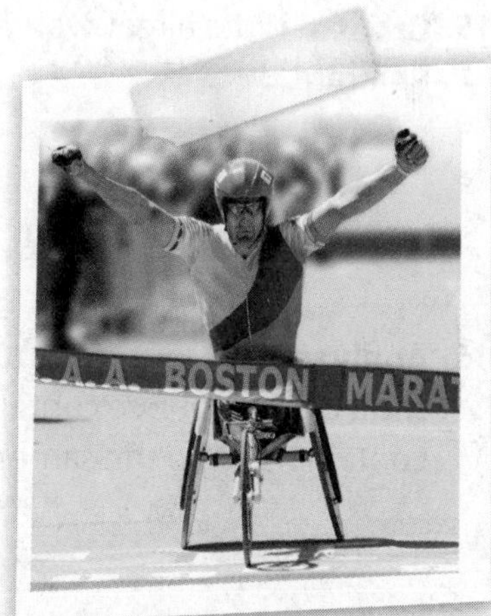

10. At Tire Depot, a pair of new tires sells for $216. The manager's special advertises the same tires selling at a rate of $380 for 4 tires. How much do you save per tire if you purchase the manager's special? ______

11. **Find the Error** Seth is trying to calculate the unit price for a package of blank compact discs on sale at 10 for $5.49. Find his mistake and correct it.

10 ÷ $5.49
$1.82 each

H.O.T. Problems Higher-Order Thinking

12. **Evaluate** Search for examples of grocery item prices in a newspaper, on television, or on the Internet. Compare unit prices of two different brands of the same item. Explain which item is the better buy.

Analyze Determine whether each statement is *sometimes, always,* or *never* true. Give an example or a counterexample.

13. A ratio is a rate.

14. A rate is a ratio.

15. **Create** Write a real-world problem that involves a rate. Then calculate the unit rate.

16. **Analyze** A 96-ounce container of orange juice costs $4.80. At what price should a 128-ounce container be sold in order for the unit rate for both containers to be the same? Explain your reasoning.

Name ____________________

Multi-Step Problem Solving

17. Makayla and her friends earn money by babysitting after school. At the end of one week, they deposit their weekly earnings at the bank. Which friend earns the most money per hour babysitting? N P MP

Name	Hours Worked	Deposit Amount ($)
Makayla	15	138.75
Gael	13	136.50
Jason	16	168.00
Cecilia	9	101.25

Ⓐ Makayla

Ⓑ Gael

Ⓒ Jason

Ⓓ Cecilia

Use a problem-solving model to solve this problem.

1 Analyze

Read the problem. Circle the information you know.
Underline what the problem is asking you to find.

2 Plan

What will you need to do to solve the problem? Write your plan in steps.

Step 1 Calculate the ________ for each person.

Step 2 Compare the unit rates to determine ________ earns the most.

3 Solve

Use your plan to solve the problem. Show your steps.

Makayla: $138.75 ÷ 15 = ________ per hour

Gael: $136.50 ÷ 13 = ________ per hour

Jason: $168 ÷ 16 = ________ per hour

Cecilia: $101.25 ÷ 9 = ________ per hour

________ earns ________ per hour, which is the greatest unit rate.

So, the correct answer is ________. Fill in that answer choice.

Read to Succeed!
Be sure to calculate each unit rate. Do not assume that a lower deposit amount will result in a lower unit rate.

4 Justify and Evaluate

How do you know your solution is accurate?

____

____

____

N = Number and Operations P = Proportionality MP = Mathematical Processes

More Multi-Step Problem Solving

Use a problem-solving model to solve each problem.

18. An automobile magazine compared the gas mileage for new cars. The distance traveled and amount of gasoline used for each car is shown in the table. Which car had the greatest gas mileage(miles per gallon)? P N MP

Car	Distance (mi)	Gasoline (gal)
Car A	650	20
Car B	426	12
Car C	515	15
Car D	280	8

Ⓐ Car A

Ⓑ Car B

Ⓒ Car C

Ⓓ Car D

19. The graph shows the amount of electricity used by one household over six months. If the cost per kilowatt hour usage is $0.12, approximately how much would it cost per day for the month of April? (*Hint:* There are 30 billable days in the month of April.)

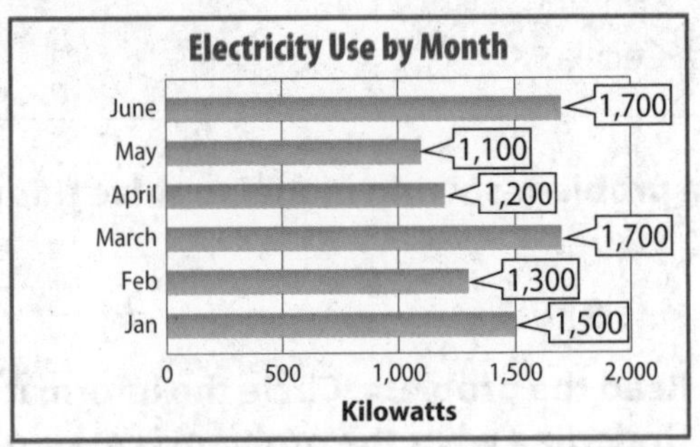

20. The graph shows the first 45 minutes of Darlene's bike trip. If she continues at a constant rate, how far will she travel in two hours? P MD MP

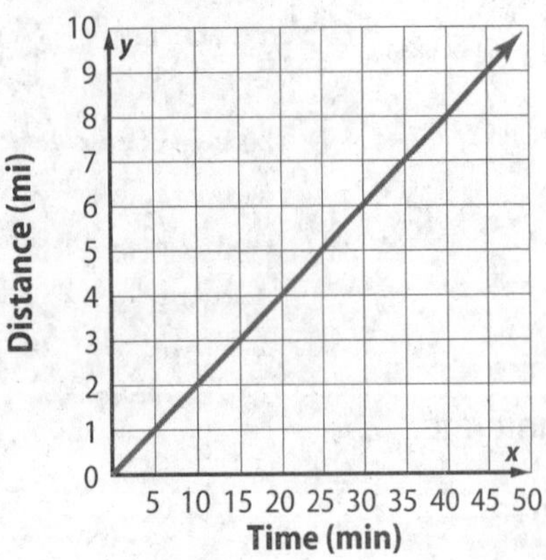

21. Pamela can run 100 meters in 12.5 seconds and Josalin can run 150 meters in 20 seconds. If they both ran a 400-meter race at this rate, how many meters ahead would Pamela cross the finish line before Josalin? P N MP

P = Proportionality N = Number and Operations MD = Measurement and Data MP = Mathematical Processes

Lesson 2

Complex Fractions and Unit Rates

Launch the Lesson: Real World

Texas Essential Knowledge and Skills

Targeted TEKS
7.4(B) Calculate unit rates from rates in mathematical and real-world problems.
Also addresses 7.4(D).

Mathematical Processes
7.1(A), 7.1(B), 7.1(F), 7.1(G)

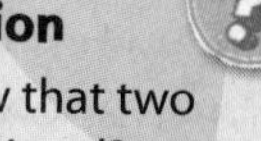

Vocabulary
complex fraction

Essential Question
HOW can you show that two objects are proportional?

Dana is skating laps to train for a speed skating competition. She can skate 1 lap in 40 seconds. How many laps can she skate in 20 seconds?

1. Write a ratio in simplest form comparing Dana's time to her number of laps.

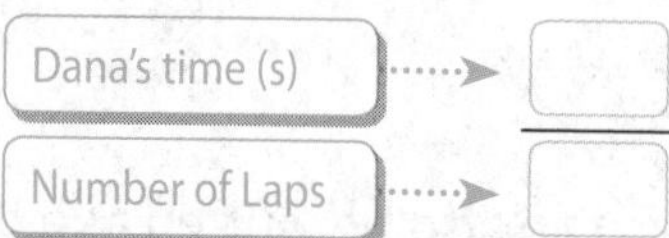

2. Suppose Dana skates for 20 seconds. How many laps will she skate?

3. Write the ratio of Dana's time from Exercise 2 to her number of laps.

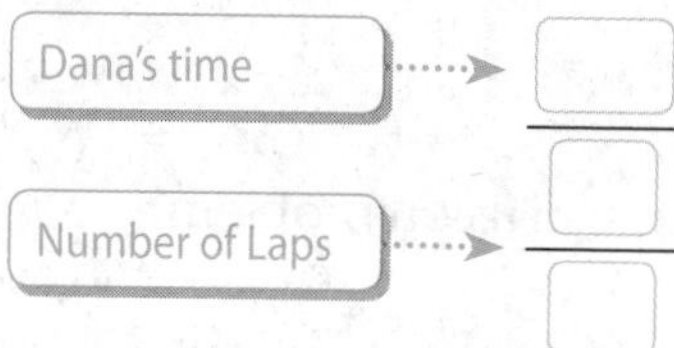

4. How could you simplify the ratio you wrote in Exercise 3?

Which MP Mathematical Processes did you use? Shade the circle(s) that applies.

Ⓐ Apply Math to the Real World.
Ⓑ Use a Problem-Solving Model.
Ⓒ Select Tools and Techniques.
Ⓓ Use Multiple Representations.
Ⓔ Organize Ideas.
Ⓕ Analyze Relationships.
Ⓖ Justify Arguments.

Work Zone

Simplify a Complex Fraction

Fractions like $\frac{20}{\frac{1}{2}}$ are called complex fractions. **Complex fractions** are fractions with a numerator, denominator, or both that are also fractions. Complex fractions are simplified when both the numerator and denominator are integers.

Examples

1. Simplify $\frac{\frac{1}{4}}{2}$.

Recall that a fraction can also be written as a division problem.

$\frac{\frac{1}{4}}{2} = \frac{1}{4} \div 2$ Write the complex fraction as a division problem.

$= \frac{1}{4} \times \frac{1}{2}$ Multiply by the reciprocal of 2, which is $\frac{1}{2}$.

$= \frac{1}{8}$ Simplify.

So, $\frac{\frac{1}{4}}{2}$ is equal to $\frac{1}{8}$.

Divide Fractions

To divide by a whole number, first write it as a fraction with a denominator of 1. Then multiply by the reciprocal.

So, $\frac{\frac{1}{4}}{2}$ can be written as $\frac{1}{4} \div \frac{2}{1}$.

2. Simplify $\frac{1}{\frac{1}{2}}$.

Write the fraction as a division problem.

$\frac{1}{\frac{1}{2}} = 1 \div \frac{1}{2}$ Write the complex fraction as a division problem.

$= \frac{1}{1} \times \frac{2}{1}$ Multiply by the reciprocal of $\frac{1}{2}$, which is $\frac{2}{1}$.

$= \frac{2}{1}$ or 2 Simplify.

So, $\frac{1}{\frac{1}{2}}$ is equal to 2.

Got It? Do these problems to find out.

a. $\frac{2}{\frac{2}{3}}$

b. $\frac{6}{\frac{1}{3}}$

c. $\frac{\frac{2}{3}}{7}$

d. $\frac{\frac{2}{4}}{2}$

a. _______

b. _______

c. _______

d. _______

Calculate Unit Rates

When the fractions of a complex fractions represent different units, you can calculate the unit rate.

Examples

3. Josiah can jog $1\frac{1}{3}$ miles in $\frac{1}{4}$ hour. Calculate his average speed in miles per hour.

Write a rate that compares the number of miles to hours.

$\dfrac{1\frac{1}{3}\text{ mi}}{\frac{1}{4}\text{ h}} = 1\frac{1}{3} \div \frac{1}{4}$ Write the complex fraction as a division problem.

$= \frac{4}{3} \div \frac{1}{4}$ Write the mixed number as an improper fraction.

$= \frac{4}{3} \times \frac{4}{1}$ Multiply by the reciprocal of $\frac{1}{4}$, which is $\frac{4}{1}$.

$= \frac{16}{3}$ or $5\frac{1}{3}$ Simplify.

So, Josiah jogs at an average speed of $5\frac{1}{3}$ miles per hour.

4. Tia is painting her house. She paints $34\frac{1}{2}$ square feet in $\frac{3}{4}$ hour. At this rate, how many square feet can she paint each hour?

Write a ratio that compares the number of square feet to hours.

$\dfrac{34\frac{1}{2}\text{ ft}^2}{\frac{3}{4}\text{ h}} = 34\frac{1}{2} \div \frac{3}{4}$ Write the complex fraction as a division problem.

$= \frac{69}{2} \div \frac{3}{4}$ Write the mixed number as an improper fraction.

$= \frac{69}{2} \times \frac{4}{3}$ Multiply by the reciprocal of $\frac{3}{4}$, which is $\frac{4}{3}$.

$= \frac{276}{6}$ or 46 Simplify.

So, Tia can paint 46 square feet per hour.

Got It? Do these problems to find out.

e. Mr. Ito is spreading mulch in his yard. He spreads $4\frac{2}{3}$ square yards in 2 hours. How many square yards can he mulch per hour?

f. Aubrey can walk $4\frac{1}{2}$ miles in $1\frac{1}{2}$ hours. Calculate her average speed in miles per hour.

e. ____________

f. ____________

Example

5. On Javier's soccer team, about $33\frac{1}{3}\%$ of the players have scored a goal. Express $33\frac{1}{3}\%$ as a fraction in simplest form.

$$33\frac{1}{3}\% = \frac{33\frac{1}{3}}{100}$$ Definition of percent

$$= 33\frac{1}{3} \div 100$$ Write the complex fraction as a division problem.

$$= \frac{100}{3} \div 100$$ Write $33\frac{1}{3}$ as an improper fraction.

$$= \frac{\overset{1}{\cancel{100}}}{3} \times \frac{1}{\underset{1}{\cancel{100}}}$$ Multiply by the reciprocal of 100, which is $\frac{1}{100}$.

$$= \frac{1}{3}$$ Simplify.

So, about $\frac{1}{3}$ of Javier's team has scored a goal.

Guided Practice

Simplify. (Examples 1 and 2)

1. $\dfrac{18}{\frac{3}{4}} =$ ______

2. $\dfrac{\frac{3}{6}}{4} =$ ______

3. $\dfrac{\frac{1}{3}}{\frac{1}{4}} =$ ______

4. Pep Club members are making spirit buttons. They make 490 spirit buttons in $3\frac{1}{2}$ hours. Calculate the number of buttons the Pep Club makes per hour. (Examples 3 and 4) ______

5. A county sales tax is $6\frac{2}{3}\%$. Express the percent as a fraction in simplest form. (Example 5) ______

6. **Building on the Essential Question** What is a complex fraction? ______

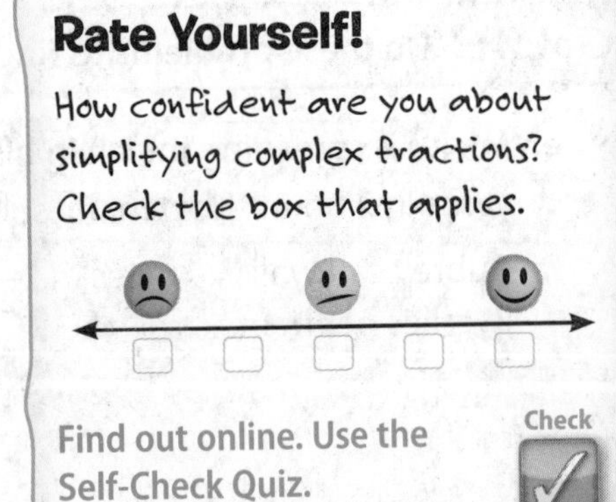

Name ______ My Homework ______

Independent Practice

7.4(B), 7.4(D), 7.4(F) TEKS

Simplify. (Examples 1 and 2)

1. $\frac{1}{\frac{2}{3}} =$ ______

2. $\frac{\frac{2}{3}}{11} =$ ______

3. $\frac{\frac{8}{9}}{6} =$ ______

4. $\frac{\frac{2}{5}}{9} =$ ______

5. $\frac{\frac{4}{5}}{10} =$ ______

6. $\frac{\frac{1}{4}}{\frac{7}{10}} =$ ______

7. Mary is making pillows for her Life Skills class. She bought $2\frac{1}{2}$ yards of fabric. Her total cost was \$15. What was the cost per yard? (Examples 3 and 4)

______

8. Doug entered a canoe race. He rowed $3\frac{1}{2}$ miles in $\frac{1}{2}$ hour. What is his average speed in miles per hour? (Examples 3 and 4)

______

9. Monica reads $7\frac{1}{2}$ pages of a mystery book in 9 minutes. What is her average reading rate in pages per minute? (Examples 3 and 4)

______

Express each percent as a fraction in simplest form. (Example 5)

10. $56\frac{1}{4}\% =$ ______

11. $15\frac{3}{5}\% =$ ______

12. $13\frac{1}{3}\% =$ ______

13. A bank is offering home loans at an interest rate of $5\frac{1}{2}\%$. Express the percent as a fraction in simplest form. (Example 5) ______

14. **Justify Arguments** The value of a mutual fund increased by $3\frac{1}{8}\%$. Express $3\frac{1}{8}\%$ as a fraction in simplest form. Justify your answer.

15. **Analyze Relationships** Karl measured the wingspan of the butterfly and the moth shown below. How many times larger is the moth than the butterfly?

Black Swallowtail Butterfly

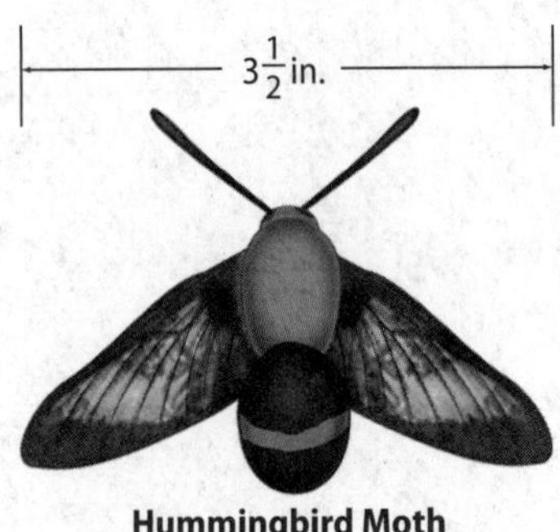

Hummingbird Moth

H.O.T. Problems Higher-Order Thinking

16. **Analyze** Explain how complex fractions can be used to solve problems involving ratios.

17. **Create** Write three different complex fractions that simplify to $\frac{1}{4}$.

18. **Evaluate** Use mental math to determine the value of $\frac{15}{124} \cdot \frac{230}{30} \div \frac{230}{124}$.

19. **Evaluate** A motorized scooter has tires with a circumference of 21.98 inches. The tires make one revolution every $\frac{1}{10}$ second. Calculate the speed of the scooter in miles per hour. Round to the nearest tenth. (*Hint:* The speed of an object spinning in a circle is equal to the circumference divided by the time it takes to complete one revolution.)

Name ______________________________

Multi-Step Problem Solving

20. Carolina and her friends went kayaking over the weekend. The distance and time traveled is shown in the table. Which person kayaked at the greatest speed, in miles per hour? N P MP

Person	Distance (mi)	Time (h)
Carolina	$3\frac{1}{2}$	$\frac{1}{2}$
Leslie	$5\frac{1}{4}$	$\frac{3}{4}$
Bryan	$4\frac{1}{2}$	$\frac{3}{4}$
Javier	$2\frac{1}{2}$	$\frac{1}{3}$

Ⓐ Carolina
Ⓑ Leslie
Ⓒ Bryan
Ⓓ Javier

Use a problem-solving model to solve this problem.

1 Analyze

Read the problem. Circle the information you know. Underline what the problem is asking you to find.

2 Plan

What will you need to do to solve the problem? Write your plan in steps.

Step 1 Calculate the __________ for each person.

Step 2 Compare the unit rates to determine __________ kayaks at the fastest rate, in miles per hour.

3 Solve

Use your plan to solve the problem. Show your steps.

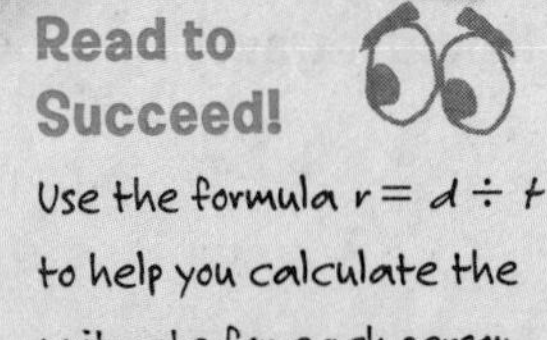

Read to Succeed!

Use the formula $r = d \div t$ to help you calculate the unit rate for each person.

Calculate each unit rate.

Carolina: $3\frac{1}{2} \div \frac{1}{2} =$ ____ mi/h   Leslie: $5\frac{1}{4} \div \frac{3}{4} =$ ____ mi/h

Bryan: $4\frac{1}{2} \div \frac{3}{4} =$ ____ mi/h   Javier: $2\frac{1}{2} \div \frac{1}{3} =$ ____ mi/h

Compare the unit rates to determine which person kayaked at the fastest rate.

Javier kayaked at a rate of ____ miles per hour, which is the fastest unit rate.

So, the correct answer is ____. Fill in that answer choice.

4 Justify and Evaluate

How do you know your solution is accurate?

____

____

____

N = Number and Operations P = Proportionality MP = Mathematical Processes

More Multi-Step Problem Solving

Use a problem-solving model to solve each problem.

21. Emma has been training for a bike race. She recorded her training times in the table below. Emma believes that if her average speed is above 15 miles per hour, then she has a good chance of winning the race. On which day(s) was Emma's average speed over 15 miles per hour? N P MP

Day	Time (hr)	Distance (mi)
Monday	$1\frac{1}{2}$	27
Wednesday	$3\frac{1}{3}$	$63\frac{1}{3}$
Saturday	$2\frac{1}{2}$	35
Sunday	$\frac{3}{4}$	9

Ⓐ Monday only
Ⓑ Saturday only
Ⓒ Monday and Wednesday
Ⓓ All four days

22. The table shows the percent commission that a sales person earns based on monthly sales. Last month, Elijah's sales totaled \$8,924. Including commission, how much did he earn last month? N P MP

Sales	Commission
under \$5,000	5%
\$5,000 – \$7,499	$9\frac{1}{2}$%
\$7,500 – \$9,999	$12\frac{1}{2}$%
\$10,000 and higher	15%

23. A cheetah is one of the fastest land running animals. A cheetah can run $17\frac{1}{2}$ miles in $\frac{1}{4}$ hour. If a cheetah ran at this rate, how far would it travel in $1\frac{1}{2}$ hours? N P MP

24. The distance between the two islands shown on the map is 210 miles. A ruler measures this distance on the map as $3\frac{1}{2}$ inches. How many miles would be represented by $1\frac{3}{4}$ inches on the map? N P MP

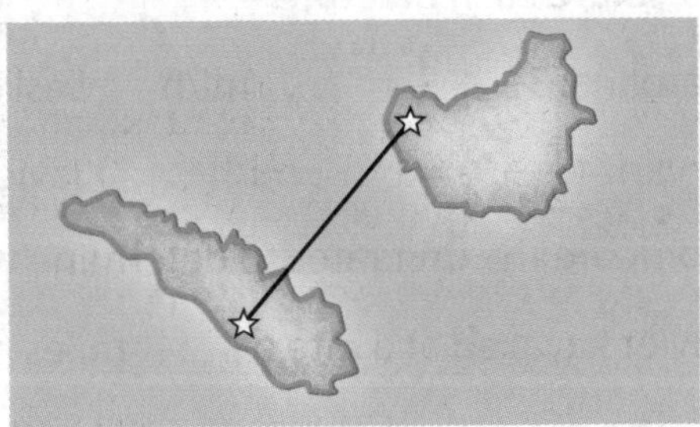

N = Number and Operations P = Proportionality MP = Mathematical Processes

Lesson 3
Convert Unit Rates

Launch the Lesson: Real World

Texas Essential Knowledge and Skills

Targeted TEKS
7.4(D) Solve problems involving ratios, rates, and percents, including multi-step problems involving percent increase and percent decrease, and financial literacy problems.
Also addresses 7.4(B).

Mathematical Processes
7.1(A), 7.1(B), 7.1(C)

Vocabulary
unit ratio
dimensional analysis

Essential Question
HOW can you show that two objects are proportional?

Squirrels, chipmunks, and rabbits are capable of running at fast speeds. The table shows the top running speeds of these animals. What is the average speed, in feet per second, for a squirrel?

Animal	Speed (mph)
Squirrel	10
Chipmunk	15
Cottontail Rabbit	30

1. How many feet are in 1 mile? 10 miles?

   1 mile = ________ feet

   10 miles = ________ feet

2. How many seconds are in 1 minute? 1 hour?

   1 minute = ________ seconds

   1 hour = ________ seconds

3. How could you determine the number of feet per second a squirrel can run?

   ____

   ____

4. Complete the following statement. Round to the nearest tenth.

   A squirrel's average speed is ☐ feet per second.

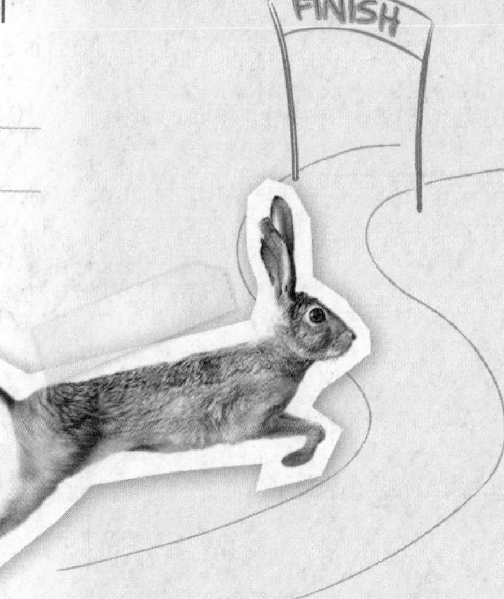

Which MP Mathematical Processes did you use? Shade the circle(s) that applies.

Ⓐ Apply Math to the Real World.
Ⓑ Use a Problem-Solving Model.
Ⓒ Select Tools and Techniques.
Ⓓ Use Multiple Representations.
Ⓔ Organize Ideas.
Ⓕ Analyze Relationships.
Ⓖ Justify Arguments.

Work Zone

Convert Rates

The relationships among some commonly used customary and metric units of measure are shown in the tables below.

Customary Units of Measure	
Smaller	**Larger**
12 inches	1 foot
16 ounces	1 pound
8 pints	1 gallon
3 feet	1 yard
5,280 feet	1 mile

Metric Units of Measure	
Smaller	**Larger**
100 centimeters	1 meter
1,000 grams	1 kilogram
1,000 milliliters	1 liter
10 millimeters	1 centimeter
1,000 milligrams	1 gram

Each of the relationships in the tables can be written as a **unit ratio**. Like a unit rate, a unit ratio is one in which the denominator is 1 unit. Below are three examples of unit ratios.

$$\frac{\text{12 inches}}{\text{1 foot}} \qquad \frac{\text{16 ounces}}{\text{1 pound}} \qquad \frac{\text{100 centimeters}}{\text{1 meter}}$$

The numerator and denominator of each of the unit ratios shown are equal. So, the value of each ratio is 1.

You can convert one rate to an equivalent rate by multiplying by a unit ratio or its reciprocal. When you convert rates, you include the units in your computation.

The process of including units of measure as factors when you compute is called **dimensional analysis**.

$$\frac{10 \text{ ft}}{1 \text{ s}} = \frac{10 \not{\text{ft}}}{1 \text{ s}} \cdot \frac{12 \text{ in.}}{1 \not{\text{ft}}} = \frac{10 \cdot 12 \text{ in.}}{1 \text{ s} \cdot 1} = \frac{120 \text{ in.}}{1 \text{ s}}$$

Example

1. A remote control car travels at a rate of 10 feet per second. How many inches per second is this?

$\frac{10 \text{ ft}}{1 \text{ s}} = \frac{10 \text{ ft}}{1 \text{ s}} \cdot \frac{12 \text{ in.}}{1 \text{ ft}}$ — Use 1 foot = 12 inches. Multiply by $\frac{12 \text{ in.}}{1 \text{ ft}}$.

$= \frac{10 \text{ ft}}{1 \text{ s}} \cdot \frac{12 \text{ in.}}{1 \text{ ft}}$ — Divide out common units.

$= \frac{10 \cdot 12 \text{ in.}}{1 \text{ s} \cdot 1}$ — Simplify.

$= \frac{120 \text{ in.}}{1 \text{ s}}$ — Simplify.

So, 10 feet per second equals 120 inches per second.

Examples

2. A swordfish can swim at a rate of 60 miles per hour. How many feet per hour is this?

You can use 1 mile = 5,280 feet to convert the rates.

$$\frac{60 \text{ mi}}{1 \text{ h}} = \frac{60 \text{ mi}}{1 \text{ h}} \cdot \frac{5{,}280 \text{ ft}}{1 \text{ mi}}$$ Multiply by $\frac{5{,}280 \text{ ft}}{1 \text{ mi}}$.

$$= \frac{60 \cancel{\text{mi}}}{1 \text{ h}} \cdot \frac{5{,}280 \text{ ft}}{1 \cancel{\text{mi}}}$$ Divide out common units.

$$= \frac{60 \cdot 5{,}280 \text{ ft}}{1 \cdot 1 \text{ h}}$$ Simplify.

$$= \frac{316{,}800 \text{ ft}}{1 \text{ h}}$$ Simplify.

A swordfish can swim at a rate of 316,800 feet per hour.

3. Marvin walks at a speed of 7 feet per second. How many feet per hour is this?

You can use 60 seconds = 1 minute and you can use 60 minutes = 1 hour to convert the rates.

$$\frac{7 \text{ ft}}{1 \text{ s}} = \frac{7 \text{ ft}}{1 \text{ s}} \cdot \frac{60 \text{ s}}{1 \text{ min}} \cdot \frac{60 \text{ min}}{1 \text{ h}}$$ Multiply by $\frac{60 \text{ s}}{1 \text{ min}}$ and $\frac{60 \text{ min}}{1 \text{ h}}$.

$$= \frac{7 \text{ ft}}{1 \cancel{\text{s}}} \cdot \frac{60 \cancel{\text{s}}}{1 \cancel{\text{min}}} \cdot \frac{60 \cancel{\text{min}}}{1 \text{ h}}$$ Divide out common units.

$$= \frac{7 \cdot 60 \cdot 60 \text{ ft}}{1 \cdot 1 \cdot 1 \text{ h}}$$ Simplify.

$$= \frac{25{,}200 \text{ ft}}{1 \text{ h}}$$ Simplify.

Marvin walks 25,200 feet in 1 hour.

and Reflect

To convert meters per hour to kilometers per hour, circle the relationship you need to know.

100 cm = 1 m

60 s = 1 min

1,000 m = 1 km

Got It? Do these problems to find out.

a. A gull can fly at a speed of 22 miles per hour. About how many feet per hour can the gull fly?

b. An AMTRAK train travels at 125 miles per hour. Convert the speed to miles per minute. Round to the nearest tenth.

a. ________

b. ________

Tutor

Example

4. The average speed of one team in a relay race is about 10 miles per hour. What is this speed in feet per second?

We can use 1 mile = 5,280 feet, 1 hour = 60 minutes, and 1 minute = 60 seconds to convert the rates.

$$\frac{10 \text{ mi}}{1 \text{ h}} = \frac{10 \text{ mi}}{1 \text{ h}} \cdot \frac{5{,}280 \text{ ft}}{1 \text{ mi}} \cdot \frac{1 \text{ h}}{60 \text{ min}} \cdot \frac{1 \text{ min}}{60 \text{ s}}$$ Multiply by distance and time unit ratios.

$$= \frac{10 \cancel{\text{mi}}}{1 \cancel{\text{h}}} \cdot \frac{5{,}280 \text{ ft}}{1 \cancel{\text{mi}}} \cdot \frac{1 \cancel{\text{h}}}{60 \cancel{\text{min}}} \cdot \frac{1 \cancel{\text{min}}}{60 \text{ s}}$$ Divide out common units.

$$= \frac{10 \cdot 5{,}280 \cdot 1 \cdot 1 \text{ ft}}{1 \cdot 1 \cdot 60 \cdot 60 \text{ s}}$$ Simplify.

$$= \frac{52{,}800 \text{ ft}}{3{,}600 \text{ s}}$$ Simplify.

$$\approx \frac{14.7 \text{ ft}}{1 \text{ s}}$$ Simplify.

The relay team runs at an average speed of about 14.7 feet per second.

Guided Practice

1. Water weighs about 8.34 pounds per gallon. About how many ounces per gallon is the weight of the water? (Examples 1 and 2) ________

2. A skydiver is falling at about 176 feet per second. How many feet per minute is he falling? (Example 3) ________

3. Lorenzo rides his bike at a rate of 5 yards per second. About how many miles per hour can Lorenzo ride his bike? (*Hint: 1 mile = 1,760 yards*) (Example 4)

4. **Building on the Essential Question** Explain why the ratio $\frac{3 \text{ feet}}{1 \text{ yard}}$ has a value of one.

Rate Yourself!

☐ I understand how to convert unit rates.

Great! You're ready to move on!

☐ I still have questions about converting unit rates.

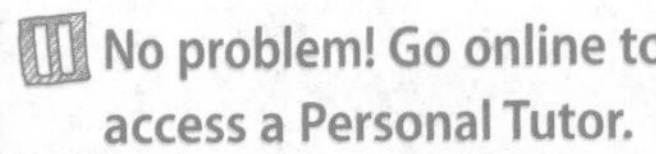
No problem! Go online to access a Personal Tutor.

Check

Independent Practice

7.4(B), 7.4(D), 7.1(A), 7.1(C) TEKS

1. A go-kart's top speed is 607,200 feet per hour. What is the speed in miles per hour? (Examples 1 and 2)

2. The fastest a human has ever run is 27 miles per hour. How many miles per minute did the human run? (Example 3)

3. A peregrine falcon can fly 322 kilometers per hour. How many meters per hour can the falcon fly? (Example 3)

4. A pipe is leaking at 1.5 cups per day. About how many gallons per week is the pipe leaking? (*Hint*: 1 gallon = 16 cups) (Example 4)

5. Charlie runs at a speed of 3 yards per second. About how many miles per hour does Charlie run? (Example 4)

6. MP **Apply Math to the Real World** Refer to the graphic novel frame below. Seth traveled 1 mile in 57.1 seconds. About how fast does Seth travel in miles per hour?

7. The speed at which a certain computer can access the Internet is 2 megabytes per second. How fast is this in megabytes per hour?

8. **Select Tools and Techniques** The approximate metric measurement of length is given for a U.S. customary unit of length. Use your estimation skills to complete the graphic organizer below. Fill in each blank with *foot*, *yard*, *inch*, or *mile*.

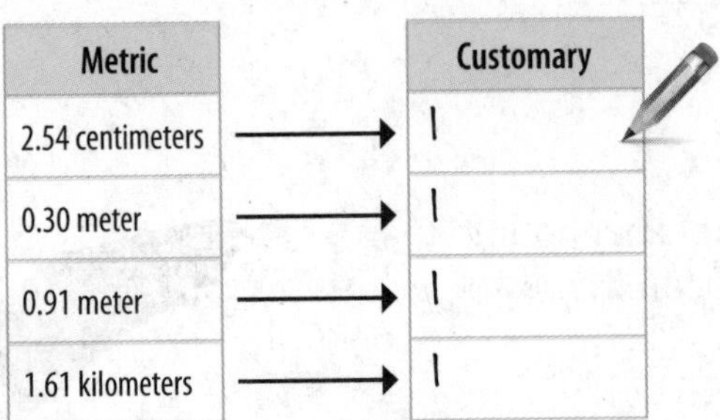

Metric		Customary
2.54 centimeters	→	1
0.30 meter	→	1
0.91 meter	→	1
1.61 kilometers	→	1

H.O.T. Problems Higher-Order Thinking

9. **Evaluate** When you convert 100 feet per second to inches per second, will there be more or less than 100 inches. Explain.

10. **Evaluate** Use the information in Exercise 8 to convert 7 meters per minute to yards per hour. Round to the nearest tenth.

11. **Evaluate** Circle the rate that does not belong with the other three. Explain your reasoning.

60 mi/h | 88 ft/s | 500 ft/min | 1440 mi/day

12. **Create** Write and solve a real-world problem in which a rate is converted.

Name ______________________________

Multi-Step Problem Solving

13. The table shows the price of almonds at three different grocery stores. What is the cost, in dollars per pound, for the cheapest almonds? N P MP

Store	Weight (oz)	Price ($)
A	64	19.96
B	80	21.75
C	112	33.95

Use a problem-solving model to solve this problem.

1 Analyze

Read the problem. Circle the information you know. Underline what the problem is asking you to find.

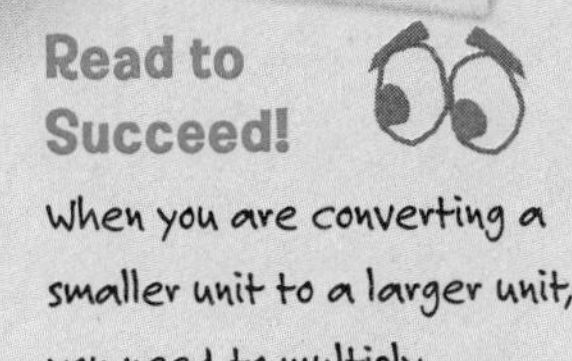

2 Plan

What will you need to do to solve the problem? Write your plan in steps.

Step 1 Calculate each __________ and convert to an equivalent rate.

Step 2 Compare the unit rates to determine __________ per pound.

3 Solve

Use your plan to solve this problem. Show your steps.

Store A: $\frac{\$19.96}{64 \text{ oz}} \cdot \frac{16 \text{ oz}}{1 \text{ lb}} = \frac{\$319.36}{64 \text{ lb}} =$ __________

Store B: $\frac{\$21.75}{80 \text{ oz}} \cdot \frac{16 \text{ oz}}{1 \text{ lb}} = \frac{\$348}{80 \text{ lb}} =$ __________

Store C: $\frac{\$33.95}{112 \text{ oz}} \cdot \frac{16 \text{ oz}}{1 \text{ lb}} = \frac{\$543.20}{112 \text{ lb}} =$ __________

Compare the unit rates. ______ < ______ < ______

Store B sells the cheapest almonds for ______ per pound. Complete the grid.

					.		
⊕	0	0	0	0		0	0
⊖	1	1	1	1		1	1
	2	2	2	2		2	2
	3	3	3	3		3	3
	4	4	4	4		4	4
	5	5	5	5		5	5
	6	6	6	6		6	6
	7	7	7	7		7	7
	8	8	8	8		8	8
	9	9	9	9		9	9

4 Justify and Evaluate

How do you know your solution is accurate?

____

____

____

N = Number and Operations P = Proportionality MP = Mathematical Processes

More Multi-Step Problem Solving

Use a problem-solving model to solve each problem.

14. The table shows the speeds of several runners on a track team. What is the speed, in feet per minute, of the fastest runner? N P MP

Runner	Distance (yd)	Time (s)
Devin	12	3
Sherwin	9	2
Zachary	34	8

15. Lian used her garden hose to fill her 15,000-gallon swimming pool in 5 hours. She plans to graph the fill rate on a coordinate grid, showing the amount of water, in pints, on the y-axis and time, in minutes on the x-axis . What will be the y-value on the coordinate grid at 1 minute? (*Hint:* There are 8 pints in one gallon.) N P MP

16. Adam painted the rectangular wall shown below in 1 hour. On average, how many square feet did he paint per minute? N P EE MP

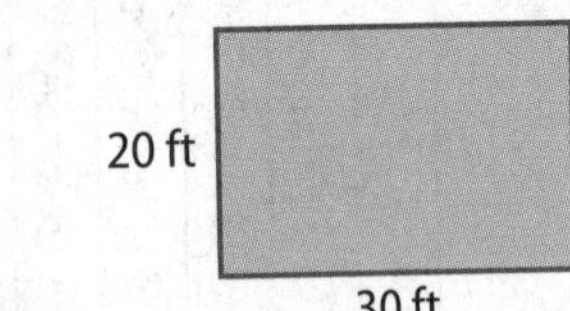

17. Use dimensional analysis to determine whether the rate 3,000 grams per week is 1,000 times faster than 3 kilograms per week. Explain. P MP

N = Number and Operations P = Proportionality EE = Expressions, Equations, and Relationships MP = Mathematical Processes

Proportional and Nonproportional Relationships

Launch the Lesson: Real World

Ms. Cochran is planning a year-end pizza party for her students. Ace Pizza offers free delivery and charges $8 per medium pizza. Complete the table to determine the cost for different numbers of pizzas ordered.

Cost ($)	8				
Pizza	1	2	3	4	5

Let's investigate the relationship between cost and number of pizzas ordered.

1. For each number of pizzas, fill in the boxes to write the relationship of the cost and number of pizzas as a ratio in simplest form.

$\frac{16}{2} = \frac{\square}{1}$ $\frac{24}{3} = \frac{\square}{\square}$

$\frac{32}{\square} = \frac{\square}{\square}$ $\frac{\square}{5} = \frac{\square}{\square}$

2. What do you notice about the simplified ratios?

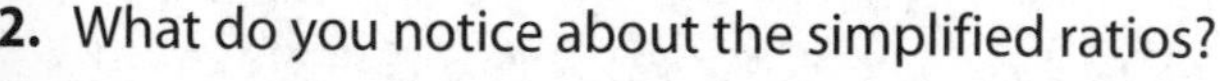

Which MP Mathematical Processes did you use? Shade the circle(s) that applies.

Ⓐ Apply Math to the Real World.
Ⓑ Use a Problem-Solving Model.
Ⓒ Select Tools and Techniques.
Ⓓ Use Multiple Representations.
Ⓔ Organize Ideas.
Ⓕ Analyze Relationships.
Ⓖ Justify Arguments.

Texas Essential Knowledge and Skills

Targeted TEKS
7.4(D) Solve problems involving ratios, rates, and percents, including multi-step problems involving percent increase and percent decrease, and financial literacy problems.

Mathematical Processes
7.1(A), 7.1(B), 7.1(C), 7.1(D), 7.1(G)

Vocab

Vocabulary
proportional
nonproportional
equivalent ratios

Essential Question
HOW can you show that two objects are proportional?

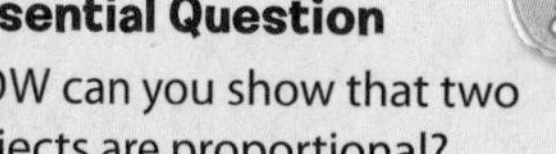

Work Zone

Identify Proportional Relationships

Two quantities are **proportional** if they have a constant ratio or unit rate. For relationships in which this ratio is not constant, the two quantities are **nonproportional**.

In the pizza example on the previous page, the cost of an order is *proportional* to the number of pizzas ordered.

$$\frac{\text{cost of order}}{\text{pizzas ordered}} = \frac{8}{1} = \frac{16}{2} = \frac{24}{3} = \frac{32}{4} = \frac{40}{5} \text{ or \$8 per pizza}$$

All of the ratios above are **equivalent ratios** because they all have the same value.

Tutor

Example

1. Andrew earns $18 per hour for mowing lawns. Is the amount of money he earns proportional to the number of hours he spends mowing? Explain.

Determine the amount of money he earns for working a different number of hours. Make a table to show these amounts.

Earnings ($)	18	36	54	72
Time (h)	1	2	3	4

For each number of hours worked, write the relationship of the amount he earned and hour as a ratio in simplest form.

$$\frac{\text{amount earned}}{\text{number of hours}} \rightarrow \frac{18}{1} \text{ or } 18 \quad \frac{36}{2} \text{ or } 18 \quad \frac{54}{3} \text{ or } 18 \quad \frac{72}{4} \text{ or } 18$$

All of the ratios between the two quantities can be simplified to 18.

The amount of money he earns is proportional to the number of hours he spends mowing.

Got It? Do this problem to find out.

a. At Lakeview Middle School, there are 2 homeroom teachers assigned to every 48 students. Is the number of students at this school proportional to the number of teachers? Explain your reasoning.

a. ________

Examples

2. Uptown Tickets charges $7 per baseball game ticket plus a $3 processing fee per order. Is the cost of an order proportional to the number of tickets ordered? Explain.

Cost ($)	10	17	24	31
Tickets Ordered	1	2	3	4

For each number of tickets, write the relationship of the cost and number of tickets as a ratio in simplest form.

$\frac{\text{cost of order}}{\text{tickets ordered}} \rightarrow \frac{10}{1}$ or 10 $\frac{17}{2}$ or 8.5 $\frac{24}{3}$ or 8 $\frac{31}{4}$ or 7.75

Since the ratios of the two quantities are not the same, the cost of an order is *not* proportional to the number of tickets ordered.

3. You can use the recipe shown to make a fruit punch. Is the amount of sugar used proportional to the amount of mix used? Explain.

Determine the amount of sugar and mix needed for different numbers of batches. Make a table to help you solve.

Cups of Sugar	$\frac{1}{2}$	1	$1\frac{1}{2}$	2
Envelopes of Mix	1	2	3	4

For each number of cups of sugar, write the relationship of the cups and number of envelopes of mix as a ratio in simplest form.

$\frac{\text{cups of sugar}}{\text{envelopes of mix}} \rightarrow \frac{\frac{1}{2}}{1}$ or 0.5 $\frac{1}{2}$ or 0.5 $\frac{1\frac{1}{2}}{3}$ or 0.5 $\frac{2}{4}$ or 0.5

All of the ratios between the two quantities can be simplified to 0.5. The amount of mix used is proportional to the amount of sugar used.

Got It? Do this problem to find out.

b. At the beginning of the year, Isabel had $120 in the bank. Each week, she deposits another $20. Is her account balance proportional to the number of weeks of deposits? Use the table below. Explain your reasoning.

Time (wk)	1	2	3
Balance ($)			

b. ______________

Tutor

Example

4. The tables shown represent the number of pages Martin and Gabriel read over time. Which situation represents a proportional relationship between the time spent reading and the number of pages read? Explain.

Pages Martin Read	2	4	6
Time (min)	5	10	15

Pages Gabriel Read	3	4	7
Time (min)	5	10	15

Write the ratios for each time period in simplest form.

$\frac{\text{pages}}{\text{minutes}} \rightarrow \frac{2}{5}, \frac{4}{10} \text{ or } \frac{2}{5}, \frac{6}{15} \text{ or } \frac{2}{5}$ $\frac{3}{5}, \frac{4}{10} \text{ or } \frac{2}{5}, \frac{7}{15}$

All of the ratios between Martin's quantities are $\frac{2}{5}$. So, Martin's reading rate represents a proportional relationship.

Guided Practice

For Exercises 1 and 2, use a table to solve. Then explain your reasoning.

1. The Vista Marina rents boats for $25 per hour. In addition to the rental fee, there is a $12 charge for fuel. Is the number of hours you can rent the boat proportional to the total cost? Explain. (Examples 1–3)

Rental Time (h)			
Cost ($)			

2. Which situation represents a proportional relationship between the hours worked and amount earned for Matt and Jane? Explain. (Example 4)

Matt's Earnings ($)	12	20	31
Time (h)	1	2	3

Jane's Earnings ($)	12	24	36
Time (h)	1	2	3

3. **Building on the Essential Question** Explain what makes two quantities proportional.

Rate Yourself!

How confident are you about determining proportional relationships? Shade the ring on the target.

Check

Find out online. Use the Self-Check Quiz.

FOLDABLES Time to update your Foldable!

Name ______________________ My Homework ______________________

Independent Practice

For Exercises 1 and 2, use a table to solve. Then explain your reasoning. (Examples 1 and 2)

1. An adult elephant drinks about 225 liters of water each day. Is the number of days the water supply lasts proportional to the number of liters of water the elephant drinks?

Time (days)	1	2	3	4
Water (L)				

____

2. An elevator *ascends*, or goes up, at a rate of 750 feet per minute. Is the height to which the elevator ascends proportional to the number of minutes it takes to get there? (Examples 1–3)

Time (min)	1	2	3	4
Height (ft)				

____

3. Which situation represents a proportional relationship between the number of laps run by each student and their time? (Example 4)

Desmond's Time (s)	146	292	584
Laps	2	4	8

Maria's Time (s)	150	320	580
Laps	2	4	6

____

____

Copy and Solve **Use a table to help you solve. Then explain your reasoning. Show your work on a separate piece of paper.**

4. Plant A is 18 inches tall after one week, 36 inches tall after two weeks, 56 inches tall after three weeks. Plant B is 18 inches tall after one week, 36 inches tall after two weeks, 54 inches tall after three weeks. Which situation represents a proportional relationship between the plants' height and number of weeks? (Example 4)

5. Determine whether the measures for the figure shown are proportional.

a. the length of a side and the perimeter

b. the length of a side and the area

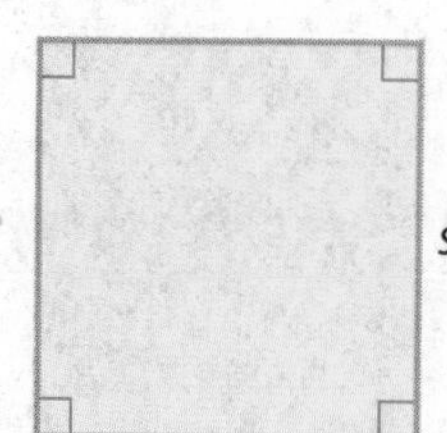

6. **MP Justify Arguments** MegaMart collects a sales tax equal to $\frac{1}{16}$ of the retail price of each purchase. The tax is sent to the state government.

a. Is the amount of tax collected proportional to the cost of an item before tax is added? Explain.

Retail Price ($)	16	32	48	64
Tax Collected ($)				

b. Is the amount of tax collected proportional to the cost of an item after tax has been added? Explain.

Retail Price ($)	16	32	48	
Tax Collected ($)				
Cost Including Tax ($)				

7. **Find the Error** Blake ran laps around the gym. His times are shown in the table. Blake is trying to decide whether the number of laps is proportional to the time. Find his mistake and correct it.

Time (min)	1	2	3	4
Laps	4	6	8	10

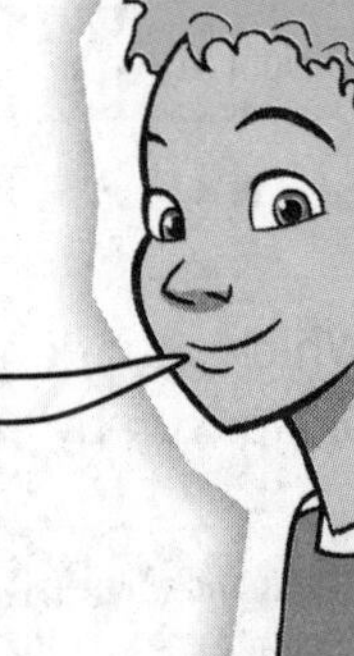

It is proportional because the number of laps always increases by 2.

H.O.T. Problems Higher-Order Thinking

8. **Analyze** Determine whether the cost for ordering multiple items that will be delivered is *sometimes, always,* or *never* proportional. Explain your reasoning.

9. **Create** Give real-world examples of two similar situations in which one is a proportional relationship and the second one is nonproportional. Then explain your reasoning.

Name ______________________________

Multi-Step Problem Solving

10. Federico pays sales tax equal to $\frac{3}{50}$ of the retail price of his purchases. If the sales tax rate remains proportional, what is the total cost, in dollars, for a purchase amount of $84? N P MP

Purchase Amount ($)	Sales Tax Amount ($)	Total Amount ($)
12	0.72	12.72
24	1.44	25.44
36	2.16	38.16
48	2.88	50.88

Use a problem-solving model to solve this problem.

1 Analyze

Read the problem. Circle the information you know.
Underline what the problem is asking you to find.

Read to Succeed!
To determine the sales tax amount, multiply the purchase amount by the fractional tax amount.

2 Plan

What will you need to do to solve the problem? Write your plan in steps.

Step 1 Determine the __________ for his purchase of $84.

Step 2 Add the purchase amount and sales tax to determine the __________.

3 Solve

Use your plan to solve the problem. Show your steps.

Determine the sales tax.

$\frac{3}{50} \times \$84 =$ __________

$84 + ________ = ________ Add.

The total amount Federico will pay for a purchase of $84 is ______.
Complete the grid.

⊕ ⊖	0–9	0–9	0–9	0–9	.	0–9	0–9

4 Justify and Evaluate

How do you know your solution is accurate?

____

____

____

____

N = Number and Operations P = Proportionality MP = Mathematical Processes

More Multi-Step Problem Solving

Use a problem-solving model to solve each problem.

11. Laurita is writing a research paper. If the relationship remains proportional, how many pages will she complete in 7 hours? N P MP

Time (hr)	Pages Completed
2	3
3	4.5

12. The table shows three membership options at a fitness center. Logan chooses the membership that represents a proportional relationship between the number of classes and the monthly cost. How much will he spend, in dollars, if he takes 12 classes in a month? N P MP

Membership	Cost
Basic	\$20 per class
Fit Plus	\$60 per month plus \$10 per class
Fit Extreme	\$75 per month plus \$30 enrollment fee

13. Carla donates 3% of her salary to charity each year. She makes \$35,000 each year. If the relationship remains proportional, how much money will she have donated after 8 years? N P MP

14. The graph shows the distance of a race car over time. Is this relationship between distance and time proportional? Justify your answers. N P MD MP

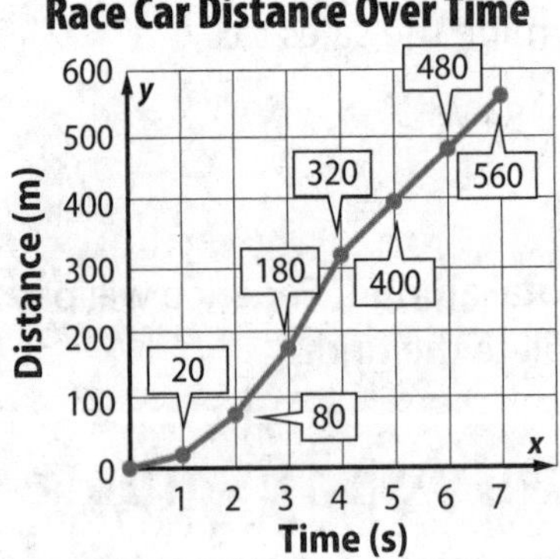

N = Number and Operations P = Proportionality MD = Measurement and Data MP = Mathematical Processes

Focus on Mathematical Processes

Draw a Diagram

Mathematical Process
7.1(B) Use a problem-solving model that incorporates analyzing given information, formulating a plan or strategy, determining a solution, justifying the solution, and evaluating the problem-solving process and the reasonableness of the solution.
Targeted TEKS 7.4(B), 7.4(D)

Science Experiment

Casey drops a ball from a height of 12 feet. It hits the ground and bounces up half as high as it fell. This is true for each successive bounce.

After how many bounces will the ball have traveled over 34 feet vertically?

Analyze *What are the facts?*

Casey dropped the ball from a height of 12 feet. It bounces up half as high for each successive bounce.

Plan *Choose a problem-solving strategy.*

I will use the ______________ strategy.

Solve *How can you apply the strategy?*

Determine the distance traveled after each bounce.
$12 \div 2 = 6, 6 \div 2 = 3, 3 \div 2 = 1.5,$
$1.5 \div 2 = 0.75, 0.75 \div 2 = 0.375$

Add the vertical distances the ball traveled.
$12 + (6 + 6) + (3 + 3) + (1.5 + 1.5) +$
$(0.75 + 0.75) =$ ☐ ft

The ball traveled over 34 feet vertically after the ☐ bounce.

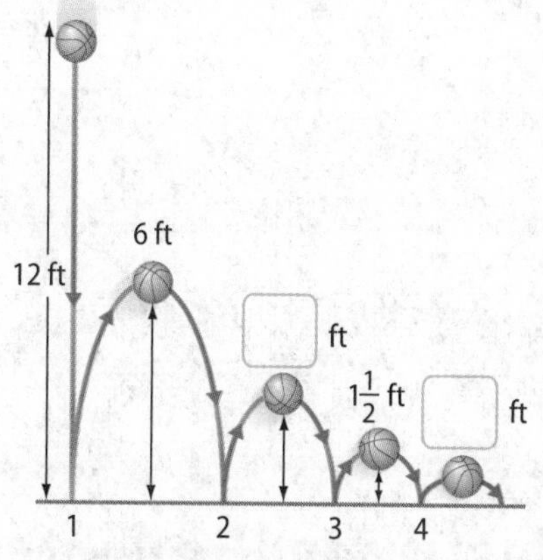

Justify and Evaluate *How do you know your solution is accurate?*

____

____

____

Travel

Mr. Garcia has driven 65 miles, which is $\frac{2}{3}$ of the way to his sister's house.

If he is traveling at a speed of 65 miles per hour, how long will it take him to drive the remaining distance to his sister's house?

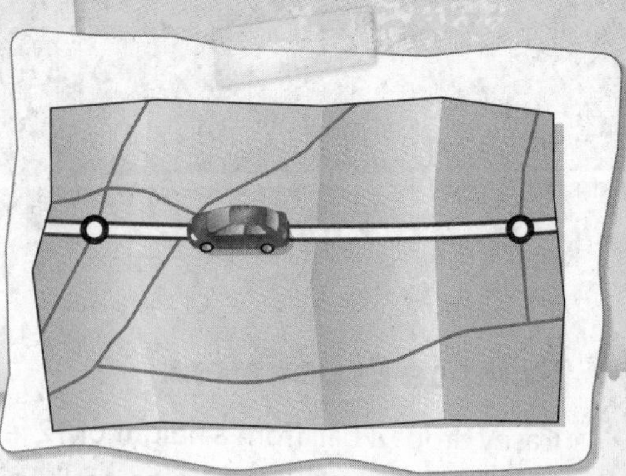

Analyze

Read the problem. Circle the information you know.
Underline what the problem is asking you to find.

2 Plan

Choose a problem-solving strategy.

I will use the _______________ strategy.

3 Solve

How can you apply the strategy?

Justify and Evaluate

How do you know your solution is accurate?

____

____

____

Multi-Step Problem Solving

Work with a small group to solve the following problems. Show your work on a separate piece of paper.

1. Pie

Marta ate a quarter of a whole pie. Edwin ate $\frac{1}{4}$ of what was left. Cristina then ate $\frac{1}{3}$ of what was left.

What fraction of the pie remains?

2. Games

Eight members of a chess club are having a tournament. In the first round, every player will play a chess game against every other player.

How many games will be in the first round of the tournament?

3. Distance

Alejandro and Pedro are riding their bikes to school. After 1 mile, they are $\frac{5}{8}$ of the way there.

How much farther do they have to go?

4. Science

The cheetah is the fastest land animal in the world. Its speed is $2\frac{3}{5}$ times that of the fastest human's speed.

If the fastest recorded speed for a human is 27.45 miles per hour, how fast can the cheetah run?

Mid-Chapter Check

Vocabulary Check

1. Define *complex fraction*. Give two examples of a complex fraction.
TEKS 7.4(B), 7.1(D)

Key Concept Check

2. Complete the graphic organizer to compare the two rates. TEKS 7.4(B), 7.1(E)

Rate 1: Texas Tech University \$22,568 for 4 years of college tuition	Compare	Rate 2: University of Houston \$18,252 for 3 years of college tuition
Unit Rate 1:		Unit Rate 2:

3. A tourist information center charges \$10 per hour to rent a bicycle. Is the rental charge proportional to the number of hours you rent the bicycle? Justify your response. TEKS 7.4(D), 7.1(A)

Multi-Step Problem Solving

4. A cruise ship is traveling at a speed of 20 knots. A knot is approximately equal to 1.151 miles per hour. What is the approximate speed the ship is traveling in yards per second? Round to the nearest tenth. P MP

Ⓐ 11.3 yards per second

Ⓑ 13.1 yards per second

Ⓒ 23.0 yards per second

Ⓓ 35.5 yards per second

P = Proportionality MP = Mathematical Processes

Lesson 5

Graph Proportional Relationships

Launch the Lesson: Vocabulary

Maps have grids to locate cities. The **coordinate plane** is a type of grid that is formed when two number lines intersect at their zero points. The number lines separate the coordinate plane into four regions called **quadrants**.

An **ordered pair** is a pair of numbers, such as (1, 2), used to locate or graph points on the coordinate plane.

The **x-coordinate** corresponds to a number on the *x*-axis. → **(1, 2)** ← The **y-coordinate** corresponds to a number on the *y*-axis.

Label the coordinate plane with the terms *ordered pair*, *x-coordinate*, and *y-coordinate*.

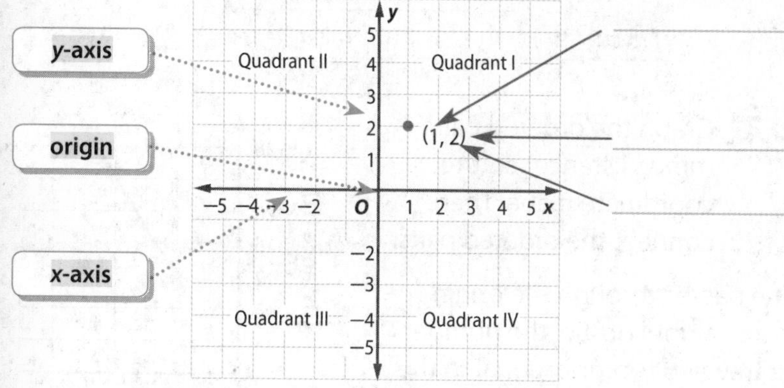

Graph points (2, 3) and (−3, −2) above. Connect the three points on the coordinate plane. Describe the graph.

____

Which MP Mathematical Processes did you use? Shade the circle(s) that applies.

Ⓐ Apply Math to the Real World.
Ⓑ Use a Problem-Solving Model.
Ⓒ Select Tools and Techniques.
Ⓓ Use Multiple Representations.
Ⓔ Organize Ideas.
Ⓕ Analyze Relationships.
Ⓖ Justify Arguments.

Texas Essential Knowledge and Skills

Targeted TEKS

7.4(D) Solve problems involving ratios, rates, and percents, including multi-step problems involving percent increase and percent decrease, and financial literacy problems. *Also addresses 7.4(A).*

Mathematical Processes

7.1(A), 7.1(B), 7.1(C), 7.1(D)

Vocabulary

coordinate plane
quadrants
ordered pair
x-coordinate
y-coordinate
y-axis
origin
x-axis

Essential Question

HOW can you show that two objects are proportional?

Work Zone

Identify Proportional Relationships

Another way to determine whether two quantities are proportional is to graph the quantities on the coordinate plane. If the graph of the two quantities is a straight line through the origin, then the two quantities are proportional.

Example

Linear Relationships

Relationships that have straight-line graphs are called linear relationships.

1. The slowest mammal on Earth is the tree sloth. It moves at a speed of 6 feet per minute. Determine whether the number of feet the sloth moves is proportional to the number of minutes it moves by graphing on the coordinate plane. Explain your reasoning.

Step 1 Make a table to find the number of feet walked for 0, 1, 2, 3, and 4 minutes.

Time (min)	0	1	2	3	4
Distance (ft)	0	6	12	18	24

Step 2 Graph the ordered pairs (time, distance) on the coordinate plane. Then connect the ordered pairs.

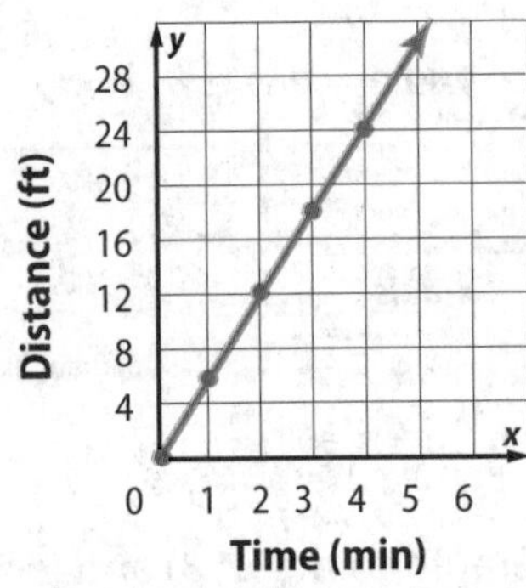

The line passes through the origin and is a straight line. So, the number of feet traveled is proportional to the number of minutes.

Got It? Do this problem to find out.

a. ______

a. James earns $5 an hour babysitting. Determine whether the amount of money James earns babysitting is proportional to the number of hours he babysits by graphing on the coordinate plane. Explain your reasoning in the work zone.

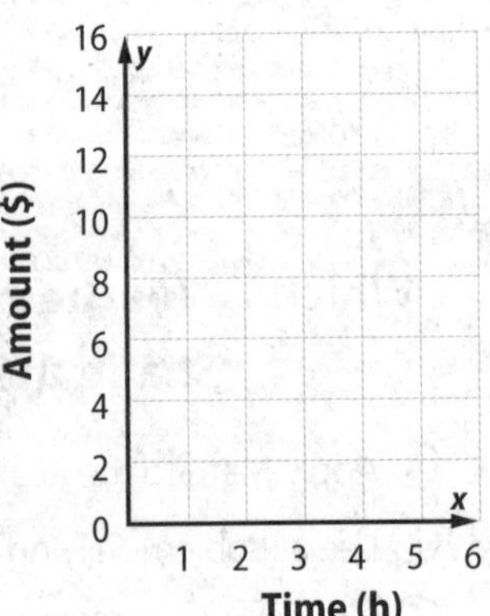

Example

Tutor

2. The cost of renting video games from Games Inc. is shown in the table. Determine whether the cost is proportional to the number of games rented by graphing on the coordinate plane. Explain your reasoning.

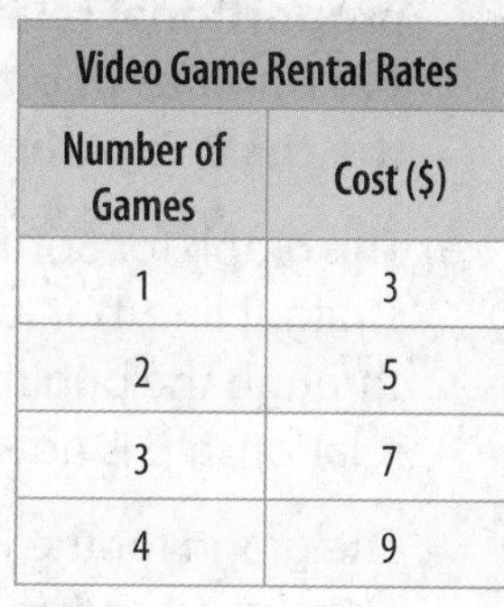

Video Game Rental Rates	
Number of Games	Cost ($)
1	3
2	5
3	7
4	9

Step 1 Write the two quantities as ordered pairs (number of games, cost).

The ordered pairs are (1, 3), (2, 5), (3, 7), and (4, 9).

Step 2 Graph the ordered pairs on the coordinate plane. Then connect the ordered pairs and extend the line to the *y*-axis.

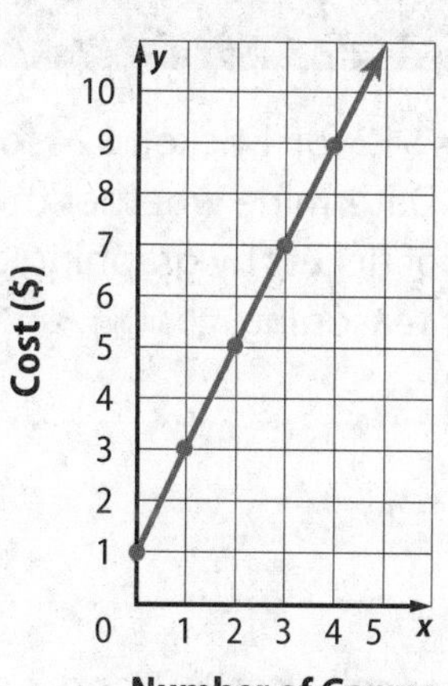

The line does not pass through the origin. So, the cost of the video games is not proportional to the number of games rented.

Check The ratios are not constant. $\frac{1}{3} \neq \frac{2}{5}$ ✓

Quick Review

When drawing a graph, include a title and labels for the horizontal and vertical axes.

Got It? **Do this problem to find out.**

b. The table shows the number of Calories an athlete burned per minute of exercise. Determine whether the number of Calories burned is proportional to the number of minutes by graphing on the coordinate plane. Explain your reasoning in the Work Zone.

Calories Burned	
Number of Minutes	Number of Calories
0	0
1	4
2	8
3	13

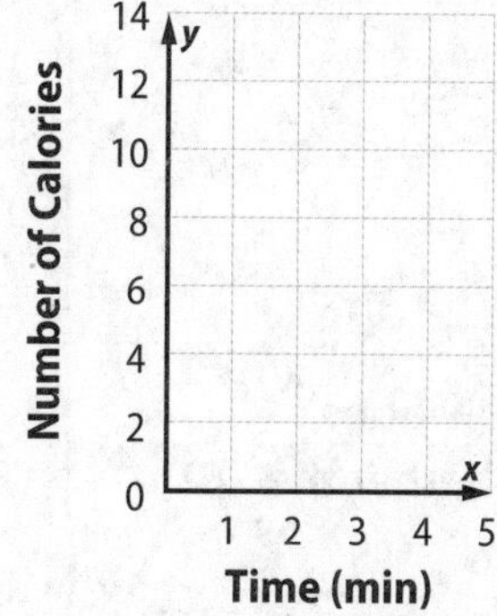

b. ______________

Example

3. Which batting cage represents a proportional relationship between the number of pitches thrown and the cost? Explain.

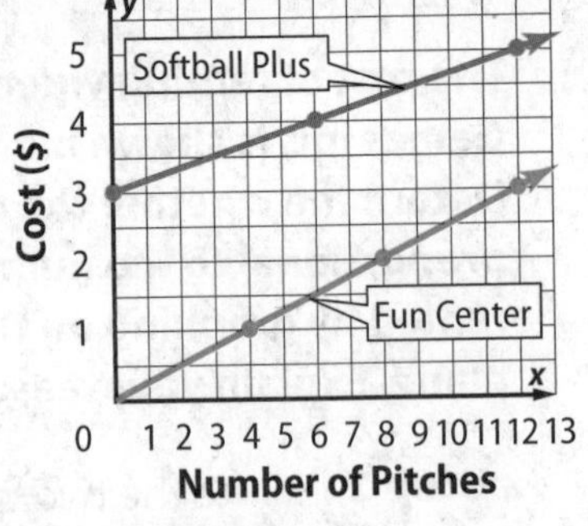

The graph for Softball Plus is a straight line, but it does not pass through the origin. So, the relationship is not proportional.

The graph for the Fun Center is a straight line through the origin. So, the relationship between the number of the pitches thrown and the cost is proportional.

Guided Practice

1. The cost of 3-D movie tickets is $12 for 1 ticket, $24 for 2 tickets, and $36 for 3 tickets. Determine whether the cost is proportional to the number of tickets by graphing on the coordinate plane. Explain your reasoning. (Examples 1 and 2)

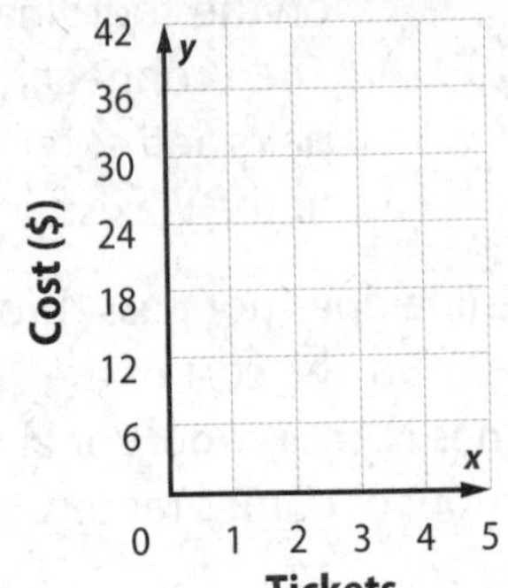

2. The number of books two stores sell after 1, 2, and 3 days is shown. Which book store represents a proportional relationship between time and books? Explain. (Example 3)

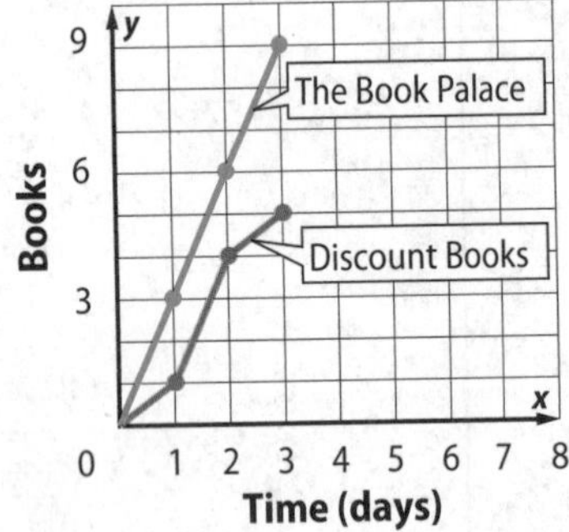

3. **Building on the Essential Question** How does graphing relationships help you determine whether the relationship is proportional or not?

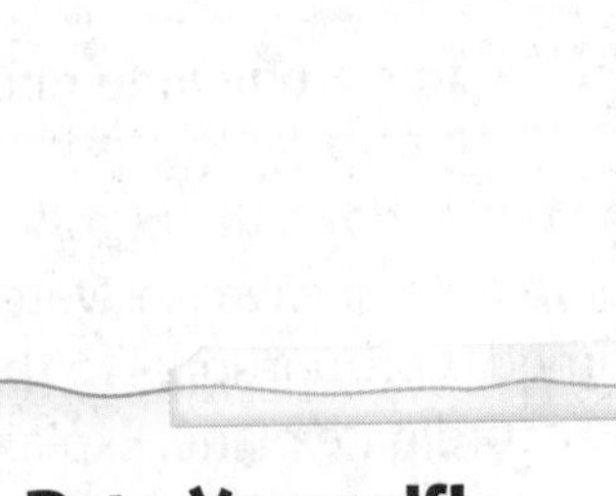

Rate Yourself!

How confident are you about identifying proportional relationships by graphing? Check the box that applies.

Find out online. Use the Self-Check Quiz.

FOLDABLES Time to update your Foldable!

Name ______________________ My Homework ______________________

Independent Practice

7.4(A), 7.4(D), 7.1(C), 7.1(D) TEKS

MP Use Multiple Representations Determine whether the relationship between the two quantities shown in each table are proportional by graphing on the coordinate plane. Explain your reasoning. (Examples 1 and 2)

1.

Savings Account	
Week	Account Balance ($)
1	125
2	150
3	175

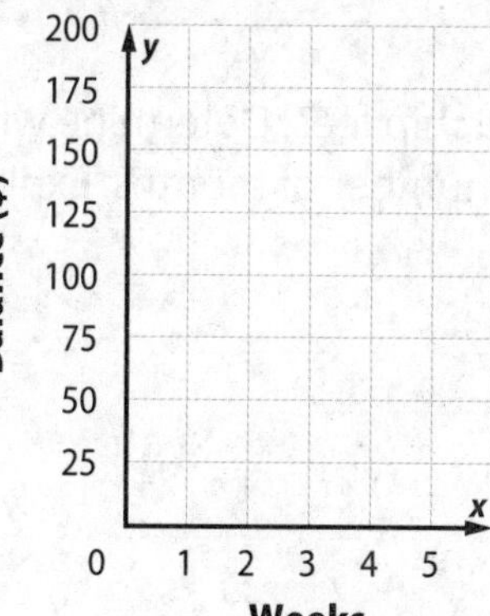

____

____

____

2.

Calories in Fruit Cups	
Servings	Calories
1	70
3	210
5	350

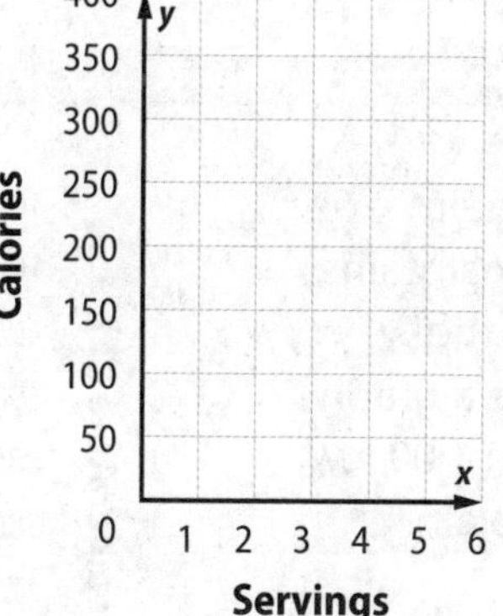

____

____

____

3. The height of two plants is recorded after 1, 2, and 3 weeks as shown in the graph at the right. Which plants' growth represents a proportional relationship between time and height? Explain. (Example 3)

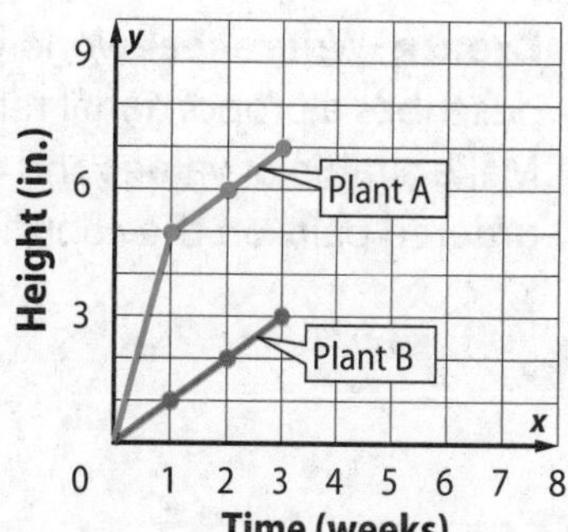

____

____

____

4. The perimeter of a square is 4 times as great as the length of any of its sides. Determine if the perimeter of a square is proportional to its side length. Explain.

5. A health club charges $35 a month for membership fees. Determine whether the cost of membership is proportional to the number of months. Explain your reasoning.

H.O.T. Problems Higher-Order Thinking

6. **Analyze** Describe some data that when graphed would represent a proportional relationship. Explain your reasoning.

7. **Evaluate** The greenhouse temperatures at certain times are shown in the table. The greenhouse maintains temperatures between 65°F and 85°F. Suppose the temperature increases at a constant rate. Create a graph of the time and temperatures at each hour from 1:00 P.M. to 8:00 P.M. Is the relationship proportional? Explain.

Time	Temperature (°F)
1:00 P.M.	66
6:00 P.M.	78.5
8:00 P.M.	83.5

Temperature (°F): 0, 65, 70, 75, 80, 85, 90, 95, 100, 105 (y)

Time: 1:00 P.M., 3:00 P.M., 5:00 P.M., 7:00 P.M. (x)

8. **Create** Write a real-world problem that describes a proportional relationship. Make a table of values and graph the ordered pairs on the coordinate plane.

Name ________________________________

Multi-Step Problem Solving

9. The amount of time it takes a car to travel a certain distance is shown in the table. Choose the statement below that best describes the appearance of the graph of the relationship between time traveled and distance traveled. P MD MP

Time (min)	Distance (mi)
10	10
20	18
35	30
45	38

Ⓐ a straight line that passes through the origin
Ⓑ a curved line that passes through the origin
Ⓒ a curved line that does not pass through the origin
Ⓓ a straight line that does not pass through the origin

Use a problem-solving model to solve this problem.

1 Analyze

Read the problem. Circle the information you know. Underline what the problem is asking you to find.

Read to Succeed!
Be sure to graph the ordered pairs on a coordinate plane to determine if the graph is a straight line.

2 Plan

What will you need to do to solve the problem? Write your plan in steps.

Step 1 __________ ordered pairs on a coordinate plane.

Step 2 Analyze the __________ to describe the relationship shown.

3 Solve

Use your plan to solve the problem. Show your steps.

Graph the ordered pairs (time, distance) on the coordinate plane. Then connect the ordered pairs with a line.

The line is __________ and __________ pass through the origin.

So, the correct answer is ____. Fill in that answer choice.

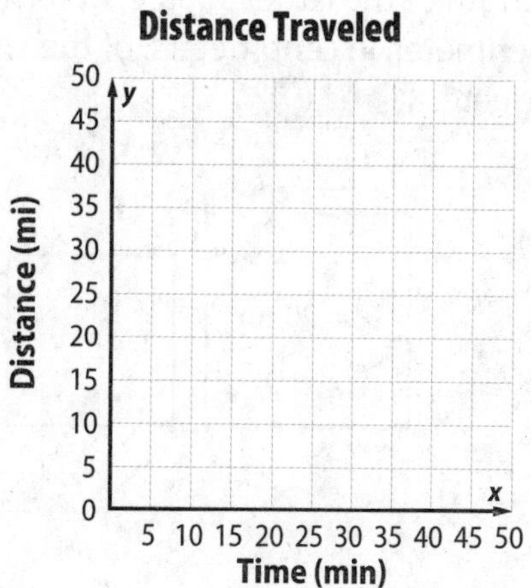

4 Justify and Evaluate

How do you know your solution is accurate?

____

____

____

P = Proportionality MD = Measurement and Data MP = Mathematical Processes

More Multi-Step Problem Solving

Use a problem-solving model to solve each problem.

10. Raisins are sometimes sold by the pound. The table below shows the cost for different weights of raisins. Choose the statement below that best describes the appearance of the graph of the relationship between weight and cost of raisins sold. P MP

Weight of Raisins (lb)	Cost ($)
1	4.60
2	9.20
4	18.40
5.5	25.30

Ⓐ a straight line that passes through the origin
Ⓑ a curved line that passes through the origin
Ⓒ a curved line that does not pass through the origin
Ⓓ a straight line that does not pass through the origin

11. The red line shows the distance traveled for five minutes by a giant tortoise. The blue line shows the distance traveled for five minutes by a three-toed sloth. If each animal kept traveling at its same rate for one hour, how much farther would the sloth have traveled than the tortoise? N P MD MP

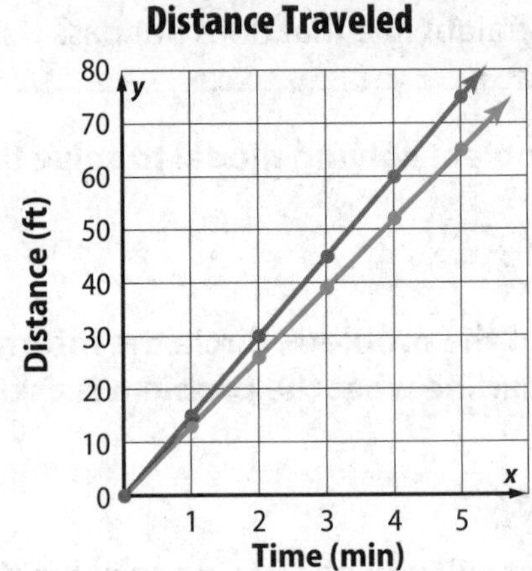

12. The relationship between the side length s of a square and the perimeter P of the square is a proportional relationship. Given that the side length of the smaller square is $\frac{4}{5}$ the side length of the larger square, determine the perimeter, in centimeters, of the smaller square. P EE MP

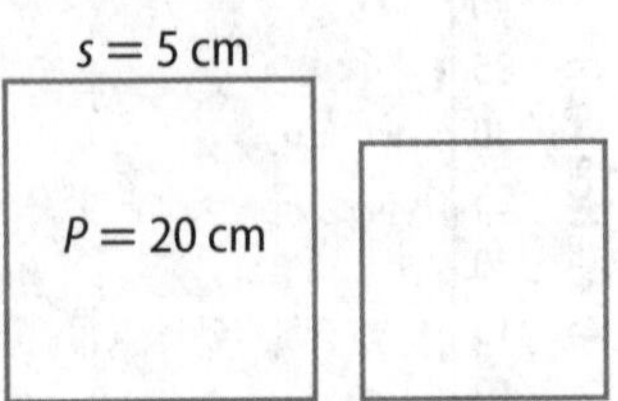

13. Jarrod is comparing gym memberships. Gym A charges $38 per month for membership, with no annual fees. Gym B charges an annual fee of $15 and a monthly membership cost of $35. Which gym charges more for a yearly membership? By how much more? Justify your response. P N MP

N = Number and Operations 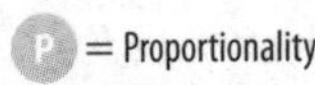 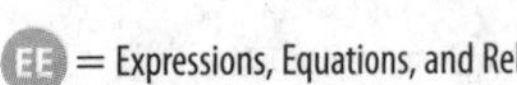 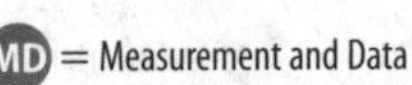 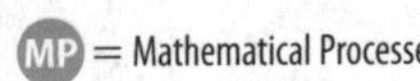
P = Proportionality EE = Expressions, Equations, and Relationships MD = Measurement and Data MP = Mathematical Processes

Hands-On Lab 5-b

Model Proportional Relationships

INQUIRY **HOW can I use multiple representations to determine how proportional and nonproportional relationships are alike and different?**

Texas Essential Knowledge and Skills

Targeted TEKS

7.4(D) Solve problems involving ratios, rates, and percents, including multi-step problems involving percent increase and percent decrease, and financial literacy problems.

Mathematical Processes

7.1(A), 7.1(C), 7.1(D), 7.1(E), 7.1(F), 7.1(G)

Albert and Bianca joined an online discussion group. Each student posted four comments. The number of replies to each of their comments is shown in the table. Determine if each data set represents a proportional relationship.

Hands-On Activity

Step 1 Arrange centimeter cubes to model the number of replies per comment as shown in the diagram below.

Student	Albert				Bianca			
Comment Number	1	2	3	4	1	2	3	4
Number of Replies								

Step 2 Complete each table. Then graph the data on the coordinate plane. You may wish to use a different color pencil for each data set.

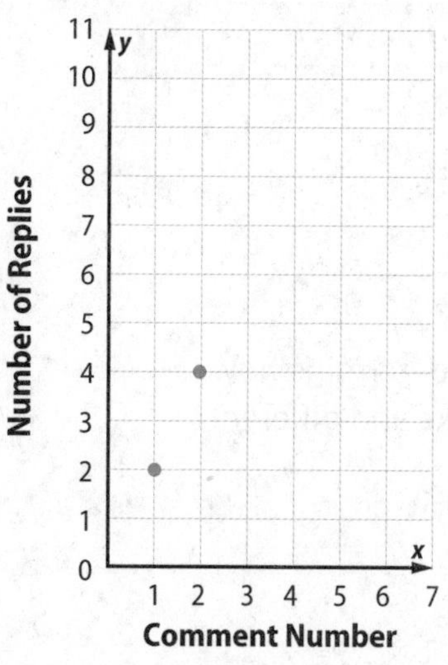

Albert's Comments	
Comment Number (x)	Number of Replies (y)
1	2
2	4
3	
4	

Bianca's Comments	
Comment Number (x)	Number of Replies (y)
1	1
2	4
3	
4	

Analyze and Reflect

Work with a partner to answer the following questions about the Activity.

1. Describe any patterns in the data.

2. Connect the ordered pairs with a straight line for each graph. Then describe the graphs.

3. Predict the next three points on the graph for each data.

4. Compare and contrast the relationships shown in each graph. What do you notice?

Create

On Your Own

5. MP **Apply Math to the Real World** Create a table and graph to describe a real-world situation that represents a proportional relationship. Then explain how you could change your situation so that it represents a nonproportional relationship.

6. **INQUIRY** HOW can I use multiple representations to determine how proportional and nonproportional relationships are alike and different?

Lesson 6

Solve Proportional Relationships

Launch the Lesson: Real World

Watch

Katie and some friends want to buy fruit smoothies. They go to a health food store that advertises a sale of 2 fruit smoothies for $5. Suppose Katie and her friends buy 6 fruit smoothies. Let's investigate the relationship between the cost and the number of fruit smoothies.

1. Fill in the boxes to write ratios that compare the cost to the number of fruit smoothies.

$$\frac{\$5}{\square \text{ smoothies}} \qquad \frac{\$\square}{6 \text{ smoothies}}$$

2. Is the cost proportional to the number of fruit smoothies for two and six smoothies? Explain.

3. Write two more rates that are proportional to $5 for 2 fruit smoothies.

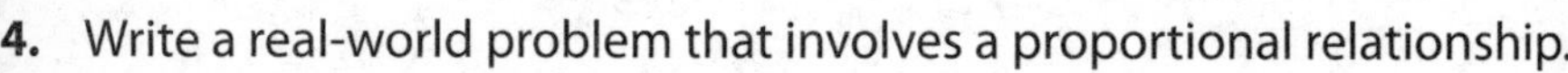

4. Write a real-world problem that involves a proportional relationship.

Texas Essential Knowledge and Skills

Targeted TEKS

7.4(D) Solve problems involving ratios, rates, and percents, including multi-step problems involving percent increase and percent decrease, and financial literacy problems.

Mathematical Processes

7.1(A), 7.1(B), 7.1(F)

Vocab

Vocabulary

proportion

cross product

Essential Question

HOW can you show that two objects are proportional?

Which MP Mathematical Processes did you use? Shade the circle(s) that applies.

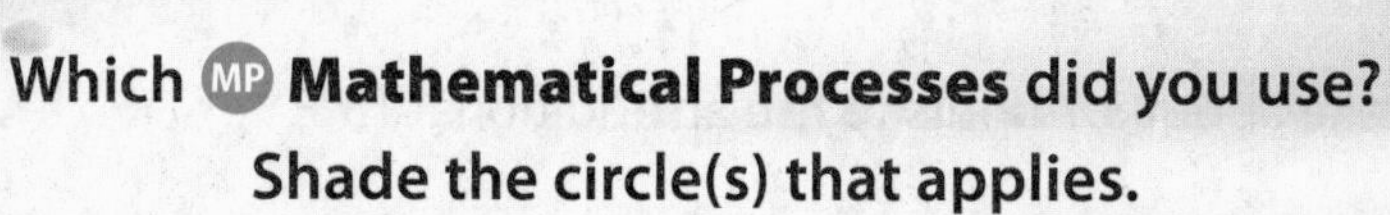

Ⓐ Apply Math to the Real World.
Ⓑ Use a Problem-Solving Model.
Ⓒ Select Tools and Techniques.
Ⓓ Use Multiple Representations.
Ⓔ Organize Ideas.
Ⓕ Analyze Relationships.
Ⓖ Justify Arguments.

Key Concept

Write and Solve Proportions

Words A **proportion** is an equation stating that two ratios or rates are equivalent.

Numbers	Algebra
$\frac{6}{8} = \frac{3}{4}$	$\frac{a}{b} = \frac{c}{d}, b \neq 0, d \neq 0$

Work Zone

Consider the following proportion.

$$\frac{a}{b} = \frac{c}{d}$$

$$\frac{a}{\cancel{b}_1} \cdot \overset{1}{\cancel{b}}d = \frac{c}{\cancel{d}_1} \cdot b\overset{1}{\cancel{d}}$$ Multiply each side by bd and divide out common factors.

$$ad = bc$$ Simplify.

The products ad and bc are called the **cross products** of this proportion. The cross products of any proportion are equal.

$$\frac{6}{8} = \frac{3}{4} \rightarrow 8 \cdot 3 = 24$$
$$\rightarrow 6 \cdot 4 = 24$$

Example

1. After 2 hours, the air temperature had risen 7°F. Write and solve a proportion to determine the amount of time it will take at this rate for the temperature to rise an additional 13°F.

Write a proportion. Let t represent the time in hours.

temperature → $\frac{7}{2} = \frac{13}{t}$ ← temperature
time → ← time

$7 \cdot t = 2 \cdot 13$ Find the cross products.

$7t = 26$ Multiply

$\frac{7t}{7} = \frac{26}{7}$ Divide each side by 7.

$t \approx 3.7$ Simplify.

It will take about 3.7 hours to rise an additional 13°F.

Got It? Do these problems to find out.

Solve each proportion.

a. $\frac{x}{4} = \frac{9}{10}$ **b.** $\frac{2}{34} = \frac{5}{y}$ **c.** $\frac{7}{3} = \frac{n}{21}$

Show your work.

a. ____________

b. ____________

c. ____________

Example

2. If the ratio of Type O to non-Type O donors at a blood drive was 37:43, how many donors would be Type O, out of 300 donors?

Type O donors → total donors → $\frac{37}{37 + 43}$ or $\frac{37}{80}$

Write a proportion. Let t represent the number of Type O donors.

Type O donors → total donors → $\frac{37}{80} = \frac{t}{300}$ ← Type O donors ← total donors

$37 \cdot 300 = 80t$ Find the cross products.

$11{,}100 = 80t$ Multiply

$\frac{11{,}100}{80} = \frac{80t}{80}$ Divide each side by 80.

$138.75 = t$ Simplify.

There would be about 139 Type O donors.

Got It? Do this problem to find out.

d. The ratio of 7th grade students to 8th grade students in a soccer league is 17:23. If there are 200 students in all, how many are in the 7th grade?

d. __________

Use Unit Rates

You can also use the unit rate to write an equation expressing the relationship between two proportional quantities.

Multi-Step Examples

3. Olivia bought 6 containers of yogurt for \$7.68. Write an equation relating the cost c to the number of yogurts y. How much would Olivia pay for 10 yogurts at this same rate?

Step 1 Determine the unit rate between cost and containers of yogurt.

$\frac{\text{cost in dollars}}{\text{containers of yogurt}} = \frac{7.68}{6}$ or \$1.28 per container

Step 2 The cost is \$1.28 times the number of containers of yogurt.

$c = 1.28y$ Let c represent the cost. Let y represent the number of yogurts.

$= 1.28(10)$ Replace y with 10.

$= 12.80$ Multiply.

The cost for 10 containers of yogurt is \$12.80.

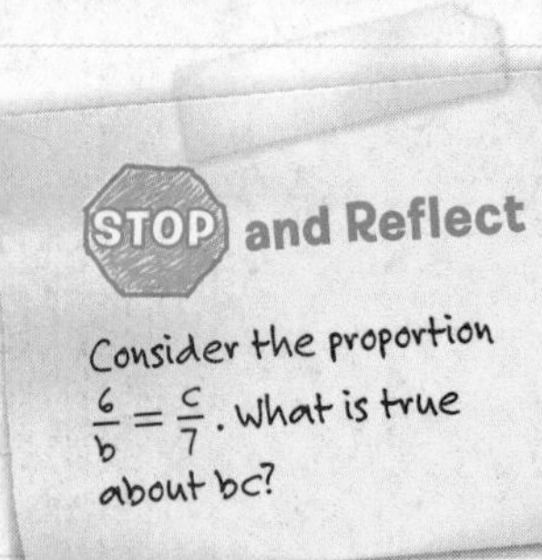

4. Jaycee bought 8 gallons of gas for $31.12. Write an equation relating the cost *c* to the number of gallons *g* of gas. How much would Jaycee pay for 11 gallons at this same rate?

Step 1 Determine the unit rate between cost and gallons.

$$\frac{\text{cost in dollars}}{\text{gasoline in gallons}} = \frac{31.12}{8} \text{ or \$3.89 per gallon}$$

Step 2 The cost is $3.89 times the number of gallons.

$c = 3.89g$ Let *c* represent the cost. Let *g* represent the number of gallons.

$= 3.89(11)$ Replace *g* with 11.

$= 42.79$ Multiply.

The cost for 11 gallons of gas is $42.79.

Got It? **Do this problem to find out.**

e. Morgan typed 2 pages in 15 minutes. Write an equation relating the number of minutes *m* to the number of pages *p* typed. How long will it take her to type 10 pages at this rate?

e. ______

Guided Practice

Solve each proportion. (Examples 1 and 2)

1. $\frac{k}{7} = \frac{32}{56}$ $k =$ ______

2. $\frac{3.2}{9} = \frac{n}{36}$ $n =$ ______

3. $\frac{41}{x} = \frac{5}{2}$ $x =$ ______

4. Trina earns $28.50 tutoring for 3 hours. Write an equation relating her earnings *m* to the number of hours *h* she tutors. Assuming the situation is proportional, how much would Trina earn tutoring for 2 hours? for 4.5 hours? (Examples 3 and 4)

______

5. **Building on the Essential Question** How do you solve a proportion?

______

______

Rate Yourself!

How confident are you about solving proportions? Check the box that applies.

☐ ☐ ☐ ☐ ☐

Find out online. Use the Self-Check Quiz.

FOLDABLES Time to update your Foldable!

Name ______________________ My Homework ______________________

Independent Practice

7.4(D), 7.1(F) TEKS

Solve each proportion. (Examples 1 and 2)

1. $\frac{1.5}{6} = \frac{10}{p}$ $p =$ ______

2. $\frac{44}{p} = \frac{11}{5}$ $p =$ ______

3. $\frac{2}{w} = \frac{0.4}{0.7}$ $w =$ ______

Assume the situations are proportional. Write and solve by using a proportion. (Examples 1 and 2)

4. Evarado paid $1.12 for a dozen eggs at his local grocery store. Determine the cost of 3 eggs.

______

5. Sheila mixed 3 ounces of blue paint with 2 ounces of yellow paint. She decided to create 20 ounces of the same mixture. How many ounces of yellow paint does Sheila need for the new mixture?

______

Assume the situations are proportional. Use the unit rate to write an equation, then solve. (Examples 3 and 4)

6. A car can travel 476 miles on 14 gallons of gas. Write an equation relating the distance *d* to the number of gallons *g*. How many gallons of gas does this car need to travel 578 miles?

______

7. Mrs. Baker paid $2.50 for 5 pounds of bananas. Write an equation relating the cost *c* to the number of pounds *p* of bananas. How much would Mrs. Baker pay for 8 pounds of bananas?

______

8. A woman who is 64 inches tall has a shoulder width of 16 inches. Write an equation relating the height *h* to the width *w*. Determine the height of a woman who has a shoulder width of 18.5 inches.

______

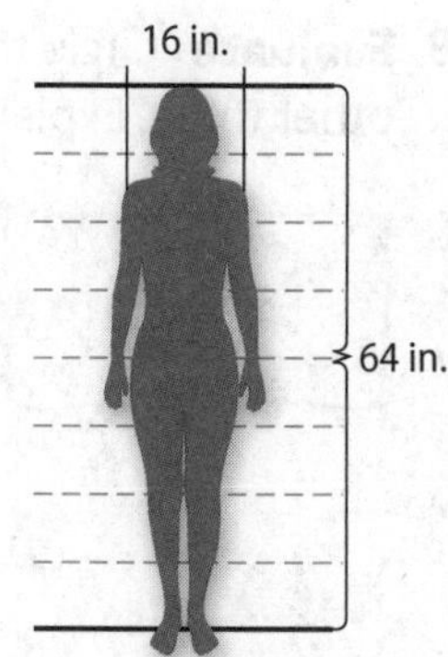

9. At an amusement park, 360 visitors rode the roller coaster in 3 hours. Write and solve a proportion to determine the number of visitors at this rate who will ride the roller coaster in 7 hours. (Examples 3 and 4)

10. MP **Analyze Relationships** Use the table to write a proportion relating the weights on two planets. Then find the missing weight. Round to the nearest tenth.

Weights on Different Planets Earth Weight = 120 pounds	
Mercury	45.6 pounds
Venus	109.2 pounds
Uranus	96 pounds
Jupiter	304.8 pounds

a. Earth: 90 pounds; Venus: ______ pounds

b. Mercury: 55 pounds; Earth: ______ pounds

c. Jupiter: 350 pounds; Uranus: ______ pounds

d. Venus: 115 pounds; Mercury: ______ pounds

H.O.T. Problems Higher-Order Thinking

Evaluate Solve each equation.

11. $\frac{2}{3} = \frac{18}{x + 5}$

12. $\frac{x - 4}{10} = \frac{7}{5}$

13. $\frac{4.5}{17 - x} = \frac{3}{8}$

14. $\frac{5}{x} = \frac{x}{45}$

15. $\frac{4}{x} = \frac{x}{9}$

16. $\frac{x}{2} = \frac{8}{x}$

17. **Analyze** A rectangle has an area 36 square units. As the length ℓ and the width w change, what do you know about their product? Is the length proportional to the width? Justify your reasoning.

Rectangle	Length	Width	Area (units^2)
A	3	12	36
B	6	6	36
C	9	4	36

18. **Evaluate** Circle the equation that does not belong with the other three. Explain your reasoning.

$\frac{x}{5} = \frac{28}{100}$ $\frac{x}{28} = \frac{5}{100}$ $\frac{28}{x} = \frac{5}{100}$ $\frac{100}{5} = \frac{28}{x}$

Name ______________________________

Multi-Step Problem Solving

19. Hugo can run 4 miles in 25 minutes. How many more miles can Hugo run in 90 minutes than in 25 minutes? Assume the situation is proportional and he always runs at the same rate. N P MP

Distance (mi)	Time (min)
4	25
m	90

Ⓐ 10.2 miles
Ⓑ 10.4 miles
Ⓒ 14.4 miles
Ⓓ 18.4 miles

Use a problem-solving model to solve this problem.

1 Analyze

Read the problem. Circle the information you know. Underline what the problem is asking you to find.

2 Plan

What will you need to do to solve the problem? Write your plan in steps.

Step 1 Calculate the __________ for Hugo's running rate. Then multiply the rate by 90 minutes to determine his distance.

Step 2 __________ the distances to determine how much __________ he runs in 90 minutes compared to 25 minutes.

3 Solve

Use your plan to solve the problem. Show your steps.

Calculate the unit rate.

4 ÷ 25 = ______ mile per minute

Determine how many miles he runs in 90 minutes.

90 × ______ = ______

Subtract to determine how much more he runs in 90 minutes.

______ − 4 = ______

So, Hugo runs ______ miles more in 90 minutes. The correct answer is ____. Fill in that answer choice.

Read to Succeed!

Don't forget to subtract! The problem asks for how much more, which tells you to subtract the distances.

4 Justify and Evaluate

How do you know your solution is accurate?

____

____

____

N = Number and Operations P = Proportionality MP = Mathematical Processes

More Multi-Step Problem Solving

Use a problem-solving model to solve each problem.

20. On average, Rai correctly answers 12 out of 18 questions in a trivia game. Assuming the situation is proportional, how many more questions is she likely to correctly answer if there are 36 questions in all? P N MP

Correct answers	Total questions
12	18
?	36

Ⓐ 12 questions
Ⓑ 18 questions
Ⓒ 20 questions
Ⓓ 24 questions

21. Kareem needs a new car and is making a decision between the three cars listed below based on fuel efficiency. Determine which car has the best fuel efficiency in kilometers per gallon. (*Hint:* 1 km $\approx$ 0.62 mile) P N MP

Car	Miles	Gallons
Car A	248	10
Car B	210	10
Car C	225	12

22. Aaron bought $\frac{1}{2}$ pound of cheese for \$6. Assuming the situation is proportional, write and solve an equation to determine how many dollars *d* Aaron will pay for $3\frac{1}{2}$ pounds of cheese *c*.

23. Taylor bought 12 more pencils this month than last month. Taylor paid \$2.88 last month and \$7.20 this month for the pencils. Assuming the situation is proportional, how many pencils did she buy this month?

P = Proportionality 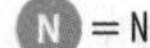 = Number and Operations EE = Expressions, Equations, and Relationships MP = Mathematical Processes

Lesson 7

Convert Between Systems

Launch the Lesson: Real World

Watch 

To raise money for a health organization, the Matthews family is participating in a 5K race. A 5K race is 5 kilometers. About how many miles is the race?

1. A kilometer is a unit of length in the metric measurement system. A mile is a measure of length in the customary measurement system. Write the following units of length under the correct measurement system.

centimeter, foot, inch, meter, millimeter, yard

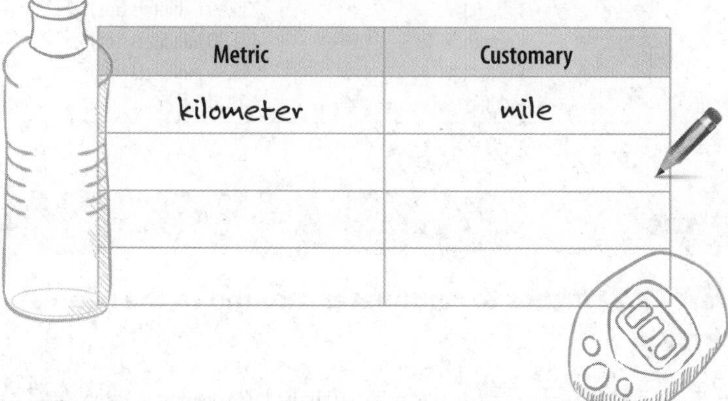

Metric	Customary
kilometer	mile

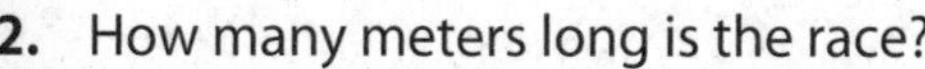

2. How many meters long is the race?

5 kilometers = ☐ meters

3. One mile is approximately 1.6 kilometers. About how many miles is the race?

5 kilometers ≈ ☐ meters

Which MP Mathematical Processes did you use? Shade the circle(s) that applies.

Ⓐ Apply Math to the Real World.
Ⓑ Use a Problem-Solving Model.
Ⓒ Select Tools and Techniques.
Ⓓ Use Multiple Representations.
Ⓔ Organize Ideas.
Ⓕ Analyze Relationships.
Ⓖ Justify Arguments.

Texas Essential Knowledge and Skills TEKS

Targeted TEKS
7.4(E) Convert between measurement systems, including the use of proportions and the use of unit rates.
Also addresses 7.3(A), 7.3(B).

Mathematical Processes
7.1(A), 7.1(B), 7.1(C)

Essential Question
HOW can you show that two objects are proportional?

Work Zone

Convert Between Measurement Systems Using Unit Rates

You can multiply by the unit-rate conversion, expressed as a fraction, to convert between customary and metric units. The table below lists common customary and metric conversions.

Customary and Metric Conversions			
Type of Measure	Customary	⟶	Metric
Length	1 inch (in.)	≈	2.54 centimeters (cm)
	1 foot (ft)	≈	0.30 meter (m)
	1 yard (yd)	≈	0.91 meter (m)
	1 mile (mi)	≈	1.61 kilometers (km)
Weight/Mass	1 pound (lb)	≈	453.6 grams (g)
	1 pound (lb)	≈	0.4536 kilogram (kg)
	1 ton (T)	≈	907.2 kilograms (kg)
Capacity	1 cup (c)	≈	236.59 milliliters (mL)
	1 pint (pt)	≈	473.18 milliliters (mL)
	1 quart (qt)	≈	946.35 milliliters (mL)
	1 gallon (gal)	≈	3.79 liters (L)

Tutor

Examples

STOP and Reflect

What metric unit of measure best corresponds to miles? to pounds? Write your answers below.

1. Convert 17.22 inches to centimeters. Round to the nearest hundredth.

Since 2.54 centimeters ≈ 1 inch, multiply by the unit rate $\frac{2.54 \text{ cm}}{1 \text{ in.}}$.

$17.22 \approx 17.22 \text{ in.} \cdot \frac{2.54 \text{ cm}}{1 \text{ in.}}$ — Multiply by $\frac{2.54 \text{ cm}}{1 \text{ in.}}$. Divide out common units.

$\approx 43.7388 \text{ cm}$ — Simplify.

So, 17.22 inches is approximately 43.74 centimeters.

2. Convert 5 kilometers to miles. Round to the nearest hundredth.

Since 1 mile ≈ 1.61 kilometers, multiply by the unit rate $\frac{1 \text{ mi}}{1.61 \text{ km}}$.

$5 \text{ km} \approx 5 \text{ km} \cdot \frac{1 \text{ mi}}{1.61 \text{ km}}$ — Multiply by $\frac{1 \text{ mi}}{1.61 \text{ km}}$. Divide out common units.

$\approx \frac{5 \text{ mi}}{1.61}$ or 3.11 mi — Simplify.

So, 5 kilometers is approximately 3.11 miles.

a. ____________

b. ____________

c. ____________

Got It? Do these problems to find out.

Complete. Round to the nearest hundredth if necessary.

a. 6 yd ≈ ■ m **b.** 1.6 cm ≈ ■ in. **c.** 17 m ≈ ■ yd

Use a Proportion to Convert

You can also use a proportion to convert between measurement systems because it allows you to easily determine equivalent ratios.

Examples

3. Convert 828.5 milliliters to cups. Round to the nearest hundredth if necessary.

$$\frac{236.59 \text{ mL}}{828.5 \text{ mL}} = \frac{1 \text{ c}}{x \text{ c}}$$ (÷ 236.59) Write the proportion. 1 c ≈ 236.59 mL

$$\approx \frac{828.5 \text{ c}}{236.59} \text{ or } 3.50 \text{ c}$$ Divide.

So, 828.5 milliliters is approximately 3.50 cups.

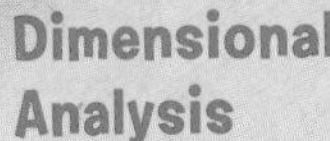

Dimensional Analysis

Recall that dimensional analysis is the process of including units of measurement when you compute.

4. Convert 3.4 quarts to milliliters. Round to the nearest hundredth if necessary.

$$\frac{1 \text{ qt}}{3.4 \text{ qt}} = \frac{946.35 \text{ mL}}{x \text{ mL}}$$ (× 946.35) Write the proportion. 946.35 mL ≈ 1 qt

$\approx 3{,}217.59$ mL Multiply.

So, 3.4 quarts is approximately 3,217.59 milliliters.

5. Convert 4.25 kilograms to pounds. Round to the nearest hundredth if necessary.

$$\frac{0.4536 \text{ kg}}{4.25 \text{ kg}} = \frac{1 \text{ lb}}{x \text{ lb}}$$ (÷ 0.4536) Write the proportion. 1 lb ≈ 0.4536 kg

$$\approx \frac{4.25 \text{ lb}}{0.4536} \text{ or } 9.37 \text{ lb}$$ Divide.

So, 4.25 kilograms is approximately 9.37 pounds.

Got It? Do these problems to find out.

Convert. Round to the nearest hundredth if necessary.

d. 7.44 c ≈ ■ mL **e.** 22.09 lb ≈ ■ kg **f.** 35.85 L ≈ ■ gal

d. ________

e. ________

f. ________

Example

6. An Olympic-size swimming pool is 50 meters long. About how many feet long is the pool? Round to the nearest hundredth.

Since 1 foot ≈ 0.30 meter, use the unit rate $\frac{1 \text{ ft}}{0.30 \text{ m}}$.

$50 \text{ m} \approx 50 \text{ m} \cdot \frac{1 \text{ ft}}{0.30 \text{ m}}$ Multiply by $\frac{1 \text{ ft}}{0.30\text{m}}$.

$\approx 50 \cancel{\text{m}} \cdot \frac{1 \text{ ft}}{0.30 \cancel{\text{m}}}$ Divide out common units, leaving the desired unit, feet.

$\approx \frac{50 \text{ ft}}{0.30}$ or 166.67 ft Divide.

An Olympic-size swimming pool is about 166.67 feet long.

Guided Practice

Convert. Round to the nearest hundredth if necessary. (Examples 1–5)

1. 3.7 yd ≈ ______ m

2. 11.07 pt ≈ ______ mL

3. 650 lb ≈ ______ kg

4. About how many feet does a team of athletes run in a 1,600-meter relay race? (Example 6) ______

5. Raheem bought 3 pounds of bananas. About how many kilograms did he buy? (Example 6) ______

6. **Building on the Essential Question** How can you use dimensional analysis to convert between measurement systems?

______

______

______

______

Rate Yourself!

Are you ready to move on? Shade the section that applies.

YES ? NO

Find out online. Use the Self-Check Quiz.

Name ______________________ My Homework ______________________

Independent Practice

7.3(A), 7.3(B), 7.1(B) TEKS

Convert. Round to the nearest hundredth if necessary. (Examples 1–5)

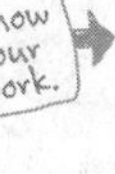

1. 5 in. ≈ ________ cm

2. 2 qt ≈ ________ mL

3. 58.14 kg ≈ ________ lb

4. 4 L ≈ ________ gal

5. 10 mL ≈ ________ c

6. 63.5 T ≈ ________ kg

7. 4.725 m ≈ ________ ft

8. 3 T ≈ ________ kg

9. 680.4 g ≈ ________ lb

10. A notebook computer has a mass of 2.25 kilograms. About how many pounds does the notebook weigh? (Example 6)

____

11. A glass bottle holds 3.75 cups of water. About how many milliliters of water can the bottle hold? (Example 6)

____

12. A Cabbage Palmetto has a height of 80 feet. What is the approximate height of the tree in meters? (Example 6)

____

 **Use a Problem-Solving Model Determine the greater amount for each situation.**

13. Which box is greater, a 1.5-pound box of raisins or a 650-gram box of raisins?

14. Which is greater a 2.75-gallon container of juice or a 12-liter container of juice?

H.O.T. Problems Higher-Order Thinking

15. Evaluate One gram of water has a volume of 1 milliliter. What is the volume of the water if it has a mass of 1 kilogram?

16. Evaluate The distance from Earth to the Sun is approximately 93 million miles. About how many gigameters is this? Round to the nearest hundredth. (*Hint: 1 gigameter is about equal to 621,118.01 miles.*)

Evaluate Order each set of measures from greatest to least.

17. 1.2 cm, 0.6 in., 0.031 m, 0.1 ft

18. 2 lb, 891 g, 1 kg, 0.02 T

19. $1\frac{1}{4}$ c, 0.4 L, 950 mL, 0.7 gal

20. 4.5 ft, 48 in., 1.3 m, 120 cm

21. Create Convert $2\frac{1}{8}$ inches and $2\frac{5}{8}$ inches to centimeters. Round to the nearest tenth. Then draw a line that measures between those measures.

Name ____________________

Multi-Step Problem Solving

22. The students in the table each made a pitcher of lemonade. About how many more liters did Serena make than Kyle? P N MP

Ⓐ 0.89 liter

Ⓑ 1.4 liters

Ⓒ 3.37 liters

Ⓓ 11.37 liters

Person	Capacity
Serena	3 gal
Morgan	3,500 mL
Charity	13 quarts
Kyle	8 L

Use a problem-solving model to solve this problem.

1 Analyze

Read the problem. Circle the information you know.
Underline what the problem is asking you to find.

2 Plan

What will you need to do to solve the problem? Write your plan in steps.

Step 1 Convert 3 gallons to ______.

Step 2 ______ the amount Kyle made from the amount of liters.

3 Solve

Use your plan to solve the problem. Show your steps.

Convert gallons to liters.

$3 \text{ gal} \cdot \frac{3.79 \text{ L}}{1 \text{ gal}} \approx$ ______ liters

Subtract the amount in liters of Kyle's pitcher from Serena's pitcher amount in liters.

______ $- 8 =$ ______

Serena made about ______ liters more than Kyle.

So, the correct answer is ______. Fill in that answer choice.

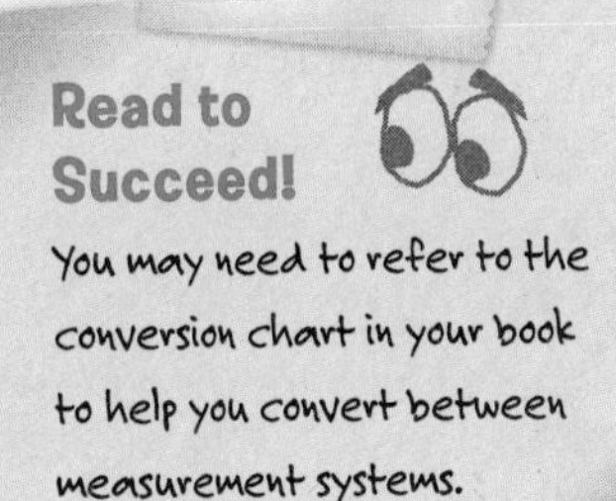

Read to Succeed!

You may need to refer to the conversion chart in your book to help you convert between measurement systems.

4 Justify and Evaluate

How do you know your solution is accurate?

____

____

____

P = Proportionality N = Number and Operations MP = Mathematical Processes

More Multi-Step Problem Solving

Use a problem-solving model to solve each problem.

23. Zaria and Vanessa each measured the length of their hands. In centimeters, about how much longer is Vanessa's hand compared to Zaria's? P N MP

Student	Length of Hand
Zaria	7 in.
Vanessa	19 cm

Ⓐ 1.22 cm

Ⓑ 1.5 cm

Ⓒ 12 cm

Ⓓ 17.78 cm

24. Three tables are going to be combined together in a row to make one long table. About how many feet long will the new table be? P N MP

Table	Length
A	4.5 feet
B	2.7 meters
C	2 yards

25. In a sauce recipe, 2 cups of ketchup are added for every 1 cup of tomato sauce. If 2.25 cups of tomato sauce are added, about how many milliliters of ketchup should be added? Round to the nearest whole number. P N MP

26. A suitcase weighing 50 pounds contains clothes, towels, and shoes. The weight distribution is shown in the circle graph below. About how much do the clothes weigh in kilograms? Round to the nearest hundredth. P N MP

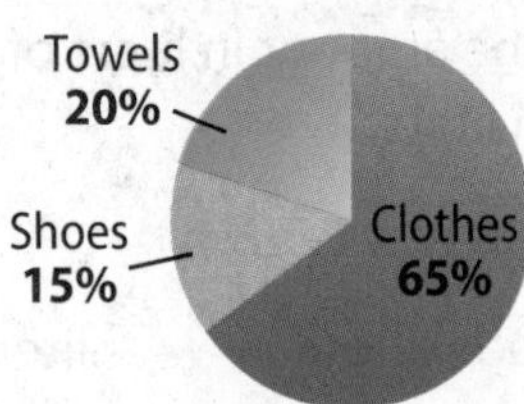

P = Proportionality N = Number and Operations MP = Mathematical Processes

Hands-On Lab 8-a
Rate of Change

INQUIRY HOW can I analyze relationships to determine how unit rate is related to rate of change?

Happy Hound is a doggie daycare where people drop off their dogs while they are at work. It costs $3 for 1 hour, $6 for 2 hours, and $9 for 3 hours of doggie daycare. Farah takes her dog to Happy Hound several days a week. Farah wants to determine if the number of hours of daycare is related to the cost.

Texas Essential Knowledge and Skills

Targeted TEKS

7.4(A) Represent constant rates of change in mathematical and real-world problems given pictorial, tabular, verbal, numeric, graphical, and algebraic representations, including $d = rt$. *Also addresses 7.4(D).*

Mathematical Processes

7.1(C), 7.1(D), 7.1(E), 7.1(G)

Hands-On Activity

Step 1 Assume the pattern in the table continues. Complete the table shown.

Happy Hound Doggie Daycare	
Number of Hours	Cost ($)
1	3
2	6
3	9
4	
5	

Step 2 The cost depends on the number of hours. So, the cost is the output y, and the number of hours is the ________. Graph the data on the coordinate plane below.

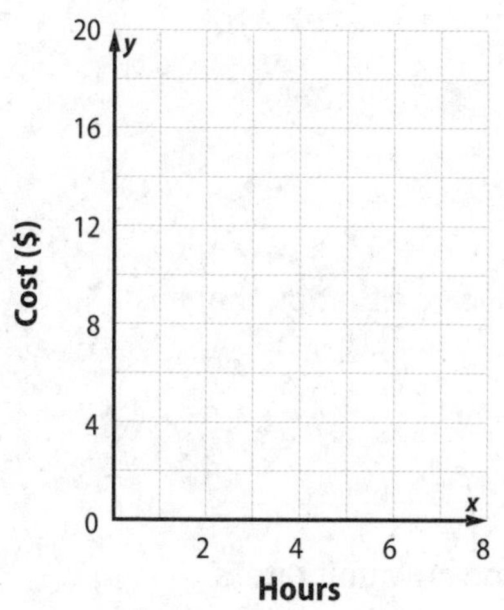

Investigate

Refer to the Investigation. Work with a partner.

1. **MP Justify Arguments** Describe the graph.

2. What is the cost per hour, or unit rate, charged by Happy Hound? ______

3. Use the graph to examine any two consecutive points. By how much does y change? By how much does x change? ______

4. The first two ordered pairs on the graph are (1, 3) and (2, 6). You can determine the *rate of change* by writing the ratio of the change in y to the change in x.

   Determine the rate of change shown in the graph. ______

Analyze and Reflect

MP Analyze Relationships Work with a partner.

5. Pampered Pooch charges $5 for 1 hour of doggie daycare, $10 for 2 hours, and $15 for 3 hours.

   a. What is the unit rate? ______

   b. What is the rate of change? ______

   c. **MP Organize Ideas** How do the rates of change for doggie daycare at Pampered Pooch and Happy Hound compare?

Create

6. **MP Apply Math to the Real World** Describe a doggie daycare situation that has a rate of change less than that of Happy Hound.

7. **INQUIRY** HOW can I analyze relationships to determine how unit rate is related to rate of change?

Lesson 8

Constant Rate of Change

Launch the Lesson: Vocabulary

A **rate of change** is a rate that describes how one quantity changes in relation to another. In some relationships, the rate of change between any two quantities is the same. These relationships have a **constant rate of change**.

Real-World Investigation

A computer programmer charges customers per line of code written. Fill in the blanks with the amount of change between consecutive numbers.

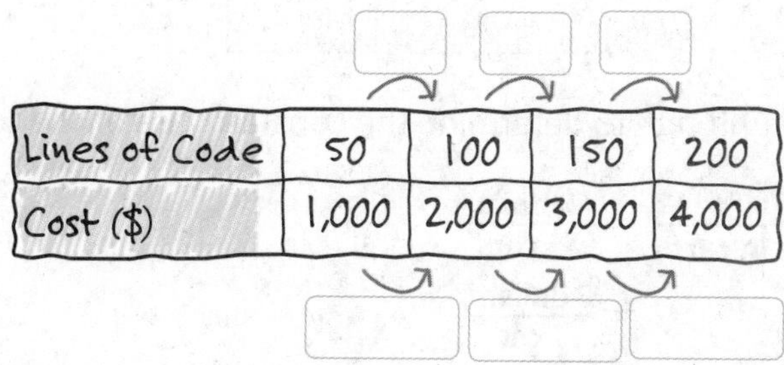

Lines of Code	50	100	150	200
Cost ($)	1,000	2,000	3,000	4,000

Label the diagram below with the terms *change in lines*, *change in dollars*, and *constant rate of change*.

$$\frac{\square}{\square} = \frac{\$1{,}000}{50 \text{ lines}}$$

$$= \frac{\$20}{1 \text{ line}} \Big\} \text{unit rate}$$

The ______________________ is $20 per line of programming code.

Which MP Mathematical Processes did you use? Shade the circle(s) that applies.

Ⓐ Apply Math to the Real World.
Ⓑ Use a Problem-Solving Model.
Ⓒ Select Tools and Techniques.
Ⓓ Use Multiple Representations.
Ⓔ Organize Ideas.
Ⓕ Analyze Relationships.
Ⓖ Justify Arguments.

Texas Essential Knowledge and Skills

Targeted TEKS

7.4(A) Represent constant rates of change in mathematical and real-world problems given pictorial, tabular, verbal, numeric, graphical, and algebraic representations, including $d = rt$. *Also addresses 7.4(D).*

Mathematical Processes

7.1(A), 7.1(B), 7.1(D)

Vocab

Vocabulary

rate of change

constant rate of change

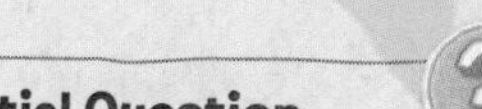

Essential Question

HOW can you show that two objects are proportional?

Work Zone

Use a Table

You can use a table to determine a constant rate of change.

Example

1. The table shows the amount of money a booster club makes washing cars for a fundraiser. Use the information to find the constant rate of change in dollars per car.

Cars Washed	
Number	Money ($)
5	40
10	80
15	120
20	160

(+5 for each Number row; +40 for each Money row)

Find the unit rate to determine the constant rate of change.

$\frac{\text{change in money}}{\text{change in cars}} = \frac{40 \text{ dollars}}{5 \text{ cars}}$ The money earned increases by $40 for every 5 cars.

$= \frac{8 \text{ dollars}}{1 \text{ car}}$ Write as a unit rate.

So, the number of dollars earned increases by $8 for every car washed.

Unit Rate
A rate of change is usually expressed as a unit rate.

Got It? Do these problems to find out.

a. The table shows the number of miles a plane traveled while in flight. Use the information to determine the approximate constant rate of change in miles per minute.

Time (min)	30	60	90	120
Distance (mi)	290	580	870	1,160

b. The table shows the number of students that buses can transport. Use the table to determine the constant rate of change in students per school bus.

Number of Buses	2	3	4	5
Number of Students	144	216	288	360

a. ________

b. ________

Use a Graph

You can also use a graph to determine a constant rate of change and to analyze points on the graph.

Examples

2. The graph represents the distance traveled while driving on a highway. Determine the constant rate of change.

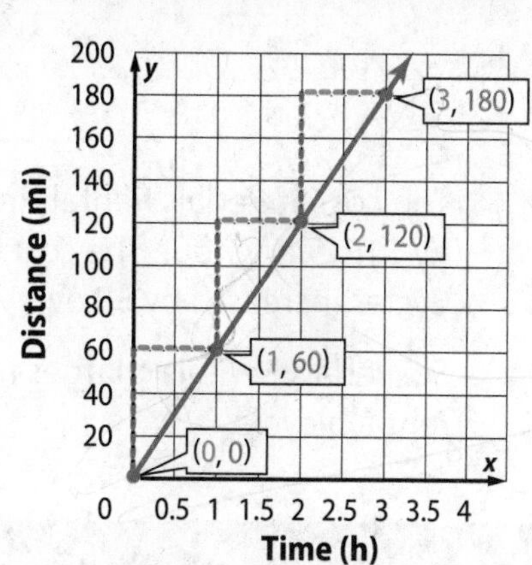

To determine the rate of change, pick any two points on the line, such as (0, 0) and (1, 60).

$$\frac{\text{change in miles}}{\text{change in hours}} = \frac{(60 - 0) \text{ miles}}{(1 - 0) \text{ hours}}$$

$$= \frac{60 \text{ miles}}{1 \text{ hour}}$$

Ordered Pairs

The ordered pair (2, 120) represents traveling 120 miles in 2 hours.

3. Explain what the points (0, 0) and (1, 60) represent.

The point (0, 0) represents traveling zero miles in zero hours. The point (1, 60) represents traveling 60 miles in 1 hour. Notice that this is the constant rate of change.

Got It? Do these problems to find out.

c. Use the graph to determine the constant rate of change in miles per hour while driving in the city.

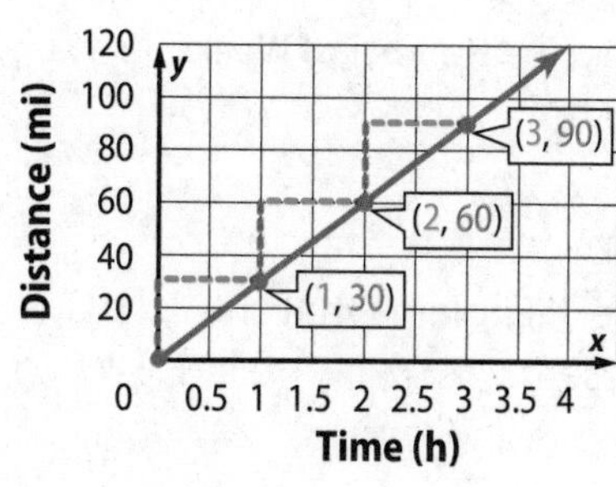

d. On the lines below, explain what the points (0, 0) and (1, 30) represent.

____

____

____

c. ____________

Example

Tutor

4. The table and graph below show the hourly charge to rent a bicycle at two different stores. Which store charges more per bicycle? Explain.

Pedals Rentals	
Time (hour)	Cost ($)
2	24
3	36
4	48

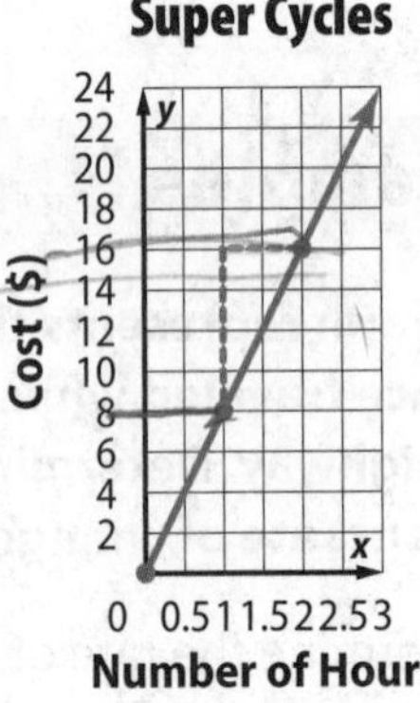

The cost at Pedals Rentals increases by $12 every hour. The cost at Super Cycles increases by $8 every hour.

So, Pedals Rentals charges more per hour to rent a bicycle.

Guided Practice

1. The table and graph below show the amount of money Mi-Ling and Daniel save each week. Who saves more each week? Explain. (Examples 1, 2, and 4)

Mi-Ling's Savings	
Time (weeks)	Savings ($)
2	$30
3	$45
4	$60

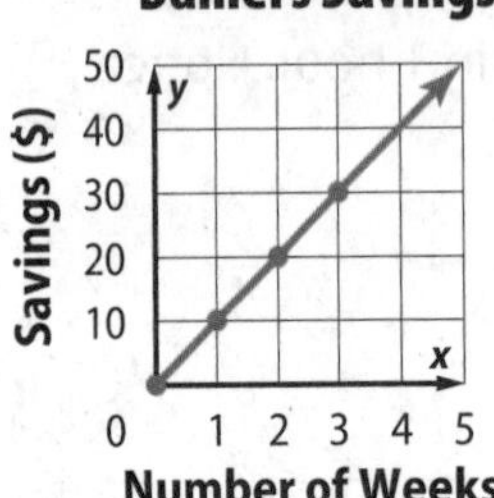

2. Refer to the graph in Exercise 1. Explain what the points (0, 0) and (1, 10) represent. (Example 3)

3. **Building on the Essential Question** How can you determine the unit rate on a graph that goes through the origin?

Rate Yourself!

Are you ready to move on? Shade the section that applies.

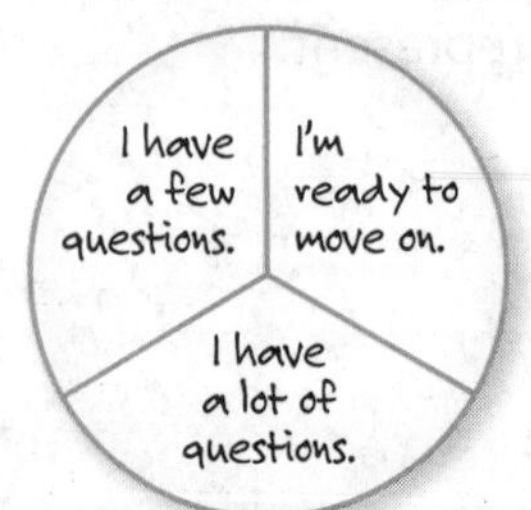

Find out online. Use the Self-Check Quiz.

Check

Name ______________________________ My Homework ______________________

Independent Practice

7.4(A), 7.4(D), 7.1(A), 7.1(D) TEKS

Determine the constant rate of change for each table. (Example 1)

1.

Time (s)	Distance (m)
1	6
2	12
3	18
4	24

______

2.

Items	Cost ($)
2	18
4	36
6	54
8	72

______

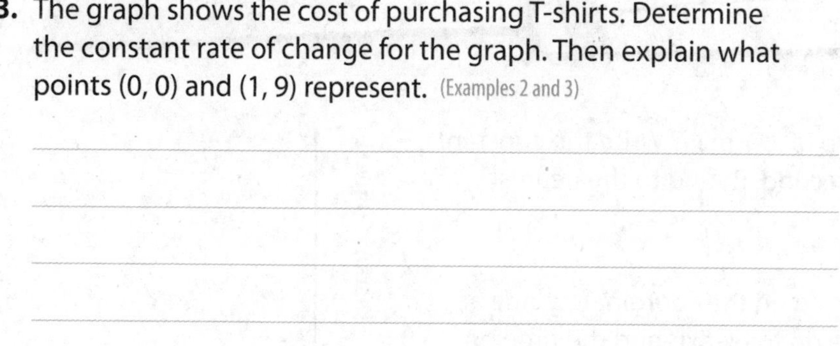

3. The graph shows the cost of purchasing T-shirts. Determine the constant rate of change for the graph. Then explain what points (0, 0) and (1, 9) represent. (Examples 2 and 3)

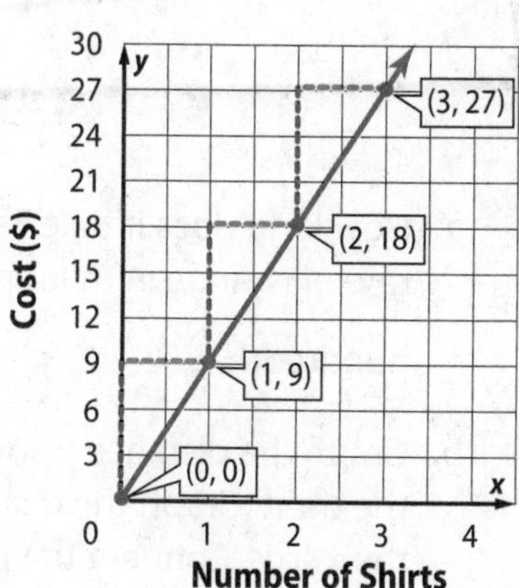

____

____

____

____

4. **MP Use Multiple Representations** The Guzman and Hashimoto families each took a 4-hour road trip. The distances traveled by each family are shown in the table and graph below. Which family averaged fewer miles per hour? Explain. (Example 4)

Guzman's Road Trip	
Time (hours)	**Distance (miles)**
2	90
3	135
4	180

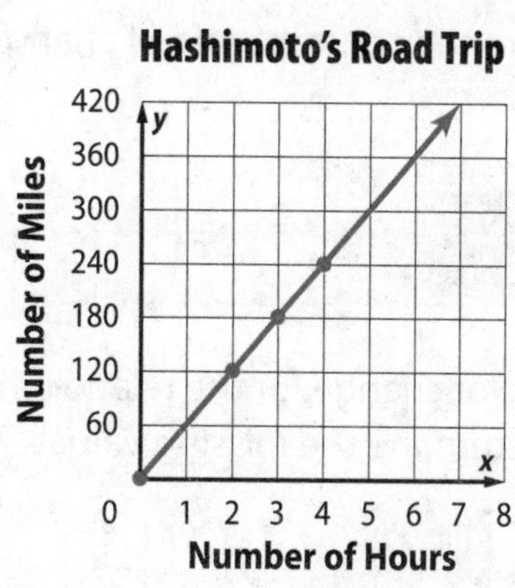

____

____

____

5. At 1:00 P.M., the water level in a pool is 13 inches. At 1:30 P.M., the water level is 18 inches. At 2:30 P.M., the water level is 28 inches. What is the constant rate of change? ______________________________

6. **Apply Math to the Real World** Refer to the lap times for Exercises **a** and **b**.

a. How long does it take Seth to race 1 mile? Write the constant rate of change in miles per second. Round to the nearest hundredth. ______

b. Graph the distance *y* and time *x* on the coordinate plane at the right. Graph the distance on the *y*-axis and the time on the *x*-axis. Connect the points with a solid line.

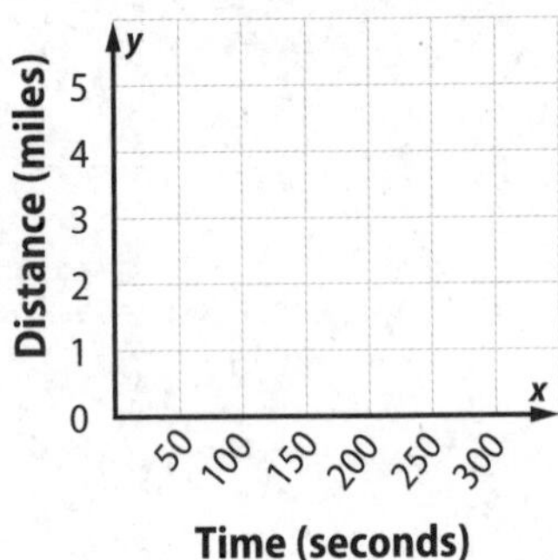

H.O.T. Problems Higher-Order Thinking

7. **Create** Make a table where the constant rate of change is 6 inches for every foot.

Feet				
Inches				

8. **Analyze** The constant rate of change for the relationship shown in the table is $8 per hour. Determine the missing values.

Time (h)	1	2	3
Earnings ($)	x	y	z

$x =$ ______ $y =$ ______ $z =$ ______

9. **Analyze** The terms in sequence *A* increase by 3. The terms in sequence *B* increase by 8. In which sequence do the terms form a steeper line when graphed as points on a coordinate plane? Justify your reasoning.

Name ______________________________

Multi-Step Problem Solving

10. The table shows the number of feet walked, given a certain amount of footsteps. Choose the set of values that would yield a constant rate of change. P N MP

Number of Footsteps	Distance Walked (ft)
5	a
10	b
15	c
25	d

Ⓐ $a = 12, b = 24, c = 36, d = 48$

Ⓑ $a = 12, b = 24, c = 36, d = 60$

Ⓒ $a = 12, b = 24, c = 48, d = 96$

Ⓓ $a = 12, b = 24, c = 46, d = 68$

Use a problem-solving model to solve this problem.

1 Analyze

Read the problem. Circle the information you know.
Underline what the problem is asking you to find.

2 Plan

What will you need to do to solve the problem? Write your plan in steps.

Step 1 Calculate the __________ using the values in the answer choices.

Step 2 Compare the __________ to determine a constant rate of change.

3 Solve

Use your plan to solve the problem. Show your steps.

A: $\frac{12}{5} =$ ____ $\frac{24}{10} =$ ____ $\frac{36}{15} =$ ____ $\frac{48}{25} =$ ____

B: $\frac{12}{5} =$ ____ $\frac{24}{10} =$ ____ $\frac{36}{15} =$ ____ $\frac{60}{25} =$ ____

C: $\frac{12}{5} =$ ____ $\frac{24}{10} =$ ____ $\frac{48}{15} =$ ____ $\frac{96}{25} =$ ____

D: $\frac{12}{5} =$ ____ $\frac{24}{10} =$ ____ $\frac{46}{15} =$ ____ $\frac{68}{25} =$ ____

Compare the unit rates to determine which one has a constant rate of change.

Answer choice ____ is the only answer choice that has a constant rate of change.

So, the correct answer is ____. Fill in that answer choice.

4 Justify and Evaluate

How do you know your solution is accurate?

____

____

P = Proportionality N = Number and Operations MP = Mathematical Processes

More Multi-Step Problem Solving

Use a problem-solving model to solve each problem.

11. The table compares number of apples purchased and the total cost. Choose which set of values would give a constant rate of change with a cost of $0.75 per apple.

Number of Apples	Cost ($)
4	a
6	b
10	c

Ⓐ $a = \$3.00, b = \$6.00, c = \$7.50$

Ⓑ $a = \$3.00, b = \$3.75, c = \$4.50$

Ⓒ $a = \$3.00, b = \$3.75, c = \$5.25$

Ⓓ $a = \$3.00, b = \$4.50, c = \$7.50$

12. Noah has been growing at a constant rate as shown in the graph below. What is his average rate of change in inches per month?

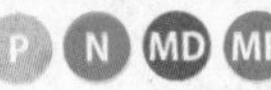

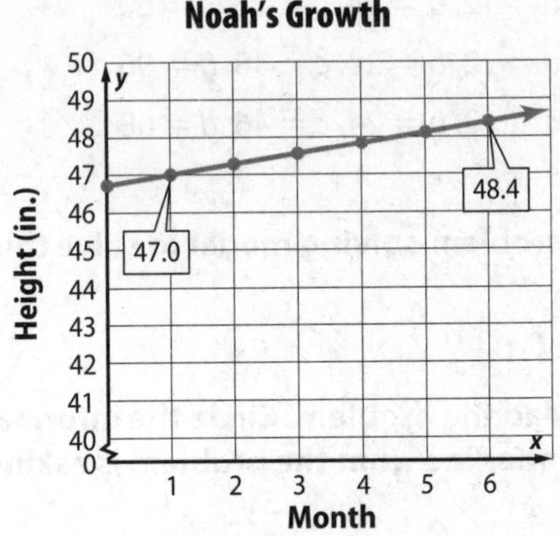

13. The table gives the distance traveled over a certain amount of time. What is the value of a that will result in a constant rate of change?

Time (hr)	Distance (mi)
3	213
5	a
8	568

14. The table below shows ordered pairs on a graph. Determine the missing value that will guarantee a constant rate of change.

x	y
a	30
$a + 2$	42
$a + 3$	?

P = Proportionality N = Number and Operations EE = Expressions, Equations, and Relationships MD = Measurement and Data MP = Mathematical Processes

Lesson 9

Constant of Proportionality

Launch the Lesson: Real World

The distance d a car travels after t hours can be represented by $d = 65t$. The table and graph also represent the situation. Let's investigate the relationship between distance and time.

Time (hours)	Distance (miles)
2	130
3	195
4	260

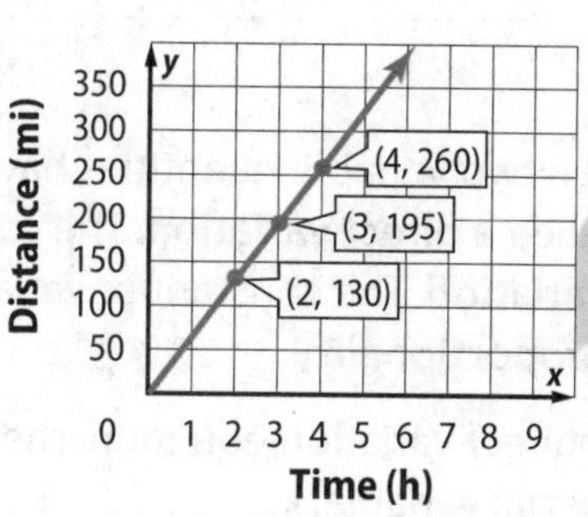

1. Determine the constant ratio.

$$\frac{\text{distance traveled}}{\text{driving time}} = \frac{130}{2} = \frac{195}{\square} = \frac{\square}{4}$$

The constant ratio is ☐ miles per hour.

2. Determine the constant rate of change.

$$\frac{\text{change in miles}}{\text{change in time}} = \square$$ miles per hour

3. Write a sentence that compares the constant rate of change and the constant ratio.

____

Texas Essential Knowledge and Skills

Targeted TEKS

7.4(C) Determine the constant of proportionality ($k = \frac{y}{x}$) within mathematical and real-world problems.

Also addresses 7.4(A).

Mathematical Processes

7.1(A), 7.1(B), 7.1(D), 7.1(F)

Vocabulary

direct variation

constant of variation

constant of proportionality

Essential Question

HOW can you show that two objects are proportional?

Which MP Mathematical Processes did you use? Shade the circle(s) that applies.

Ⓐ Apply Math to the Real World.
Ⓑ Use a Problem-Solving Model.
Ⓒ Select Tools and Techniques.
Ⓓ Use Multiple Representations.
Ⓔ Organize Ideas.
Ⓕ Analyze Relationships.
Ⓖ Justify Arguments.

Key Concept

Direct Variation

Work Zone

Words A relationship is a direct variation when the ratio of *y* to *x* is a constant, *k*. We say *y* varies directly with *x*.

Symbols $\frac{y}{x} = k$ or $y = kx$, where $k \neq 0$

Example $y = 3x$

Model

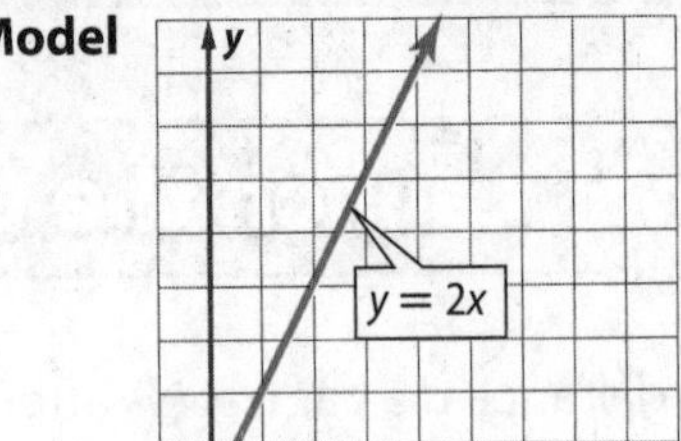

When two variable quantities have a constant ratio, their relationship is called a **direct variation**. The constant ratio is called the **constant of variation**. The constant of variation is also known as the **constant of proportionality**.

In a direct variation equation, the constant of proportional is assigned a special variable, *k*.

Tutor

Real World

Example

1. The height of the water as a pool is being filled is shown in the graph. Determine the rate in inches per minute.

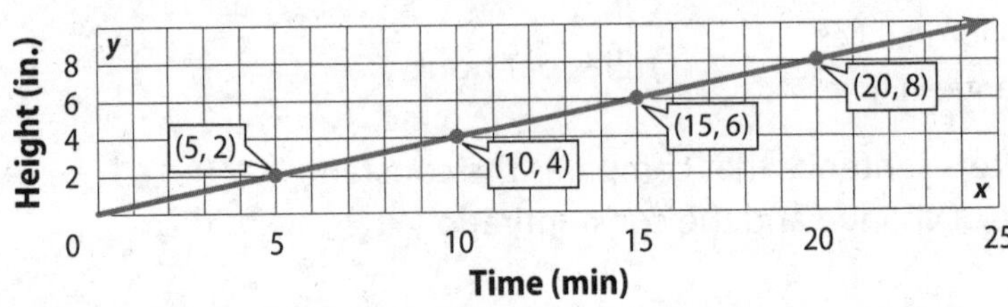

Direct Variation

When a relationship varies directly, the graph will always go through the origin, (0, 0). Also, the unit rate *r* is located at (1, *r*).

Since the graph of the data forms a line, the rate of change is constant. Use the graph to determine the constant of proportionality.

$\frac{\text{height}}{\text{time}} \rightarrow \quad \frac{2}{5} \text{ or } \frac{0.4}{1} \quad \frac{4}{10} \text{ or } \frac{0.4}{1} \quad \frac{6}{15} \text{ or } \frac{0.4}{1} \quad \frac{8}{20} \text{ or } \frac{0.4}{1}$

The pool fills at a rate of 0.4 inch every minute.

Got It? Do this problem to find out.

a. __________

a. Two minutes after a diver enters the water, he has descended 52 feet. After 5 minutes, he has descended 130 feet. At what rate is the scuba diver descending?

Example

2. The equation $y = 10x$ represents the amount of money y Julio earns for x hours of work. Identify the constant of proportionality. Explain what it represents in this situation.

$y = kx$
$\downarrow$
$y = 10x$

Compare the equation to $y = kx$, where k is the constant of proportionality.

The constant of proportionality is 10. So, Julio earns $10 for every hour that he works.

Got It? Do this problem to find out.

Show your work.

b. The distance y traveled in miles by the Chang family in x hours is represented by the equation $y = 55x$. Identify the constant of proportionality. Then explain what it represents.

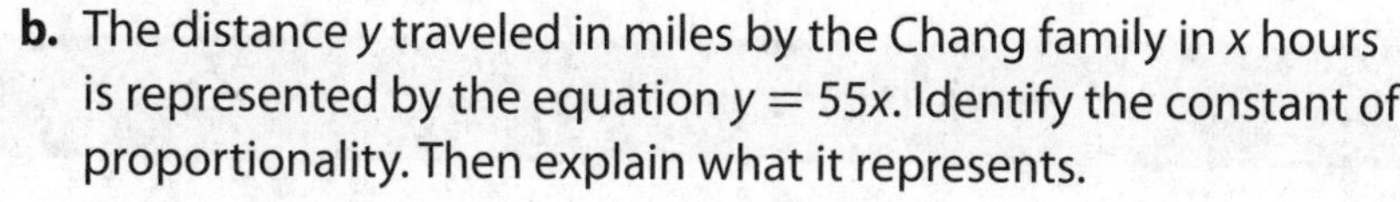

b. ____________

Determine Direct Variation

Not all situations with a constant rate of change are proportional relationships. In other words, they are not all direct variations.

Example

3. Pizzas cost $8 each plus a $3 delivery charge. Show the cost of 1, 2, 3, and 4 pizzas. Is there a direct variation?

Number of Pizzas	1	2	3	4
Cost ($)	$11	$19	$27	$35

$\frac{\text{cost}}{\text{number of pizzas}} \rightarrow \frac{11}{1}, \frac{19}{2}$ or 9.5, $\frac{27}{3}$ or 9, $\frac{35}{4}$ or 8.75

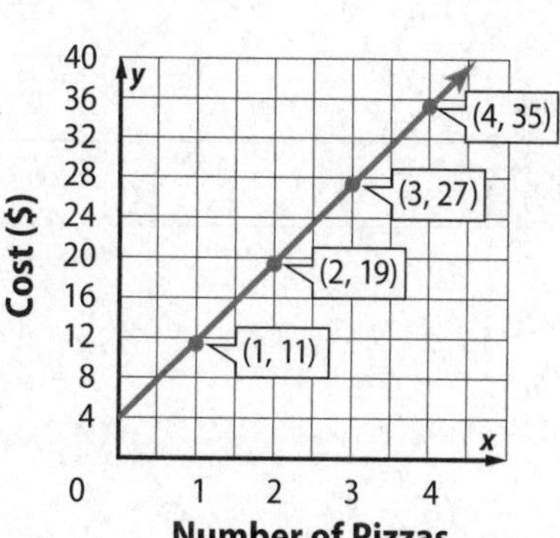

There is no constant ratio and the line does not go through the origin. So, there is no direct variation.

Got It? Do this problem to find out.

c. Two pounds of cheese cost $8.40. Show the cost of 1, 2, 3, and 4 pounds of cheese. Is there a direct variation? Explain.

Weight (lb)	Cost ($)

y
21
18
15
12
9
6
3
0
1 2 3 4 5 x
Cost ($)
Weight (lb)

c. ____________

Example

4. Determine whether the relationship is a direct variation. If so, state the constant of proportionality.

Time, x	1	2	3	4
Wages ($), y	12	24	36	48

Compare the ratios to check for a common ratio.

$\frac{\text{wages}}{\text{time}} \longrightarrow \frac{12}{1} \quad \frac{24}{2} \text{ or } \frac{12}{1} \quad \frac{36}{3} \text{ or } \frac{12}{1} \quad \frac{48}{4} \text{ or } \frac{12}{1}$

Since the ratios are the same, the relationship is a direct variation. The constant of proportionality is $\frac{12}{1}$.

Guided Practice

1. The number of cakes baked varies directly with the number of hours the caterers work. What is the ratio of cakes baked to hours worked? (Examples 1 and 2) ________

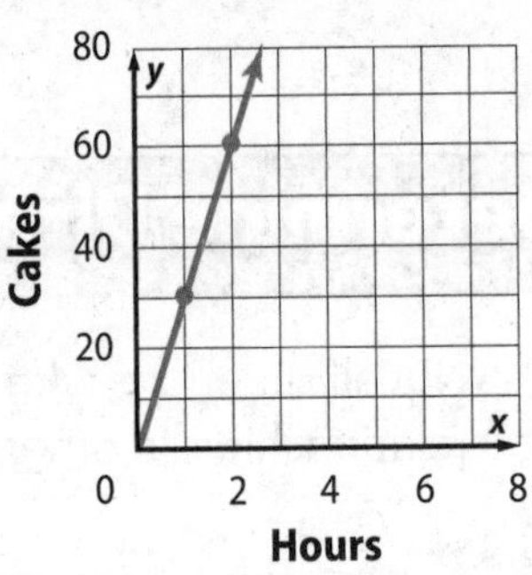

2. An airplane travels 780 miles in 4 hours. Make a table and graph to show the mileage for 2, 8, and 12 hours. Is there a direct variation? Explain.

(Examples 3 and 4) ________

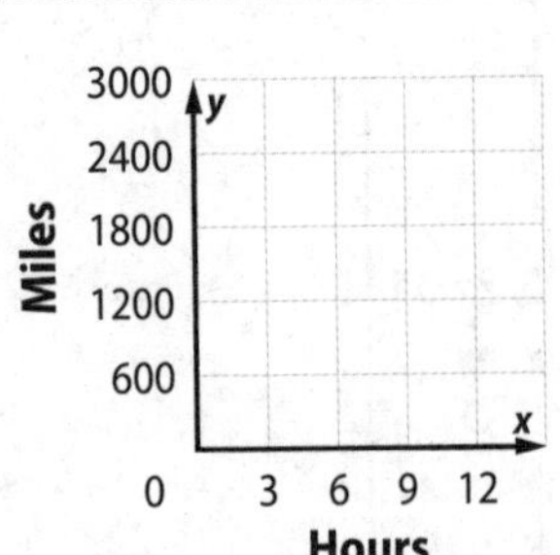

Hours			
Miles			

3. **Building on the Essential Question** How can you determine if a relationship is a direct variation from an equation? a table? a graph? ________

Rate Yourself!

How confident are you about direct variation? Check the box that applies.

Find out online. Use the Self-Check Quiz.

Name ______________________ My Homework ______________________

Independent Practice

7.4(A), 7.4(C), 7.1(D), 7.1(F) TEKS

1. Veronica is mulching her front yard. The total weight of mulch varies directly with the number of bags of mulch.

   What is the rate of change? (Example 1) ______________________

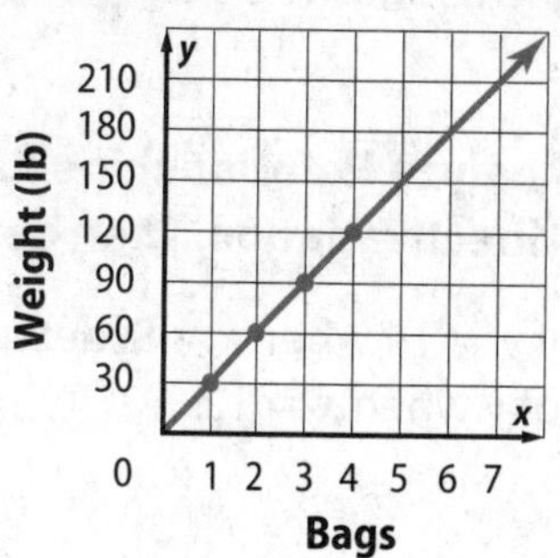

2. The Spanish club held a car wash to raise money. The equation $y = 5x$ represents the amount of money y club members made for washing x cars. Identify the constant of proportionality. Then explain what it represents in this situation. (Example 2) ______________________

   ____

3. MP **Use Multiple Representations** A technician charges $25 per hour plus $50 for a house call to repair home computers. Make a table and a graph to show the cost for 1, 2, 3, and 4 hours of home computer repair service. Is there a direct variation? (Example 3)

Time (h)				
Charge ($)				

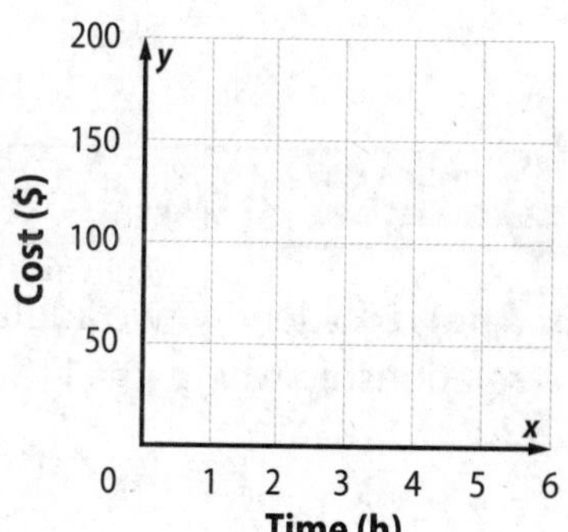

____

____

Determine whether each relationship is a direct variation. If so, state the constant of proportionality. (Example 4)

4.

Pictures, x	3	4	5	6
Profit, y	24	32	40	48

____

5.

Minutes, x	185	235	275	325
Cost, y	60	115	140	180

____

6.

Year, x	5	10	15	20
Height, y	12.5	25	37.5	50

____

7.

Game, x	2	3	4	5
Points, y	4	5	7	11

____

8. At a 33-foot depth underwater, the pressure is 29.55 pounds per square inch (psi). At a depth of 66 feet, the pressure reaches 44.4 psi. At what rate is the pressure increasing? ______

Analyze Relationships If y varies directly with x, write an equation for the direct variation. Then determine each value.

9. If $y = 14$ when $x = 8$, determine the value of y when $x = 12$.

______

10. Determine the value of y when $x = 15$ if $y = 6$ when $x = 30$.

______

11. If $y = -6$ when $x = -24$, determine the value of x when $y = -7$.

______

12. Determine the value of x when $y = 14$, if $y = 7$ when $x = 8$.

______

H.O.T. Problems Higher-Order Thinking

13. **Analyze** Identify two additional values for x and y in a direct variation relationship where $y = 11$ when $x = 18$.

$x =$ ______ $y =$ ______ and $x =$ ______ $y =$ ______

14. **Analyze** Determine the value of y when $x = 14$ if y varies directly with x^2, and $y = 72$ when $x = 6$. ______

15. **Create** Tom is drawing rectangles in which the length varies directly with the width. One of his rectangles has a width of 2 centimeters and a length of 3.6 centimeters. Draw and label a rectangle with a width of 3.5 centimeters that could be one of Tom's rectangles. Then determine the perimeter.

______

Name ___

Multi-Step Problem Solving

16. The graph shows the distance a car travels over a certain amount of time. What is the ratio of kilometers traveled to the time in hours? (*Hint*: 1 mi ≈ 1.61 km) P EE MP

Ⓐ 40 kilometers per hour

Ⓑ 64.4 kilometers per hour

Ⓒ 80 kilometers per hour

Ⓓ 128.80 kilometers per hour

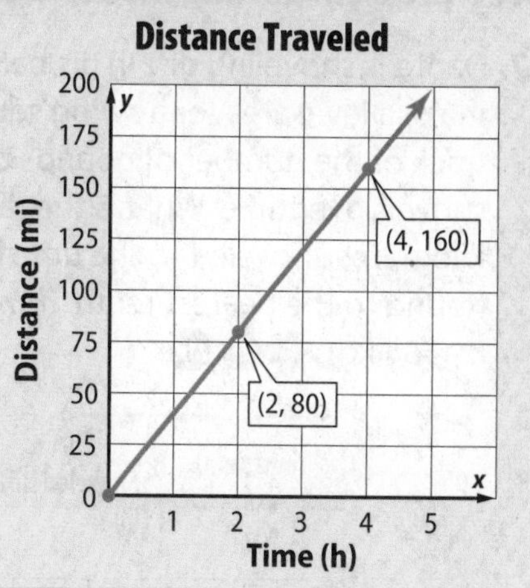

Use a problem-solving model to solve this problem.

1 Analyze

Read the problem. Circle the information you know.
Underline what the problem is asking you to find.

2 Plan

What will you need to do to solve the problem? Write your plan in steps.

Step 1 Use the graph to determine the constant of ___.

Step 2 Convert miles to ___.

Read to Succeed!

Use the symbols $y = kx$ to help you determine the ratios from the graph.

3 Solve

Use your plan to solve the problem. Show your steps.

$\frac{80}{2} =$ ___ $\frac{160}{4} =$ ___ The rate of change is ___ miles per hour.

Convert miles to kilometers.

$\frac{40 \text{ mi}}{1 \text{ h}} \times \frac{1.61 \text{ km}}{1 \text{ h}} \approx$ ___

The car traveled about ___ kilometers per hour.

So, the correct answer is ___. Fill in that answer choice.

4 Justify and Evaluate

How do you know your solution is accurate?

___

___

___

P = Proportionality EE = Expressions, Equations, and Relationships MP = Mathematical Processes

More Multi-Step Problem Solving

Use a problem-solving model to solve each problem.

17. Dante is shoveling dirt in his backyard to make a level area for a swing set. He keeps track of the number of pounds of dirt he shovels over time. What is the ratio of kilograms shoveled to the time in minutes? Round to the nearest tenth. (*Hint*: 1 lb $\approx$ 0.4536 kg) P EE MP

Time (min)	Dirt Shoveled (lb)
20	100
45	225

Ⓐ 2.3 kilograms per minute

Ⓑ 4.5 kilograms per minute

Ⓒ 5 kilograms per minute

Ⓓ 11.0 kilograms per minute

18. The table shows the wages Ramona earned for the number of hours she spent babysitting. If her wage is a direct variation of hours babysitting, how many hours does she need to babysit to earn $60? N P MP

Hours Babysitting	Wage ($)
2	15
3	22.50
5	37.50

19. Reynaldo needs to purchase cupcakes for the after-school picnic. The table shows the price of different numbers of cupcakes. How many cupcakes can Reynaldo purchase with $45?

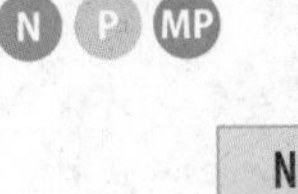

Number of Cupcakes	Price ($)
3	6.75
6	13.50
12	27.00

20. Change one y-value in the table below so that it represents a direct variation. Explain your reasoning, and identify the constant of proportionality. N P MP

x	11	25	41	58
y	27.5	62.5	100	145

N = Number and Operations P = Proportionality EE = Expressions, Equations, and Relationships MP = Mathematical Processes

21ST CENTURY CAREER

Biomechanical Engineering

Did you know that more than 700 pounds of force are exerted on a 140-pound long-jumper during the landing? Biomechanical engineers understand how forces travel through the shoe to an athlete's foot and how the shoes can help reduce the impact of those forces on the legs. If you are curious about how engineering can be applied to the human body, a career in biomechanical engineering might be a great fit for you.

Mathematical Process TEKS
7.1(A) Apply mathematics to problems arising in everyday life, society, and the workplace.

Targeted TEKS 7.4(A), 7.4(D)

Is This the Career for You?

Are you interested in a career as a biomechanical engineer? Take some of the following courses in high school.

- Biology
- Calculus
- Physics
- Trigonometry

Explore college and careers at ccr.mcgraw-hill.com

Start Off on the Right Foot

Use the information in the graph to solve each problem.

1. Determine the constant rate of change for the data shown in the graph below Exercise 2. Interpret its meaning.

2. Is there a proportional relationship between the weight of an athlete and the forces that are generated from running? Explain your reasoning.

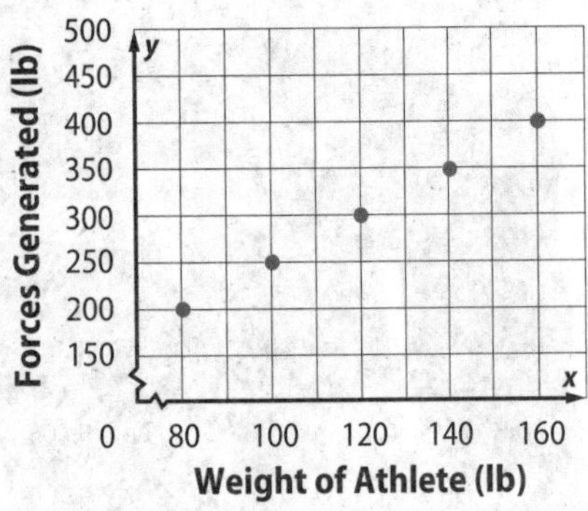

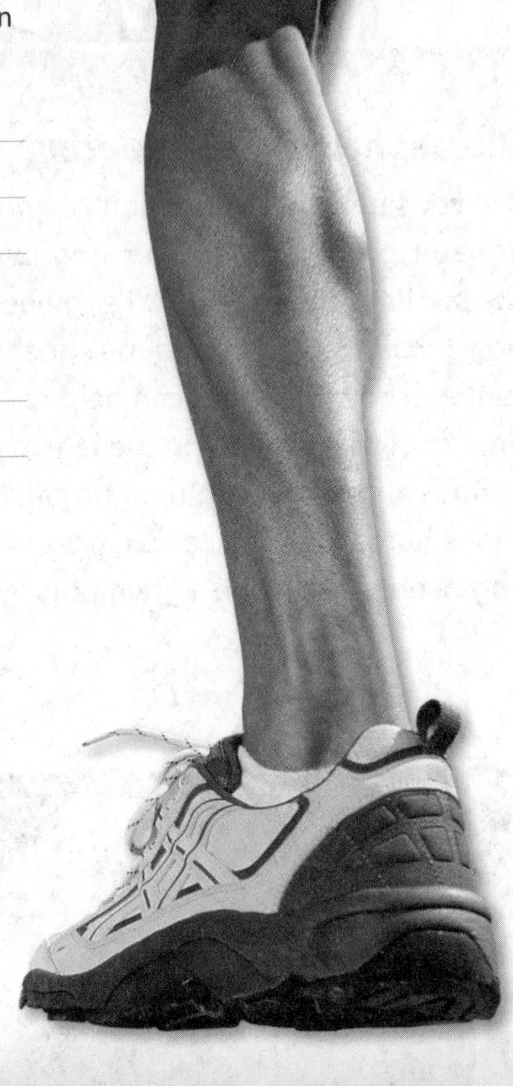

Career Project

It's time to update your career portfolio! Use the Internet or another source to research the fields of biomechanical engineering, biomedical engineering, and mechanical engineering. Write a brief summary comparing and contrasting the fields. Then prepare and present a brief oral presentation to your classmates describing how they are all related. At the end, ask any clarifying questions.

What subject in school is the most important to you? How would you use that subject in this career?

Chapter Review

Vocabulary Check

Work with a partner to complete each sentence using the vocabulary list at the beginning of the chapter. Take turns saying each sentence aloud while the other student listens carefully. Then circle the word that completes the sentence in the word search.

1. A ____________ is a ratio that compares two quantities with different kinds of units.
2. A rate that has a denominator of 1 unit is called a ____________ rate.
3. A pair of numbers used to locate a point in the coordinate plane is an ____________ pair.
4. (0, 0) represents the ____________
5. A ____________ variation is the relationship between two variable quantities with a constant ratio.
6. A ____________ fraction has a fraction in the numerator, denominator, or both.
7. One of the four regions into which a coordinate plane is separated is called a ____________.
8. A ____________ is an equation stating that two ratios or rates are equal.
9. The rate of ____________ describes how one quantity changes in relation to another.
10. ____________ analysis is the process of including units of measurement when you compute.

I	U	M	H	P	G	N	B	W	Z	A	F	X	O	Q	G	H	W	M	E	M	P
L	Z	E	O	X	V	D	H	B	T	U	S	A	A	U	X	E	L	P	M	O	C
U	Y	K	N	N	N	U	L	S	N	H	K	D	Z	A	J	U	R	W	X	T	I
G	A	B	V	X	Y	X	P	C	Y	E	L	M	E	D	C	H	A	N	G	E	U
G	O	J	Y	L	C	S	T	F	G	P	Y	J	V	R	T	R	T	Y	F	O	V
A	Q	N	N	L	W	I	L	T	M	R	R	F	J	A	E	D	E	V	O	Y	M
M	N	I	P	U	O	I	C	Z	J	M	W	O	C	N	Z	D	X	X	C	A	A
A	T	G	N	N	I	E	L	B	A	M	K	B	P	T	O	T	R	G	Z	U	F
R	H	I	A	E	R	Z	G	A	T	R	U	O	X	O	S	G	M	O	N	H	M
U	T	R	Z	I	A	H	R	S	A	Y	F	Y	Z	F	R	L	U	E	R	D	E
N	C	O	D	T	G	C	F	A	O	X	O	M	W	B	T	T	O	K	W	X	W
I	L	S	E	M	G	D	I	M	E	N	S	I	O	N	A	L	I	P	T	Z	N
Y	H	M	R	L	C	O	I	E	Z	R	S	A	V	L	Z	B	P	O	E	Y	L
X	S	W	C	C	W	G	J	W	U	D	G	A	I	W	I	E	Y	C	N	O	D
J	U	U	V	K	O	Z	Z	D	H	J	K	G	W	Z	P	U	K	M	F	W	J
A	G	A	L	R	B	K	Z	X	X	Q	M	H	P	L	P	M	N	B	W	T	V

Key Concept Check 

Use Your FOLDABLES

Use your Foldable to help review the chapter. Share your Foldable with a partner and take turns summarizing what you learned in this chapter, while the other partner listens carefully. Ask for or give help of any concept if needed. TEKS 7.1(E)

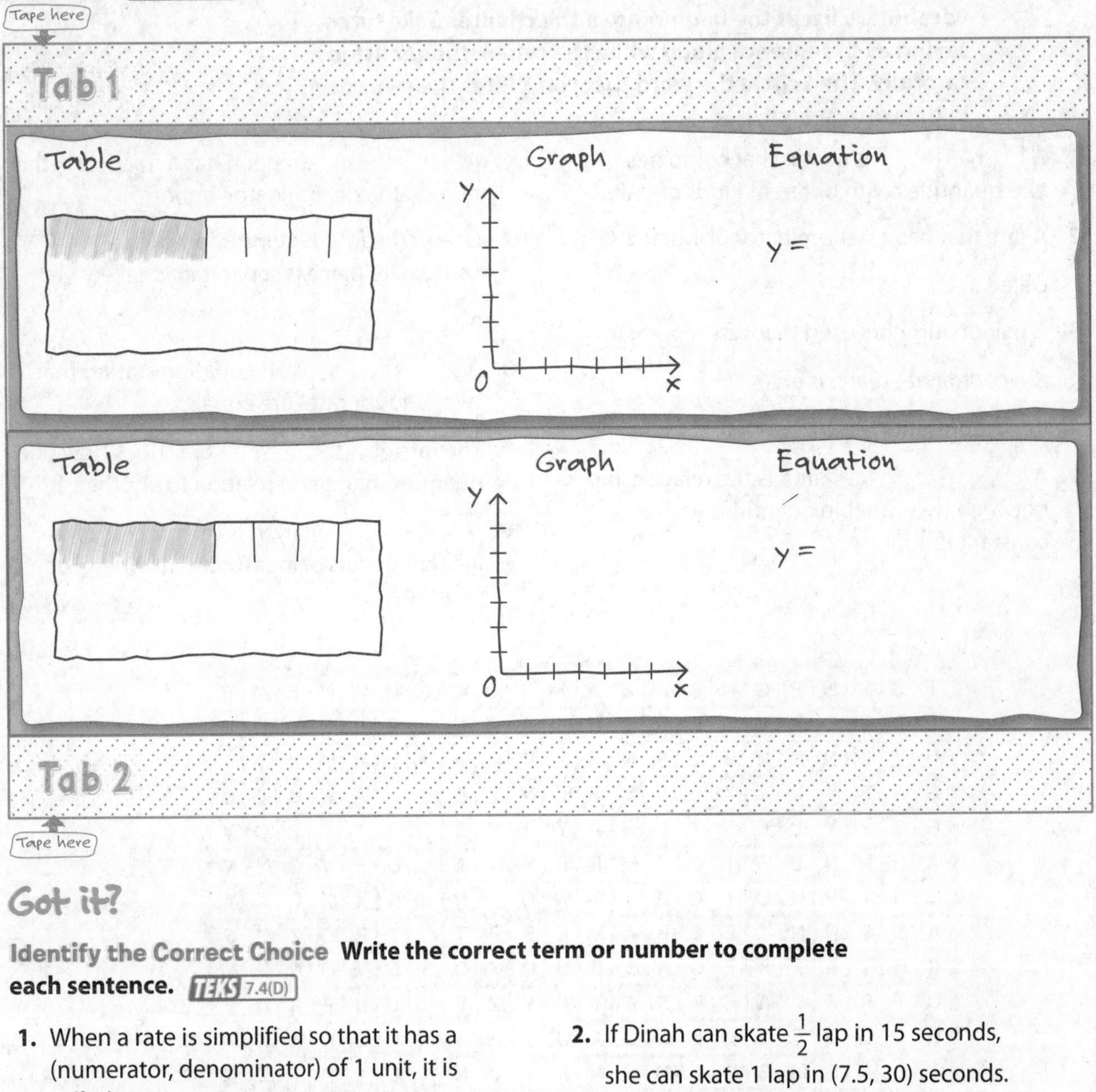

Tape here

Tab 1

Table

Graph

Equation

y

0

x

$y =$

Table

Graph

Equation

y

0

x

$y =$

Tab 2

Tape here

Got it?

Identify the Correct Choice Write the correct term or number to complete each sentence. TEKS 7.4(D)

1. When a rate is simplified so that it has a (numerator, denominator) of 1 unit, it is called a unit rate.

2. If Dinah can skate $\frac{1}{2}$ lap in 15 seconds, she can skate 1 lap in (7.5, 30) seconds.

3. Two quantities are (proportional, nonproportional) if they have a constant ratio or unit rate.

4. When two quantities have a constant ratio, their relationship is called a (direct, nonproportional) variation.

Multi-Step Problem Solving

5. Kylee is biking from her house to her grandmother's house. Every two seconds she travels 48 feet. After she has traveled 400 feet, her brother leaves their house on his bike to catch up with her. Every three seconds he travels 78 feet. If Kylee and her brother continue traveling at these rates, how long will it take her brother to catch up to her? Justify your solution. P N MP

1 Analyze

2 Plan

3 Solve

4 Justify and Evaluate

Got it?

6. A short course meter pool is shown. What is the perimeter of the pool in feet? Justify your solution. P N MP

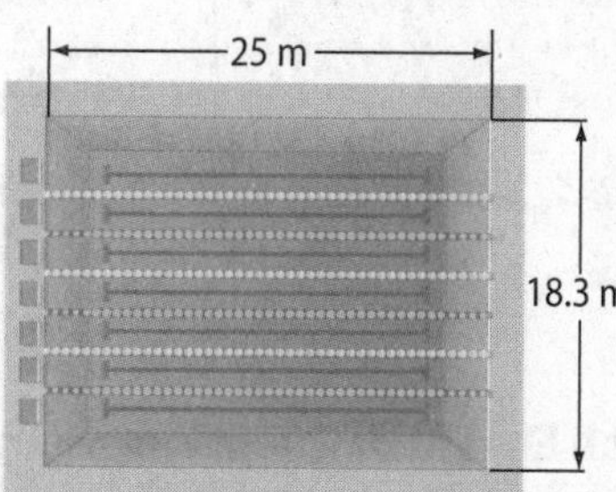

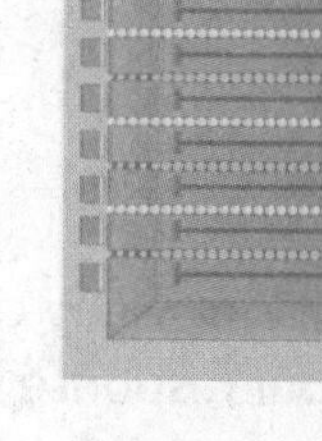

N = Number and Operations P = Proportionality MP = Mathematical Processes

Reflect

Answering the Essential Question

Use what you learned about ratios and proportional reasoning to complete the graphic organizer. TEKS 7.1(D), 7.1(F), 7.1(G)

Essential Question

HOW can you show that two objects are proportional?

... with a table?	... with a graph?	... with an equation?

Answer the Essential Question. HOW can you show that two objects are proportional? Verbally share your response with a partner, asking for and giving help if needed.

Chapter 3
Apply Proportionality to Percent

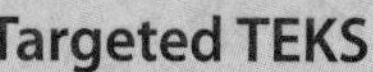

Texas Essential Knowledge and Skills

Targeted TEKS

7.4 The student applies mathematical process standards to represent and solve problems involving proportional relationships. *Also addresses 7.13.*

Mathematical Processes

7.1, 7.1(A), 7.1(B), 7.1(C), 7.1(D), 7.1(E), 7.1(F), 7.1(G)

Essential Question

HOW can percent help you understand situations involving money?

Math in the Real World

Biking The fundraising goal for each rider in the Texas 4000 is \$4,500. One rider has already raised \$3,150. Fill in the graph below to show the percent of the goal achieved.

Go Online! www.connectED.mcgraw-hill.com

Watch  Worksheets  Vocab  Tutor  Tools  Check

What Tools Do You Need?

Vocabulary

discount	percent equation	percent proportion	selling price
gratuity	percent of change	principal	simple interest
markdown	percent of decrease	sales tax	tip
markup	percent of increase		

Studying Math

Draw a Picture Drawing a picture can help you better understand numbers. For example, a *number map* shows how numbers are related to each other.

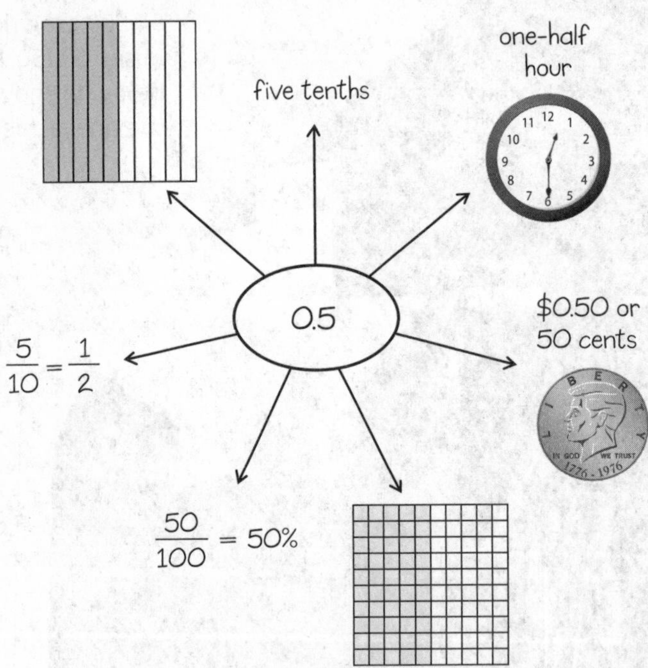

In the space below, work with a partner to make a number map for 0.75. Ask your partner or teacher for help if needed. Then share your number maps with a partner.

When Will You Use This?

Marisol, Blake, and Hiroshi in

Amusement Park Prices

Your Turn! **You will solve this problem in the chapter.**

Are You Ready?

Quick Review

Review 5.3(E), 6.5(C) TEKS

Example 1

Evaluate $240 \times 0.03 \times 5$.

$240 \times 0.03 \times 5$

$= 7.2 \times 5$ Multiply 240 by 0.03.

$= 36$ Simplify.

Example 2

Express 0.35 as a percent.

$0.35 = 35\%$ Move the decimal point two places to the right and add the percent symbol.

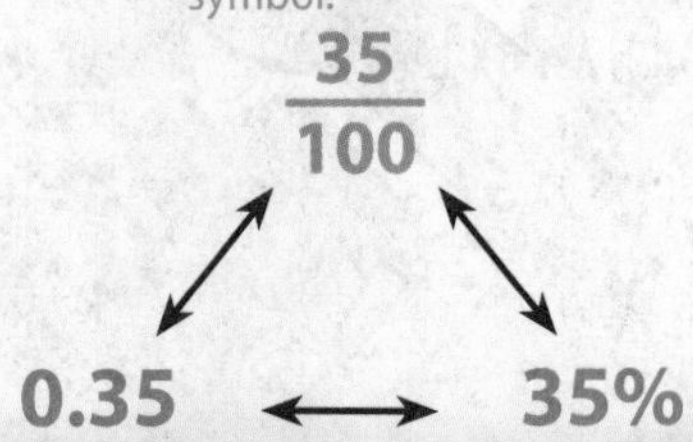

Quick Check

Multiply Decimals **Determine each product.**

1. $300 \times 0.02 \times 8 =$ ______

show your work.

2. $85 \times 0.25 \times 3 =$ ______

3. Suppose Nicole saves $2.50 every day. How much money will she have in 4 weeks? ______

Decimals and Percents **Express each decimal as a percent.**

4. $0.675 =$ ______

5. $0.725 =$ ______

6. $0.95 =$ ______

7. Approximately 0.92 of a watermelon is water. What percent represents this decimal? ______

How Did You Do?

Which problems did you answer correctly in the Quick Check? Shade those exercise numbers below.

① ② ③ ④ ⑤ ⑥ ⑦

Use the Foldable throughout this chapter to help you learn about percents.

 cut on all dashed lines

fold on all solid lines

 tape to page 296

Percents

percent proportion

percent equation

FOLDABLES®

Use the Foldable throughout this chapter to help you learn about percents.

fold on all solid lines

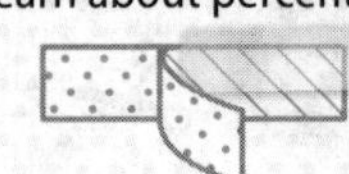

Definition

Definition

page 296

Hands-On Lab 1-a

Percent Diagrams

INQUIRY **HOW can I use multiple representations to solve real-world problems about percents?**

Texas Essential Knowledge and Skills

Targeted TEKS
7.4(D) Solve problems involving ratios, rates, and percents, including multi-step problems involving percent increase and percent decrease, and financial literacy problems.

Mathematical Processes
7.1(A), 7.1(C), 7.1(D), 7.1(E), 7.1(F)

One fourth of the students in Mrs. Singh's music class chose a guitar as their favorite musical instrument. There are 24 students in Mrs. Singh's music class. How many students chose a guitar as their favorite musical instrument?

What do you know? ______

What do you need to find? ______

Hands-On Activity 1

Bar diagrams can be used to represent a part of a whole as a fraction and as a percent.

Step 1 The bar diagram represents 100% of the class. Shade the bar diagram to show that $\frac{1}{4}$ or ☐% of the class chose guitar as their favorite instrument.

				100%

|---☐%---|

Step 2 There are ☐ students in Mrs. Singh's music class. Divide the number of students equally into 4 sections. Fill in the number in each section.

|-------------------- 24 students --------------------|

				100%

|---☐%---|

So, ☐ students chose a guitar as their favorite musical instrument.

Hands-On Activity 2

There are 500 seventh-grade students at Heritage Middle School. Sixty percent of them play a musical instrument. How many seventh-grade students play a musical instrument?

Step 1 Supply the missing information for the second bar.

percent 100%

students ☐ total students

Step 2 Divide each bar into ten equal parts. Write 10% in each section of the first bar.

percent **10%** 100%

students ☐ total students

Step 3 Determine what number to write in each section of the second bar. Fill in that number.

percent **10%** 100%

students ☐ total students

Step 4 Shade 60% of the first bar and an equal amount on the second bar.

percent **10%** 100%

students ☐ total students

Since ☐ % corresponds to 6 sections, count the number of students in 6 sections. There are ☐ seventh-grade students who play a musical instrument.

Work with a partner. Use bar diagrams to solve each problem.

1. The seventh-grade class at Fort Couch Middle School has a goal of selling 300 tickets to the annual student versus teacher basketball game. The eighth-grade class has a goal of selling 400 tickets.

   a. By the end of the first week, the eighth-grade students sold 30% of their goal. How many tickets has the eighth grade sold? ______

   percent [   ] 100%

   tickets [   ] [ ]

   b. The seventh grade sold 60% of their goal. How many tickets do the students still need to sell? Explain. ______

   ______

   ______

   ______ [   ] 100%

   ______ [   ] [ ]

2. MP **Justify Arguments** The graph shows the results of a survey asking 500 teens about their allowances. How many teens did not receive between $10 and $20? Explain.

   ______

   ______

Weekly Allowance

10% more than $20

15% less than $10

75% $10–$20

______ [   ] [ ] %

______ [   ] [ ]

Analyze and Reflect

Collaborate

MP Organize Ideas Work with a partner to complete the graphic organizer about percent and bar diagrams. The first one is done for you.

	Percent	Rate per 100	Whole	Part
	30%	$\frac{30}{100}$	150	45
3.	40%	$\frac{40}{100}$	150	
4.	50%	$\frac{50}{100}$	150	

5. **MP Analyze Relationships** Use the pattern in the table above to determine 80% of 150. ______

Create

On Your Own

MP Apply Math to the Real World Write a real-world problem for the bar diagrams shown. Then solve your problem.

6.

10%	10%	10%	10%	10%	10%	10%	10%	10%	10%	100%
25	25	25	25	25	25	25	25	25	25	250

7.

25%	25%	25%	25%	100%
15	15	15	15	60

8. **INQUIRY** HOW can I use multiple representations to solve real-world problems about percents?

Lesson 1

Percent of a Number

Launch the Lesson: Real World

Some students are collecting money for a local pet shelter. They have raised 60% of their $2,000 goal. Shade the dog bones to show how much money they have raised. Then complete the table to show the fraction-decimal-percent equivalents.

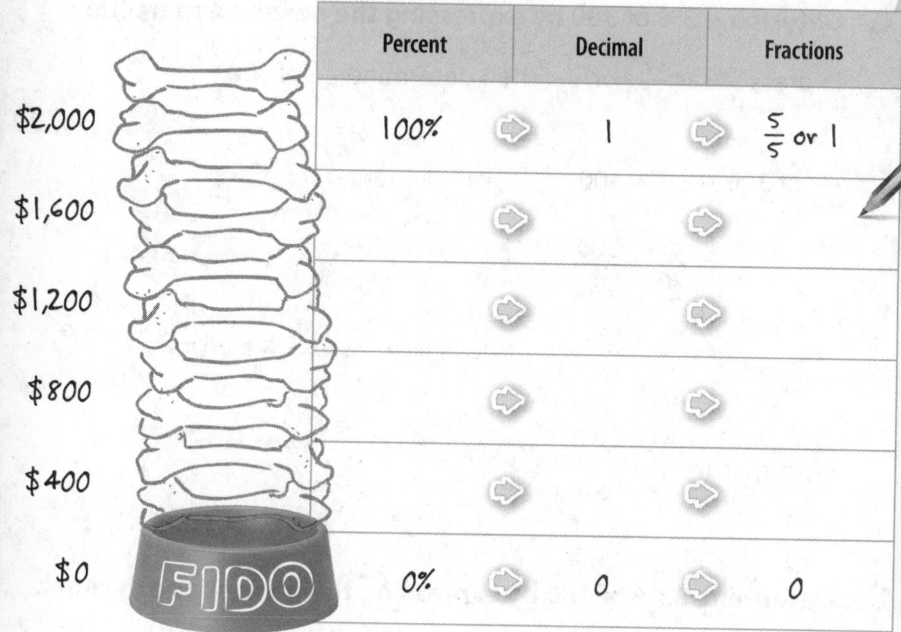

Percent	Decimal	Fractions
100%	1	$\frac{5}{5}$ or 1
0%	0	0

Texas Essential Knowledge and Skills

TEKS

Targeted TEKS

7.4(D) Solve problems involving ratios, rates, and percents, including multi-step problems involving percent increase and percent decrease, and financial literacy problems.

Mathematical Processes

7.1(A), 7.1(B), 7.1(C)

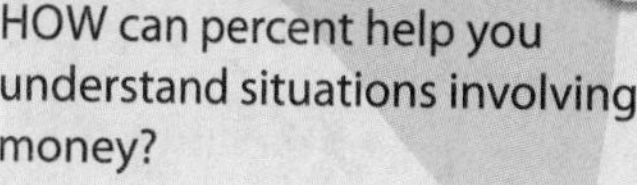

Essential Question

HOW can percent help you understand situations involving money?

1. How much money did they raise? Justify your solution.

2. **Create** Write two different multiplication equations that can each be used to find 60% of $2,000.

Which MP Mathematical Processes did you use? Shade the circle(s) that applies.

Ⓐ Apply Math to the Real World.
Ⓑ Use a Problem-Solving Model.
Ⓒ Select Tools and Techniques.
Ⓓ Use Multiple Representations.
Ⓔ Organize Ideas.
Ⓕ Analyze Relationships.
Ⓖ Justify Arguments.

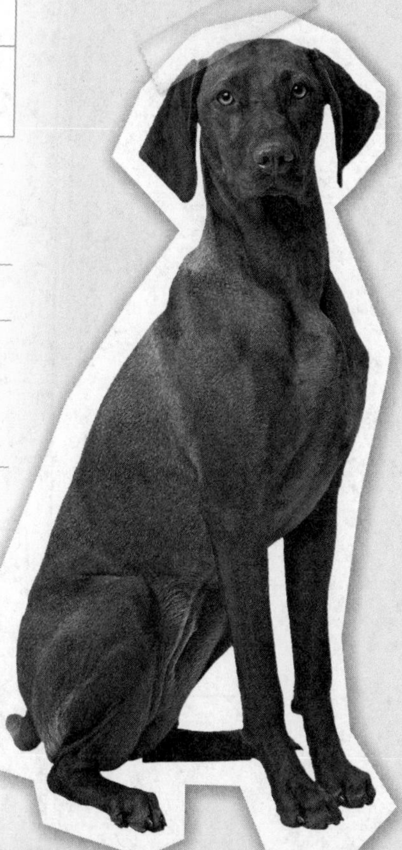

Work Zone

Determine the Percent of a Number

To determine the percent of a number such as 60% of 2,000, you can use either of the following methods.

- Express the percent as a fraction and then multiply.
- Express the percent as a decimal and then multiply.

Examples

Percent as a Rate

Determine a percent of a quantity as a rate per 100. For example, 5% of a quantity means $\frac{5}{100}$ times the quantity.

1. Determine 5% of 300 by expressing the percent as a fraction.

Express 5% as $\frac{5}{100}$ or $\frac{1}{20}$. Then determine $\frac{1}{20}$ of 300.

$\frac{1}{20}$ of $300 = \frac{1}{20} \times 300$ — Write a multiplication expression.

$= \frac{1}{\cancel{20}_1} \times \frac{\cancel{300}^{15}}{1}$ — Write 300 as $\frac{300}{1}$. Divide out common factors.

$= \frac{1 \times 15}{1 \times 1}$ — Multiply numerators and denominators.

$= \frac{15}{1}$ or 15 — Simplify.

So, 5% of 300 is 15.

2. Determine 25% of 180 by expressing the percent as a decimal.

Express 25% as 0.25. Then multiply 0.25 and 180.

$$\begin{array}{r} 180 \\ \times \quad 0.25 \\ \hline 900 \\ + \; 3{,}600 \\ \hline 45.00 \end{array}$$

0.25 ← two decimal places

45.00 ← two decimal places

So, 25% of 180 is 45.

Got It? Do these problems to find out.

Determine the percent of each number.

a. 40% of 70

b. 15% of 100

c. 55% of 160

d. 75% of 280

a. ______

b. ______

c. ______

d. ______

Use Percents Greater Than 100%

Percents that are greater than 100% can be written as improper fractions, mixed numbers, or decimals greater than 1.

$$150\% = \frac{150}{100} = \frac{3}{2} = 1\frac{1}{2} = 1.5$$

Examples

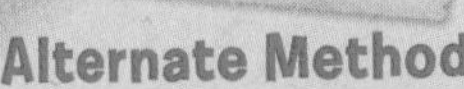

Alternate Method
You can solve Example 3 using a decimal, and you can solve Example 4 using a fraction.

3. Determine 120% of 75 by expressing the percent as a fraction.

Express 120% as $\frac{120}{100}$ or $\frac{6}{5}$. Then determine $\frac{6}{5}$ of 75.

$\frac{6}{5}$ of $75 = \frac{6}{5} \times 75$ — Write a multiplication expression.

$= \frac{6}{\cancel{5}_1} \times \frac{\cancel{75}^{15}}{1}$ — Write 75 as $\frac{75}{1}$. Divide out common factors.

$= \frac{6 \times 15}{1 \times 1}$ — Multiply numerators and denominators.

$= \frac{90}{1}$ or 90 — Simplify.

So, 120% of 75 is 90.

4. Determine 150% of 28 by expressing the percent as a decimal.

Express 150% as 1.5. Then determine 1.5 of 28.

$$\begin{array}{r} 28 \\ \times\ 1.5 \\ \hline 140 \\ +\ 280 \\ \hline 42.0 \end{array}$$

× 1.5 ← one decimal place

42.0 ← one decimal place

So, 150% of 28 is 42.

Got It? Do these problems to find out.

Determine the percent of each number.

e. 150% of 20

f. 160% of 35

e. ______

f. ______

Multi-Step Example

5. Refer to the graph. If 275 students took the survey, how many can be expected to have at least 3 televisions in each of their houses?

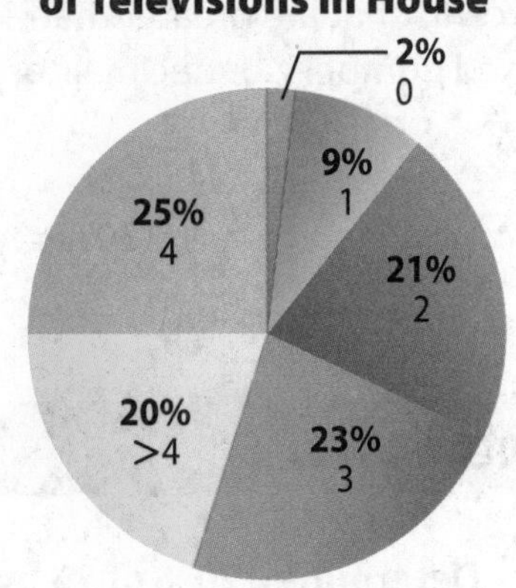

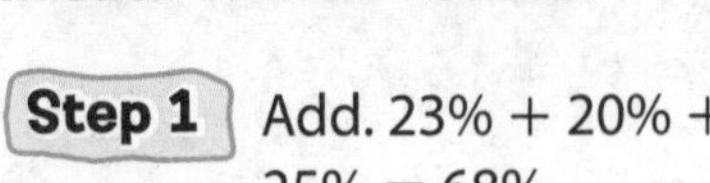
Step 1 Add. 23% + 20% + 25% = 68%

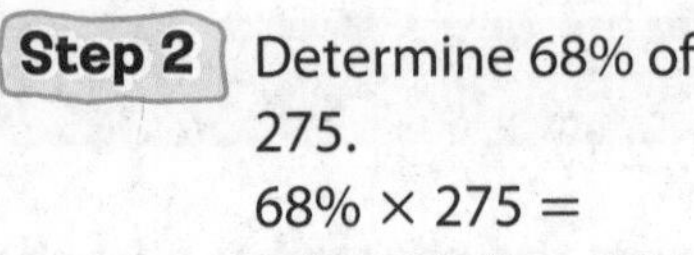
Step 2 Determine 68% of 275.

68% × 275 =

0.68 × 275 = 187

So, 187 students can be expected to have at least 3 televisions.

Guided Practice

Determine each number. Round to the nearest tenth if necessary. (Examples 1–4)

1. 8% of 50 = ______

2. 95% of 40 = ______

3. 110% of 70 = ______

4. Financial Literacy Mackenzie wants to buy a backpack that costs $50. If the tax rate is 6.5%, how much did she pay in total? (Example 5)

______

5. **Building on the Essential Question** Give an example of a real-world situation in which you would determine the percent of a number. ______

______

______

Rate Yourself!

Are you ready to move on? Shade the section that applies.

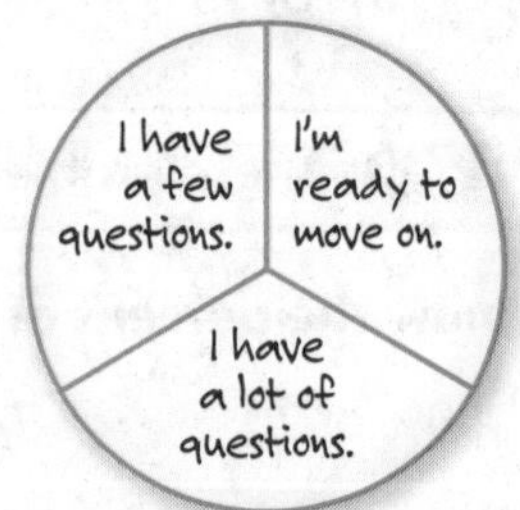

Find out online. Use the Self-Check Quiz.

Name ________________ My Homework ________________

Independent Practice

7.4(D), 7.1(A) TEKS

Determine each number. Round to the nearest tenth if necessary. (Examples 1–4)

1. 65% of 186 = ________

2. 45% of \$432 = ________

3. 23% of \$640 = ________

4. 130% of 20 = ________

5. 175% of 10 = ________

6. 150% of 128 = ________

7. 32% of 4 = ________

8. 5.4% of 65 = ________

9. 23.5% of 128 = ________

10. Suppose there are 20 questions on a multiple-choice test. If 25% of the answers are choice B, how many of the answers are *not* choice B? (Example 5)

____

11. MP **Apply Math to the Real World** Refer to the graphic novel frame below. Determine the dollar amount of the group discount each student would receive at each park.

____

12. **Financial Literacy** In addition to her salary, Ms. Lopez earns a 3% *commission*, or fee paid based on a percent of her sales, on every vacation package that she sells. One day, she sold the three vacation packages shown. Fill in the table for each packages' commission. What was her total commission?

Package	Sale Price	Commission
#1	$2,375	
#2	$3,950	
#3	$1,725	

____

Copy and Solve For Exercises 13–21, determine each number. Round to the nearest hundredth. Show your work on a separate piece of paper.

13. $\frac{4}{5}$% of 500

14. $5\frac{1}{2}$% of 60

15. $20\frac{1}{4}$% of 3

16. 1,000% of 99

17. 520% of 100

18. 0.15% of 250

19. 200% of 79

20. 0.3% of 80

21. 0.28% of 50

H.O.T. Problems Higher-Order Thinking

22. **Evaluate** Suppose you add 10% of a number to the number, and then you subtract 10% of the total. Is the result *greater than, less than,* or *equal to* the original number? Explain your reasoning.

23. **Analyze** When is it easiest to determine the percent of a number using a fraction? using a decimal?

24. **Analyze** If you calculated the percent of a number and the product is greater than the number, what do you know about the percent? Explain.

25. **Create** Give two examples of real-world situations in your life in which you would determine the percent of a number.

Name ____________________

Multi-Step Problem Solving

26. The table shows how much Alfonso earns per week at his summer job. He wants to put 30% of his earnings into a savings account. How much should he deposit into a savings account? P FL MP

Ⓐ $360

Ⓑ $400

Ⓒ $1,200

Ⓓ $3,600

Week	Money Earned ($)
1	100
2	150
3	250
4	75
5	175
6	125
7	115
8	210

Use a problem-solving model to solve this problem.

1 Analyze

Read the problem. Circle the information you know. Underline what the problem is asking you to find.

2 Plan

What will you need to do to solve the problem? Write your plan in steps.

Step 1 ______ the money Alfonso makes for all 8 weeks.

Step 2 Determine ______ of his earnings.

Read to Succeed!

Alfonso wants to save a percentage of his earnings. You can eliminate answer choice D, since the amount is more than he earns.

3 Solve

Use your plan to solve the problem. Show your steps.

100 + 150 + 250 + 75 + 175 + 125 + 115 + 210 = ______ Add.

Determine 30% of ______. 0.3 × ______ = ______

Alfonso will need to put ______ into his savings account.

So, the correct answer is ______. Fill in that answer choice.

4 Justify and Evaluate

How do you know your solution is accurate?

____

____

____

P = Proportionality FL = Personal Financial Literacy MP = Mathematical Processes

More Multi-Step Problem Solving

Use a problem-solving model to solve each problem.

27. Ella and her family normally pay $165 per month for electricity. The utility company is adding a 5% tax to help fund research for eco-friendly energy sources. How much tax will Ella's family pay for the entire year?

Ⓐ $990.00

Ⓑ $99.00

Ⓒ $66.00

Ⓓ $8.25

28. The local newspaper asked people to vote for their favorite candidate for mayor. The results are shown. If 2,500 people voted, how many more people voted for Candidate B than Candidate C? N P MP

Candidate	Percent of Vote
A	20
B	56
C	24

29. Mr. Jenkins buys a hat for $18 and a coat for $63. He has a coupon that allows him to get 15% off the total cost. He pays with four $20 bills. How much change should he receive, in dollars? N P FL MP

30. Rodrigo is at the mall shopping for new shoes. Two stores are offering a special deal on the pair of shoes he wants. How much is each store charging, and which is a better deal? N P MP

Store	Original Cost	Percent Discount
A	$70	15
B	$85.50	40

N = Number and Operations P = Proportionality FL = Personal Financial Literacy MP = Mathematical Processes

Lesson 2

Percent and Estimation

Launch the Lesson: Real World

Suppose 200 people are surveyed to determine how they learned to play an instrument. The results are shown in the table below. Estimate each percent. Choose an estimate that can be represented by a fraction that is easy to use. Then, express each estimated percent as a fraction in simplest form.

Type of Teaching	Actual Percent	Estimated Percent	Fractions
Private Lessons	42%	40%	$\frac{2}{5}$
Lessons at School	32%		
Self-Taught	26%		

Texas Essential Knowledge and Skills

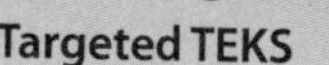

Targeted TEKS

7.4(D) Solve problems involving ratios, rates, and percents, including multi-step problems involving percent increase and percent decrease, and financial literacy problems.

Mathematical Processes

7.1(A), 7.1(B), 7.1(F), 7.1(G)

Essential Question

HOW can percent help you understand situations involving money?

1. About how many people took lessons at school?

2. Sarah estimates the percent of people who taught themselves to play an instrument as 25%, and then she found $\frac{1}{4}$ of 200. Would her answer be less than or greater than the actual number of people who were self taught? Explain.

3. About how many more people took lessons at school than self-taught lessons?

Which MP Mathematical Processes did you use? Shade the circle(s) that applies.

Ⓐ Apply Math to the Real World.
Ⓑ Use a Problem-Solving Model.
Ⓒ Select Tools and Techniques.
Ⓓ Use Multiple Representations.
Ⓔ Organize Ideas.
Ⓕ Analyze Relationships.
Ⓖ Justify Arguments.

Work Zone

Estimate the Percent of a Number

Sometimes an exact answer is not needed when using percents. One way to estimate the percent of a number is to use a fraction.

Another method for estimating the percent of a number is first to determine 10% of the number and then multiply.

$$70\% = 7 \cdot 10\%$$

So, 70% equals 7 times 10% of a number.

Real World Multi-Step Examples

1. Jodi has paid 62% of the $500 she owes for her loan. Estimate how much she still needs to pay.

Step 1 Estimate 62% of 500.

62% of $500 \approx 60\%$ of 500 — $62\% \approx 60\%$

$\approx \frac{3}{5} \cdot 500$ — $60\% = \frac{6}{10}$ or $\frac{3}{5}$

≈ 300 — Multiply.

Step 2 $500 - 300 = 200$ — Subtract.

So, Jodi still owes about $200.

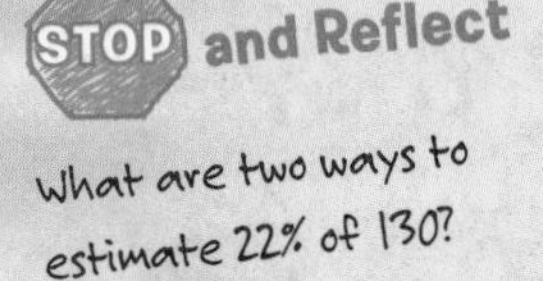

What are two ways to estimate 22% of 130? Explain below.

2. Marita and four of her friends ordered a pizza that cost $14.72. She is responsible for 20% of the bill. About how much money will she need to pay?

Step 1 Determine 10% of $15.00.

10% of $\$15.00 = 0.1 \cdot \$15.00$

$= \$1.50$ — To multiply by 10%, move the decimal point one place to the left.

Step 2 20% of $15.00 is 2 times 10% of $15.00.

$2 \cdot \$1.50 = \$3.00$ — Multiply.

So, Marita should pay about $3.00.

a. ____________

Got It? Do this problem to find out.

a. Dante plans to put 80% of his paycheck into a savings account and spend the other 20%. His paycheck this week was $295. About how much money will he put into his savings account?

Percents Greater Than 100 or Less Than 1

You can also estimate when the percent is greater than 100 or less than 1.

Check for Reasonableness
When the percent is greater than 100, the estimate will always be greater than the number.

Example

3. Estimate 122% of 50.

122% is about 120%.

$120\% \text{ of } 50 = 100\% \text{ of } 50 + 20\% \text{ of } 50$ 120% = 100% + 20%

$= (1 \cdot 50) + \left(\frac{1}{5} \cdot 50\right)$ 100% = 1 and 20% = $\frac{1}{5}$

$= 50 + 10$ or 60 Simplify.

So, 122% of 50 is about 60.

Got It? Do these problems to find out.

b. 174% of 200   **c.** 298% of 45   **d.** 347% of 80

b. ____________

c. ____________

d. ____________

Real World Multi-Step Example

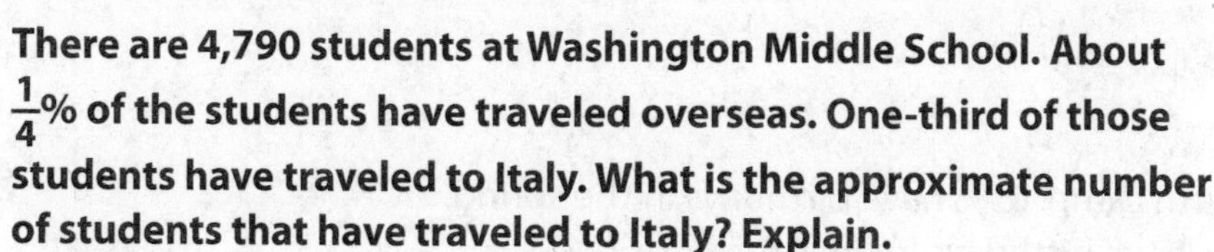

4. There are 4,790 students at Washington Middle School. About $\frac{1}{4}$% of the students have traveled overseas. One-third of those students have traveled to Italy. What is the approximate number of students that have traveled to Italy? Explain.

Step 1 $\frac{1}{4}$% is one fourth of 1%. 4,790 is about 4,800.

$1\% \text{ of } 4{,}800 = 0.01 \cdot 4{,}800$ Write 1% as 0.01.

$= 48$ Multiply.

$\frac{1}{4}$ of 48 is 12. About 12 students have traveled overseas.

Step 2 Determine one third of 12.

One third of 12 is $\frac{1}{3} \cdot 12$ or 4.

So, about 4 students have traveled to Italy.

Got It? Do this problem to find out.

e. Financial Literacy A county receives $\frac{3}{4}$% of a state sales tax. A city in that county receives half of that amount. About how much money would the county receive from the sale of a computer that costs $1,020?

e. ____________

Example

Tutor

5. This year, 639 students attended a summer camp. Of those who attended this year, 0.5% also attended summer camp last year. About how many students attended the summer camp two years in a row?

0.5% is half of 1%.

$1\% \text{ of } 639 = 0.01 \cdot 639$

≈ 6

So, 0.5% of 639 is about $\frac{1}{2}$ of 6 or 3.

About 3 students attended summer camp two years in a row.

Guided Practice

Estimate. (Examples 1–4)

1. 52% of 10 ≈ ______

2. 79% of 489 ≈ ______

3. 151% of 70 ≈ ______

4. $\frac{1}{2}$% of 82 ≈ ______

5. Of the 78 teenagers at a youth camp, 63% have birthdays in the spring. About how many teenagers have birthdays in the spring? (Example 2)

______

6. About 0.8% of the land in Maine is federally owned. If Maine has 19,847,680 acres, about how many acres are *not* federally owned? (Example 5) ______

7. **Building on the Essential Question** How can you estimate the percent of a number? ______

Rate Yourself!

How confident are you about estimating percents? Shade the ring on the target.

Check

Find out online. Use the Self-Check Quiz.

Name _______________ My Homework _______________

Independent Practice

7.4(D), 7.1(B), 7.1(F), 7.1(G) TEKS

Estimate. (Examples 1–4)

1. 47% of 70 ≈ ______

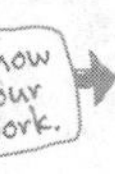

2. 39% of 120 ≈ ______

3. 21% of 90 ≈ ______

4. 65% of 152 ≈ ______

5. 72% of 238 ≈ ______

6. 132% of 54 ≈ ______

7. 224% of 320 ≈ ______

8. $\frac{3}{4}$% of 168 ≈ ______

9. 0.4% of 510 ≈ ______

10. **Financial Literacy** Carlie spent $42 at the salon. Her mother loaned her the money. Carlie will pay her mother 15% of $42 each week until the loan is repaid. About how many weeks will it take Carlie to repay her mother? (Example 2) ______

11. The United States has 12,383 miles of coastline. If 0.8% of the coastline is located in Georgia, about how many miles of coastline are in Georgia? (Example 5) ______

12. MP **Use a Problem-Solving Model** Use the graph shown.

a. About how many more hours does Avery spend sleeping than doing the activities in the "other" category? Justify your answer.

______

b. What is the approximate number of minutes Avery spends each day on extracurricular activities?

______

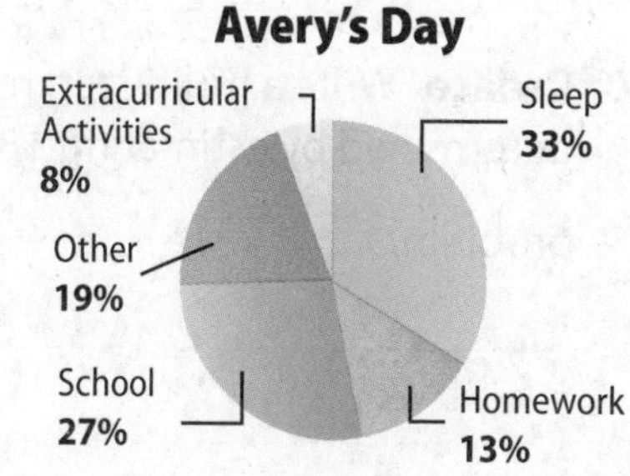

Estimate.

13. 67% of 8.7 ≈ ______

14. 54% of 76.8 ≈ ______

15. 10.5% of 238 ≈ ______

16. The average white rhinoceros gives birth to a single calf that weighs about 3.8% as much as its mother. If the mother rhinoceros weighs 3.75 tons, about how many pounds does its calf weigh? ______

17. The students at Monroe Junior High sponsored a canned food drive. The seventh-grade class collected 129% of its canned food goal. Their goal was to collect 200 cans.

a. About how many more cans did the seventh-graders collect than their goal? ______

b. The eighth-graders collected 50% *more* than the seventh-graders. About how many cans did the eighth-graders collect? ______

H.O.T. Problems Higher-Order Thinking

18. Evaluate Explain how you could determine $\frac{3}{8}$% of \$800.

19. Analyze Is an estimate for the percent of a number always, sometimes, or never greater than the actual percent of the number? Give an example or a counterexample to support your answer.

20. Create Write a multi-step real-world problem in which the answer can be determined by estimating 18% of 30. Then explain how you would solve the problem. ______

Name ______________________________

Multi-Step Problem Solving

21. The students at Elgin Middle School voted on a new mascot. The principal found that 19% of each grade chose a tiger for a new mascot. About how many more 7th graders voted for a tiger than 8th graders? P N MP

Grade	Number of Students
6	149
7	168
8	123

Ⓐ 4 students

Ⓑ 10 students

Ⓒ 34 students

Ⓓ 44 students

Use a problem-solving model to solve this problem.

1 Analyze

Read the problem. Circle the information you know.
Underline what the problem is asking you to find.

2 Plan

What will you need to do to solve the problem? Write your plan in steps.

Step 1 Estimate ________ of 170 and 120.

Step 2 ________ to determine the difference.

3 Solve

Use your plan to solve the problem. Show your steps.

Estimate of 7th graders.

19% of $168 \approx 0.2 \times 170$

$\approx$ ______

Estimate of 8th graders.

19% of $123 \approx 0.2 \times 120$

$\approx$ ______

______ − ______ = ______ Subtract.

About ______ more 7th graders voted for a tiger than 8th graders.

So, the correct answer is ______. Fill in that answer choice.

Read to Succeed!
You can also estimate using an equivalent fraction to determine the number of students.

4 Justify and Evaluate

How do you know your solution is accurate?

____

____

____

P = Proportionality N = Number and Operations MP = Mathematical Processes

More Multi-Step Problem Solving

Use a problem-solving model to solve each problem.

22. Elena works on a farm that has three types of animals. There are a total of 47 animals. About how many more cows are there than chickens? N P MD MP

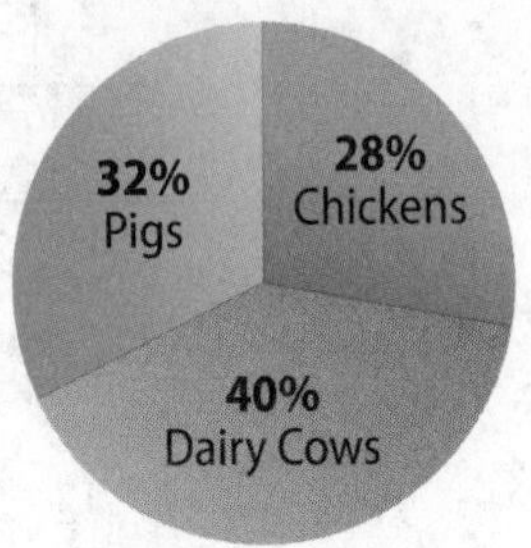

Ⓐ 2 cows
Ⓑ 5 cows
Ⓒ 12 cows
Ⓓ 564 cows

23. Brad borrowed money from his sister to buy a new video game that costs $62. He has paid back 78% of the cost of the game. About how much money does he still owe his sister, in dollars? N P FL MP

24. Dana buys the camping supplies shown below. About how many dollars does she spend if sales tax is 6%? N P FL MP

Item	Cost ($)
Sleeping bag	29
Tent	52
Flashlight	18

25. The table shows the number of shots taken and the percent made by the top female basketball players. Estimate who made the most shots and about how many more shots were made than the next best player.

Player	Shots Taken	Percent Made
Rosa	301	43
Domenica	384	52
Melinda	501	50

N = Number and Operations  = Proportionality 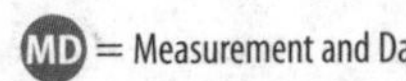 = Measurement and Data  = Personal Financial Literacy 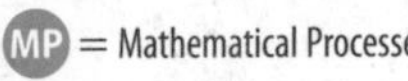 = Mathematical Processes

Hands-On Lab 3-a

Find Percents

INQUIRY **HOW can I select tools and techniques to solve real-world problems about percents?**

The eighth grade had 300 tickets to sell to the school play and the seventh grade had 250 tickets to sell. One hour before the show, the eighth grade had sold 225 tickets and the seventh grade had sold 200 tickets. Complete the investigation below to determine which grade sold the greater percent of tickets.

Texas Essential Knowledge and Skills TEKS

Targeted TEKS

7.4(D) Solve problems involving ratios, rates, and percents, including multi-step problems involving percent increase and percent decrease, and financial literacy problems.

Mathematical Processes

7.1(C), 7.1(D), 7.1(E)

Hands-On Activity

Step 1 The bar diagrams below show 100% for each grade. Label the total tickets to be sold above each bar. Divide each bar into 10 equal sections. So, each section will represent 10%.

☐ tickets

eighth grade ☐ 100%

☐ tickets

seventh grade ☐ 100%

Step 2 Determine the number that belongs in each section for both of the bars. Then write that number in the sections.

Eighth grade: $300 \div 10 =$ ☐

Seventh grade: $250 \div 10 =$ ☐

Step 3 Determine the number of sections to shade for each bar. Then shade the sections.

Eighth grade: $225 \div 30 =$ ☐

Seventh grade: $200 \div 25 =$ ☐

The eighth grade sold ☐ % of their tickets. The seventh grade sold ☐ % of their tickets.

The ________ grade sold the greater percent of their tickets.

Work with a partner. Show your work using bar diagrams.

1. **Select Tools and Techniques** Vanlue Middle School has 600 students and Memorial Middle School has 450 students. Vanlue has 270 girls and Memorial has 225 girls. Which school has the greater percent of girls? Explain.

Vanlue: ☐ students — 100%

Memorial: ☐ students — 100%

Create

On Your Own

Work with a partner to answer the following question.

2. **Apply Math to the Real World** Seventy-five students were in the audience for a 3-D screening of a movie. Fifty students were in the audience for a 2-D screening of the same movie. Describe a situation in which the percent of students who went to the 2-D screening is greater than the percent of students who went to the 3-D screening.

3. **INQUIRY** HOW can I select tools and techniques to solve real-world problems about percents?

Lesson 3

The Percent Proportion

Launch the Lesson: Real World

The tires on a monster truck weigh approximately 2 tons. The entire truck weighs about 6 tons. About what percent of the monster truck's weight is the tires?

1. Write the ratio of tire weight to total weight as a fraction.

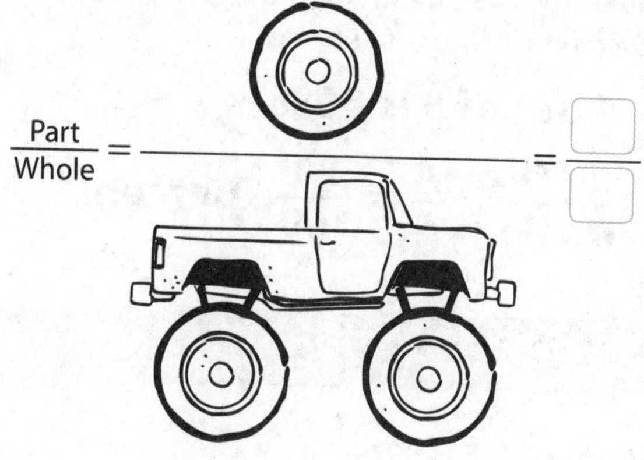

2. Draw a model to represent the fraction.

3. Express the fraction as a decimal to the nearest hundredth.

4. About what percent of the monster truck's weight is the tires?

Which MP Mathematical Processes did you use? Shade the circle(s) that applies.

Ⓐ Apply Math to the Real World.
Ⓑ Use a Problem-Solving Model.
Ⓒ Select Tools and Techniques.
Ⓓ Use Multiple Representations.
Ⓔ Organize Ideas.
Ⓕ Analyze Relationships.
Ⓖ Justify Arguments.

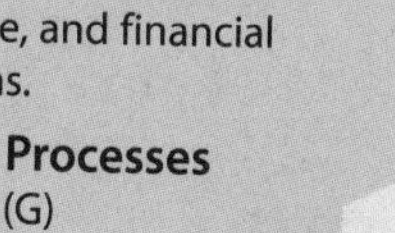

Texas Essential Knowledge and Skills

Targeted TEKS

7.4(D) Solve problems involving ratios, rates, and percents, including multi-step problems involving percent increase and percent decrease, and financial literacy problems.

Mathematical Processes

7.1(A), 7.1(B), 7.1(G)

Vocabulary

percent proportion

Essential Question

HOW can percent help you understand situations involving money?

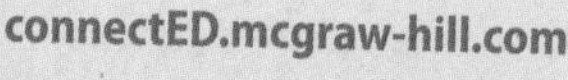

Key Concept

Use the Percent Proportion

Type	Example	Proportion
Determine the Percent	What percent of 5 is 4?	$\frac{4}{5} = \frac{n}{100}$
Determine the Part	What number is 80% of 5?	$\frac{p}{5} = \frac{80}{100}$
Determine the Whole	4 is 80% of what number?	$\frac{4}{w} = \frac{80}{100}$

Work Zone

In a **percent proportion**, one ratio or fraction compares part of a quantity to the whole quantity. The other ratio is the equivalent percent written as a fraction with a denominator of 100.

4 out of 5 is 80%

$$\frac{\text{part}}{\text{whole}} \quad \frac{4}{5} = \frac{80}{100} \Big\} \text{ percent}$$

Watch Tutor

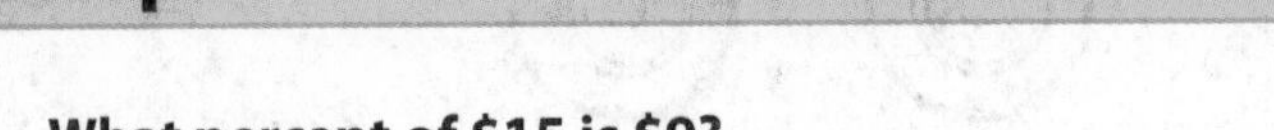

Example

The Percent Proportion
The word *of* is usually followed by the whole.

1. What percent of \$15 is \$9?

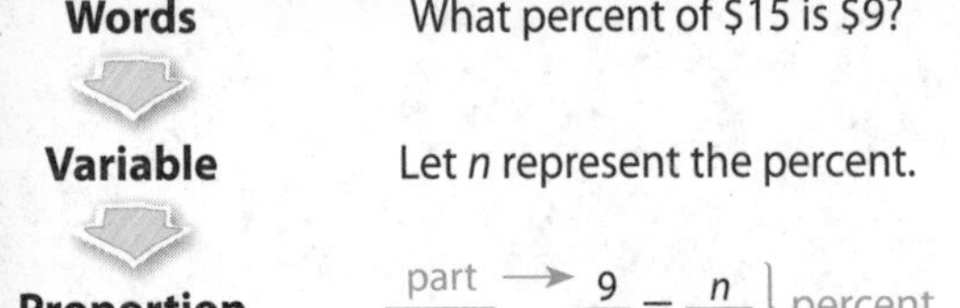

Words What percent of \$15 is \$9?

Variable Let n represent the percent.

Proportion $\frac{\text{part}}{\text{whole}} \rightarrow \frac{9}{15} = \frac{n}{100} \Big\}$ percent

$\frac{9}{15} = \frac{n}{100}$ Write the proportion.

$9 \cdot 100 = 15 \cdot n$ Determine the cross products.

$900 = 15n$ Simplify.

$\frac{900}{15} = \frac{15n}{15}$ Divide each side by 15.

$60 = n$

So, \$9 is 60% of \$15.

You can use a bar diagram to check your answer.

3	6	9	12	15
20%	40%	60%	80%	100%

0%

Show your work.

a. ______________

b. ______________

Got It? Do these problems to find out.

a. What percent of 25 is 20? **b.** \$12.75 is what percent of \$50?

Examples

Tutor

2. What number is 40% of 120?

Words What number is 40% of 120?

Variable Let p represent the part.

Proportion $\frac{\text{part} \rightarrow p}{\text{whole} \rightarrow 120} = \frac{40}{100}$ } percent

$\frac{p}{120} = \frac{40}{100}$ Write the proportion.

$p \cdot 100 = 120 \cdot 40$ Determine the cross products.

$100p = 4,800$ Simplify.

$\frac{100p}{100} = \frac{4,800}{100}$ Divide each side by 100.

$p = 48$

So, 48 is 40% of 120.

Use a bar diagram to check your answer.

24	48	72	96	120

0% 20% 40% 60% 80% 100%

3. 18 is 25% of what number?

Words 18 is 25% of what number?

Variable Let w represent the whole.

Proportion $\frac{\text{part} \rightarrow 18}{\text{whole} \rightarrow w} = \frac{25}{100}$ } percent

$\frac{18}{w} = \frac{25}{100}$ Write the proportion.

$18 \cdot 100 = w \cdot 25$ Determine the cross products.

$1,800 = 25w$ Simplify.

$\frac{1,800}{25} = \frac{25w}{25}$ Divide each side by 25.

$72 = w$

So, 18 is 25% of 72.

Use a bar diagram to check your answer.

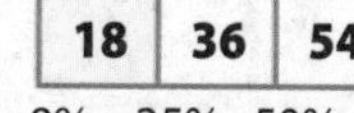

18	36	54	72

0% 25% 50% 75% 100%

Got It? Do these problems to find out.

c. What number is 5% of 60?

d. 12% of 85 is what number?

e. 40% of what number is 26?

f. 84 is 75% of what number?

STOP and Reflect

In the proportion $\frac{3}{20} = \frac{15}{100}$, identify the part, whole, and percent.

part = ______

whole = ______

percent = ______

Show your work.

c. ______

d. ______

e. ______

f. ______

Multi-Step Example

4. The average adult male Western Lowland gorilla eats about 33.5 pounds of fruit each day. How much food does the average adult male gorilla eat each day that is *not* fruit?

Western Lowland Gorilla's Diet	
Food	**Percent**
Fruit	67%
Seeds, leaves, stems, and pith	17%
Insects/ insect larvae	16%

Step 1 You know that 33.5 pounds is the part. You need to determine the whole.

$$\frac{33.5}{w} = \frac{67}{100}$$ Write the proportion.

$$33.5 \cdot 100 = w \cdot 67$$ Determine the cross products.

$$3{,}350 = 67w$$ Simplify.

$$\frac{3{,}350}{67} = \frac{67w}{67}$$ Divide each side by 67.

$$50 = w$$

Step 2 Subtract to determine the food that is *not* fruit.

$$50 - 33.5 = 16.5$$

The average adult male gorilla eats 16.5 pounds of food that is *not* fruit each day.

Guided Practice

Determine each number. Round to the nearest tenth if necessary. (Examples 1–3)

1. What percent of $90 is $9? ______

2. What number is 2% of 35? ______

3. 62 is 90.5% of what number? ______

4. Brand A cereal contains 10 cups of cereal per box. How many cups of cereal are in Brand B cereal? (Example 4)

______

5. Building on the Essential Question How can you use the percent proportion to solve real-world problems?

Rate Yourself!

How confident are you about using the percent proportion? Shade the ring on the target.

Find out online. Use the Self-Check Quiz.

FOLDABLES Time to update your Foldable!

Name ______________________ My Homework ______________________

Independent Practice

7.4(D), 7.1(A), 7.1(B), 7.1(G) TEKS

Determine each number. Round to the nearest tenth if necessary. (Examples 1–3)

1. What percent of 60 is 15? ________

2. What number is 15% of 60? ________

3. 9 is 12% of which number? ________

4. 12% of 72 is what number? ________

5. What percent of 50 is 18? ________

6. 12 is 90% of what number? ________

7. A pair of sneakers is on sale as shown. This is 75% of the original price. How much less than the original price is the sale price? (Example 4)

____

8. Of the 60 books on a bookshelf, 24 are nonfiction.

What percent of the books are *not* nonfiction? (Example 4) ________

Determine each number. Round to the nearest hundredth if necessary.

9. 40 is 50% of what number? ________

10. 12.5% of what number is 24? ________

11. What percent of 300 is 0.6? ________

12. What number is 0.5% of 8? ________

Determine each number. Round to the nearest hundredth if necessary.

Planet	Radius (km)
Mercury	r
Mars	$r + 957$
Jupiter	$29.3r$

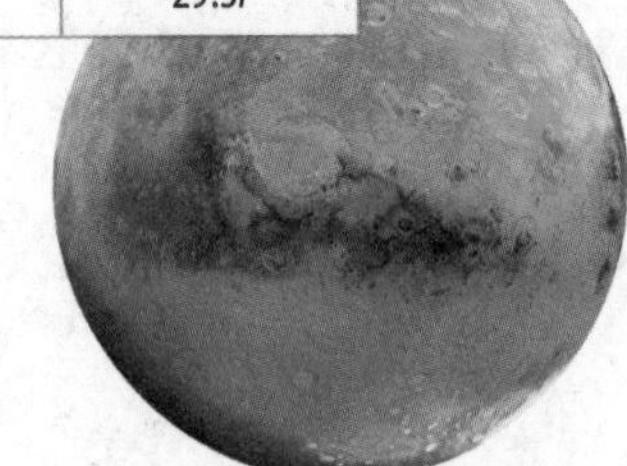

13. **STEM** Use the table. Mercury's radius is 2,440 kilometers.

   a. Mercury's radius is what percent of Jupiter's radius?

   b. If the radius of Mars is about 13.7% of Neptune's radius, what is the radius of Neptune?

   c. Earth's radius is about 261.4% of Mercury's radius. What is the radius of Earth?

H.O.T. Problems Higher-Order Thinking

14. **Analyze** Seventy percent of the 100 students in a middle school cafeteria bought their lunch. Some of the students that bought their lunch leave the cafeteria to attend an assembly. Now only 60% of the remaining students bought their lunch. How many students are remaining in the cafeteria?

   Explain.

15. **Analyze** Without calculating, arrange the following from greatest to least value. Justify your reasoning.

   20% of 100, 20% of 500, 5% of 100

16. **Create** Write a real-world problem involving a percent that can be solved by using the proportion $\frac{3}{b} = \frac{60}{100}$. Then solve the proportion.

Name ______________________________

Multi-Step Problem Solving

17. The recommended caloric intake for boys ages 9–13 is 1,800 Calories per day. The table shows what percent of the Calories should be divided into different nutrients. How many daily Calories should *not* come from protein? P N MP

Nutrient	Percent of Daily Calories
Carbohydrates	45
Fat	20
Protein	35

Ⓐ 810
Ⓑ 990
Ⓒ 1,170
Ⓓ 1,440

Use a problem-solving model to solve this problem.

1 Analyze

Read the problem. Circle the information you know. Underline what the problem is asking you to find.

2 Plan

What will you need to do to solve the problem? Write your plan in steps.

Step 1 Determine the percent of daily Calories that do *not come from* ____________.

Step 2 Write a ____________ to determine the number of Calories.

3 Solve

Use your plan to solve the problem. Show your steps.

$100\% - 35\% =$ ______ Subtract.

$\frac{p}{1,800} = \frac{\quad}{100}$ Write the proportion.

$p =$ ______

The daily Calories that should *not* come from protein is ______.

So, the correct answer is ___. Fill in that answer choice.

Read to Succeed!
You can add the percent of daily Calories that come from Carbohydrates and fat to determine the percent that does not come from protein.

4 Justify and Evaluate

How do you know your solution is accurate?

____

____

____

N = Number and Operations P = Proportionality MP = Mathematical Processes

More Multi-Step Problem Solving

Use a problem-solving model to solve each problem.

18. Carlos is saving up to buy two new books. He has saved 60% of the cost of one book that costs $18, and 30% of the cost of another book that costs $21. How much more does he need to save? P N MP

Ⓐ $17.10
Ⓑ $18.20
Ⓒ $21.30
Ⓓ $21.90

19. Hasina entered a raffle 5 times and there are 125 entries. She decided to buy 15 more raffle tickets. By what percent does her chance of winning increase? Round to the nearest percent. P N MP

20. Rudy took a test and earned a 92%. Camilo earned an 88% on the same test. If Rudy answered 46 questions correctly, how many more questions did he answer correctly than Camilo? P N MP

21. Alma bought a rocking chair for $266. She used a coupon to save some money. If she paid $226.10 for the chair, what percent discount did Alma get on the chair? P N MP

N = Number and Operations P = Proportionality MP = Mathematical Processes

Lesson 4

The Percent Equation

Launch the Lesson: Vocabulary

You have used a percent proportion to determine the missing part (p), percent (n), or whole (w). You can also use a **percent equation**.

Label the diagram that shows the relationship between the percent proportion and the percent equation with the terms *part, whole,* and *percent*. Use each term once.

$\frac{\text{part}}{\text{whole}} =$ ________ Write the percent proportion.

$\frac{\text{part}}{\text{whole}} \cdot \text{whole} = \text{percent} \cdot$ ________ Multiply each side by the whole.

________ $=$ percent $\cdot$ whole Divide out common factors to obtain the percent equation.

The percent equation is ____________________.

Texas Essential Knowledge and Skills

Targeted TEKS

7.4(D) Solve problems involving ratios, rates, and percents, including multi-step problems involving percent increase and percent decrease, and financial literacy problems.

Mathematical Processes

7.1(A), 7.1(B)

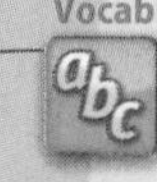

Vocabulary

percent equation

Essential Question

HOW can percent help you understand situations involving money?

Real-World Investigation

A survey found that 16% of all seventh-graders at Lincoln Middle school think that tarantulas are the scariest creatures. There are 150 seventh-graders at the school. How would you write a percent equation to determine how many seventh-graders said that tarantulas are the scariest creatures? Explain how you determined the equation.

BOO!

Ⓐ Apply Math to the Real World.
Ⓑ Use a Problem-Solving Model.
Ⓒ Select Tools and Techniques.
Ⓓ Use Multiple Representations.
Ⓔ Organize Ideas.
Ⓕ Analyze Relationships.
Ⓖ Justify Arguments.

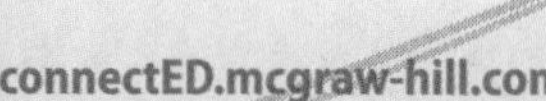

Key Concept

Use the Percent Equation

Type	Example	Equation
Determine the Percent	3 is what percent of 6?	$3 = n \cdot 6$
Determine the Part	What number is 50% of 6?	$p = 0.5 \cdot 6$
Determine the Whole	3 is 50% of what number?	$3 = 0.5 \cdot w$

Work Zone

You can use the percent equation to solve problems that involve percent.

3 is 50% of 6

$$\underbrace{3}_{\text{part}} = \underbrace{0.5}_{\text{percent}} \times \underbrace{6}_{\text{whole}}$$

Note that the percent is written as a decimal.

Tutor

Example

Percent Equation
A percent must always be converted to a decimal or a fraction when it is used in an equation.

1. What number is 12% of 150?

Do you need to determine the percent, part, or whole? ______

Estimate $0.10 \cdot 150 = 15$

part = percent · whole

$p = 0.12 \cdot 150$ — Write the percent equation. 12% = 0.12

$p = 18$ — Multiply.

So, 18 is 12% of 150.

18 is close to the estimate of 15. So, the answer is reasonable. You can also check your answer using the percent proportion.

Check $\frac{18}{150} \stackrel{?}{=} \frac{12}{100}$

$18 \cdot 100 \stackrel{?}{=} 150 \cdot 12$

$1{,}800 = 1{,}800$ ✓

a. ______

b. ______

c. ______

d. ______

Got It? Do these problems to find out.

Write an equation for each problem. Then solve.

a. What is 6% of 200?

b. Determine 72% of 50.

c. What is 14% of 150?

d. Determine 50% of 70.

Example

Tutor 

2. **21 is what percent of 40?**

Do you need to determine the percent, part, or whole? ______

Estimate $\frac{21}{40} \approx \frac{1}{2}$ or 50%

part = percent · whole

$21 = n \cdot 40$ Write the percent equation.

$\frac{21}{40} = \frac{40n}{40}$ Divide each side by 40.

$0.525 = n$ Simplify.

So, 21 is 52.5% of 40.

Check 52.5% ≈ 50% ✓

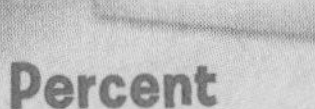

Percent

Remember to write the decimal as a percent in your final answer.

Got It? Do these problems to find out.

Write an equation for each problem. Then solve. Round to the nearest tenth if necessary.

e. What percent of 40 is 9?

f. 27 is what percent of 150?

e. ______

f. ______

Example

Tutor

3. **13 is 26% of what number?**

Do you need to determine the percent, part, or whole? ______

Estimate $26\% \approx \frac{1}{4}$, $13 \approx 12$, and $\frac{1}{4}$ of $48 = 12$

part = percent · whole

$13 = 0.26 \cdot w$ Write the percent equation. 26% = 0.26

$\frac{13}{0.26} = \frac{0.26w}{0.26}$ Divide each side by 0.26.

$50 = w$ Simplify.

So, 13 is 26% of 50.

Check 50 ≈ 48. ✓

Got It? Do these problems to find out.

Write an equation for each problem. Then solve. Round to the nearest tenth if necessary.

g. 39 is 84% of what number?

h. 26% of what number is 45?

g. ______

h. ______

Multi-Step Example

4. **A survey found that 25% of people aged 18–24 gave up their home phone and only use a cell phone. Of the people who only use a cell phone, 35% of them use their cell phone to browse the Internet. If 1,141 people only use a cell phone to browse the Internet, how many people were surveyed?**

Step 1 Determine how many people only use a cell phone.

$1{,}141 = 0.35 \cdot w$ Write the percent equation. 35% = 0.35

$\frac{1{,}141}{0.35} = \frac{0.35w}{0.35}$ Divide each side by 0.35. Use a calculator.

$3{,}260 = w$ Simplify.

Step 2 Determine how many people were surveyed.

$3{,}260 = 0.25 \cdot w$ Write the percent equation. 25% = 0.25

$\frac{3{,}260}{0.25} = \frac{0.25w}{0.25}$ Divide.

$13{,}040 = w$ Simplify.

About 13,040 people were surveyed.

Guided Practice

Write an equation for each problem. Then solve. Round to the nearest tenth if necessary. (Examples 1–3)

1. What number is 88% of 300? ______

2. 24 is what percent of 120? ______

3. 3 is 12% of what number? ______

4. A local bakery sold 60 loaves of bread in one day. If 65% of these were sold in the afternoon, how many loaves were *not* sold in the afternoon? (Example 4) ______

5. **Building on the Essential Question** When might it be easier to use the percent equation rather than the percent proportion? ______

Rate Yourself!

Are you ready to move on? Shade the section that applies.

YES ? NO

Find out online. Use the Self-Check Quiz. Check

FOLDABLES Time to update your Foldable!

Name ______________________ My Homework ______________________

Independent Practice

7.4(D), 7.1(B), 7.1(F) TEKS

Write an equation for each problem. Then solve. Round to the nearest tenth if necessary. (Examples 1–3)

1. 75 is what percent of 150? ________

2. 84 is 60% of what number? ________

3. What number is 65% of 98? ________

4. Determine 39% of 65. ________

5. Determine 24% of 25. ________

6. What number is 53% of 470? ________

7. Ruben bought 6 new books for his collection. This increased his collection by 12%. How many books does he have now? (Example 4)

____

8. A store sold 550 video games during the month of December. If this made up 12.5% of its yearly video game sales, about how many video games did the store sell all year? (Example 4)

____

9. **MP Use a Problem-Solving Model** About 142 million people in the United States watch online videos. Use the graph that shows what types of videos they watch.

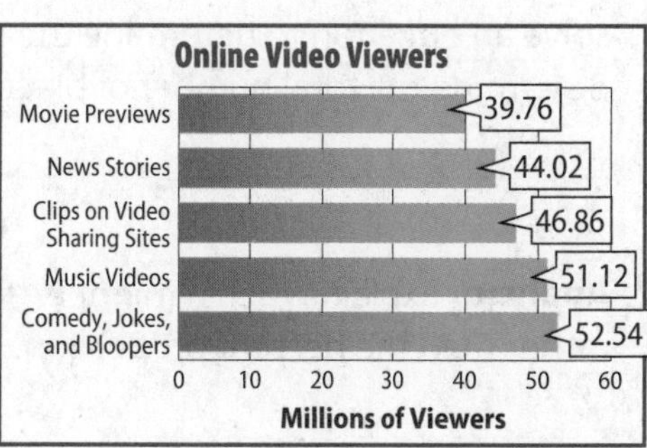

a. About what percent of viewers do *not* watch comedy, jokes, and bloopers? ________

b. About what percent more watch clips on video sharing sites than news stories?

____

Write an equation for each problem. Then solve. Round to the nearest tenth if necessary.

10. Determine 135% of 64. ______

11. What number is 0.4% of 82.1? ______

12. 450 is 75.2% of what number? ______

13. What percent of 200 is 230? ______

H.O.T. Problems Higher-Order Thinking

14. **Create** Write a percent problem for which the percent is greater than 100 and the part is known. Use the percent equation to solve your problem to determine the whole.

______

15. **Evaluate** If you need to determine the percent of a number, explain how you can predict whether the part will be *less than*, *greater than*, or *equal* to the number.

______

16. **Create** A museum has 50 pieces of art to display in an exhibit. Of these, 11 are photos and 39 are color paintings. The manager wants to add more photos so they represent 25% of the pieces of art at the museum. Write and solve an equation to determine the number of photos to be added. Then determine the total number of pieces of art in the exhibit.

______

17. **Analyze** Explain when it might be more efficient to use the percent equation rather than the percent proportion.

______

Name ______________________________

Multi-Step Problem Solving

18. Three friends work on a sales team. The table shows their sales for the month of January. What percent of the team's total sales was sold by Inali and Nigel? Express your answer as a decimal. N P MP

Employee	January Sales ($)
Inali	28,000
Nigel	32,000
Sydney	20,000

Use a problem-solving model to solve this problem.

1 Analyze

Read the problem. Circle the information you know. Underline what the problem is asking you to find.

2 Plan

What will you need to do to solve the problem? Write your plan in steps.

Step 1 Determine the __________ and sales from Inali and Nigel.

Step 2 Determine the __________ of the total sales was from Inali and Nigel.

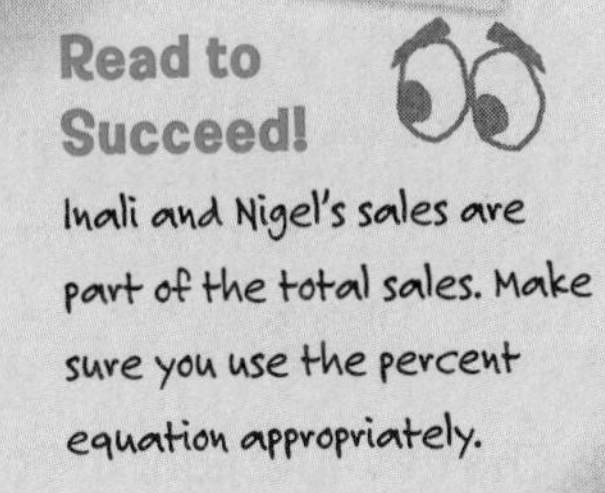

3 Solve

Use your plan to solve the problem. Show your steps.

Total sales: 28,000 + 32,000 + 20,000 = __________ Add.

Inali and Nigel: 28,000 + 32,000 = __________ Add.

Use the percent equation to determine the percent.

__________ $= n \cdot$ __________

$n =$ __________

Inali and Nigel sold __________ of the team's total sales. Complete the grid.

					.		
⊕	0	0	0	0		0	0
⊖	1	1	1	1		1	1
	2	2	2	2		2	2
	3	3	3	3		3	3
	4	4	4	4		4	4
	5	5	5	5		5	5
	6	6	6	6		6	6
	7	7	7	7		7	7
	8	8	8	8		8	8
	9	9	9	9		9	9

4 Justify and Evaluate

How do you know your solution is accurate?

____

____

____

N = Number and Operations P = Proportionality MP = Mathematical Processes

More Multi-Step Problem Solving

Use a problem-solving model to solve each problem.

19. The table shows the distribution of entries for a science fair. The middle school consists of grades 6 through 8, and the high school consists of grades 9 through 12. What percent more of science projects are completed by middle school students than high school students? Express your answer as a decimal. N P MP

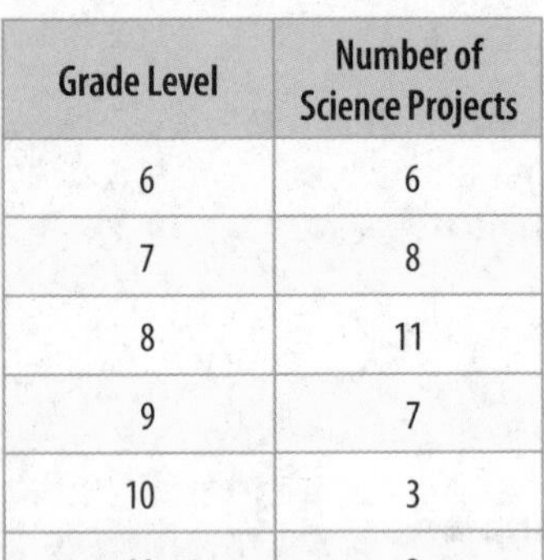

Grade Level	Number of Science Projects
6	6
7	8
8	11
9	7
10	3
11	3
12	2

20. The circle graph shows the types of movies Abul watched last year. If he saw a total of 40 movies, how many more independent movies did he see than drama and action movies combined? N P MD MP

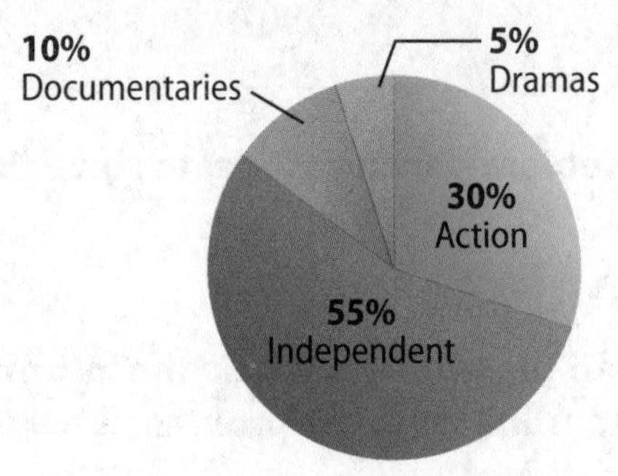

21. The low-fuel light in Sophia's car comes on when her fuel tank is 10% full. If she has used 18.2 gallons when the light comes on, how many gallons does her fuel tank hold? Round to the nearest tenth. N P MP

22. An art dealer sells art for two galleries. He makes 25% commission on sales at Gallery A and 35% commission on sales at Gallery B. Will the higher commission rate always result in a higher monthly commission income? Justify your reasoning. N P MP

N = Number and Operations  P = Proportionality 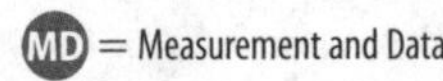 MD = Measurement and Data 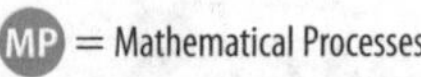 MP = Mathematical Processes

Focus on Mathematical Processes

Determine Reasonable Answers

Vacations

Wesley's family spent $1,400 on a trip to the Grand Canyon. They spent 35% of the total on a helicopter flight. Wesley estimates that his family spent about $450 on the flight.

Determine whether Wesley's estimate is reasonable.

Mathematical Process
7.1(B) Use a problem-solving model that incorporates analyzing given information, formulating a plan or strategy, determining a solution, justifying the solution, and evaluating the problem-solving process and the reasonableness of the solution.

Targeted TEKS 7.4(D)

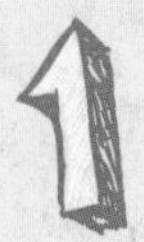

1 Analyze *What are the facts?*

- Wesley's family spent $1,400 on vacation and 35% of that was spent on a helicopter flight.
- Wesley estimates that 35% is about $450.

2 Plan *Choose a problem-solving strategy.*

I will use the ________________ strategy.

3 Solve *How can you apply the strategy?*

Fill in each section of the diagram with 10% of $1,400.

|—— $1,400 ——|

|—— 35% ——|

35% equals three and a half sections of the bar diagram.

Add three and a half sections to get a total of ☐.

Since $450 is close to ☐, his estimate was reasonable.

4 Justify and Evaluate *How do you know your solution is reasonable?*

____

____

____

Don't forget the tip!

At a local Italian restaurant, Brett's bill was $17.50. He decides to leave an 18% tip for the server.

Is $3.50 a reasonable tip?

Analyze

Read the problem. Circle the information you know.
Underline what the problem is asking you to find.

Plan

Choose a problem-solving strategy.

I will use the ______________________ strategy.

Solve

How can you apply the strategy?

Justify and Evaluate

How do you know your solution is reasonable?

____

____

____

Multi-Step Problem Solving

Work with a small group to solve the following problems. Show your work on a separate piece of paper.

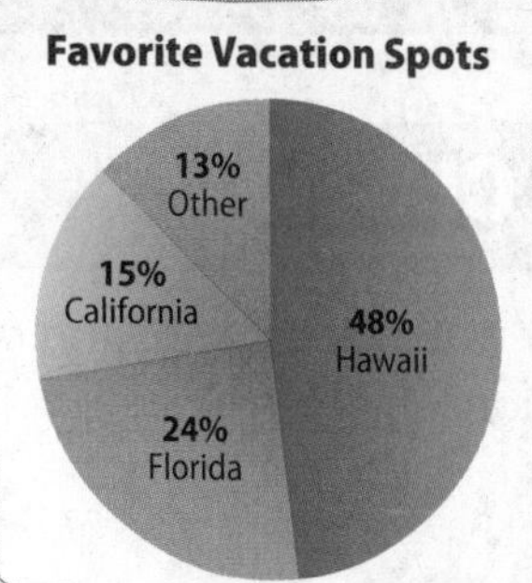

1. Travel

A travel agency surveyed 140 families about their favorite vacation spots.

Is it reasonable to say that 24 more families chose Hawaii over Florida? Explain.

2. Exercise

A survey showed that 61% of middle school students do some kind of physical activity every day. Of those students, 9% play on the football team.

Suppose there are 828 middle school students in your school. About how many students play on the football team?

3. Clubs

Of the 36 students in the environmental club, 15 are boys and 21 are girls. The president of the club wants to add more boys so that the boys represent 50% of the students in the club.

Write and solve an equation to determine the number of boys to be added. Then determine the total number of students in the club.

4. Bowling

In bowling, you get a spare when you knock down the ten pins in a total of two throws.

How many possible ways are there to get a spare?

Vocab

Vocabulary Check

1. Write a few sentences to compare and contrast the percent equation and the percent proportion. TEKS 7.4(D), 7.1(D)

Key Concept Check

2. Complete the graphic organizer by providing a real-world example of each scenario. TEKS 7.4(D), 7.1(E)

Determine the Part	Determine the Whole	Determine the Percent

3. MP **Select Tools and Techniques** A computer costs \$849.75 and the hard drive is 61.3% of the total cost. What is a reasonable estimate for the cost of the hard drive? TEKS 7.4(D), 7.1(C)

Multi-Step Problem Solving

4. Ayana has 220 coins in her piggy bank. Of those, 45% are pennies. There are one ninth as many dimes as pennies. Of the remaining coins, 30% are quarters. The rest are nickels. What is the total value of the coins in her piggy bank? N P MP

   Ⓐ \$14.19　　Ⓒ \$22.80
   Ⓑ \$15.75　　Ⓓ \$27.95

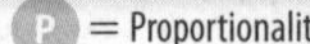

N = Number and Operations　P = Proportionality　MP = Mathematical Processes

Hands-On Lab 5-a

Model Percent of Change

INQUIRY HOW can you use multiple representations to model a percent of change?

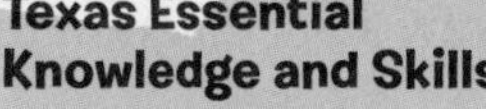

Texas Essential Knowledge and Skills

Targeted TEKS

7.4(D) Solve problems involving ratios, rates, and percents, including multi-step problems involving percent increase and percent decrease, and financial literacy problems.

Mathematical Processes

7.1(C), 7.1(D), 7.1(E), 7.1(G)

The admission price for the state fair has increased by 50% in the last five years. The admission price was $6 five years ago. What is the current admission price? Do the activity below to find out.

Hands-On Activity

Use a bar diagram.

Step 1 The bar diagram represents 100%.

price 5 years ago = $6	100%

Since 50% = $\frac{1}{2}$, divide the bar diagram in half. Fill in the missing information.

price 5 years ago = ☐

$3		100%

Step 2 The admission price increased by 50%. Complete the bar diagram that represents 150% of the price 5 years ago.

price 5 years ago = ☐ — increase

$3			150%

current price = ☐

So, the current admission price is ☐ + ☐ or ☐.

Investigate

Work with a partner to solve the following problems.

1. The height of a tree was 8 feet. After a year, the tree's height increased by 25%.

   Draw a bar diagram to determine the new height of the tree? ______

2. MP **Apply Math to the Real World** The model below describes the following scenario: Ryan put $160 in a bank account. After 2 months, the total in his account decreased by 25%. Fill in the amount in Ryan's account after 2 months.

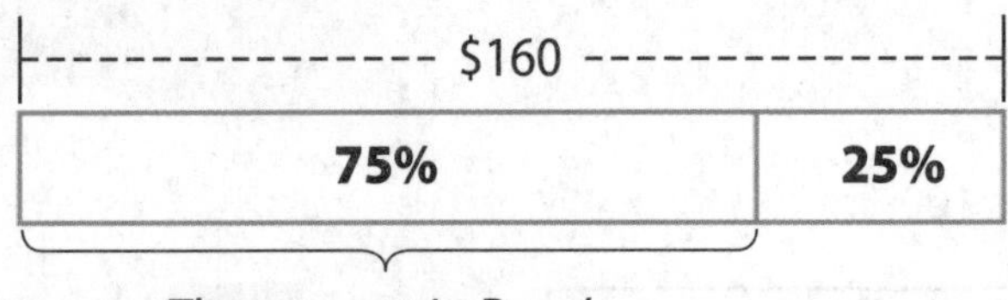

The amount in Ryan's account after 2 months is ☐.

Analyze and Reflect

Work with a partner to answer the following question.

3. MP **Organize Ideas** Refer to Exercise 1. How can you determine the new amount of a quantity that has increased over a period of time?

______

______

______

Create

4. Write two different ways you can determine 125% of 8.

______

______

5. **INQUIRY** HOW can you use multiple representations to model a percent of change?

______

______

Lesson 5

Percent of Change

Launch the Lesson: Real World

Watch

The Indy 500 is one of the world's great motor races. The table shows the average speed of the winning race cars for various years. Determine the amounts of increase for the speed from 1922 to 1955 and from 1955 to 2010.

Year	Speed (mph)
1922	94
1955	128
2010	162

1. Determine the speed increase from 1922 to 1955. Then determine the speed increase from 1955 to 2010. What do you notice?

   ____

2. Compare the speed increase from 1922 to 1955 to the original speed in 1922. Express the ratio as a percent rounded to the nearest whole percent. ________

3. Compare the speed increase from 1955 to 2010 to the original speed in 1955. Express the ratio as a percent rounded to the nearest whole percent. ________

4. Why are the amounts of increase the same but the percents different? ______________________________

Which MP Mathematical Processes did you use? Shade the circle(s) that applies.

Ⓐ Apply Math to the Real World.
Ⓑ Use a Problem-Solving Model.
Ⓒ Select Tools and Techniques.
Ⓓ Use Multiple Representations.
Ⓔ Organize Ideas.
Ⓕ Analyze Relationships.
Ⓖ Justify Arguments.

Texas Essential Knowledge and Skills

Targeted TEKS

7.4(D) Solve problems involving ratios, rates, and percents, including multi-step problems involving percent increase and percent decrease, and financial literacy problems.

Mathematical Processes

7.1(A), 7.1(B), 7.1(C), 7.1(E), 7.1(G)

Vocab

Vocabulary

percent of change
percent of increase
percent of decrease

Essential Question

HOW can percent help you understand situations involving money?

Key Concept

Percent of Change

Words A **percent of change** is a ratio that compares the change in quantity to the original amount.

Equation $\text{percent of change} = \frac{\text{amount of change}}{\text{original amount}}$

Work Zone

When you compare the amount of change to the original amount in a ratio, you are determining the percent of change. The percent of change is based on the original amount.

If the original quantity is increased, then it is called a **percent of increase**. If the original quantity is decreased, then it is called a **percent of decrease**.

$$\text{percent of increase} = \frac{\text{amount of increase}}{\text{original amount}}$$

$$\text{percent of decrease} = \frac{\text{amount of decrease}}{\text{original amount}}$$

Examples

1. Determine the percent of change in the cost of gasoline from 1970 to 2010. Round to the nearest whole percent if necessary.

Since the 2010 price is greater than the 1970 price, this is a percent of increase.

Step 1 Determine the amount of increase.
$\$2.95 - \$1.30 = \$1.65$

Step 2 Determine the percent of increase.

$$\begin{aligned} \text{percent of increase} &= \frac{\text{amount of increase}}{\text{original amount}} \\ &= \frac{\$1.65}{\$1.30} && \text{Substitution} \\ &\approx 1.27 && \text{Simplify.} \\ &\approx 127\% && \text{Write 1.27 as a percent.} \end{aligned}$$

The cost of gasoline increased by about 127% from 1970 to 2010.

Percents
In the percent of change formula, the decimal repesenting the percent of change must be written as a percent.

2. Yusuf bought a DVD recorder for \$280. Now it is on sale for \$220. Determine the percent of change in the price. Round to the nearest whole percent if necessary.

The new price is less than the original, so this is a percent of decrease.

Step 1 Determine the amount of decrease.
\$280 − \$220 = \$60

Step 2 Determine the percent of decrease.

$$\text{percent of decrease} = \frac{\text{amount of decrease}}{\text{original amount}}$$

$$= \frac{\$60}{\$280} \quad \text{Substitution}$$

$$\approx 0.21 \quad \text{Simplify.}$$

$$\approx 21\% \quad \text{Write 0.21 as a percent.}$$

The price of the DVD recorder decreased by about 21%.

Percent of Change
Always use the original amount as the whole when finding percent of change.

Got It? Do these problems to find out.

Show your work.

a. Determine the percent of change from 10 yards to 13 yards.

b. The price of a radio was \$20. It is on sale for \$15. What is the percent of change in the price of a radio?

a. ________

b. ________

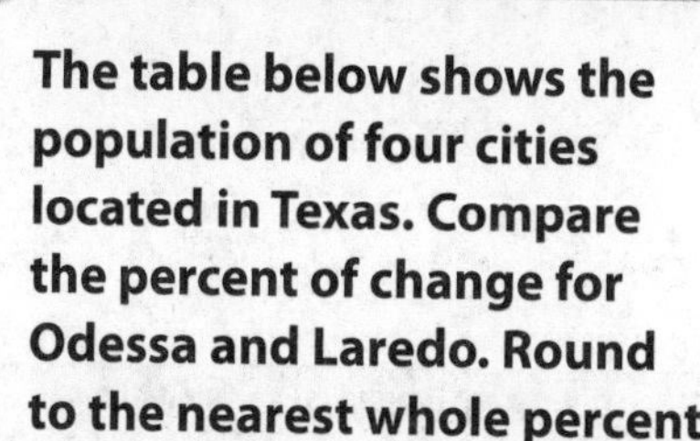

Multi-Step Example

Tutor

3. The table below shows the population of four cities located in Texas. Compare the percent of change for Odessa and Laredo. Round to the nearest whole percent.

City	Population 2000	Population 2010
El Paso	679,622	800,647
Odessa	121,123	137,130
Laredo	193,117	250,304
Victoria	111,663	115,384

Step 1 Determine the amounts of increase for each city.
Odessa: 137,130 − 121,123 = 16,007
Laredo: 250,304 − 193,117 = 57,187

Step 2 Determine the percent of increase for each city.
Odessa: 16,007 ÷ 121,130 is about 13%
Laredo: 57,187 ÷ 193,117 is about 30%

So, Laredo, Texas, had the greatest percent of increase from 2000 to 2010.

Got It? Do this problem to find out.

c. Compare the percent of change for El Paso and Victoria. Round to the nearest whole percent.

c. ________

Multi-Step Example

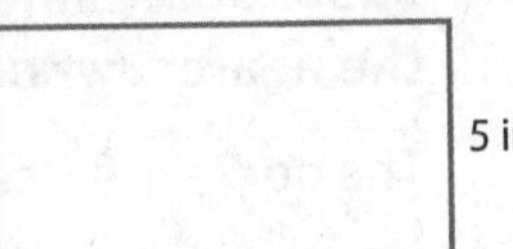

4. The dimensions of the rectangle shown are decreased by 25%. Determine the percent of change in the area of the rectangle. Round to the nearest hundredth.

(Rectangle: 10 in. by 5 in.)

Step 1 Determine the new dimensions of the rectangle.
Length: $10 \cdot 0.25 = 2.5$ $\quad 10 - 2.5 = 7.5$
Width: $5 \cdot 0.25 = 1.25$ $\quad 5 - 1.25 = 3.75$

Step 2 Determine the area of the original rectangle and the smaller rectangle.
Original: $10 \cdot 5 = 50$ in^2
Smaller: $7.5 \cdot 3.75 = 28.13$ in^2

Step 3 Determine the percent decrease in areas.
$50 - 28.13 = 21.87$
$\frac{21.87}{50}$ is about 0.44

So, the area of the smaller rectangle is about 44% smaller.

Guided Practice

Determine each percent of change. Round to the nearest whole percent if necessary. State whether the percent of change is an *increase* or a *decrease*. (Examples 1 and 2)

1. 30 inches to 24 inches _______

2. \$126 to \$150 _______

3. The table shows the allowances of two friends. Compare the percent of change for the two friends. Round to the nearest whole percent. (Example 3) _______

Friend	Original Weekly Allowance	Weekly Allowance Increase
Taylor	\$14	\$22
Pablo	\$13	\$21

4. **Building on the Essential Question** Explain how two amounts of change can be the same but the percents of change can be different.

Rate Yourself!

How confident are you about percent of change? Check the box that applies.

Find out online. Use the Self-Check Quiz.

Name ________________________________ My Homework ________________________

Independent Practice

7.4(D), 7.1(C), 7.1(E), 7.1(G) TEKS

Determine each percent of change. Round to the nearest whole percent if necessary. State whether the percent of change is an *increase* or a *decrease*. (Examples 1 and 2)

1. 15 yards to 18 yards

2. 100 acres to 140 acres

3. \$15.60 to \$11.70

4. 125 centimeters to 87.5 centimeters

5. 1.6 hours to 0.95 hour

6. 132 days to 125.4 days

7. Financial Literacy The first and second quarter earnings of two sporting goods stores are shown in the table. Which store had the greater percent of change in the second quarter? Round to the nearest whole percent. (Example 3)

Earnings (\$)		
	All-Sports Gear	Performance Plus Sports
Quarter 1	21,430	17,216
Quarter 2	22,329	19,214

For each situation, determine each percent of change. Round to the nearest whole percent if necessary. State whether the percent of change is an *increase* or a *decrease*. (Examples 1 and 2)

8. Three months ago, Santos could walk 2 miles in 40 minutes. Today he can walk 2 miles in 25 minutes.

9. Last school year the enrollment of Genoa Middle School was 465 students. This year the enrollment is 525.

10. Use the graph shown to determine the percent of change in CD sales from 2011 to 2012.

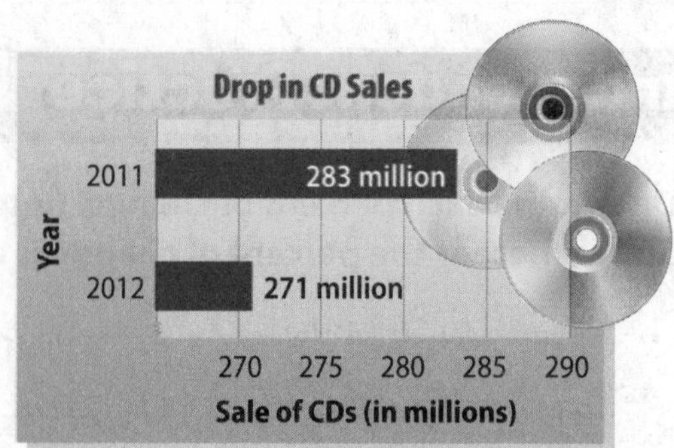

11. Refer to the rectangle at the right. Suppose the side lengths are doubled.

a. Determine the percent of change in the perimeter.

b. Determine the percent of change in the area.

12. MP **Select Tools and Techniques** Find examples of data reflecting change over a period of time in a newspaper or magazine, on television, or on the Internet. Determine the percent of change. Explain whether the data show a percent of increase or decrease.

13. **Find the Error** Dario is determining the percent of change from $52 to $125. Find his mistake and correct it.

H.O.T. Problems Higher-Order Thinking

14. **Evaluate** The costs of two sound systems were decreased by $10. The original costs of the systems were $90 and $60. Without calculating, which had a greater percent of decrease? Explain.

15. **Analyze** If a quantity increases by 25% and then decreases by 25%, will the result be the original quantity? Explain.

16. **Create** Write and solve a percent of change problem using the quantities 17.5 and 25, and state whether there is a percent of increase or decrease.

Name ______________________________

Multi-Step Problem Solving

17. The track and field coach records Ian's 400-meter race times during several practices. How much greater was the percent of change from practice 1 to practice 2 than from practice 2 to practice 3? Round to the nearest tenth. N P MP

Practice	Time (s)
1	63
2	60
3	58

Ⓐ 1.5%
Ⓑ 3.3%
Ⓒ 4.8%
Ⓓ 7.9%

Use a problem-solving model to solve this problem.

1 Analyze

Read the problem. Circle the information you know.
Underline what the problem is asking you to find.

2 Plan

What will you need to do to solve the problem? Write your plan in steps.

Step 1 Determine the ______________ between each practice.

Step 2 ______________ to determine how much greater the percent of change was between each practices.

3 Solve

Use your plan to solve the problem. Show your steps.

practice 1 to practice 2

$\frac{63 - 60}{63} =$ ______________

practice 2 to practice 3

$\frac{60 - 58}{60} =$ ______________

Write each as a percent, then subtract.

_______ − _______ = _______

Ian's percent of decrease was _______ greater between practice 1 and 2.

So, the correct answer is _______. Fill in that answer choice.

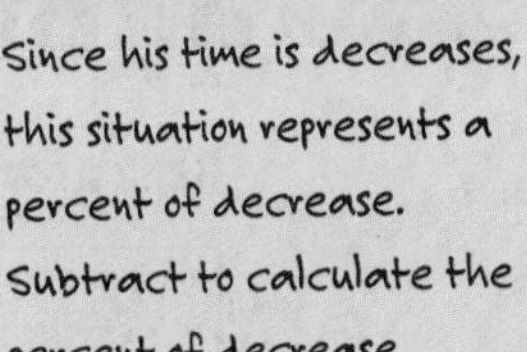

Since his time is decreases, this situation represents a percent of decrease. Subtract to calculate the percent of decrease.

4 Justify and Evaluate

How do you know your solution is accurate?

____

____

____

N = Number and Operations P = Proportionality MP = Mathematical Processes

More Multi-Step Problem Solving

Use a problem-solving model to solve each problem.

18. The table shows Dashawna's science grade during four grading periods. How much greater was the percent change in her grade from grading period 1 to 2, than from grading period 2 to 3? Round to the nearest tenth. N P MP

Grading Period	Grade
1	92%
2	96%
3	99%
4	96%

Ⓐ 1.0%

Ⓑ 1.2%

Ⓒ 3.1%

Ⓓ 4.3%

19. Earth follows an elliptical orbit around the Sun. At its nearest point on the orbit, it is about 147 million kilometers from the Sun. At its farthest point, it is about 152 million kilometers away. What is the percent change, rounded to the nearest tenth, from its nearest point to its farthest? N P MP

20. The graph below shows Alexa's bank account balance over the past four months. Between which months is the percent of increase the greatest? N P MD FL MP

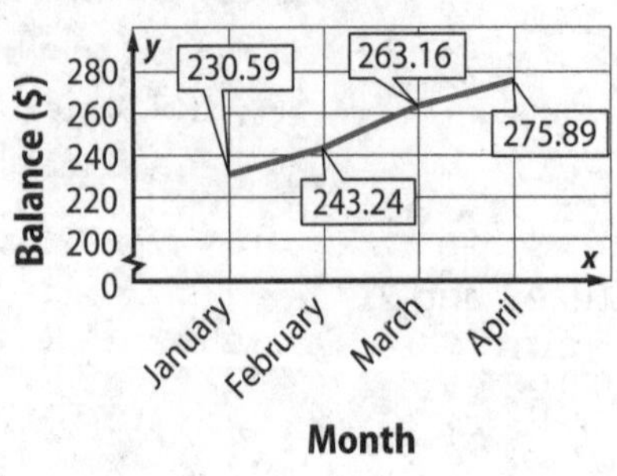

21. Is the percent increase from A to B greater than or less than the percent decrease from B to A? Explain your answer. N P MP

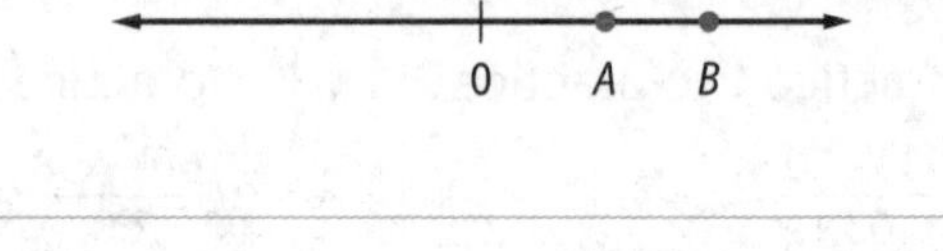

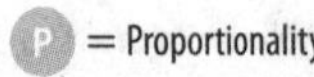

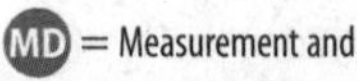

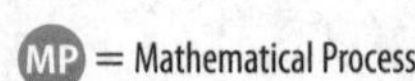

MP = Mathematical Processes

Lesson 6

Financial Literacy: Sales Tax, Tips, and Markup

Launch the Lesson: Real World

Alonso plans to buy a new kayak that costs $2,100. But when he buys the kayak, it actually costs more because he lives in a county where there is a 7% sales tax. What is the total amount he will pay?

1. Complete the diagram.

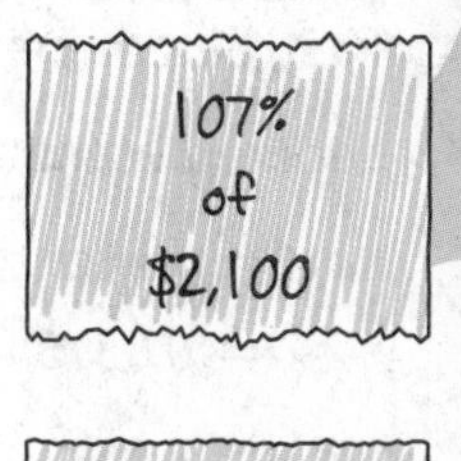

_____ + _____ = _____

2. What is the amount of tax he will pay? ________

3. Fill in the receipt at the right. What is the total cost? ________

4. What is 107% of $2,100? How does this compare to Alonso's total cost? ____________________

5. On Alonso's kayaking trip, hiring a guide costs $50. Alonso wants to give the guide a 10% tip. Explain two different ways to determine the total amount after the tip.

____

____

____

Texas Essential Knowledge and Skills

Targeted TEKS

7.4(D) Solve problems involving ratios, rates, and percents, including multi-step problems involving percent increase and percent decrease, and financial literacy problems.

Mathematical Processes

7.1(A), 7.1(B), 7.1(C)

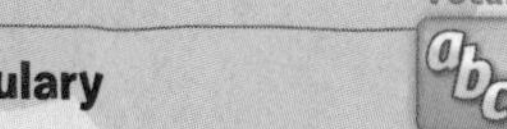

Vocab

Vocabulary

sales tax

tip

gratuity

markup

selling price

Essential Question

HOW can percent help you understand situations involving money?

Which MP Mathematical Processes did you use? Shade the circle(s) that applies.

Ⓐ Apply Math to the Real World.

Ⓑ Use a Problem-Solving Model.

Ⓒ Select Tools and Techniques.

Ⓓ Use Multiple Representations.

Ⓔ Organize Ideas.

Ⓕ Analyze Relationships.

Ⓖ Justify Arguments.

Work Zone

Sales Tax and Total Cost

Sales tax is an additional amount of money charged on items that people buy. The total cost of an item is the regular price plus the sales tax.

Example

1. Drew wants to buy exercise equipment that costs \$140 and the sales tax is 5.75%. What is the total cost of the equipment?

Method 1 **Add sales tax to the regular price.**

First, determine the sales tax.

Let t represent the sales tax.

part = percent × whole	Write the percent equation.
$t = 0.0575 \times 140$	$5.75\% = 0.0575$
$t = 8.05$	Multiply.

Next, add the sales tax to the regular price.
$\$8.05 + \$140 = \$148.05$

Method 2 **Add the percent of tax to 100%.**

$100\% + 5.75\% = 105.75\%$ Add the percent of tax to 100%.

Let t represent the total.

part = percent × whole	Write the percent equation.
$t = 1.0575 \times 140$	$105.75\% = 1.0575$
$t = \$148.05$	Multiply.

The total cost of the exercise equipment is \$148.05.

Got It? **Do this problem to find out.**

a. __________

a. What is the total cost of a sweatshirt if the regular price is \$42 and the sales tax is $5\frac{1}{2}\%$?

Tips and Markups

A **tip** or **gratuity** is a small amount of money in return for a service. The total price is the regular price of the service plus the tip.

A store sells items for more than it pays for those items. The amount of increase is called the **markup**. The **selling price** is the amount the customer pays for an item.

Examples

Tutor

2. A customer wants to tip 15% on a restaurant bill that is $35. What will be the total bill with tip?

Method 1 **Add the tip to the regular price.**

First, determine the tip. Let t represent the tip.

part = percent × whole

$t = 0.15 \times 35$ 15% = 0.15

$t = 5.25$ Multiply.

Next, add the tip to the bill.

$5.25 + $35 = $40.25 Add.

Method 2 **Add the percent of tip to 100%.**

100% + 15% = 115% Add the percent of tip to 100%.

The total cost is 115% of the bill. Let t represent the total.

part = percent × whole

$t = 1.15 \times 35$ 115% = 1.15

$t = 40.25$ Multiply.

Using either method, the total cost of the bill with tip is $40.25.

3. A haircut costs $20. Sales tax is 4.75%. Is $25 sufficient to cover the haircut with tax and a 15% tip?

Step 1 Sales tax is 4.75% and the tip is 15%, so together they will be 19.75%.

Step 2 Let t represent the tax and tip.

part = percent × whole

$t = 0.1975 \times 20$ 0.15 + 0.0475 = 0.1975

$t = 3.95$ Multiply.

Step 3 $20 + $3.95 = $23.95 Add.

Since $23.95 < $25, $25 is sufficient to cover the total cost.

Mental Math

10% of a number can be found by moving the decimal one place to the left. 10% of $20 is $2. So, 20% of $20 is $4.

Got It? **Do these problems to find out.**

b. Scott wants to tip his taxicab driver 20%. If his commute costs $15, what is the total cost?

c. Determine the total cost of a spa treatment of $42 including 6% tax and 20% tip.

b. ____________

c. ____________

Multi-Step Example

Markup

In Example 4, you could determine the selling price by determining 125% of the amount the store pays.

4. A store pays $56 for a GPS navigation system. The markup is 25%. How much more is the selling price than what the store paid for it?

Step 1 First, determine the markup. Let m represent the markup.

part = percent × whole	Write the percent equation.
$m = 0.25 \times 56$	25% = 0.25
$m = 14$	Mulitply.

Step 2 Next, add the markup to the amount the store pays.

$14 + $56 = $70 — Add.

The selling price of the GPS navigation system is $70.

Step 3 Subtract to determine the difference in prices.

$70 - 56 = 14$

So, the selling price is $14 more than what the store paid for it.

Guided Practice

Determine the total cost to the nearest cent. (Examples 1 and 2)

1. $2.95 notebook; 5% tax ______

2. $28 lunch; 15% tip ______

3. Jaimi went to have a manicure that cost $30. She wanted to tip the technician 20% and tax is 5.75%. How much did she spend total for the manicure? (Example 3)

______

4. Determine the selling price and amount of increase of a $62.25 karaoke machine with a 60.5% markup. (Example 4)

______

5. **Building on the Essential Question** Describe two methods for determining the total price of a bill that includes a 20% tip. Which method do you prefer? ______

______

______

Rate Yourself!

How well do you understand determining sales tax, tips, and markups? Circle the image that applies.

Clear — Somewhat Clear — Not So Clear

Find out online. Use the Self-Check Quiz.

Name ______________________ My Homework ______________________

Independent Practice

7.4(D), 7.1(A) TEKS

Determine the total cost to the nearest cent. (Examples 1 and 2)

1. \$58 bill; 20% tip ________

Show your work.

2. \$43 dinner; 18% gratuity ________

3. \$1,500 computer; 7% tax ________

4. \$46 shoes; 2.9% tax ________

5. **Financial Literacy** A restaurant bill comes to \$28.35. Determine the total cost if the tax is 6.25% and a 20% tip is left on the amount before tax. (Example 3) ________

6. Toru takes his dog to be groomed. The fee to groom the dog is \$75 plus 6.75% tax. Is \$80 enough to pay for the service? Explain. (Example 3)

7. Determine the selling price and amount of increase of a \$270 bicycle with a 24% markup. (Example 4)

8. Determine the selling price and amount of increase of a \$450 painting with a 45% markup. (Example 4)

9. What is the sales tax on the chair shown if the tax rate is 5.75%? ________

10. A store pays \$10 for a bracelet, and the markup is 115%. A customer will also pay a $5\frac{1}{2}$% sales tax. What will be the total cost of the bracelet to the nearest cent? ________

11. The bill for lunch was $7. The sales tax in Dallas, Texas, is 8.25%. If you have $9.50, what is the maximum amount you can give for a tip and still cover the food bill and sales tax? About what percent of the food bill would this tip be? Explain.

12. **Which One Doesn't Belong?** In each pair, the first value is the regular price of an item and the second value is the price with gratuity. Identify the pair that does not belong with the other three. Explain your reasoning to a classmate.

$30, $34.50	$54, $64.80	$16, $18.40	$90, $103.50

H.O.T. Problems Higher-Order Thinking

13. **Analyze** The Leather Depot buys a coat from a supplier for $90 wholesale and marks up the price by 40%. If the retail price is $134.82, what is the sales tax? ______

14. **Create** Give an example of the regular price of an item and the total cost including sales tax if the tax rate is 5.75%.

15. **Analyze** An electronics store marks all items with a 20% markup. Including tax, Sydney paid $38.52 for a video game. If the sales tax rate is 7%, how much did the electronics store pay for the game? ______

16. **Analyze** Use the Internet to find the sales tax rate for Indiana and Alabama. Using each state's tax rate, determine how much more you would pay for an item that costs $100 in Indiana compared to Alabama.

Name ____

Multi-Step Problem Solving

17. Takara orders the rib basket meal at a barbecue restaurant. She wants to leave an 18% tip. Sales tax is 6.5% at the restaurant. She also buys one bottle of barbecue sauce, plus tax. How much does Takara spend, in dollars? N P FL MP

Purchase	Price ($)
Rib basket	21
Barbecue sauce	15

Use a problem-solving model to solve this problem.

1 Analyze

Read the problem. Circle the information you know. Underline what the problem is asking you to find.

2 Plan

What will you need to do to solve the problem? Write your plan in steps.

Step 1 Determine the __________ for just the meal.

Step 2 Determine the __________. Then add the tip, sales tax, and total bill.

Read to Succeed!
Takara only wants to leave a tip for the meal and not the bottle of sauce. Be sure to only determine the tip for the meal.

3 Solve

Use your plan to solve the problem. Show your steps.

Tip: $\$21 \times 0.18 =$ ______

Total Bill: $\$21 + \$15 =$ ______

Sales Tax: $\$36 \times 0.065 =$ ______

Add the tip, sales tax, and total bill.

______ + ______ + ______ = ______

Takara spends ______ at the restaurant. Complete the grid.

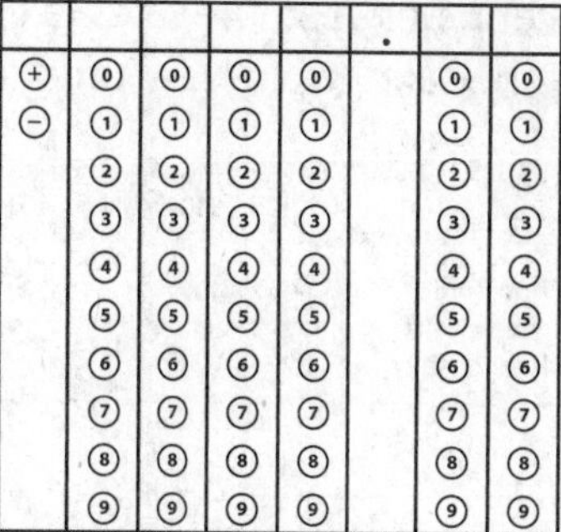

4 Justify and Evaluate

How do you know your solution is accurate?

____

____

____

N = Number and Operations P = Proportionality FL = Personal Financial Literacy MP = Mathematical Processes

More Multi-Step Problem Solving

Use a problem-solving model to solve each problem.

18. Brian has $24 worth of pizzas delivered to his house for a $3 delivery fee. He pays 7% sales tax and a 15% tip, which are both calculated on the total price before the delivery fee. How much change does he receive, in dollars, if he pays with two $20 bills? N P FL MP

19. Yoselin bought a broken antique table at a garage sale for $30. She plans to repair and paint it before reselling it. Her supplies will cost $45 plus 6% sales tax. She takes the amount that she spent on the table and increases the price by 100%. How much does she charge for the table, in dollars? Round to the nearest cent, if necessary. N P FL MP

20. Two customers buy the same couch, but live in different states. The table shows the couch pricing information. What is the difference, in percent, between the sales tax in New Jersey and the sales tax in New York? N P FL MP

Location	Price before tax	Price after tax
New York	$2,500	$2,600
New Jersey	$2,000	$2,140

21. Umar sells personalized sports T-shirts at the City Sports Festival. Each shirt costs him $15 to make. The bar graph shows the number of shirts he sold last weekend. He charged a 50% markup on Friday and Saturday, and then lowered it to 30% on Sunday to increase sales. On which day did he make the most money? Justify your answers. N P FL MD MP

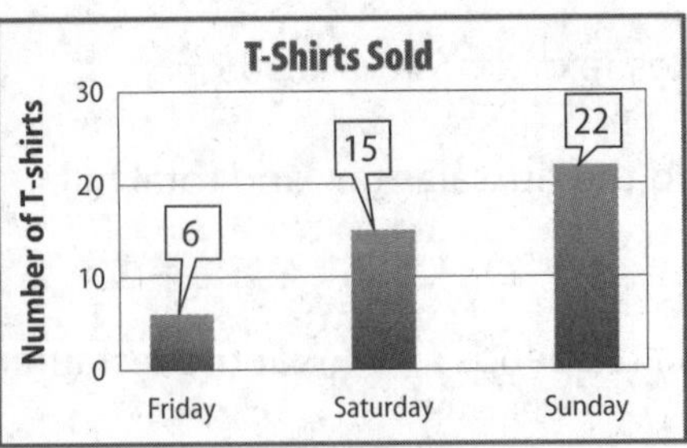

N = Number and Operations P = Proportionality FL = Personal Financial Literacy MD = Measurement and Data MP = Mathematical Processes

Lesson 7
Discount

Launch the Lesson: Real World

A pass at a water park is $58 dollars at the beginning of the season. The cost of the pass decreases each month. Each month 10% is taken off the price of a season pass. Determine the discounted price for August by completing the diagram below.

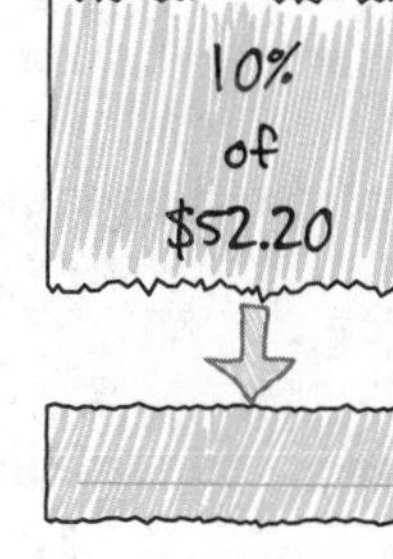

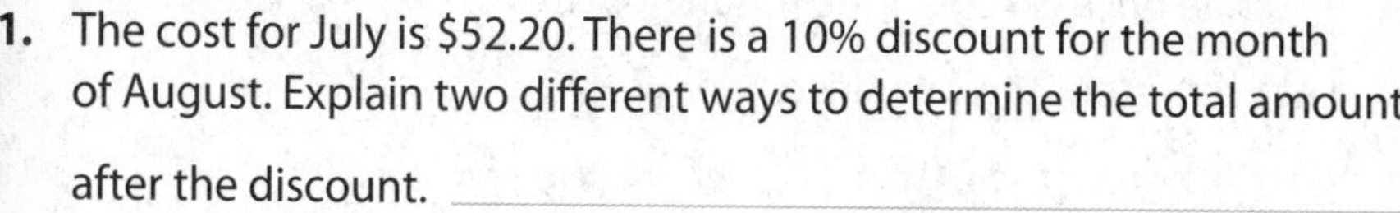

Texas Essential Knowledge and Skills

Targeted TEKS
7.4(D) Solve problems involving ratios, rates, and percents, including multi-step problems involving percent increase and percent decrease, and financial literacy problems.

Mathematical Processes
7.1(A), 7.1(B), 7.1(E)

Vocabulary
discount
markdown

Essential Question
HOW can percent help you understand situations involving money?

1. The cost for July is $52.20. There is a 10% discount for the month of August. Explain two different ways to determine the total amount after the discount. ______

______

Which MP Mathematical Processes did you use? Shade the circle(s) that applies.

Ⓐ Apply Math to the Real World.
Ⓑ Use a Problem-Solving Model.
Ⓒ Select Tools and Techniques.
Ⓓ Use Multiple Representations.
Ⓔ Organize Ideas.
Ⓕ Analyze Relationships.
Ⓖ Justify Arguments.

Work Zone

Determine Sale Price and Original Price

Discount or **markdown** is the amount by which the regular price of an item is reduced. The sale price is the regular price minus the discount.

Example

1. A DVD normally costs \$22. This week it is on sale for 25% off the original price. What is the sale price of the DVD?

Original Price
\$22

Sale Price | 25%

Method 1 **Subtract the discount from the regular price.**

First, determine the amount of the discount.

Let d represent the discount.

part = percent × whole	Write the percent equation.
$d = 0.25 \times 22$	$25\% = 0.25$
$d = 5.50$	Multiply.

Next, subtract the discount from the regular price.
$\$22 - \$5.50 = \$16.50$

Method 2 **Subtract the percent of discount from 100%.**

$100\% - 25\% = 75\%$	Subtract the discount from 100%.

The sale price is 75% of the regular price.

Let s represent the sale price.

part = percent × whole	Write the percent equation.
$s = 0.75 \times 22$	$75\% = 0.75$
$s = 16.5$	Multiply.

The sale price of the DVD is \$16.50.

a. ________

Got It? Do this problem to find out.

a. A shirt is regularly priced at \$42. It is on sale for 15% off of the regular price. What is the sale price of the shirt?

Multi-Step Example

2. A boogie board that has a regular price of $69 is on sale at a 35% discount. What is the sale price with 7% tax?

Step 1 Determine the amount of the discount.

Let d represent the discount.

part = percent × whole	Write the percent equation.
$d = 0.35 \times 69$	35% = 0.35
$d = 24.15$	Multiply.

Step 2 Subtract the discount from the regular price.

$69 − $24.15 = $44.85

Step 3 The percent of tax is applied after the discount is taken.

7% of $44.85 = 0.07 • 44.85	Write 7% as a decimal.
= 3.14	The tax is $3.14.
$44.85 + $3.14 = $47.99	Add the tax to the sale price.

The sale price of the boogie board including tax is $47.99.

Got It? Do this problem to find out.

b. A CD that has a regular price of $15.50 is on sale at a 25% discount. What is the sale price with 6.5% tax?

b. ________

Multi-Step Example

3. A cell phone is on sale for 30% off. If the sale price is $239.89, what is the original price?

The sale price is 100% − 30% or 70% of the original price.

Let p represent the original price.

part = percent × whole	
$239.89 = 0.7 \times p$	
$\frac{239.89}{0.7} = \frac{0.7p}{0.7}$	Divide each side by 0.7.
$342.70 = p$	Simplify.

The original price is $342.70.

Percent Equation

Remember that in the percent equation, the percent must be written as a decimal. Since the sale price is 70% of the original price, use 0.7 to represent 70% in the percent equation.

Got It? Do this problem to find out.

c. Determine the original price if the sale price of a phone is $205.50.

c. ________

Multi-Step Example

4. Clothes Are Us and Ratcliffe's are having sales. At Clothes Are Us, a pair of sneakers is on sale for 40% off the regular price of $50. At Ratcliffe's, the same brand of sneakers is discounted by 30% off of the regular price of $40. Which store has the better sale price? Explain.

Determine the sale price of the sneakers at each store.

Clothes Are Us	**Ratcliffe's**
60% of \$50 = 0.6 × \$50	70% of \$40 = 0.7 × \$40
= \$30	= \$28
The sale price is \$30.	The sale price is \$28.

Since \$28 < \$30, the sale price at Ratcliffe's is the better buy.

Show your work.

Got It? Do this problem to find out.

d. ______________

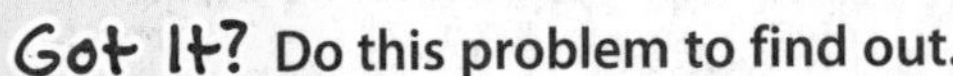

d. If the sale at Clothes Are Us was 50% off, which store would have the better buy? Explain.

Guided Practice

1. Mary and Roberto bought identical backpacks at different stores. Mary's backpack originally cost \$65 and was discounted 25%. Roberto's backpack originally cost \$75 and was on sale for 30% off of the original price. Which backpack was the better buy? Explain. (Examples 1, 2 and 4)

____

2. A pair of in-line skates is on sale for \$90. If this price represents a 9% discount from the original price, what is the original price to the nearest cent? (Example 3)

____

3. **Building on the Essential Question** Describe two methods for determining the sale price of an item that is discounted 30%.

____

____

____

Rate Yourself!

Are you ready to move on? Shade the section that applies.

I have a few questions. | I'm ready to move on. | I have a lot of questions.

Find out online. Use the Self-Check Quiz.

Name ______________________ My Homework ______________________

Independent Practice

7.4(D), 7.1(A), 7.1(E) TEKS

Determine the sale price to the nearest cent. (Examples 1 and 2)

1. $64 jacket; 20% discount ________

2. $1,200 TV; 10% discount ________

3. $7.50 admission; 20% off; 5.75% tax ________

4. $4.30 makeup; 40% discount; 6% tax ________

5. A bottle of hand lotion is on sale for $2.25. If this price represents a 50% discount from the original price, what is the original price to the nearest cent? (Example 3)

____

6. A tennis racket at Sport City costs $180 and is discounted 15%. The same model racket costs $200 at Tennis World and is on sale for 20% off. Which store is offering the better deal? Explain. (Example 4)

____

____

7. MP **Apply Math to the Real World** Refer to the graphic novel frame below.

a. Determine the price that a student would pay including the group discount for each amusement park. ________

b. Which is the best deal? ________

8. The Wares want to buy a new computer. The regular price is $1,049. The store is offering a 20% discount and a sales tax of 5.25% is added after the discount.

What is the total cost? ______

Determine the original price to the nearest cent.

9. calendar: discount, 75%;

sale price, $2.25 ______

10. telescope: discount, 30%;

sale price, $126 ______

11. MP **Organize Ideas** Compare and contrast tax and discount.

Tax

Discount

H.O.T. Problems Higher-Order Thinking

12. **Create** Give an example of the sale price of an item and the total cost including sales tax if the tax rate is 5.75% and the item is 25% off.

13. **Analyze** A store is having a sale in which all items are discounted 20%. Including tax, Colin paid $21 for a picture. If the sales tax rate is 5%, what was the original price of the picture? ______

14. **Analyze** Describe two methods for determining the sale price of an item that is discounted 30%. Which method do you prefer? Explain.

Name ______________________________

Multi-Step Problem Solving

15. At the end of the summer season, a garden store discounts all of its summer merchandise. The table shows the discounts for beach umbrellas. Which umbrella would be the least expensive to purchase after the discount and a 6% tax? P N FL MP

Umbrella	Original Price ($)	Percent Discount
A	75	30
B	68	20
C	85	40
D	80	35

Ⓐ Umbrella A
Ⓑ Umbrella B
Ⓒ Umbrella C
Ⓓ Umbrella D

Use a problem-solving model to solve this problem.

1 Analyze

Read the problem. Circle the information you know.
Underline what the problem is asking you to find.

2 Plan

What will you need to do to solve the problem?
Write your plan in steps.

Step 1 Determine the amount of __________ for each umbrella.

Step 2 Apply the __________ after the discount is applied.

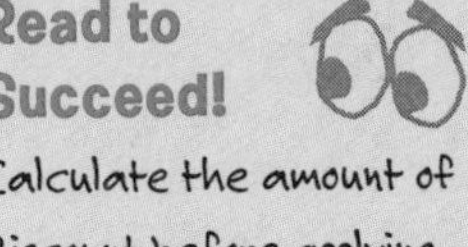

Read to Succeed!
Calculate the amount of discount before applying the tax to determine the final price.

3 Solve

Use your plan to solve the problem. Show your steps.

Discount: A: $\$75 \times 0.7 =$ ______ B: $\$68 \times 0.8 =$ ______

C: $\$85 \times 0.6 =$ ______ D: $\$80 \times 0.65 =$ ______

Tax: A: $\$52.50 \times 1.06 =$ ______ B: $\$54.40 \times 1.06 =$ ______

C: $\$51.00 \times 1.06 =$ ______ D: $\$52.00 \times 1.06 =$ ______

The least expensive umbrella is __________.

So, the correct answer is _____. Fill in that answer choice.

4 Justify and Evaluate

How do you know your solution is accurate?

____

____

____

N = Number and Operations P = Proportionality FL = Personal Financial Literacy MP = Mathematical Processes

More Multi-Step Problem Solving

Use a problem-solving model to solve each problem.

16. The table shows the percent discount that a customer will save based on the original cost of an item. If Jeremy buys a $35 item and an $80 item, how much will he spend after the discount is applied to each item? N P FL MP

Original Cost	Percent Discount
Under $50	10
$50–$100	20
over $100	25

Ⓐ $95.50
Ⓑ $86.25
Ⓒ $19.50
Ⓓ $28.75

17. A pair of jeans that regularly cost $75 is on sale for 30% off. Javier has a coupon for an additional 15% off, which is calculated after the initial discount. How much will Javier pay for the jeans, in dollars? Round to the nearest cent. N P FL MP

18. Christian was excited when he saw an ad for a local electronics store in the newspaper that was going out of business. Everything in the store was 40% off. He would like to purchase a new television that originally costs $1,250. How many months would it take him to pay for the television if he paid $75 each month? N P FL MP

19. Maria purchased a new jacket for $78.12. The original price of the jacket was discounted 20%, and Maria had to pay a 5% sales tax. What was the original price of the jacket? N P FL MP

N = Number and Operations P = Proportionality FL = Personal Financial Literacy MP = Mathematical Processes

Lesson 8

Financial Literacy: Simple Interest

Launch the Lesson: Vocabulary

Principal is the amount of money deposited or borrowed.
Simple interest is the amount paid or earned for the use of money.

The simple interest formula is shown below. Fill in the diagram using the words *interest*, *principal*, *rate*, and *time*.

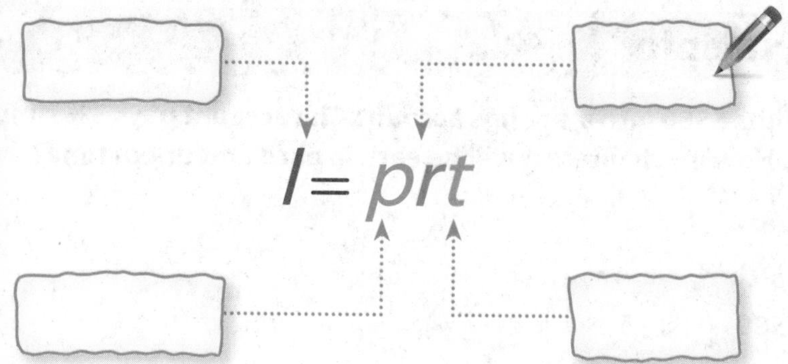

Texas Essential Knowledge and Skills

Targeted TEKS

7.4(D) Solve problems involving ratios, rates, and percents, including multi-step problems involving percent increase and percent decrease, and financial literacy problems. *Also addresses 7.13(E).*

Mathematical Processes

7.1(A), 7.1(B), 7.1(G)

Vocabulary

principal

simple interest

Essential Question

HOW can percent help you understand situations involving money?

Real-World Link

Mrs. Ramirez is investing $400 in a savings account at a simple interest rate of 2% to purchase a laptop computer. She plans on investing the money for 18 months.

Based on this real-world situation, fill in the blanks with the correct numbers. Express the rate as a decimal. Time is expressed in years.

principal = ☐ rate = ☐ time = ☐ years

Which MP Mathematical Processes did you use? Shade the circle(s) that applies.

Ⓐ Apply Math to the Real World.
Ⓑ Use a Problem-Solving Model.
Ⓒ Select Tools and Techniques.
Ⓓ Use Multiple Representations.
Ⓔ Organize Ideas.
Ⓕ Analyze Relationships.
Ⓖ Justify Arguments.

Key Concept

Simple Interest Formula

Words Simple interest I is the product of the principal p, the annual interest rate r, and the time t, expressed in years.

Symbols $I = prt$

Work Zone

If you have a savings account, the bank pays you interest for the use of your money. Use the formula $I = prt$ to determine the amount of interest that will be earned.

Real World

Tutor

Examples

Arnold puts \$580 into a savings account. The account pays 3% simple interest. How much interest will he earn in each amount of time?

1. 5 years

$I = prt$	Formula for simple interest
$I = 580 \cdot 0.03 \cdot 5$	Replace p with \$580, r with 0.03, and t with 5.
$I = 87$	Simplify.

So, Arnold will earn \$87 in interest in 5 years.

2. 6 months

6 months $= \frac{6}{12}$ or 0.5 year	Write the time as years.
$I = prt$	Formula for simple interest
$I = 580 \cdot 0.03 \cdot 0.5$	$p = \$580, r = 0.03, t = 0.5$
$I = 8.7$	Simplify.

So, Arnold will earn \$8.70 in interest in 6 months.

Show your work.

a. ______________

b. ______________

Got It? Do these problems to find out.

a. Jenny puts \$1,560 into a savings account. The account pays 2.5% simple interest. How much interest will she earn in 3 years?

b. Marcos invests \$760 into a savings account. The account pays 4% simple interest. How much interest will he earn after 5 years?

Interest on Loans and Credit Cards

If you borrow money from a bank, you pay the bank interest for the use of their money. You also pay interest to a credit card company if you have an unpaid balance. Use the formula $I = prt$ to determine the amount of interest owed.

Examples

Tutor

STOP and Reflect

Explain in the space below how you would determine the simple interest on a \$500 loan at a 6% interest rate for 18 months.

3. Rondell's parents borrow \$6,300 from the bank for a new car. The interest rate is 6% per year. How much simple interest will they pay if they take 2 years to repay the loan?

$I = prt$	Formula for simple interest
$I = 6{,}300 \cdot 0.06 \cdot 2$	Replace p with \$6,300, r with 0.06, and t with 2.
$I = 756$	Simplify.

Rondell's parents will pay \$756 in interest in 2 years.

4. Derrick's dad bought new tires for \$900 using a credit card. His card has an interest rate of 19%. If he has no other charges on his card and does not make a payment, how much money will he owe after one month?

Step 1

$I = prt$	Formula for simple interest
$I = 900 \cdot 0.19 \cdot \frac{1}{12}$	Replace p with \$900, r with 0.19, and t with $\frac{1}{12}$.
$I = 14.25$	Simplify.

The interest owed after one month is \$14.25.

Step 2 The total amount owed would be \$900 + \$14.25 or \$914.25.

Got It? **Do these problems to find out.**

c. Mrs. Hanover borrows \$1,400 at a rate of 5.5% per year. How much simple interest will she pay if it takes 8 months to repay the loan?

d. An office manager charged \$425 worth of office supplies on a credit card. The credit card has an interest rate of 9.9%. How much money will he owe at the end of one month if he makes no other charges on the card and does not make a payment?

c. ________

d. ________

Example

5. Luis is taking out a car loan for $5,000. He plans on paying off the car loan in 2 years. At the end of 2 years, Luis will have paid $300 in interest. What is the simple interest rate on the car loan?

$I = prt$ — Formula for simple interest

$300 = 5{,}000 \cdot r \cdot 2$ — Replace I with 300, p with 5,000, and t with 2.

$300 = 10{,}000r$ — Simplify.

$\frac{300}{10{,}000} = \frac{10{,}000r}{10{,}000}$ — Divide each side by 10,000.

$0.03 = r$

The simple interest rate is 0.03 or 3%.

Got It? **Do this problem to find out.**

e. ___________

e. Maggie is taking out a student loan for $2,600. She plans on paying off the loan in 3 years. At the end of 3 years, Maggie will have paid $390 in interest. What is the simple interest rate on the student loan?

Guided Practice

1. The Masters family financed a computer that cost $1,200. If the interest rate is 19%, how much will the family owe for the computer after one month if no payments are made? (Examples 1–4) ___________

2. Samantha received a loan from the bank for $4,500. She plans on paying off the loan in 4 years. At the end of 4 years, Samantha will have paid $900 in interest. What is the simple interest rate on the bank loan? (Example 5)

____

3. **Building on the Essential Question** How can you use a formula to determine simple interest?

____

____

____

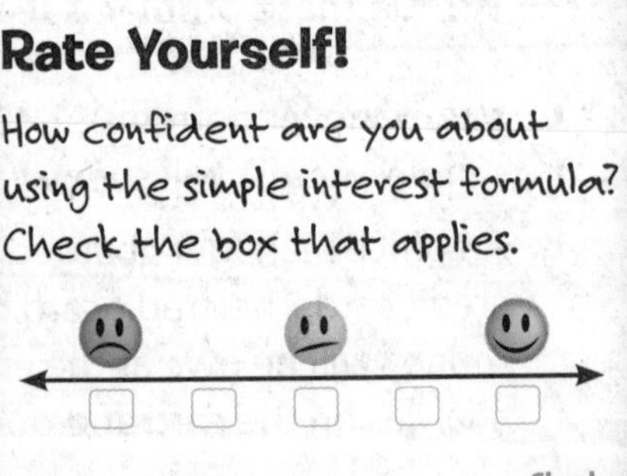

Name _______________ My Homework _______________

Independent Practice

7.4(D), 7.1(A) TEKS

Determine the simple interest earned to the nearest cent for each principal, interest rate, and time. (Examples 1 and 2)

1. \$640, 3%, 2 years ________

Show your work.

2. \$1,500, 4.25%, 4 years ________

3. \$580, 2%, 6 months ________

4. \$1,200, 3.9%, 8 months ________

Determine the simple interest paid to the nearest cent for each loan amount, interest rate, and time. (Example 3)

5. \$4,500, 9%, 3.5 years ________

6. \$290, 12.5%, 6 months ________

7. Leon charged \$75 at an interest rate of 12.5%. How much will Leon have to pay after one month if he makes no payments? (Example 4)

____

8. Jamerra received a \$3,000 car loan. She plans on paying off the loan in 2 years. At the end of 2 years, Jamerra will have paid \$450 in interest. What is the simple interest rate on the car loan? (Example 5)

____

9. MP **Justify Arguments** Pablo has \$4,200 to invest for college.

a. If Pablo invests \$4,200 for 3 years and earns \$630, what is the simple interest rate? ________

b. Pablo's goal is to have \$5,000 after 4 years. Is this possible if he invests with a rate of return of 6%? Explain. ________

____

10. Financial Literacy The table shows interest owed for a home improvement loan based on how long it takes to pay off the loan.

a. How much more interest is owed on $900 for 9 months than for 6 months? Round to the nearest hundredth.

b. Does the interest rate increase at a constant rate?

Explain.

Time	Rate
6 months	2.4%
9 months	2.9%
12 months	3.0%
18 months	3.1%

H.O.T. Problems Higher-Order Thinking

11. Evaluate Suppose you earn 3% on a $1,200 deposit for 5 years. Explain how the simple interest is affected if the rate is increased by 1%. What happens if the time is increased by 1 year?

12. Analyze Dustin bought a $2,000 computer with a credit card. The minimum payment each month is $35. Each month, 1% of the unpaid balance is added to the amount he owes.

a. If Dustin pays only $35 the first month, what will he owe the second month?

b. If Dustin makes the minimum payment, what will he owe the third month?

13. Evaluate Compare the two investments below. Which will have a greater account balance in the given time periods? Explain.

Investment A
Principal: $1,500
Interest Rate: 3%
Time: 30 years

Investment B
Principal: $1,500
Interest Rate: 4.5%
Time: 15 years

Name ____________________

Multi-Step Problem Solving

14. Donte is buying a car that costs $8,000. He is deciding between a 3-year loan and a 4-year loan. Use the rates in the table to determine how much money he will save if he chooses the 3-year loan instead of the 4-year loan. P FL N MP

Time (y)	Simple Interest (%)
3	2.25
4	2.5
5	3

Ⓐ $60 Ⓒ $100

Ⓑ $20 Ⓓ $260

Use a problem-solving model to solve this problem.

1 Analyze

Read the problem. Circle the information you know. Underline what the problem is asking you to find.

2 Plan

What will you need to do to solve the problem? Write your plan in steps.

Step 1 Determine the __________ for each loan.

Step 2 Subtract to determine how much __________ he will save.

3 Solve

Use your plan to solve the problem. Show your steps.

Use the simple interest formula.

3 year loan: $I = 8{,}000 \cdot 0.0225 \cdot 3 =$ ______

4 year loan: $I = 8{,}000 \cdot 0.025 \cdot 4 =$ ______

______ − ______ = ______ Subtract.

Donte would save ______ if he chooses a 3-year loan.

So, the correct answer is ______. Fill in that answer choice.

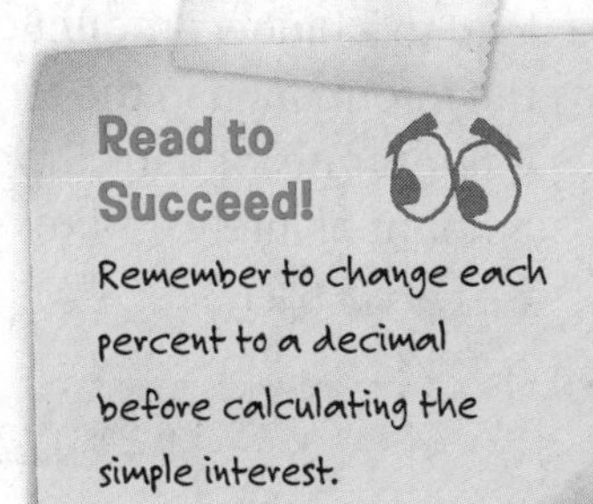

4 Justify and Evaluate

How do you know your solution is accurate?

____

____

____

N = Number and Operations P = Proportionality FL = Personal Financial Literacy MP = Mathematical Processes

More Multi-Step Problem Solving

Use a problem-solving model to solve each problem.

15. Evan has $4,000 that he wants to put into a savings account until he leaves for college, which will be 6 years from now. How much more money will he have in his savings account if he chooses Bank B instead of Bank A? P FL N MP

Bank	Interest Rate
Bank A	4.5%
Bank B	4.9%

Ⓐ $16
Ⓑ $96
Ⓒ $1,176
Ⓓ $1,080

16. Isabel has $1,500 to deposit into a savings account with a 3.2% interest rate. She wants to wait until she earns $240 in interest before withdrawing the money. How many years will she have to wait before she can withdraw the money? P FL N MP

17. A higher interest rate and a longer loan term lead to a higher amount of interest. Given the information in the table, what percent interest rate for Bank B would make the amount of interest from each bank the same?

	Bank A	Bank B
Interest rate	4.2%	■
Term	4 year	5 year
Principal	$4,000	$4,000

18. Alex is buying a car that costs $18,000. He will make a down payment of $2,000, and the tax rate is 7%. He is considering a 5-year loan with an interest rate of 6.2%. What is the total cost of the car including tax and interest over the life of the loan? P FL N MP

N = Number and Operations P = Proportionality FL = Personal Financial Literacy MP = Mathematical Processes

Spreadsheet Lab 8-b

Compound Interest

INQUIRY HOW can I analyze relationships to determine how compound interest is different from simple interest?

Jin Li's parents deposit $2,000 in a college savings account. The account pays an interest rate of 4% compounded annually. Complete the Hands-On Activity to determine how much money will be in the account after 9 years.

Texas Essential Knowledge and Skills TEKS

Targeted TEKS
7.4(D) Solve problems involving ratios, rates, and percents, including multi-step problems involving percent increase and percent decrease, and financial literacy problems.
Also addresses 7.13(E).

Mathematical Processes
7.1(C), 7.1(D), 7.1(F)

Hands-On Activity

Compound interest is interest earned on the original principal and on interest earned in the past. At the end of each time period, the interest earned is added to the principal, which becomes the new principal for the next time period.

A computer spreadsheet is a useful tool for quickly performing calculations involving compound interest. To perform a calculation in a spreadsheet cell, first enter the equals sign. For example, enter =A4+B4 to determine the sum of Cells A4 and B4.

Create a spreadsheet like the one shown.

Compound Interest

◇	A	B	C	D
1	Rate	0.04		
2				
3	Principal	Interest	New Principal	Time (YR)
4	$2000.00	$80.00	$2080.00	1
5	$2080.00	$83.20	$2163.20	2
6	$2163.20	$86.53	$2249.73	3
7	$2249.73	$89.99	$2339.72	4
8	$2339.72	$93.59	$2433.31	5
9	$2433.31	$97.33	$2530.64	6
10	$2530.64	$101.23	$2631.86	7
11	$2631.86	$105.27	$2737.14	8
12				

Sheet 1 Sheet 2 Sheet 3

The interest rate is entered as a decimal.

The spreadsheet evaluates the formula A4×B1.

The interest is added to the principal every year. The spreadsheet evaluates the formula A4+B4.

What formula would the spreadsheet use to determine the new principal at the end of Year 9? ______________________

So, the account will have a balance of ____________ after 9 years.

Investigate

Work with a partner. Create spreadsheets for the situations below.

1. Lakeesha deposits $1,500 into a Young Savers account. The account receives 4% interest compounded annually. What is the balance in Lakeesha's account after 2 years? after 3 years?

   2 Years: ____________ 3 Years: ____________

2. Michael deposits $2,650 into an account. The interest rate on the account is 6% compounded annually. What is the balance in Michael's account after 2 years? after 3 years?

   2 Years: ____________ 3 Years: ____________

On Your Own

Analyze and Reflect

3. MP **Analyze Relationships** Suppose Elijah deposited $1,000 into a bank account paying 4.75% interest compounded annually. At the same time, Lily deposits $1,000 in a separate account that pays 5% simple interest. Elijah and Lily withdraw the money from their accounts after 6 years. Predict who made more money. Explain.

On Your Own

Create

4. MP **Apply Math to the Real World** Write a real-world problem that involves compound interest. Then create a spreadsheet and solve your problem.

5. INQUIRY HOW can I analyze relationships to determine how compound interest is different from simple interest?

21ST CENTURY CAREER

Video Game Designer

Are you passionate about computer gaming? You might want to explore a career in video game design. A video game designer is responsible for a game's concept, layout, character development, and game-play. Game designers use math and logic to compute how different parts of a game will work.

Mathematical Process
7.1(A) Apply mathematics to problems arising in everyday life, society, and the workplace.

Targeted TEKS 7.4(D)

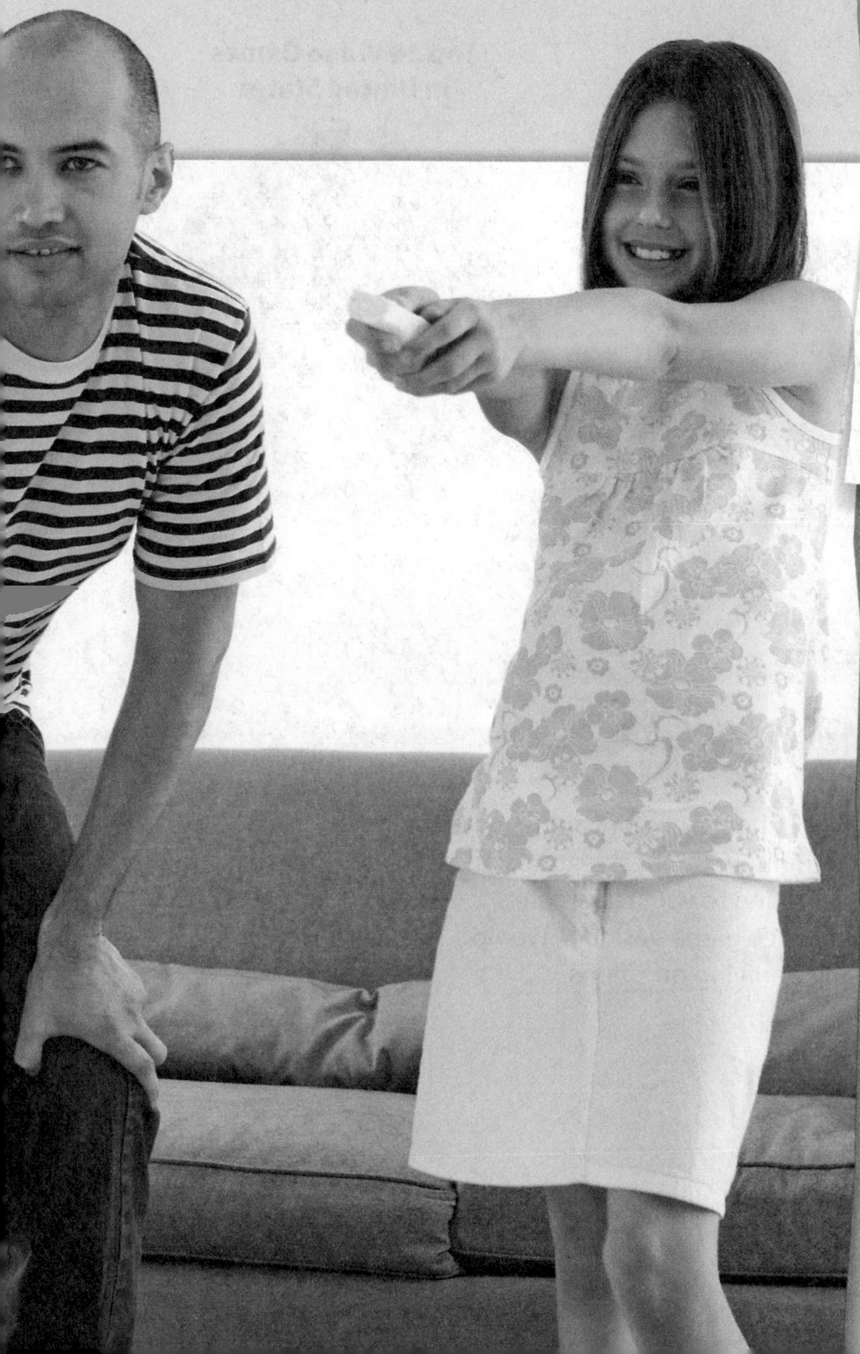

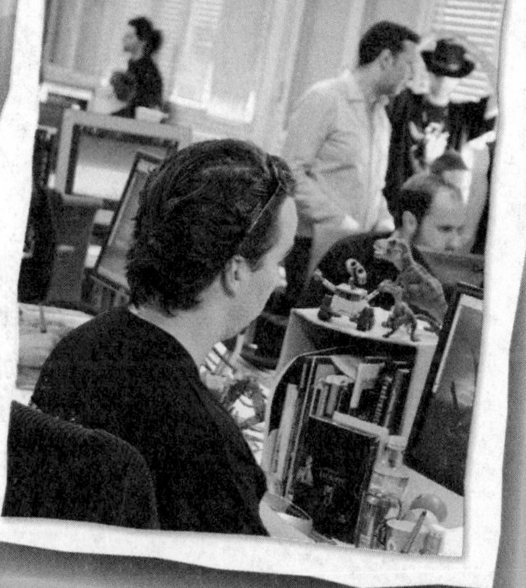

Is This the Career for You?

Are you interested in a career as a video game designer? Take some of the following courses in high school.

- 3-D Digital Animation
- Introduction to Computer Literacy
- Introduction to Game Development

Explore college and careers at ccr.mcgraw-hill.com

All Fun and Games

Use the information in the circle graph and the table to solve the problems below.

1. How many of the top 20 video games sold were sports games? ______________
2. Out of the top 20 video games sold, how many more music games were there than racer games? ______________
3. In Week 1, the total sales for a video game were $2,374,136. What percent of the total sales was from the United States? Round to the nearest whole percent. ______________
4. Determine the percent of change in sales of the video game from Week 1 to Week 3 in Japan. Round to the nearest whole percent.

____

5. Which country had a greater percent decrease in sales from Week 1 to Week 2: Japan or the United States? Explain.

____

Video Game Sales History		
Week	Japan Sales ($)	U.S. Sales ($)
1	580,510	1,213,264
2	185,528	415,320
3	149,045	263,825

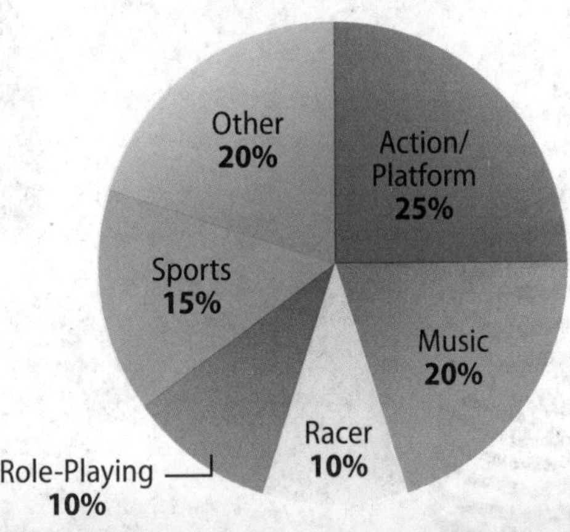

TEKS Career Project

It's time to update your career portfolio! Choose one of your favorite video games. Make a list of what you think are the best features of the game. Then prepare a brief oral presentation to your classmate describing any changes that you, as a video game designer, would make to the game. At the end, ask any clarifying questions.

List the strengths you have that would help you succeed in this career.

-
-
-
-
-

Chapter Review

Vocabulary Check

Work with a partner to complete the crossword puzzle using the vocabulary list at the beginning of the chapter. Take turns reading each sentence aloud while the other student listens carefully.

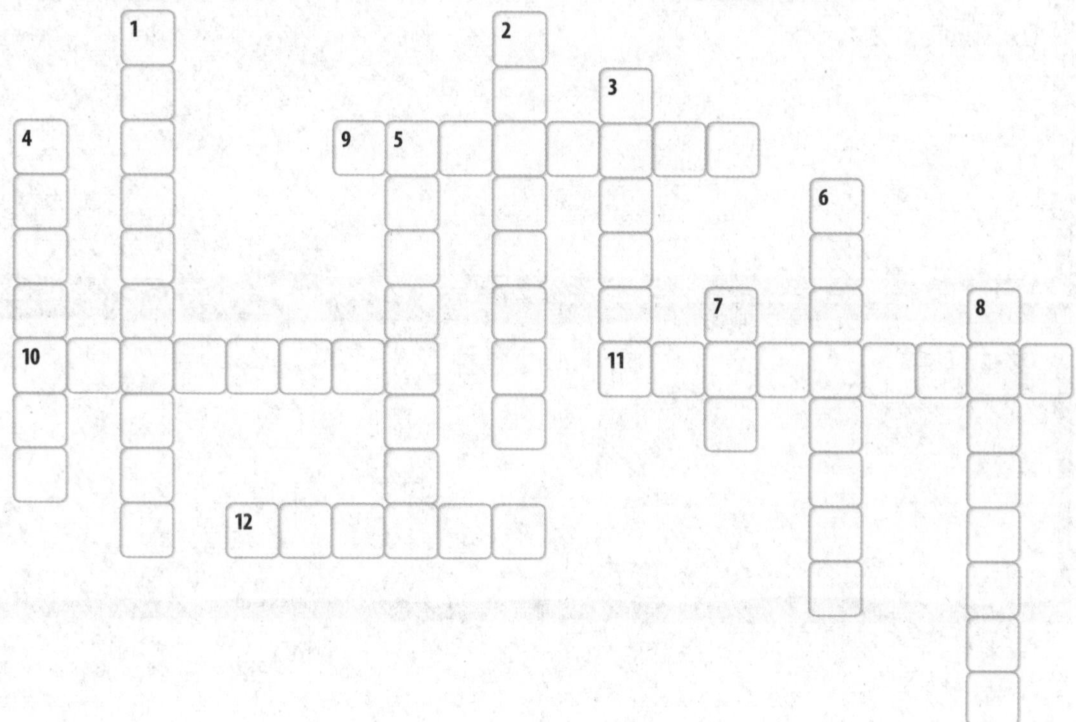

Down

1. statement that two ratios are equal
2. amount that the regular price is reduced
3. difference between what a store pays for an item and what a customer pays
4. price that a customer pays for an item
5. mathematical sentence stating that two expressions are equal
6. another term for the term in 2 down
7. gratuity
8. additional amount of money charged to items that people buy

Across

9. type of percent when the final amount is less than the original amount
10. amount paid or earned for the use of money
11. amount of money deposited or borrowed
12. type of percent that compares the final and original amounts

Key Concept Check

Use Your FOLDABLES

Use your Foldable to help review the chapter. Share your Foldable with a partner and take turns summarizing what you learned in this chapter, while the other partner listens carefully. Ask for and give help of any concept if needed. TEKS 7.1(E)

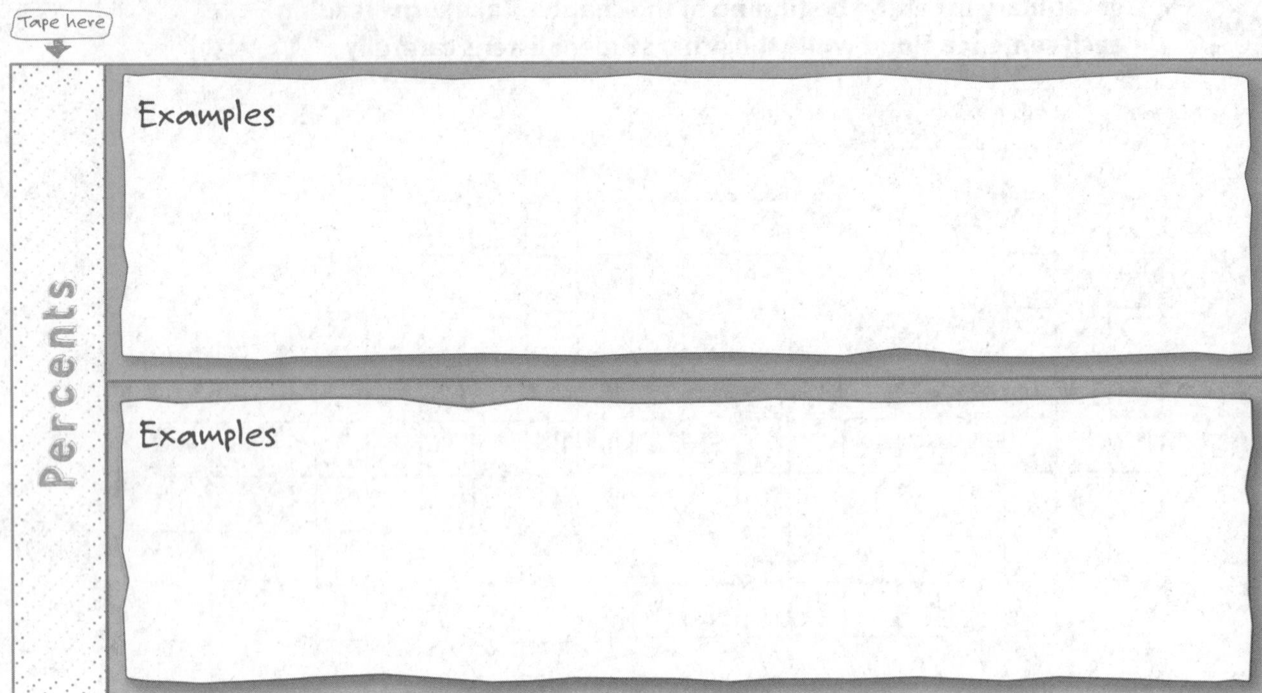

Got it?

Match each equation with its solution. TEKS 7.4(D)

1. $0.15w = 45$	**a.** 125%
2. $15 = 20n$	**b.** 12
3. $0.3(60) = p$	**c.** 300
4. $600n = 750$	**d.** 18
5. $0.15(80) = x$	**e.** 75%
6. $20 = 0.8w$	**f.** 25

Multi-Step Problem Solving

7. The table shows the results of a survey in which 175 randomly selected students were asked what type of food they wanted for an end-of-year celebration. The school will order food for 1,200 students. Each order will serve one student. How many more orders of Tex-Mex should they order than Italian? Justify your solution. N P MP

Type of Food	Percent
Subs	32
Tex-Mex	56
Italian	12

1 Analyze

2 Plan

3 Solve

4 Justify and Evaluate

Got it?

8. Margie and three of her friends went to a restaurant. The bill was \$47.02. Sales tax of 6% is added to the bill and a 15% tip is left on the amount after the tax is added. The four friends split the bill before the tip, and Margie decides to pay for the tip herself. How more did Margie pay than each of her friends? Round to the nearest cent. Justify your solution. N P MP

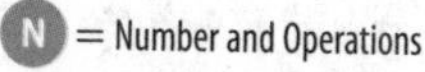

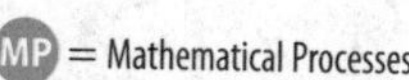

Reflect

Answering the Essential Question

Use what you learned about percent to complete the graphic organizer. For each situation, circle an arrow to show if the final amount would be greater or less than the original amount. Then write a real-world percent problem and an equation that models it. TEKS 7.1(D), 7.1(F), 7.1(G)

Essential Question

HOW can percent help you understand situations involving money?

Sales Tax	Simple Interest	Discount
⇧ ⇩	⇧ ⇩	⇧ ⇩
Equation:	Equation:	Equation:

Answer the Essential Question. HOW can percent help you understand situations involving money? Verbally share your response with a partner, asking for and giving help if needed.

Chapter 4

Apply Proportionality to Geometry

Texas Essential Knowledge and Skills

Targeted TEKS

7.5 The student applies mathematical process standards to use geometry to describe or solve problems involving proportional relationships. *Also addresses 7.8, 7.9.*

Mathematical Processes

7.1, 7.1(A), 7.1(B), 7.1(C), 7.1(D), 7.1(E), 7.1(F), 7.1(G)

Essential Question

HOW can proportional relationships be applied to geometry?

Math in the Real World

Rio Grande Wild Turkeys are found throughout Texas. The adult turkey is about 48 inches in length. The northern mockingbird is smaller than the turkey. If it is $\frac{1}{6}$ the size of the turkey, fill in the blank with the correct measurement for the length of the mockingbird in the drawing.

What Tools Do You Need?

Vocab

Vocabulary

attribute
center
circle
circumference
diameter
pi (π)
radius
scale
scale drawing
scale factor
scale model
similar figures

Studying Math

Power Notes *Power notes* are similar to lesson outlines, but they are simpler to organize. Power notes use the numbers 1, 2, 3, and so on. You can have more than one detail under each power. You can even add drawings or examples to your power notes.

Power 1: This is the main idea.

Power 2: This provides details about the main idea.

Power 3: This provides details about Power 2. and so on...

Work with a partner to complete the following sample of power notes for this chapter. Then share your notes with a partner, discussing any differences.

1: Circles

2: Circumference

3: ______________________________

3: ______________________________

2: Area

3: ______________________________

When Will You Use This?

Raul, Caitlyn, and Jamar in

Campfire Song

Wow! Kayaking sure is fun! Camp is turning out to be a blast!

If Caitlyn hadn't rescued me, I'd be going in circles for hours! It took me forever to get it straight!

Now I'm so hungry I could eat a kayak!

Well, you can do that if you want to, Jamar! As for me, I need to get back to the cabin and get my camera before dinner.

Gotcha!

After that, Raul and I need to get to the campfire early to practice our song.

Song?

♪

Yes! We have been preparing a song for the campfire tonight!

Oh yeah! That's tonight! So... um, where is the campfire exactly?

I don't know. I thought you knew!

Jamar? Do you know where it is, or how far away it is?

And Jamar saves the day! I brought a map! We can figure out how far it is from here.

CABIN

LAKE

ROPES COURSE

1 SQ CM = 75 YARDS

MESS HALL

PICNIC AREA

CAMPFIRE

Awesome! Jamar, you are the greatest!

Maybe you can use your greatness to get us to dinner quickly! I'm getting hungry!

Your Turn! **You will solve this problem in the chapter.**

Are You Ready?

Quick Review

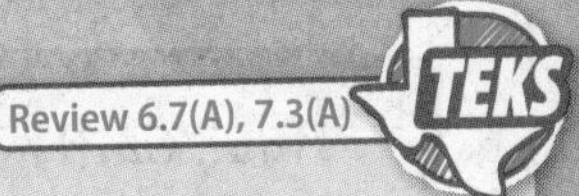

Example 1

Evaluate 2^3.

$2^3 = 2 \cdot 2 \cdot 2$

$= 8$

Example 2

Express 5 • 5 • 5 in exponential form.

5 is the base. It is used as a factor 3 times. So, the exponent is 3.

$5 \cdot 5 \cdot 5 = 5^3$

Example 3

Determine 3.14 × 4.

$3.14 \times 4 = 12.56$ Multiply.

Example 4

Determine $\frac{22}{7} \times 14$.

$\frac{22}{7} \times 14 = \frac{22}{7} \times \frac{14}{1}$ Write 14 as $\frac{14}{1}$.

$= \frac{22}{\cancel{7}_1} \times \frac{\cancel{14}^2}{1}$ Divide 7 and 14 by their GCF.

$= \frac{44}{1}$ or 44 Multiply.

Quick Check

Exponents **Evaluate each expression.**

1. $2^2 =$ ______

2. $3^3 =$ ______

3. $4^2 =$ ______

4. Express 4 • 4 • 4 • 4 in exponential form. ______

Rational Number Operations **Multiply.**

5. $3.14 \times 8 =$ ______

6. $\frac{22}{7} \times 28 =$ ______

7. $3.14 \times 11 =$ ______

Which problems did you answer correctly in the Quick Check? Shade those exercise numbers below.

1 2 3 4 5 6 7

Use this Foldable throughout this chapter to help you learn about proportionality and geometry.

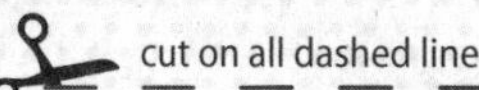

cut on all dashed lines

fold on all solid lines

tape to page 356

Similar Figures

angles	scale
sides	scale factor
similar figures	scale drawing

Scale Drawings

Use this Foldable throughout this chapter to help you learn about proportionality and geometry.

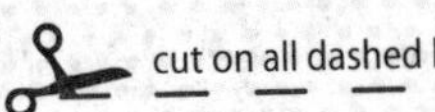

cut on all dashed lines

fold on all solid lines

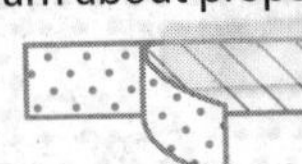

tape to page 356

page 356

Words

Example

Write about it

page 356

Words

Example

Write about it

Words

Example

Picture

Tab 2

Tab 1

Hands-On Lab 1-a

Investigate Online Maps and Scale Drawings

INQUIRY HOW can I select tools and techniques to determine how the zoom feature of an online map is like a scale drawing?

Texas Essential Knowledge and Skills TEKS

Targeted TEKS
7.5(C) Solve mathematical and real-world problems involving similar shape and scale drawings.

Mathematical Processes
7.1(C), 7.1(D), 7.1(E), 7.1(F)

Maps and blueprints are *scale drawings* of the locations and buildings they represent. Unlike maps printed on paper, online map services allow users the opportunity to view a location from different distances.

Maps | Directions | Info

Start Here | Country

Business or Name: Name of your School

Address or location

City: Your Town | State | Zip Code

Hands-On Activity 1

Step 1 Use the online map service provided to you by your teacher. Locate your school on a map.

Step 2 Measure the length of the scale bar in centimeters on the online map. Determine the scale distance of the map. Write these values in the Original View table in Step 4.

Step 3 Click on the satellite or aerial view. Use the zoom feature to zoom in until your school shows up on the map.

Step 4 Measure the length of the scale bar in centimeters. Determine the new scale distance for the map. Write these values in the Zoom View table.

Original View	
Scale Bar	
Scale Distance	

Zoom View	
Scale Bar	
Scale Distance	

1. What happens when you use the zoom feature?

2. Describe the appearance of the map as you zoomed in.

Investigate

Collaborate

MP Select Tools and Techniques Work with a partner to answer the following questions about using an online map service.

3. Locate the local public library on the map. Write the scale bar and scale distance values in the Original View table below Exercise 4.

4. Click on the satellite or aerial view. Use the zoom feature to zoom in until the building shows up on the map. Write the scale bar and scale distance values in the Zoom View table.

Original View	
Scale Bar	
Scale Distance	

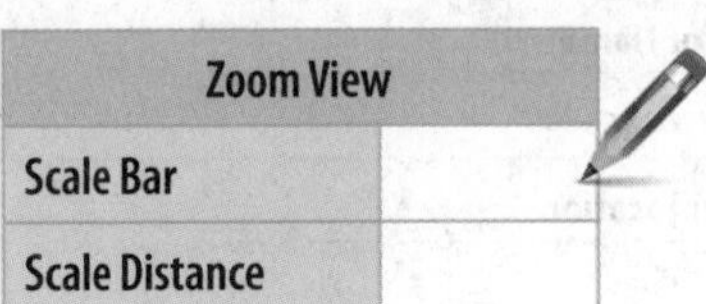

Zoom View	
Scale Bar	
Scale Distance	

Analyze and Reflect

Collaborate

Work with a partner to answer the following questions about using an online map.

5. Refer to Activity 1. Write a ratio $\frac{\text{scale bar}}{\text{scale distance}}$ for the original view and the zoom view.

Original View: ______ Zoom View: ______

6. How many times bigger is the zoom view?

7. How does zooming in affect the scale on the map?

8. When using the zoom feature on an online map, what changes and what stays the same?

Hands-On Activity 2

The diagram shown represents a garden. The scale is 1 centimeter = 30 meters. That means that each square on the grid measures 1 centimeter by 1 centimeter, or 30 meters by 30 meters.

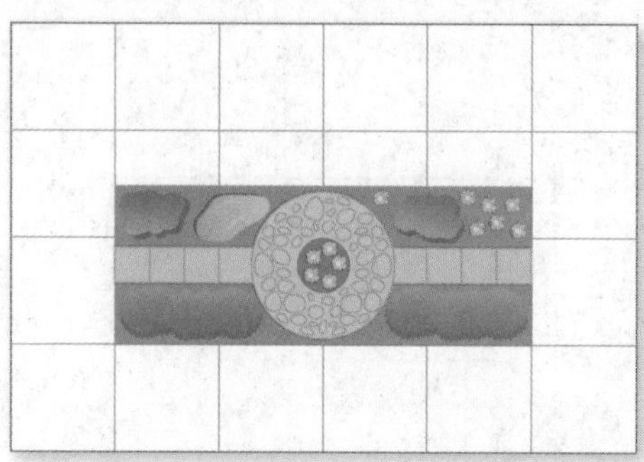

Step 1 Write the length and width of the drawing of the garden.

Length: ________ centimeters Width: ________ centimeters

Step 2 Use the scale to determine the dimensions of the garden.

Length: ________ meters Width: ________ meters

Step 3 On the grid below, draw the garden so that the scale is 1 centimeter = 10 meters. Write the dimensions of your drawing.

Length: ________ centimeters Width: ________ centimeters

9. Use the scale on your drawing to compute the dimensions of the garden. How do the dimensions compare to the dimensions in Step 2?

Length: ________ meters Width: ________ meters

Investigate

Work with a partner to answer the following questions about reproducing a scale drawing.

10. Recreate the drawing of the baseball diamond below using the new scale.

current scale: 1 unit = 15 ft
new scale: 1 unit = 30 ft

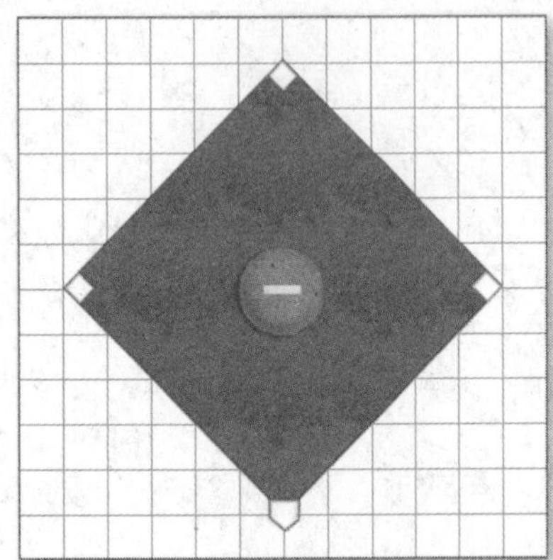

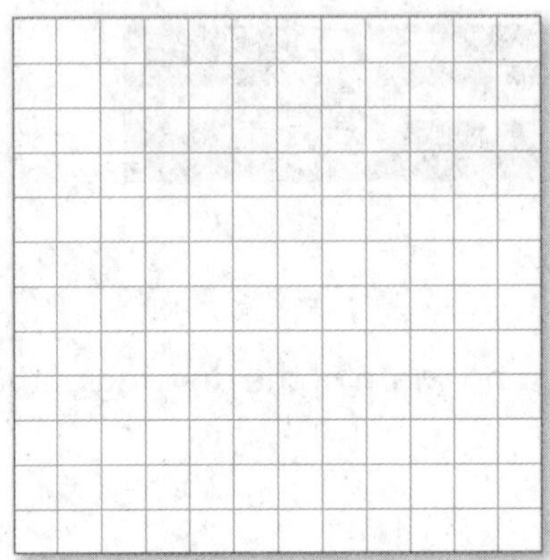

11. A drawing of the Statue of Liberty is 3 inches tall. The scale is 1 inch = 50 feet. How tall would the drawing be if the scale were 0.5 inch = 100 feet? ______________________

Analyze and Reflect

12. MP **Analyze Relationships** The triangle shown in the drawing has an area of 40 square feet. What is the scale of the drawing? ______________________

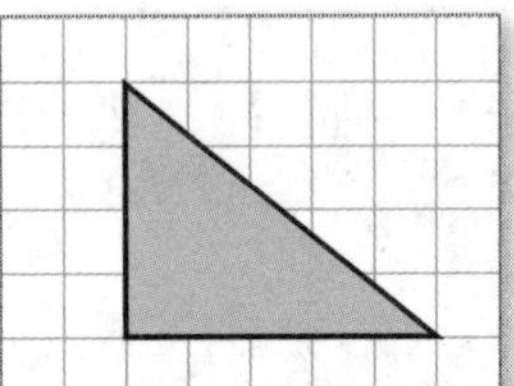

Create

13. MP **Use Multiple Representations** Using a separate piece of grid paper, create a map of your classroom or a room in your home. Identify the scale you used. ______________________

14. INQUIRY HOW can I select tools and techniques to determine how the zoom feature of an online map is like a scale drawing?

____

____

____

Lesson 1

Scale Drawings

Launch the Lesson: Real World

Texas Essential Knowledge and Skills

Targeted TEKS

7.5(C) Solve mathematical and real-world problems involving similar shape and scale drawings.

Mathematical Processes

7.1(A), 7.1(B), 7.1(C), 7.1(E)

Vocabulary

scale drawing
scale model
scale
scale factor

Essential Question

HOW can proportional relationships be applied to geometry?

Architects make detailed drawings of rooms and buildings. Conner made a drawing of a bedroom. Follow the steps below to make a model of a room of your choosing.

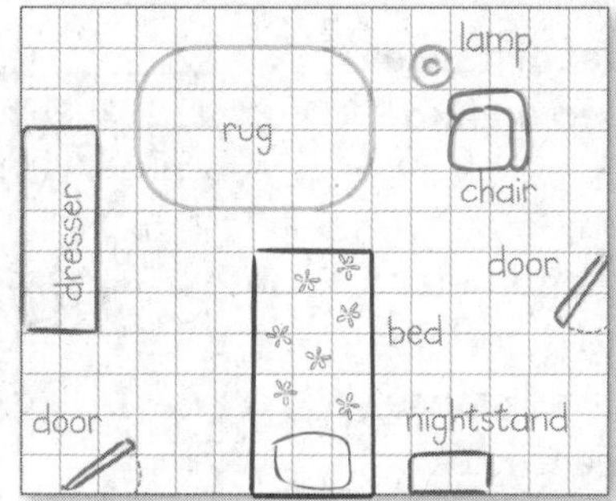

Step 1 Measure the length of three objects in the room. Record each length to the nearest $\frac{1}{2}$ foot in the table below.

Object	Length (ft)	Length (units)

Step 2 Let 1 unit represent 2 feet. So, 4 units = 8 feet. Convert all your measurements to units. Record these values.

Step 3 On grid paper, make a drawing of your room like the one shown above.

Which MP Mathematical Processes did you use? Shade the circle(s) that applies.

Ⓐ Apply Math to the Real World.
Ⓑ Use a Problem-Solving Model.
Ⓒ Select Tools and Techniques.
Ⓓ Use Multiple Representations.
Ⓔ Organize Ideas.
Ⓕ Analyze Relationships.
Ⓖ Justify Arguments.

Work Zone

Use a Scale Drawing or a Scale Model

Scale drawings and **scale models** are used to represent objects that are too large or too small to be drawn or built at actual size. The **scale** gives the ratio that compares the measurements of the drawing or model to the measurements of the real object. The measurements on a drawing or model are proportional to the measurements on the actual object.

Example

1. What is the actual distance between Hagerstown and Annapolis?

Step 1 Use a centimeter ruler to determine the map distance betweenthe two cities. The map distance is about 4 centimeters.

Step 2 Write and solve a proportion using the scale. Let d represent the actual distance between the cities.

	Scale		Length	
map →	1 centimeter	=	4 centimeter	← map
actual →	24 miles		d miles	← actual

$$\frac{1 \text{ centimeter}}{24 \text{ miles}} = \frac{4 \text{ centimeter}}{d \text{ miles}}$$

$$1 \times d = 24 \times 4 \quad \text{Cross products}$$

$$d = 96 \quad \text{Simplify.}$$

The distance between the cities is about 96 miles.

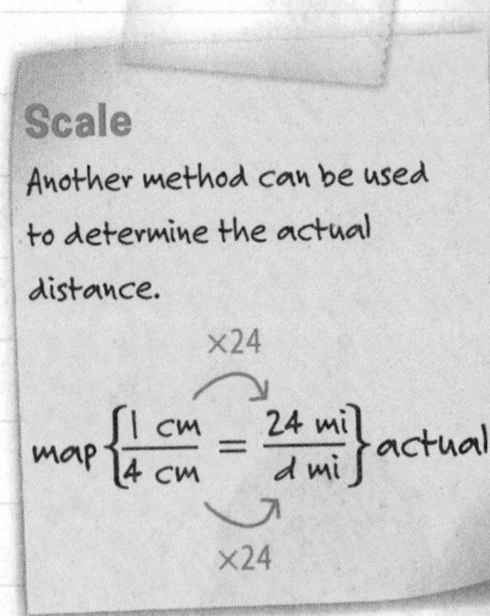

Got It? Do this problem to find out.

a. On the map of Texas shown, determine the actual distance between Mount Vernon and Dallas. Use a ruler to measure.

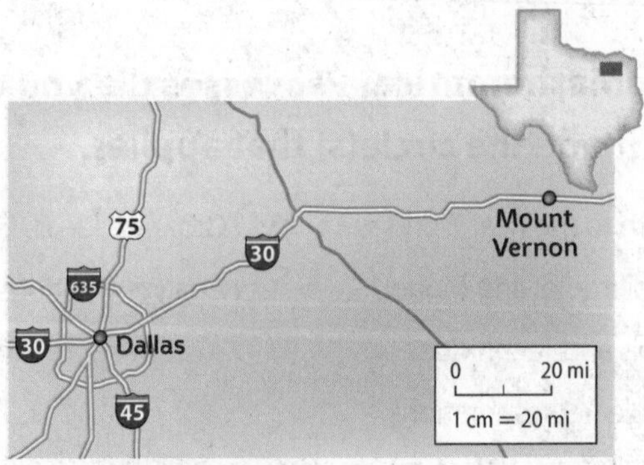

Show your work.

a. ________

Example

Tutor

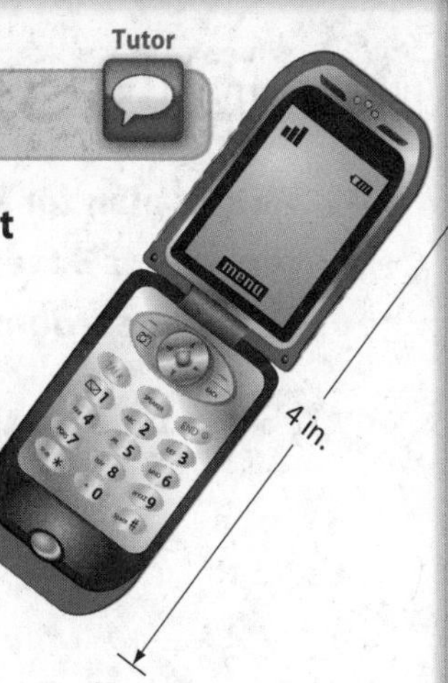

2. A graphic artist is creating an advertisement for this cell phone. If she uses a scale of 5 inches = 1 inch, what is the length of the cell phone on the advertisement?

Write a proportion using the scale. Let a represent the length of the advertisement cell phone.

	Scale		Length	
advertisement →	5 inches	=	a inches	← advertisement
actual →	1 inch		4 inches	← actual

$5 \cdot 4 = 1 \cdot a$ Cross products

$20 = a$ Simplify.

The length of the cell phone on the advertisement is 20 inches long.

Scale

The scale is the ratio of the drawing or model measure to the actual measure. It is not always the ratio of a smaller measure to a larger measure.

Got It? Do this problem to find out.

b. A scooter is $3\frac{1}{2}$ feet long. Determine the length of a scale model of the scooter if the scale is 1 inch = $\frac{3}{4}$ feet.

b. ______________

Determine a Scale Factor

A scale expressed as a ratio without units in simplest form is called the **scale factor**.

Example

Tutor

3. Determine the scale factor of a model sailboat if the scale is 1 inch = 6 feet.

$\frac{1 \text{ inch}}{6 \text{ feet}} = \frac{1 \text{ inch}}{72 \text{ inches}}$ Convert 6 feet to inches.

$= \frac{1}{72}$ Divide out the common units.

The scale factor is $\frac{1}{72}$.

Got It? Do this problem to find out.

c. What is the scale factor of a model car if the scale is 1 inch = 2 feet?

c. ______________

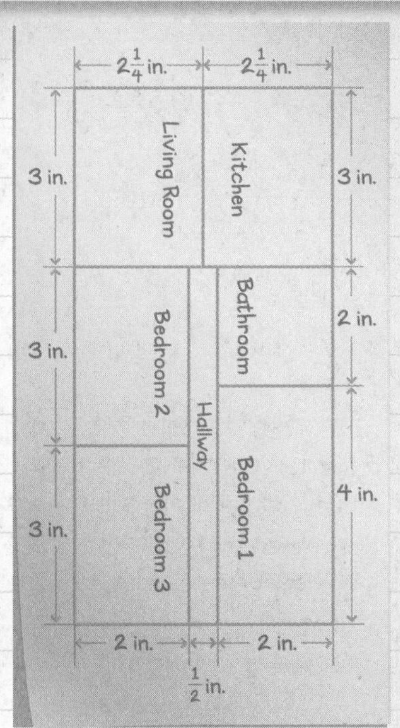

Multi-Step Example

4. A floor plan for a home is shown at the left where $\frac{1}{2}$ inch represents 3 feet of the actual home. What is the actual area of bedroom 1?

Step 1 **Length of Bedroom 1**

$\frac{\frac{1}{2} \text{ in.}}{3 \text{ ft}} = \frac{4 \text{ in.}}{\ell}$ ← floor plan ← actual

$\frac{1}{2}\ell = 12$ Find cross products.

$\ell = 24$ Divide each side by $\frac{1}{2}$.

Step 2 **Width of Bedroom 1**

$\frac{\frac{1}{2} \text{ in.}}{3 \text{ ft}} = \frac{2 \text{ in.}}{w}$ ← floor plan ← actual

$\frac{1}{2}w = 6$ Find cross products.

$w = 12$ Divide each side by $\frac{1}{2}$.

So, the area of bedroom 1 is 24 × 12 or 288 square feet.

Got It? **Do this problem to find out.**

Show your work.

d. What is the actual area of bedroom 3?

d. ______

Guided Practice

1. On a map, the distance from Falls City, Texas, to Pleasanton, Texas, measures 2 centimeters. What is the actual distance if the scale of the map shows that 1 centimeter is equal to 30 kilometers? (Example 1)

______

2. An engineer makes a model of a bridge using a scale of 1 inch = 3 yards. The length of the actual bridge is 50 yards. What is the length of the model? (Example 2)

______

3. Julie is constructing a scale model of her room. The rectangular room is $10\frac{1}{4}$ inches by 8 inches. If 1 inch represents 2 feet of the actual room, what is the scale factor and the actual area of the room? (Examples 3 and 4)

______

4. **Building on the Essential Question** Explain how you could use a map to estimate the actual distance between El Paso, Texas, and Lubbock, Texas.

______

______

Rate Yourself!

How well do you understand scale drawings? Circle the image that applies.

Clear

Somewhat Clear

Not So Clear

Find out online. Use the Self-Check Quiz.

FOLDABLES Time to update your Foldable!

Independent Practice

7.5(C), 7.1(A), 7.1(C) TEKS

Select Tools and Techniques Determine the actual distance between each pair of locations in Texas. Use a ruler to measure. (Example 1)

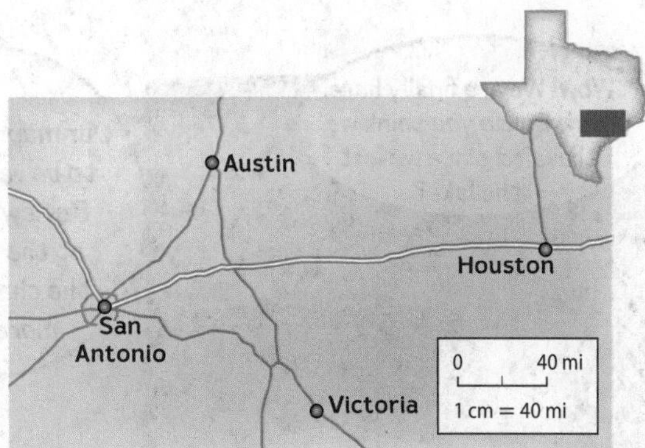

1. Houston and San Antonio ______

2. Austin and Victoria ______

Determine the length of each model. Then determine the scale factor.
(Examples 2 and 3)

3.

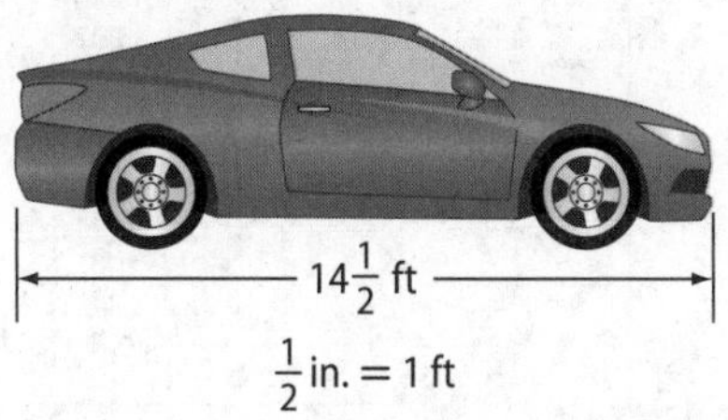

$\frac{1}{2}$ in. = 1 ft

4.

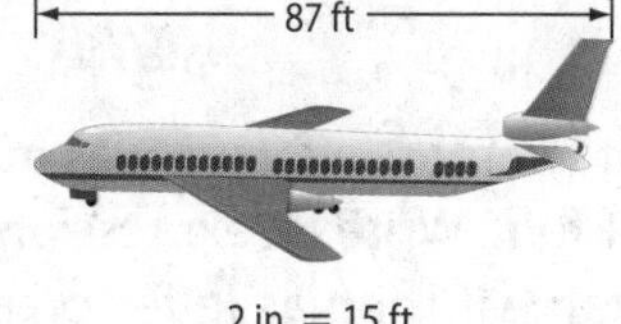

2 in. = 15 ft

5. A model of an apartment is shown where $\frac{1}{4}$ inch represents 3 feet in the actual apartment. Determine the actual area of the master bedroom. (Example 4)

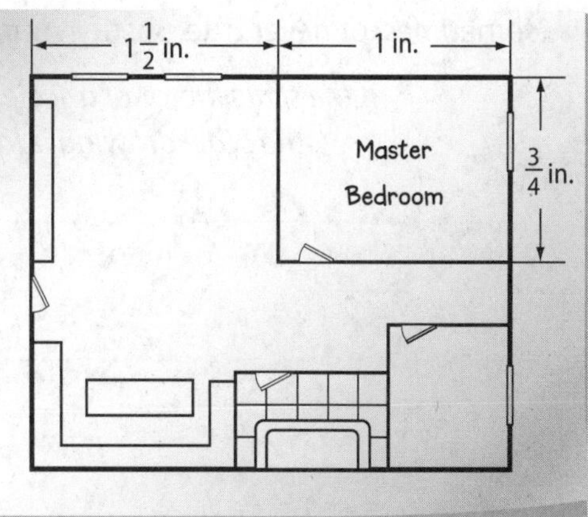

6. MP **Apply Math to the Real World** Refer to the graphic novel frame at the beginning of the chapter. The scale on the map shows that 1 centimeter is equal to 75 yards. If the red line represents the path they took, how far have Raul, Caitlyn, and Jamar traveled since they left the lake? The red line is 17 centimeters long. ______

H.O.T. Problems Higher-Order Thinking

7. **Create** On the grid paper, create a scale drawing of an insect in your science book. Include the scale that you used.

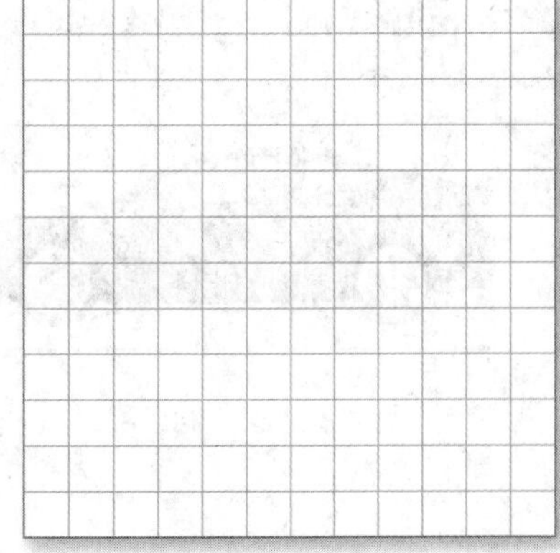

8. **Create** A statue of Thomas Jefferson was made using a scale of 3 feet = 1 foot. Write an expression to represent the height of the statue if Thomas Jefferson is *x* feet in height. Then determine his actual height if the height of the statue is $18\frac{1}{2}$ feet.

______

9. **Evaluate** Determine whether the following statement is *always*, *sometimes*, or *never* true. Justify your reasoning.

If the scale factor of a scale drawing is greater than one, the scale drawing is larger than the actual object.

______

Name ______________________________

Multi-Step Problem Solving

10. Roger is building a storage shed. The blue print uses a scale of 1 inch = 3 feet. How many square feet of storage room will Roger have? N P MP

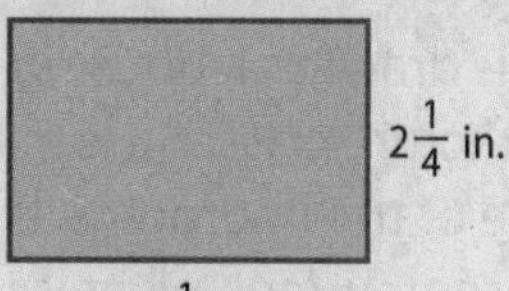

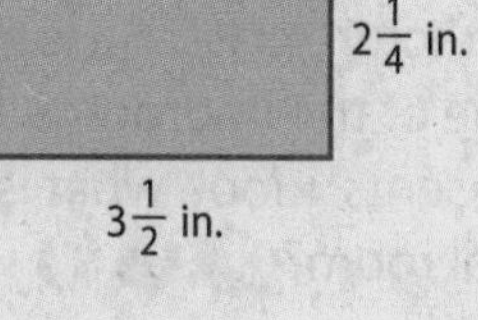

Ⓐ $23\frac{5}{8}$ ft^2 Ⓒ $65\frac{7}{8}$ ft^2

Ⓑ $55\frac{1}{8}$ ft^2 Ⓓ $70\frac{7}{8}$ ft^2

Use a problem-solving model to solve this problem.

1 Analyze

Read the problem. Circle the information you know. Underline what the problem is asking you to find.

2 Plan

What will you need to do to solve the problem? Write your plan in steps.

Step 1 Use the ______________ to determine the dimensions of the storage shed.

Step 2 Multiply the length by the width to determine the ________.

3 Solve

Use your plan to solve the problem. Show your steps.

$\frac{1 \text{ in.}}{3 \text{ ft}} = \frac{3\frac{1}{2} \text{ in.}}{\ell \text{ ft}}$ $\ell =$ ______ $\frac{1 \text{ in.}}{3 \text{ ft}} = \frac{2\frac{1}{4} \text{ in.}}{w \text{ ft}}$ 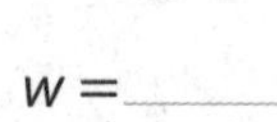 $w =$ ______

Determine the area.

______ × ______ = ______

The area of Roger's storage shed is ______ square feet.

So, the correct answer is ____. Fill in that answer choice.

Read to Succeed!
Make sure you use the scale factor to determine the dimensions of the shed before calculating the area.

4 Justify and Evaluate

How do you know your solution is accurate?

____

____

____

N = Number and Operations P = Proportionality MP = Mathematical Processes

More Multi-Step Problem Solving

Use a problem-solving model to solve each problem.

11. Cory is drawing a housing plan for his architecture class. He is making a scale model of one of the bedrooms. If the scale is 3 inches represents 1 foot, what is the area of the actual room? P N MP

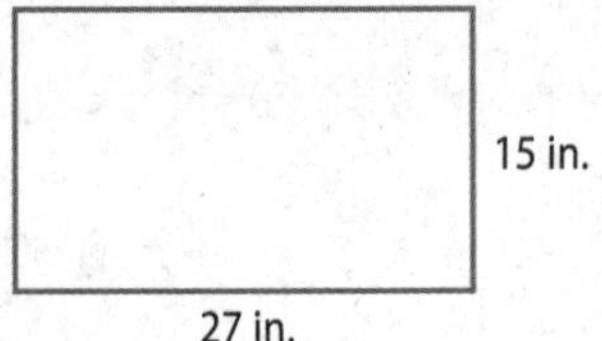

Ⓐ 45 square feet
Ⓑ 48 square feet
Ⓒ 54 square feet
Ⓓ 63 square feet

12. Shantel wants to know the area of the gymnasium floor at her school. She found a scale drawing that shows the square gym measured $4\frac{1}{2}$ inches long. If the scale is 1 inch = 5 feet, what is the actual area of the gym in square feet? P N MP

13. Elisha was born in Aruba but now lives in the U.S. She wants to determine the length of the island of Aruba. Using the scale map below, determine the length of Aruba in yards, from Cudarebe to Ceru Colorado. P MD MP

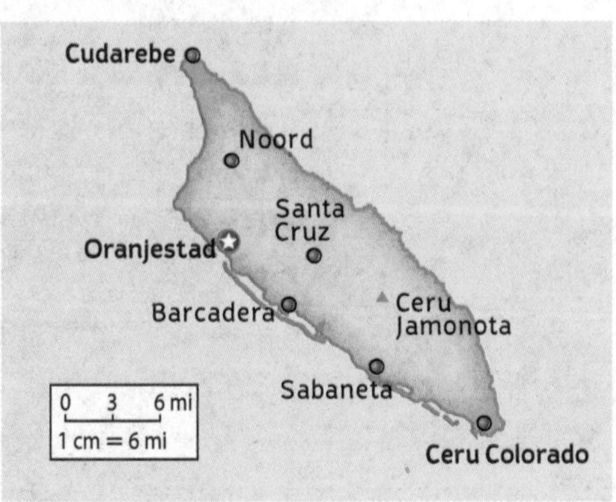

14. Tevon plans to tile a friend's kitchen. On a scale drawing, the rectangular kitchen is 6 inches by 8 inches. The scale shows that 1 inch equal $1\frac{1}{2}$ feet. Use this information to determine how much it would cost to use Travertine, in dollars. P N MP

Tile Style	Cost per Square feet ($)
Ceramic	6.50
Marble	8.00
Travertine	9.75

N = Number and Operations P = Proportionality MD = Measurement and Data MP = Mathematical Processes

Hands-On Lab 2-a

Similar Triangles

INQUIRY HOW can I select tools and techniques to determine how two triangles are related if they have the same shape, but different sizes?

Texas Essential Knowledge and Skills

Targeted TEKS

7.5(A) Generalize the critical attributes of similarity, including ratios within and between similar shapes. *Also addresses 7.5(C).*

Mathematical Processes

7.1(C), 7.1(D), 7.1(E), 7.1(F), 7.1(G)

Triangles, like the ones shown below, are used in the design of many structures, including buildings, bridges, and amusement park rides. The triangles used often have some attributes that are the same. An **attribute** is a characteristic of a figure, such as side and angle measures. You can compare attributes using ratios between the triangles.

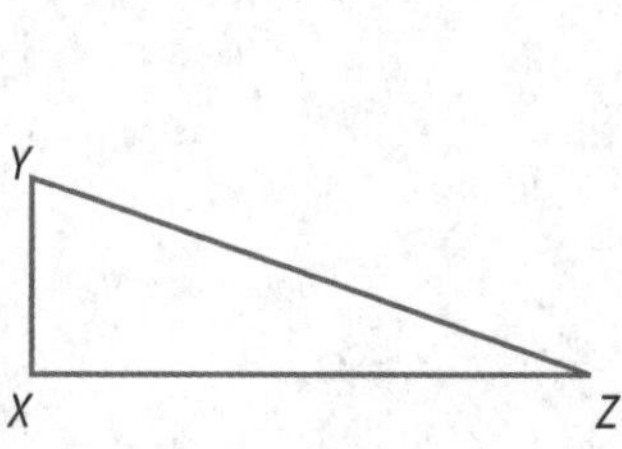

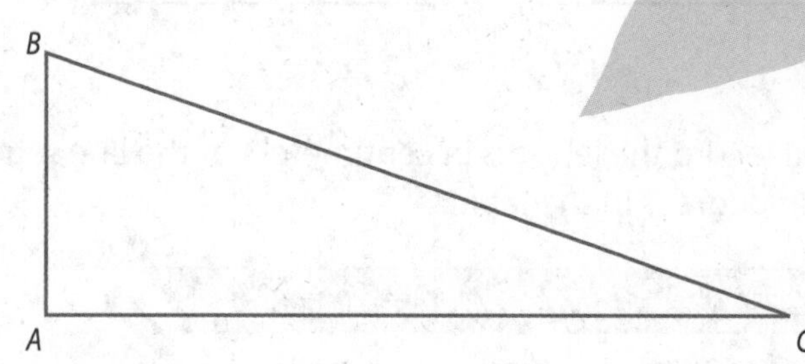

Hands-On Activity 1

Step 1 Measure and record the lengths in centimeters of the line segments and angles in degrees in the table.

$\triangle XYZ$		$\triangle ABC$	
$XY =$	$m\angle X =$	$AB =$	$m\angle A =$
$XZ =$	$m\angle Y =$	$AC =$	$m\angle B =$
$YZ =$	$m\angle Z =$	$BC =$	$m\angle C =$

1. What do you notice about the measure of the corresponding angles of the triangles? ______

Step 2 Express the lengths of the corresponding sides between the triangles as ratios.

$\frac{AB}{XY} =$ ______ $\frac{AC}{XZ} =$ ______ $\frac{BC}{YZ} =$ ______

2. What do you notice about the ratios of the corresponding sides between the triangles? ______

Hands-On Activity 2

You can compare attributes using ratios within the triangles as well.

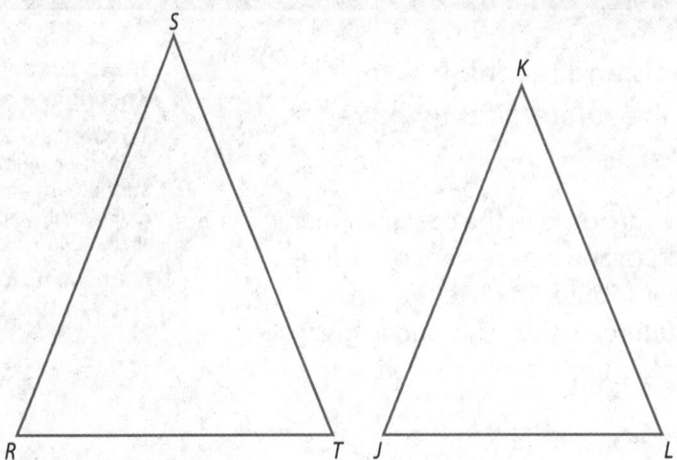

Step 1 Measure and record the lengths in centimeters of the line segments and angles in degrees in the table.

$\triangle RST$		$\triangle JKL$	
$RS =$	$m\angle R =$	$JK =$	$m\angle J =$
$ST =$	$m\angle S =$	$KL =$	$m\angle K =$
$RT =$	$m\angle T =$	$JL =$	$m\angle L =$

3. What do you notice about the measure of the corresponding angles of the triangles? ______

4. Compare the sides lengths of the triangles above. What do you notice?

______

Step 2 Express the lengths of the corresponding sides within the triangles as ratios. Round to the nearest thousandth.

$\frac{RT}{RS} =$ ______ $\frac{RT}{ST} =$ ______

$\frac{JL}{JK} =$ ______ $\frac{JL}{KL} =$ ______

5. What do you notice about the ratios of the corresponding sides within the triangles? ______

Work with a partner.

6. **MP Select Tools and Techniques** On the grid, draw and label triangle *XYZ*, using a scale factor of $\frac{1}{3}$.

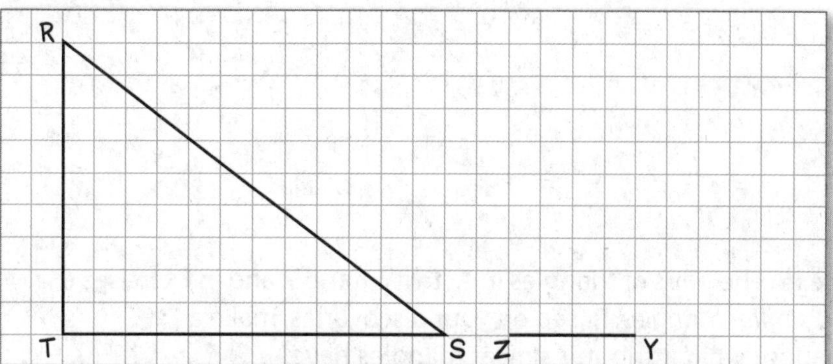

a. Determine the ratios of the corresponding sides for each triangle.

Between Triangles | **Within Triangles**

$\frac{XZ}{RT}$ = ______ $\frac{YZ}{ST}$ = ______ $\frac{RT}{ST}$ = ______ $\frac{XZ}{YZ}$ = ______

b. What do you notice about the ratios of corresponding sides between triangles? Within triangles? ______

7. **MP Select Tools and Techniques** On the grid, draw and label triangle *MNO*, using a scale factor of 2.

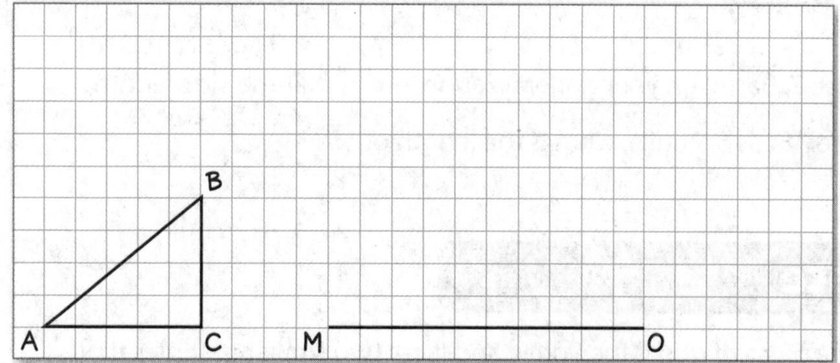

a. Determine the ratios of the corresponding sides for each triangle.

Between Triangles | **Within Triangles**

$\frac{MO}{AC}$ = ______ $\frac{NO}{BC}$ = ______ $\frac{BC}{AC}$ = ______ $\frac{NO}{MO}$ = ______

b. What do you notice about the ratios of corresponding sides between triangles? Within triangles? ______

Analyze and Reflect

Collaborate

Work with a partner.

8. **MP Organize Ideas** Refer to Exercises 6 and 7. What do you notice about the scale factors used to draw the new triangles?

9. **MP Organize Ideas** The pairs of triangles in Activity 1 and 2 and in Exercises 6 and 7 are called *similar triangles*. Based on your discoveries, make a generalization about what attributes similar triangles have.

10. Refer to Exercise 6. Based on your generalization, given that the side length of $\overline{RS}$ in triangle *RST* is 15 units, what is the length of $\overline{XY}$? ______

11. Refer to Exercise 7. Based on your generalization, given that the side length of $\overline{AB}$ in triangle *ABC* is 6.5 units, what is the length of $\overline{MN}$? ______

Create

On Your Own

12. **Create** Using a piece of grid paper, draw and label two similar triangles that have a ratio between their corresponding sides of $\frac{1}{2}$.

13. **INQUIRY** HOW can I select tools and techniques to determine how two triangles are related if they have the same shape, but different sizes?

Lesson 2

Critical Attributes of Similar Figures

Launch the Lesson: Real World

Elsa drew the two rectangles below as part of a design. She stated that she drew the larger rectangle first and used a scale factor of $\frac{1}{2}$ to draw the smaller rectangle. Is Elsa's statement correct? Explain.

Collaborate Follow the steps to discover how the rectangles are related.

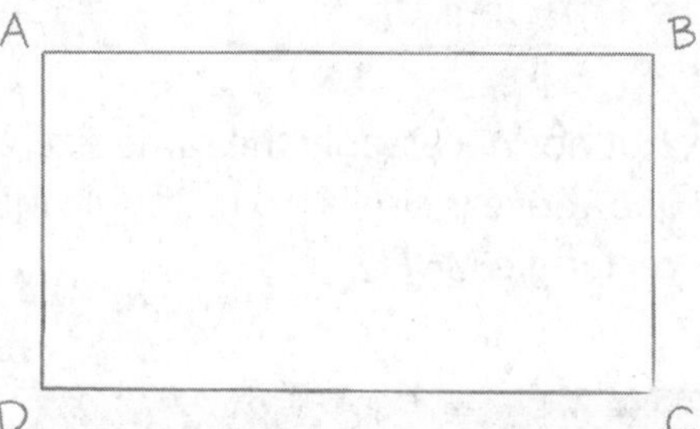

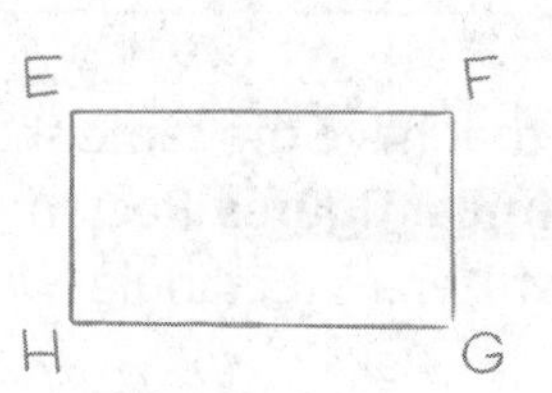

1. Using a centimeter ruler, measure the sides of the two rectangles. Record the results in the table at the right.

Figure	Length (cm)		Width (cm)	
ABCD	*AB*	*CD*	*BC*	*AD*
EFGH	*EF*	*GH*	*FG*	*EH*

2. Are the side lengths between rectangles proportional? Explain.

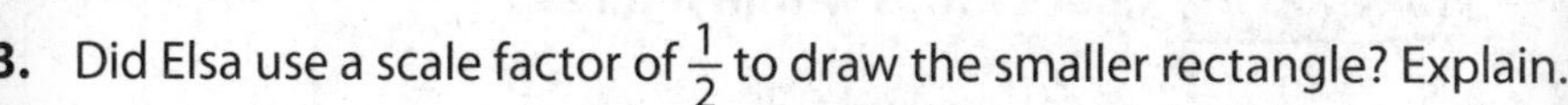

3. Did Elsa use a scale factor of $\frac{1}{2}$ to draw the smaller rectangle? Explain.

Which MP Mathematical Processes did you use? Shade the circle(s) that applies.

Ⓐ Apply Math to the Real World.
Ⓑ Use a Problem-Solving Model.
Ⓒ Select Tools and Techniques.
Ⓓ Use Multiple Representations.
Ⓔ Organize Ideas.
Ⓕ Analyze Relationships.
Ⓖ Justify Arguments.

Texas Essential Knowledge and Skills

Targeted TEKS

7.5(A) Generalize the critical attributes of similarity, including ratios within and between similar shapes. *Also addresses 7.5(C).*

Mathematical Processes

7.1(A), 7.1(B)

Vocabulary

similar figures

Essential Question

HOW can proportional relationships be applied to geometry?

Key Concept

Identify Similar Figures

Words If two figures have congruent corresponding angles and the ratios of their corresponding sides are equivalent, then they are similar.

Model

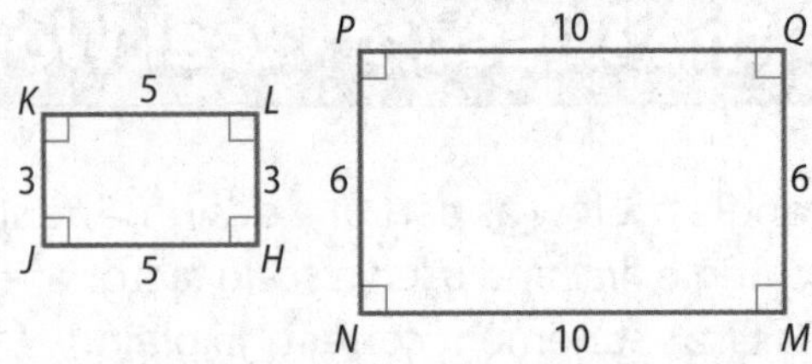

Symbols $\frac{MN}{HJ} = \frac{10}{5}$ or 2 $\frac{NP}{JK} = \frac{6}{3}$ or 2 $\frac{PQ}{KL} = \frac{10}{5}$ or 2 $\frac{QM}{LH} = \frac{6}{3}$ or 2

Work Zone

Proportionality

Another way to say that the ratios of corresponding sides are equivalent is to say the sides are proportional.

Figures that have the same shape, but not necessarily the same size, are called **similar figures**. Rectangle *HJKL* above is similar to rectangle *MNPQ*. This is written as rectangle *HJKL* ~ rectangle *MNPQ*.

Example

1. Determine whether trapezoid *ABCD* is similar to trapezoid *HJKL*. Explain.

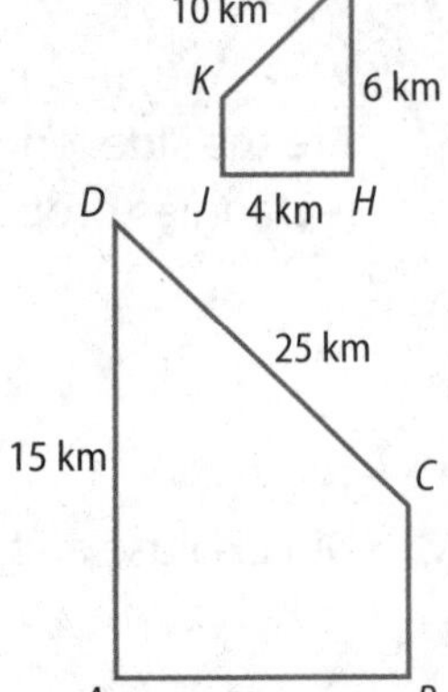

Method 1 **Check ratios between figures.**

$\frac{AB}{HJ} = \frac{10}{4}$ or $2\frac{1}{2}$ $\frac{CD}{KL} = \frac{25}{10}$ or $2\frac{1}{2}$

$\frac{AD}{HL} = \frac{15}{6}$ or $2\frac{1}{2}$

Method 2 **Check ratios within figures.**

$\frac{AB}{AD} = \frac{10}{15}$ or $\frac{2}{3}$ $\frac{HJ}{HL} = \frac{4}{6}$ or $\frac{2}{3}$

Since the ratios between and within figures are equivalent, the trapezoids are similar.

Got It? **Do this problem to find out.**

a. Determine whether $\triangle ABC$ is similar to $\triangle XYZ$. Explain.

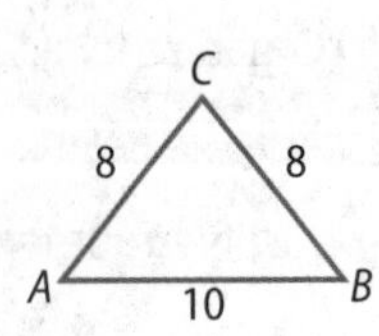

a. ______________

Determine Missing Measures

Key Concept

Work Zone

If you know that two figures are similar, you can determine missing measures.

Words If two polygons are similar, then

- their corresponding angles are congruent and
- the ratios of their corresponding sides are equivalent.

Model

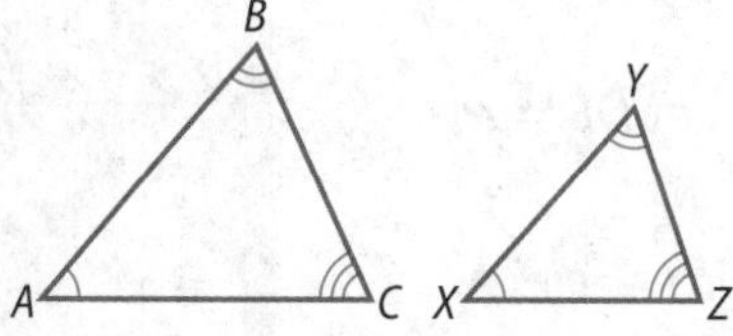

$\triangle ABC \sim \triangle XYZ$

Symbols $\angle A \cong \angle X$, $\angle B \cong \angle Y$, $\angle C \cong \angle Z$, and $\frac{AB}{XY} = \frac{BC}{YZ} = \frac{AC}{XZ}$

You can use a proportion or the scale factor to determine the measure of the sides of similar figures when some measures are known.

Example

Tutor

2. The figures are similar. Determine the missing measure.

Since $\triangle ABC \sim \triangle DEF$, the corresponding angles are congruent and the ratios of the corresponding sides between figures are equivalent.

E
x cm
D
12 cm
F

$\frac{BC}{EF} = \frac{AC}{DF}$ Write a proportion.

$\frac{6}{x} = \frac{4}{12}$ $BC = 6$, $EF = x$, $AC = 4$, and $DF = 12$.

$6 \cdot 12 = x \cdot 4$ Determine the cross products.

$72 = 4x$ Simplify.

$18 = x$ Division Property of Equality

The length of $\overline{EF}$ is 18 centimeters.

Got It? Do these problems to find out.

Show your work.

b.

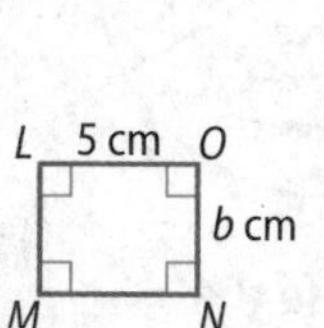

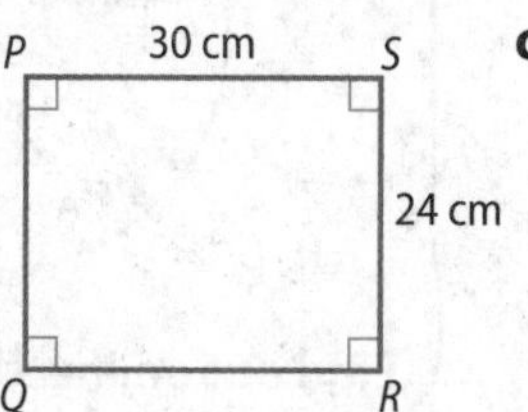

c.

K
a cm
14 cm
J
L

b. ________

c. ________

Example

3. An architect is using similar triangles to design a decorative window for the entrance of a new office building. If $\triangle ABC \sim \triangle DEF$, determine the length of segment *DF*.

Determine the scale factor by determining the ratio of corresponding sides between figures with known lengths.

scale factor: $\frac{BC}{EF} = \frac{18}{9}$ or 2

$\overline{DF}$ corresponds to $\overline{AC}$. Let $DF = m$ and $AC = 25.5$.

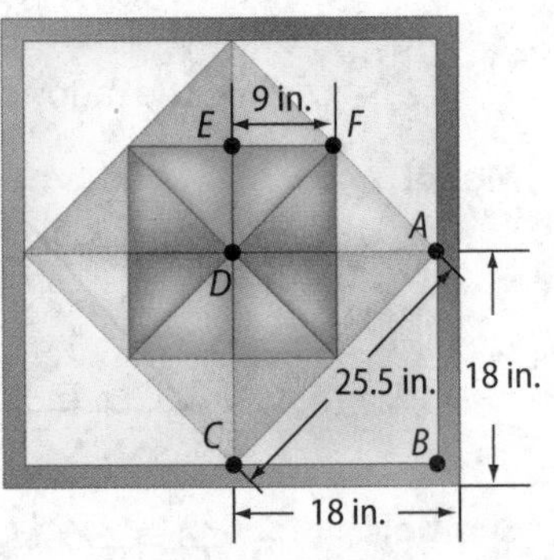

$2m = 25.5$	Write the equation.
$m = 12.75$	Divide each side by 2.

So, the length of *DF* is 12.75 inches.

Guided Practice

Determine whether each pair of polygons is similar. Explain. (Example 1)

1.

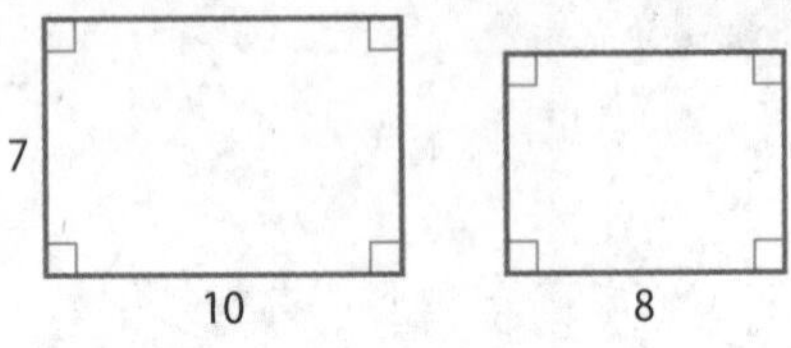

2.

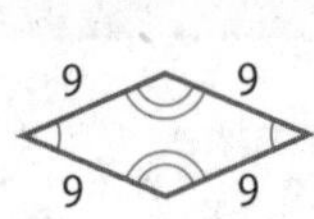

3. The two quadrilaterals are similar. Determine the missing side measure.

(Example 2)

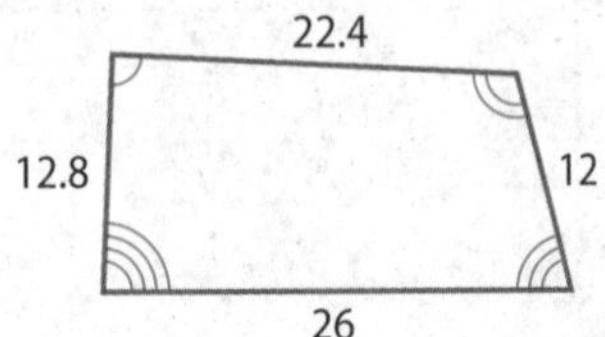

4. **Building on the Essential Question** Write a generalization you can make about the ratios of corresponding sides between similar figures and within similar figures.

Rate Yourself!

Are you ready to move on? Shade the section that applies.

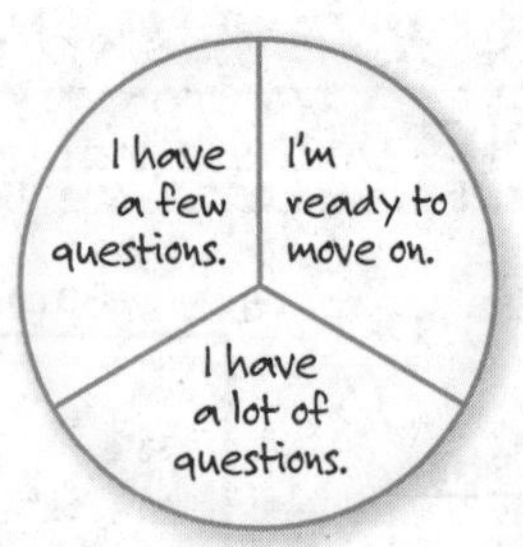

Find out online. Use the Self-Check Quiz.

FOLDABLES Time to update your Foldable!

Name ________________ My Homework ________________

Independent Practice

Determine whether each pair of polygons is similar. Explain. (Example 1)

1.

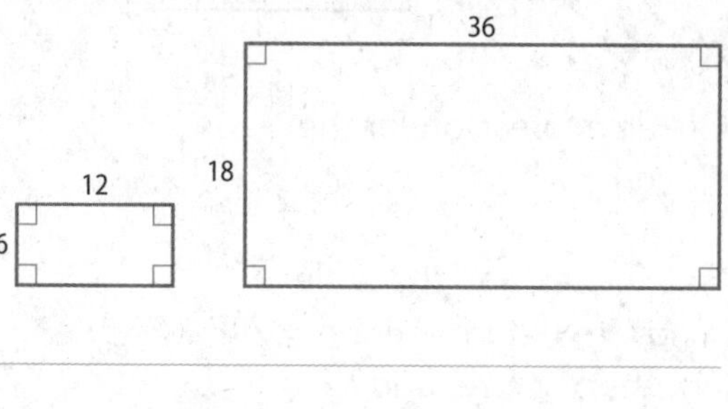

2.

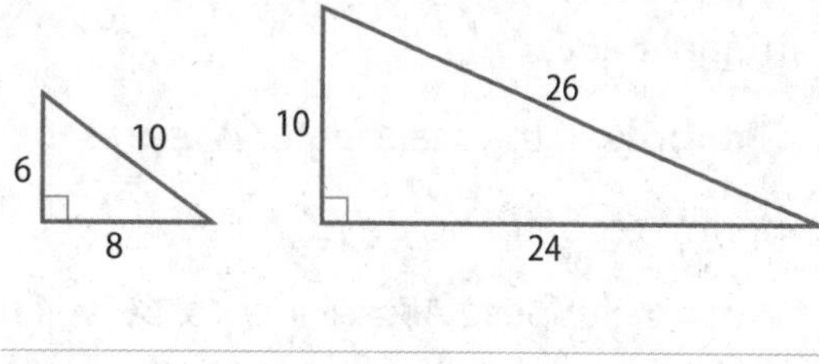

Each pair of polygons is similar. Determine the missing side measures.
(Example 2)

3.

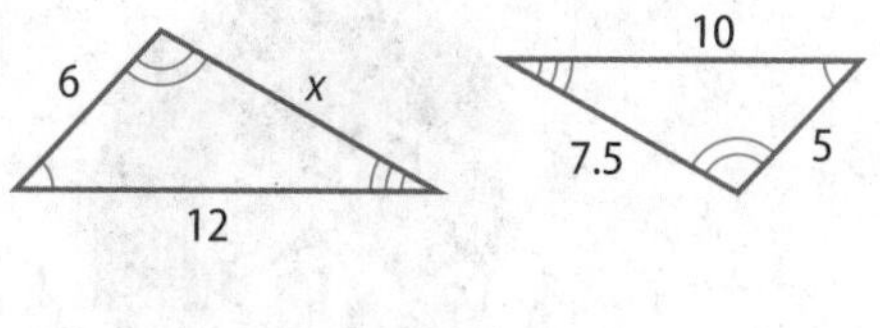

4.

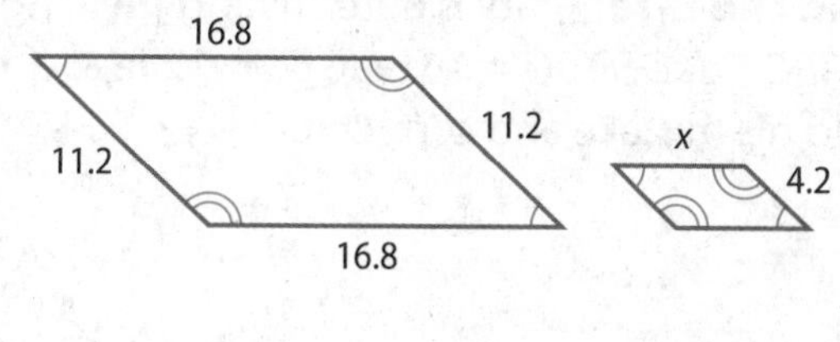

5. A rectangular blue tile has a length of 4.25 inches and a width of 6.75 inches. A similar red tile has a length of 12.75 inches. What is the width of the red tile? (Example 3) ________________

6. Triangle *LMN* is similar to triangle *RST*. What is the value of *LN* if *RT* is 9 inches, *MN* is 21 inches, and *ST* is 7 inches? (Example 3) ________________

For Exercises 7–9, use the following information.

Quadrilateral *ABCD* ~ quadrilateral *WXYZ*. $AD = 18$ feet, $CD = 27$ feet, and $YZ = 10.8$ feet.

7. Write a proportion that can be used to determine *WZ* using ratios *between* the two figures. Then determine *WZ*.

8. Write a proportion that can be used to determine WZ using ratios *within* each of the two figures. Then determine *WZ*.

9. Compare the two proportions you wrote.

10. **MP Use Multiple Representations** In this problem, you will investigate the relationship between the perimeters of similar figures. In the figures at the right, triangle *ABC* ~ triangle *XYZ*.

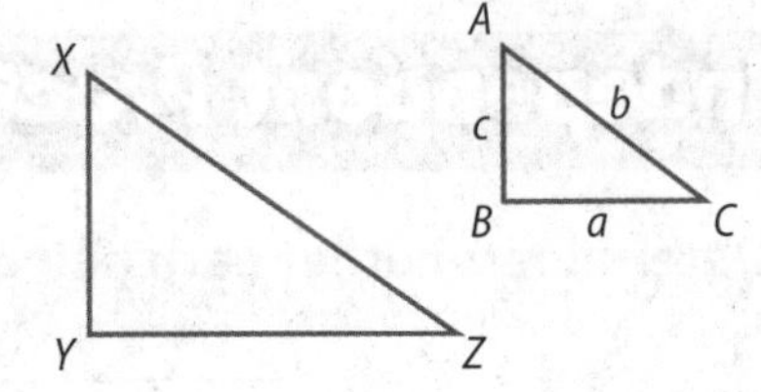

a. **Symbols** Write an expression for the perimeter of triangle *ABC*. ______

b. **Symbols** If the scale factor is represented by *d*, write an expression for the perimeter of triangle *XYZ*. ______

c. **Words** Suppose $AB = 3$ inches, $BC = 4$ inches, $AC = 5$ inches, and the scale factor from triangle *ABC* to triangle *XYZ* is 2. Explain how to determine the perimeter of triangle *XYZ* without calculating the lengths of $\overline{XY}$, $\overline{YZ}$, and $\overline{XZ}$.

______

______

11. **Find the Error** Raul is determining the length of $\overline{AB}$ where $\triangle ABC \sim \triangle DEF$, $BC = 16$ feet, $EF = 12$ feet, and $DE = 18$ feet. Find his mistake and correct it.

______

______

______

______

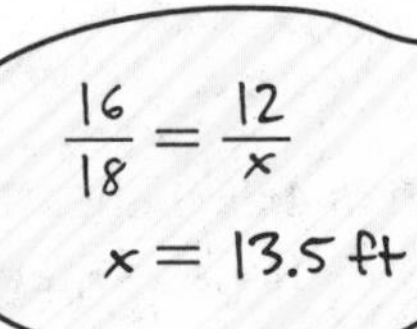

H.O.T. Problems Higher-Order Thinking

12. **Create** Using a scale factor of $\frac{2}{3}$, draw and label a rectangle similar to rectangle *ABCD*.

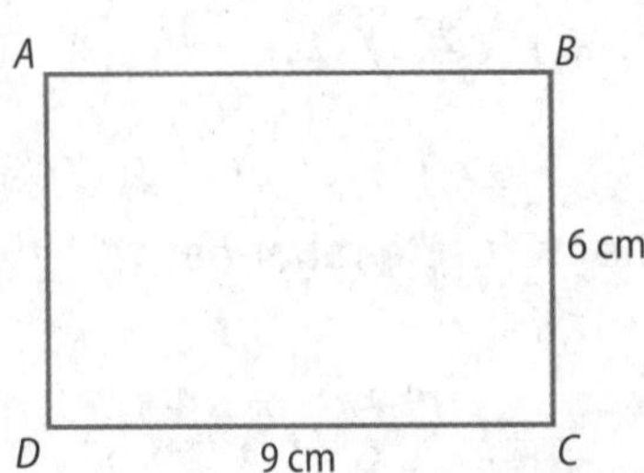

13. **Analyze** Suppose you have two triangles. Triangle *A* is similar to triangle *B*, and the measures of the sides of triangle *A* are less than the measures of the sides of triangle *B*. The scale factor is 0.25. Which is the original triangle? Explain.

______

______

______

______

Name ______________________________

Multi-Step Problem Solving

14. The two rectangles are similar. What is the perimeter of the larger rectangle, in meters? (P) (N) (MP)

6 m | 12 m | 10 m

Use a problem-solving model to solve this problem.

1 Analyze

Read the problem. Circle the information you know. Underline what the problem is asking you to find.

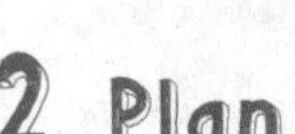

2 Plan

What will you need to do to solve the problem? Write your plan in steps.

Step 1 Determine the ______________ of the larger rectangle.

Step 2 Add the dimensions of the larger rectangle to determine the ________.

Read to Succeed!

When writing a proportion, make sure you use the correct corresponding sides to determine the missing side.

3 Solve

Use your plan to solve the problem. Show your steps.

Determine the missing measure of the larger rectangle.

$\frac{6\text{ m}}{10\text{ m}} = \frac{12\text{ m}}{x\text{ m}}$ $\quad x =$ ______

Add the dimensions of the larger rectangle to determine the perimeter.

$10 + 10 +$ ______ $+$ ______ $=$ ______

The perimeter of the larger rectangle is ______ meters.
Complete the grid.

					.		
+	0	0	0	0		0	0
−	1	1	1	1		1	1
	2	2	2	2		2	2
	3	3	3	3		3	3
	4	4	4	4		4	4
	5	5	5	5		5	5
	6	6	6	6		6	6
	7	7	7	7		7	7
	8	8	8	8		8	8
	9	9	9	9		9	9

4 Justify and Evaluate

How do you know your solution is accurate?

____

____

____

(P) = Proportionality (N) = Number and Operations (MP) = Mathematical Processes

More Multi-Step Problem Solving

Use a problem-solving model to solve each problem.

15. The two triangles below are similar. What is the perimeter of the larger triangle? P N MP

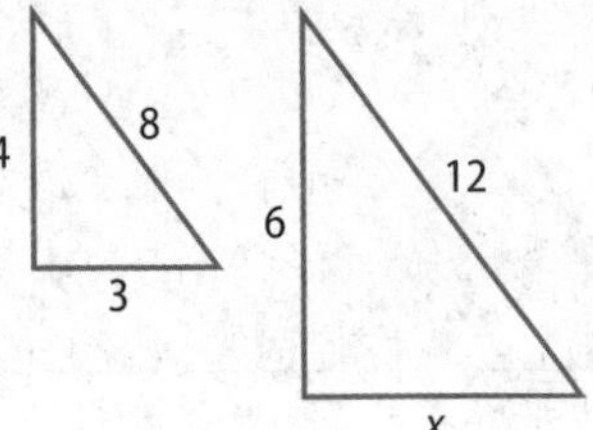

16. Rhonda is making copies of a photograph. The photo is 24 centimeters wide and has a length of 32 centimeters. If she makes a copy that is 12 centimeters long, what is the area of the copy? P N MP

17. Rectangle X is $\frac{1}{3}$ foot long and $\frac{5}{6}$ foot wide. Which rectangle(s) listed below are similar to Rectangle X? P N MP

Rectangle	Length	Width
Rectangle A	10 in.	16 in.
Rectangle B	7.2 in.	18 in.
Rectangle C	12 in.	13 in.
Rectangle D	13 in.	32.5 in.

18. The same number is added to the length and width of the rectangle below to form a new rectangle. Will the rectangles be similar? Explain. P EE MP

5 m

12 m

N = Number and Operations 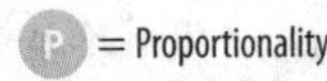

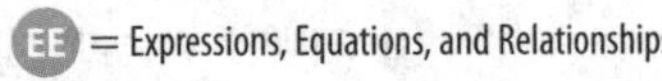

MP = Mathematical Processes

Focus on Mathematical Processes
Make a Model

Science Project

Jordan is making a model of Mount Saint Helens for a science project. The height of the actual volcano is about 2,550 meters. She uses a scale of 75 meters equals 1 centimeter.

What is the height of the volcano in inches for Jordan's model? Round to the nearest hundredth. (Hint: 1 inch ≈ 2.54 cm)

Mathematical Process
7.1(B) Use a problem-solving model that incorporates analyzing given information, formulating a plan or strategy, determining a solution, justifying the solution, and evaluating the problem-solving process and the reasonableness of the solution.

Targeted TEKS 7.5(C)

Analyze ***What are the facts?***

- The height of the actual volcano is about 2,550 meters.
- The scale for her model is 75 meters = 1 centimeter.

Plan ***Choose a problem-solving strategy.***

I will use the ______ strategy.

Solve ***How can you apply the strategy?***

The scale is 75 meters = 1 centimeter.
Write and solve a proportion using the scale.

$$\frac{75\text{ m}}{1\text{ cm}} = \frac{\square\text{ m}}{x\text{ cm}}$$

$$75 \cdot x = 1 \cdot \square$$

$$x = \square\text{ cm}$$

Convert centimeters to inches.

$$34\text{ cm} \approx 34\text{ cm} \cdot \frac{1\text{ in.}}{2.54\text{ cm}}$$

$$\approx \frac{34\text{ in.}}{2.54} \text{ or } \square \text{ in.}$$

So, Jordan's model has a height of approximately ______ inches.

Justify and Evaluate ***How do you know your solution is accurate?***

______

______

Portraits

Alicia created a portrait that is 10 inches wide by 13 inches long. She wants to put it in a frame that is $2\frac{1}{4}$ inches wide on each side.

What is the area of the framed portrait?

Analyze

Read the problem. Circle the information you know.
Underline what the problem is asking you to find.

Plan

Choose a problem-solving strategy.

I will use the ______________________________ strategy.

Solve

How can you apply the strategy?

Justify and Evaluate

How do you know your solution is reasonable?

Multi-Step Problem Solving

Work with a small group to solve the following problems. Show your work on a separate piece of paper.

1. Tables

Members of Student Council are setting up square tables end-to-end for an awards banquet. Each table will seat one person on each side.

How many square tables will they need to put together for 32 people? Explain.

2. Tile

The diagram shows the design of a tile border around a swimming pool that measures 10.5 meters by 6 meters. Each tile is a square measuring 1.5 meters on each side.

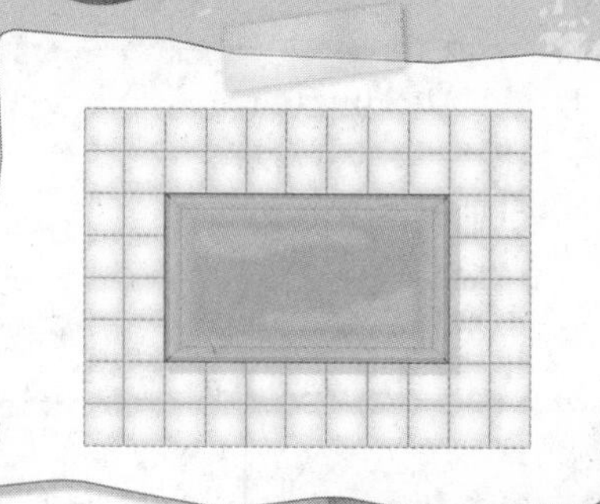

Explain a method you could use to determine the area of just the tile border. Then solve.

3. Classes

Faith, Sebastián, and Guadalupe take French, Spanish, and German. No person's language class begins with the same letter as their first name. Sebastián's best friend takes French.

Which language does each person take?

4. Money

Corri received money for her birthday. She let Lakisha borrow \$4.50 and spent half of the remaining money. The next day she received \$10 from her uncle. After spending \$12.50 at the movies, she still had \$7.75 left.

How much money did she receive for her birthday?

Vocabulary Check

1. List two attributes of a pair of similar figures. TEKS 7.5(A), 7.1(D)

Key Concept Check

2. Complete the graphic organizer about similar figures. TEKS 7.5(C), 7.1(E)

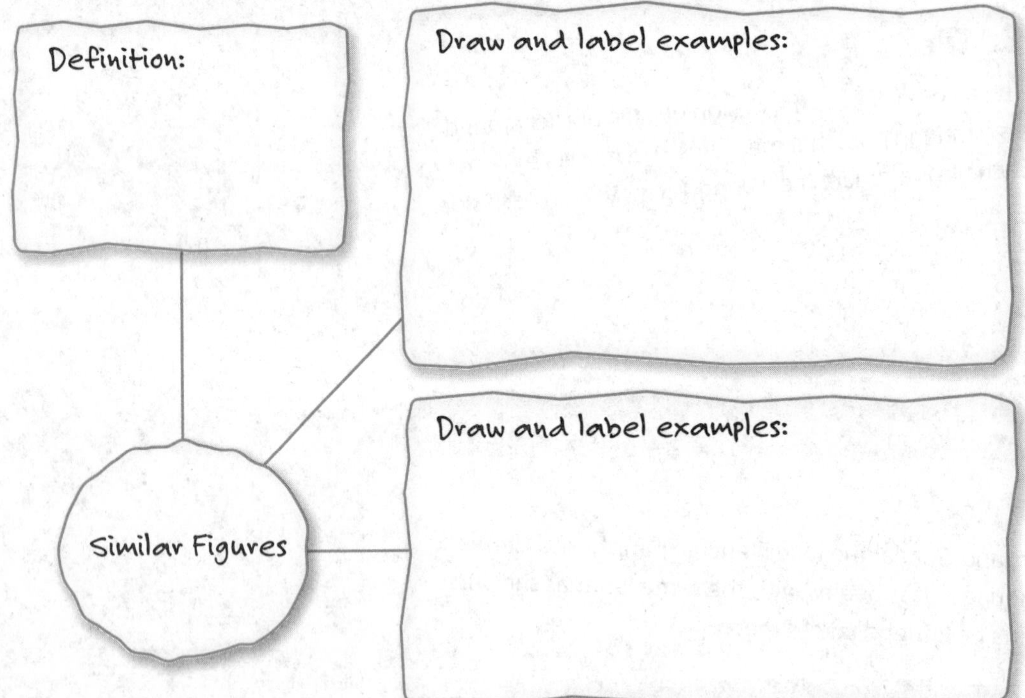

Multi-Step Problem Solving

3. Keshawn enlarges a rectangular photograph to make a poster that is similar to the photograph. The photograph is 4 inches wide and 6 inches long. The poster is $4\frac{1}{4}$ feet long. What is the area of the poster? TEKS 7.5(C) P N MP

   Ⓐ $2\frac{5}{6}$ ft
   Ⓒ $14\frac{1}{6}$ ft
   Ⓑ $12\frac{1}{24}$ ft^2
   Ⓓ 24 in^2

P = Proportionality N = Number and Operations MP = Mathematical Processes

Hands-On Lab 3-a

Changes in Perimeter and Area

INQUIRY **HOW can I analyze relationships to determine how changes in dimensions affect perimeter and area?**

Mallory's family has a small vegetable garden that is 4 feet long and 2 feet wide. Her family decides to expand their garden and double the dimensions of their garden. How will this affect the planting area and fence needed around the perimeter?

Texas Essential Knowledge and Skills TEKS

Targeted TEKS
7.5(A) Generalize the critical attributes of similarity, including ratios within and between similar shapes. *Also addresses 7.5(C).*

Mathematical Processes
7.1(C), 7.1(D), 7.1(E), 7.1(F)

Hands-On Activity

Step 1 Draw the small vegetable garden on the graph paper at the right. Let each square grid represent 1 square foot.

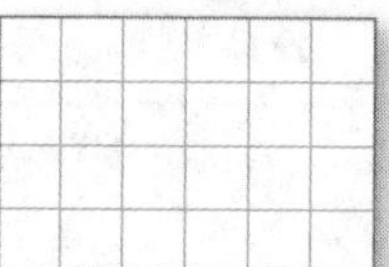

Step 2 Determine the perimeter and area.

$P =$ ____________________

$A =$ ____________________

Step 3 Mallory's family doubles the dimensions of the garden. Draw the new garden at the right. Determine the new perimeter and area.

$P =$ ____________________

$A =$ ____________________

1. How did the perimeter change from the first to the second garden?

____

2. How did the planting area change from the first to the second garden?

____

Work with a partner to complete the table that gives the new perimeter and area when a rectangle is changed by different scale factors. The first one is done for you.

	Scale Factor	Length (in.)	Width (in.)	Perimeter (in.)	Area (in^2)
	1	4	12	32	48
3.	3	12	36		
4.	4				
5.	$\frac{1}{2}$				
6.	$\frac{1}{4}$				

Analyze and Reflect

Collaborate

7. How does the perimeter change when the original dimensions are changed by a factor of 2? by 3? by $\frac{1}{4}$? The area? ______

Create

On Your Own

8. **Connect Models to Rules** Write a rule that you can use to determine the perimeter of a rectangle when the rectangle's dimensions are changed by a scale factor of *x*.

______

9. **Connect Models to Rules** Write a rule that you can use to determine the area of a rectangle when the rectangle's dimensions are changed by a scale factor of *x*.

______

10. **INQUIRY** HOW can I analyze relationships to determine how changes in dimensions affect perimeter and area?

______

______

______

Lesson 3

Changes in Dimension

Launch the Lesson: Real World

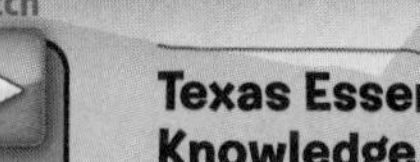

Texas Essential Knowledge and Skills

Targeted TEKS

7.5(C) Solve mathematical and real-world problems involving similar shape and scale drawings. *Also addresses 7.5(A).*

Mathematical Processes

7.1(A), 7.1(B), 7.1(C), 7.1(E)

Essential Question

HOW can proportional relationships be applied to geometry?

Mr. Blackwell is doubling the size of his dog house. The floors are rectangular. The perimeter of the original floor is 12 feet and the area is 8 square feet. Follow the steps below to determine how the perimeter and area change when the dimensions are doubled.

$2\ell + 2w$	Perimeter P of a rectangle is $2\ell + 2w$
$\square(2\ell) + \square(2w)$	Double each dimension. The scale factor is 2.
$\square(2\ell + 2w)$	Distributive Property
$2(\square)$	$P = 2\ell + 2w$

The perimeter is multiplied by the scale factor $\square$.

ℓw	Area A of a rectangle is ℓw
$(\square\ell)(\square w)$	Double each dimension. The scale factor is 2.
$\square(\ell w)$	Simplify.
$2^2(\ell w)$	Write 4 as a power of 2.
$2^2(\square)$	$A = \ell w$

The area is multiplied by the square of the scale factor.

Describe how the perimeter and area of Mr. Blackwell's dog house will change when the dimensions area doubled.

___

___

Which MP Mathematical Processes did you use? Shade the circle(s) that applies.

Ⓐ Apply Math to the Real World.
Ⓑ Use a Problem-Solving Model.
Ⓒ Select Tools and Techniques.
Ⓓ Use Multiple Representations.
Ⓔ Organize Ideas.
Ⓕ Analyze Relationships.
Ⓖ Justify Arguments.

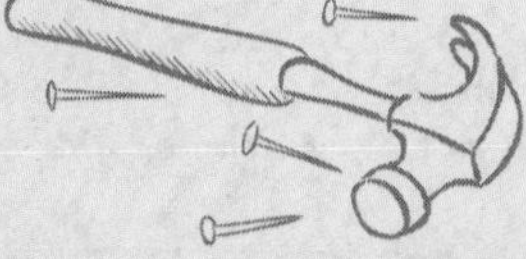

Key Concept

Changing Dimensions: Effect on Perimeter

Work Zone

Words If the dimensions of a polygon are multiplied by *x*, then the perimeter of the polygon changes by a factor of *x*.

Model

Figure A

Figure B

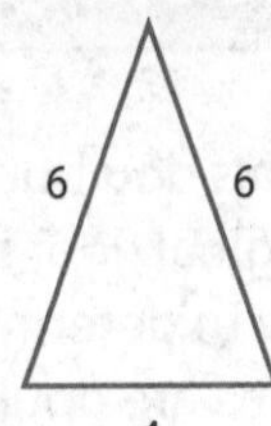

Example The dimensions of Figure A are multiplied by 2 to produce Figure B.

$\underbrace{\text{perimeter of Figure A}}_{8} \cdot 2 = \underbrace{\text{perimeter of Figure B}}_{16}$

Notice that all the dimensions of the figure must change using the same factor, *x*.

Tutor

Example

1. Suppose the side lengths of the parallelogram at the right are tripled. What effect would this have on the perimeter? Justify your answer.

The dimensions are 3 times greater.

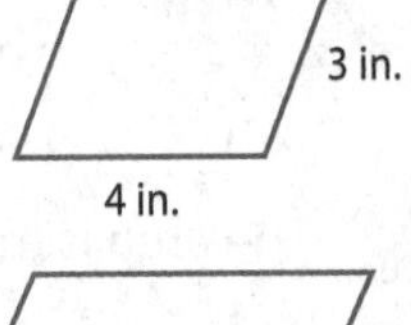

original perimeter: $2(4) + 2(3) = 14$ in.

new perimeter: $2(12) + 2(9) = 42$ in.

Show your work.

compare perimeters: 42 in. ÷ 14 in. = 3

So, the perimeter is 3 times the perimeter of the original figure.

Got It? Do this problem to find out.

a. Suppose the side lengths of the trapezoid at the right are multiplied by $\frac{1}{2}$. What effect would this have on the perimeter? Justify your answer.

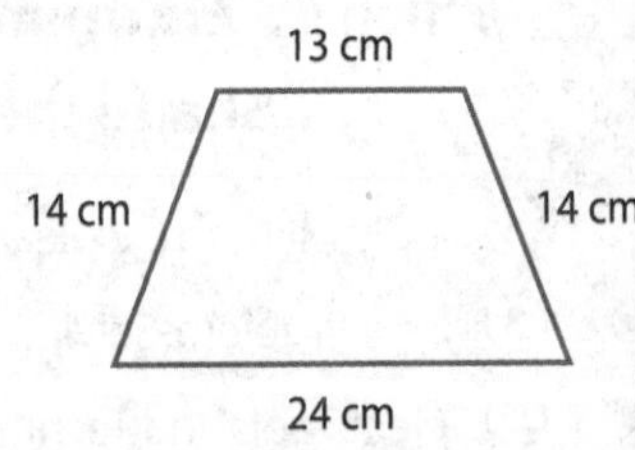

a. ______

Changing Dimensions: Effect on Area

Key Concept

Words If the dimensions of a polygon are multiplied by x, then the area of the polygon changes by $x \cdot x$ or x^2.

Model

Figure A

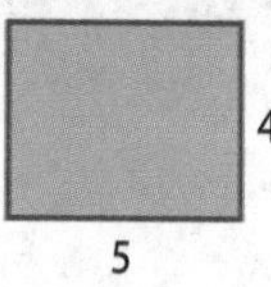

Figure B

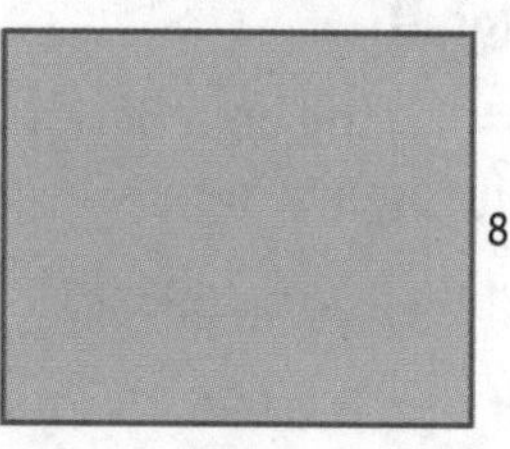

Example The dimensions of Figure A are multiplied by 2 to produce Figure B.

$$\underbrace{\text{area of Figure A}}_{20} \cdot 2^2 = \underbrace{\text{area of Figure B}}_{80}$$

$$20 \cdot 4 = 80$$

Notice that all the dimensions of the figure must change using the same factor, x.

Example

2. The side lengths of the triangle at the right are multiplied by 5. What effect would this have on the area? Justify your answer.

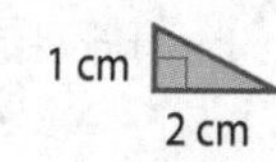

The dimensions are 5 times greater.

original area: $\frac{1}{2} \cdot 2 \cdot 1 = 1 \text{ cm}^2$

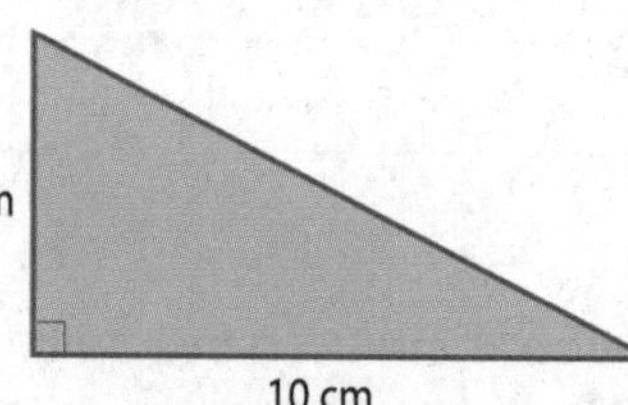

new area: $\frac{1}{2} \cdot 10 \cdot 5 = 25 \text{ cm}^2$

compare areas:

$25 \text{ cm}^2 \div 1 \text{ cm}^2 = 25$ or 5^2.

So, the area is 5^2 or 25 times the area of the original figure.

Got It? Do this problem to find out.

b. A rectangle measures 2 feet by 4 feet. Suppose the side lengths are multiplied by 2.5. What effect would this have on the area? Justify your answer.

b. ______________

Example

Tutor

3. A stop sign is in the shape of a regular octagon. Sign A shown at the right has an area of 309 square inches. What is the area of sign B?

Since $8 \times 1.5 = 12$, the area of sign B is 1.5^2 times the area of sign A.

$309 \cdot 1.5^2 = 309 \cdot 2.25$ or 695.25

So, the area of sign B is 695.25 square inches.

Guided Practice

Refer to the figure at the right for Exercises 1 and 2. Justify your answers.
(Examples 1–2)

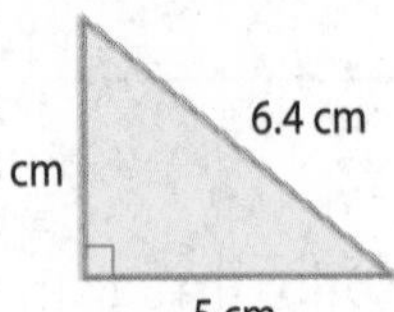

1. Each side length is doubled. Describe the change in the perimeter.

2. Each side length is tripled. Describe the change in the area.

3. Different sizes of regular hexagons are used in a quilt. Each small hexagon has side lengths of 4 inches and an area of 41.6 square inches. Each large hexagon has side lengths of 8 inches. What is the area of each large hexagon? (Example 3) ____________

4. **Building on the Essential Question** How can exponents help you determine the area of a rectangle if each side length is multiplied by *x*? ____________

Rate Yourself!

How confident are you about changes in dimensions? Check the box that applies.

☐ ☐ ☐ ☐ ☐

Find out online. Use the Self-Check Quiz.

Check

Name ________________________ My Homework ________________

Independent Practice

7.5(A), 7.5(C), 7.1(G) TEKS

1. Each side length of the parallelogram at the right is multiplied by 4. Describe the change in the perimeter. Justify your answer. (Example 1)

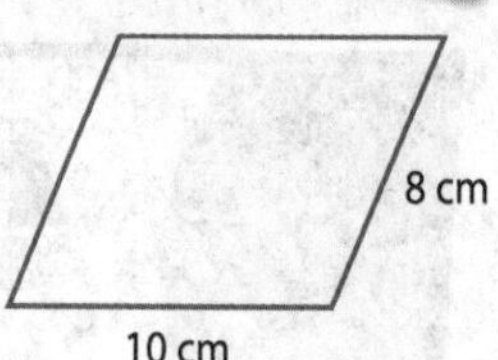

2. The base and height of the triangle at the right are multiplied by 4. Describe the change in the area. Justify your answer. (Example 2)

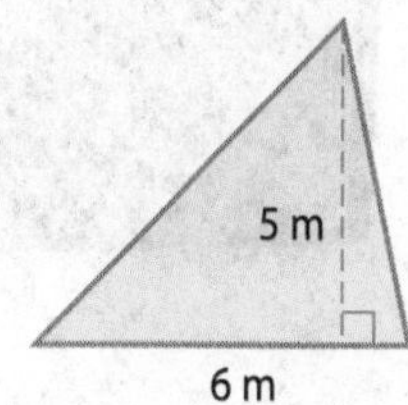

3. Each side length of the rectangle is multiplied by $\frac{1}{3}$. Describe the change in the area. Justify your answer. (Example 2)

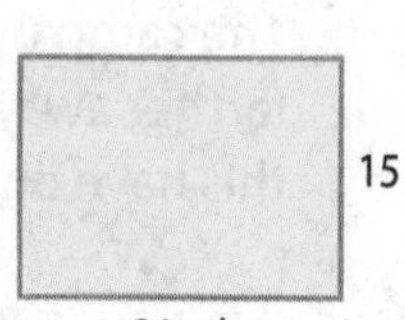

4. Different sizes of regular pentagons are used in a stained glass window. Each small pentagon has side lengths of 4 inches and an area of 27.5 square inches. Each large pentagon has side lengths of 8 inches. What is the area of each large pentagon? (Example 3)

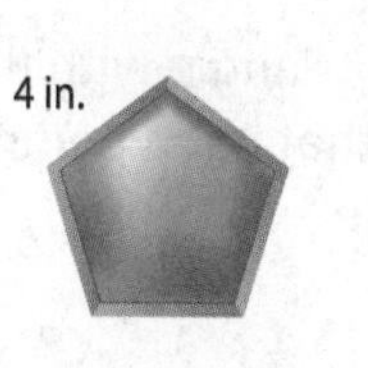

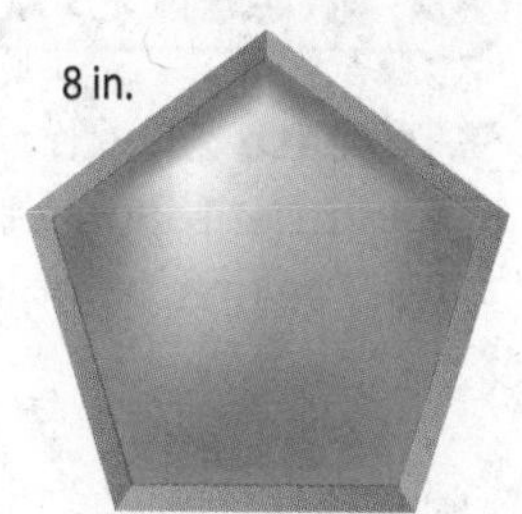

5. MP **Justify Arguments** A dollhouse has a bed with dimensions $\frac{1}{12}$ the size of a queen-size bed. A queen-size bed has an area of 4,800 square inches, and a length of 80 inches. What are the side lengths of the dollhouse bed? Justify your answer.

6. **MP Apply Math to the Real World** Refer to the graphic novel below. The cabin, ropes course, and mess hall form a triangle.

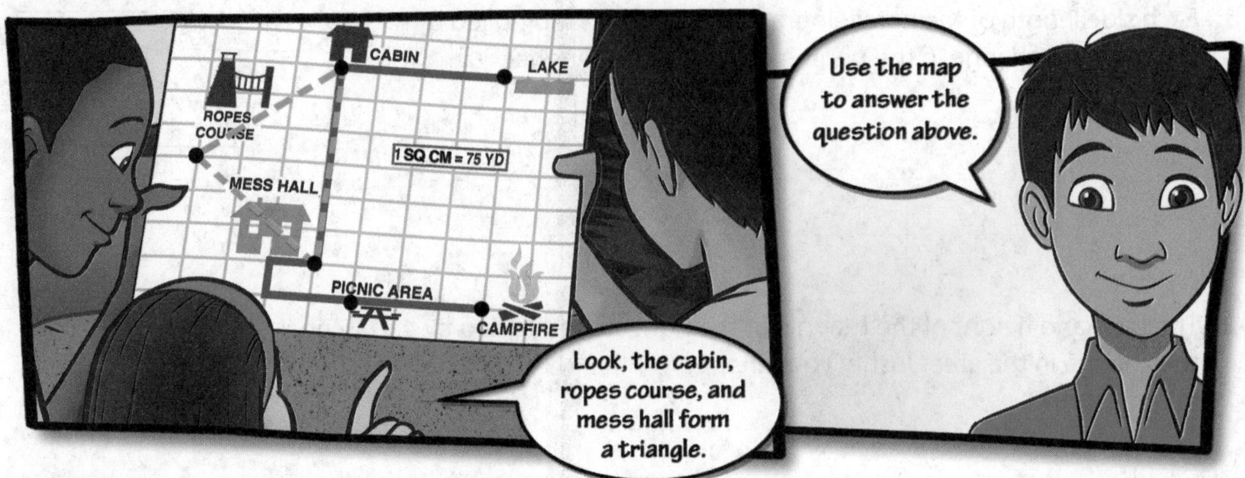

a. What is the area of the triangle shown on the map? ____________

b. The camp owner is remodeling the campsite. The ropes course was moved farther away so that height of the triangle is now 6 units. What effect did this have on the area?

____

____

H.O.T. Problems Higher-Order Thinking

7. **Create** Sketch a triangle with the side lengths labeled. Sketch and label another triangle that has a perimeter two times greater than the perimeter of the first triangle.

8. **Analyze** The corresponding side lengths of two figures have a ratio of $\frac{a}{b}$. What is the ratio of the perimeters? the ratio of the areas?

____

9. **Analyze** The larger square shown has a perimeter of 48 units. The smaller square inside has a perimeter that is 2 times smaller. What are the side lengths of the larger and smaller square? Explain.

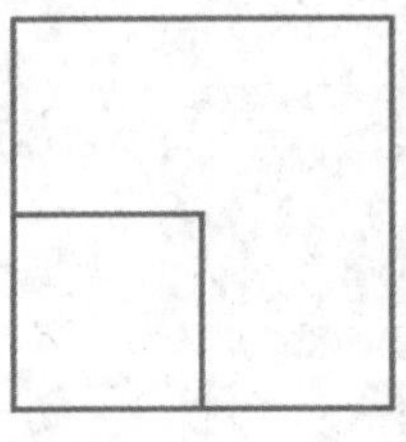

____

____

____

Name ______________________________

Multi-Step Problem Solving

10. The side lengths of the smaller triangle are multiplied by the same number to create a larger triangle with a base of 1 foot and height of $\frac{1}{2}$ foot. How many times greater is the area of the larger triangle? P N MP

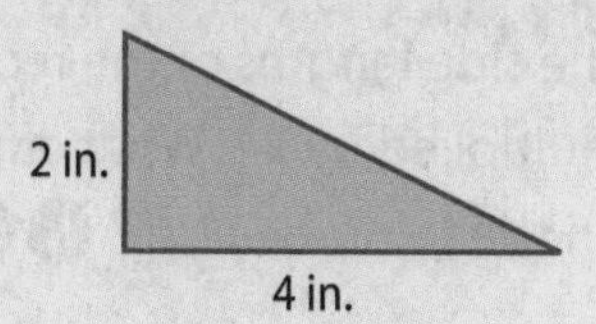

Ⓐ 3
Ⓑ 4
Ⓒ 9
Ⓓ 36

Use a problem-solving model to solve this problem.

1 Analyze

Read the problem. Circle the information you know.
Underline what the problem is asking you to find.

2 Plan

What will you need to do to solve the problem? Write your plan in steps.

Step 1 Determine the ______ of the smaller triangle.

Step 2 Convert the dimensions of the larger triangle to ______, determine the area, then compare the ______.

3 Solve

Use your plan to solve the problem. Show your steps.

Determine the area of the smaller triangle.

$\frac{1}{2} \times 2 \times 4 =$ ______

Determine the area of the larger triangle in inches.

1 ft = ______ $\frac{1}{2}$ ft = ______ $\frac{1}{2} \times 12 \times 6 =$ ______

______ ÷ ______ = ______

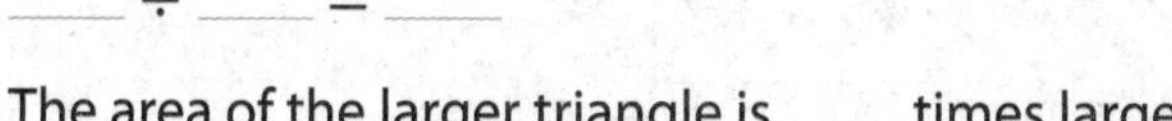

The area of the larger triangle is ______ times larger.

So, the correct answer is ______. Fill in that answer choice.

Read to Succeed!
Remember to convert the units of the larger triangle to inches before comparing the area of each triangle.

4 Justify and Evaluate

How do you know your solution is accurate?

____
____
____

P = Proportionality N = Number and Operations MP = Mathematical Processes

More Multi-Step Problem Solving

Use a problem-solving model to solve each problem.

11. The side lengths of the rectangle below are multiplied by $2\frac{3}{4}$. What effect would this have on the perimeter? P N MP

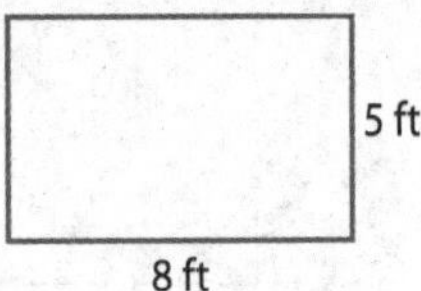

Ⓐ The perimeter will be $1\frac{3}{4}$ times greater.

Ⓑ The perimeter will be $2\frac{3}{4}$ times greater.

Ⓒ The perimeter will be $2\frac{5}{8}$ times greater.

Ⓓ The perimeter will be 3 times greater.

12. The dimensions of the rectangles listed in the table will all be multiplied by 3. What is the combined area of the enlarged rectangles in meters? P N MP

Rectangle	Length (cm)	Width (cm)
Rectangle A	4	5
Rectangle B	6	6
Rectangle C	7	9

13. The Pentagon in Washington, D.C. is a regular pentagon. Juan made two scale models of the Pentagon. The perimeter of the larger model is how many times greater than the perimeter of the smaller model? (*Hint:* 1 inch ≈ 2.54 cm) P N MP

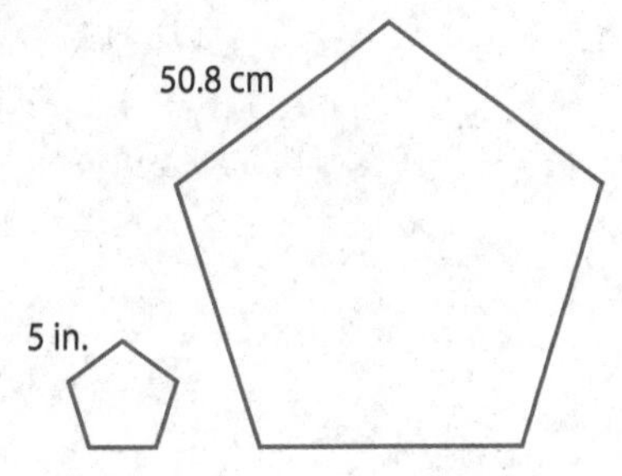

14. The area of Rectangle B is 5 times greater than the area of Rectangle A. Give possible dimensions for each rectangle. Justify your answer. P N MP

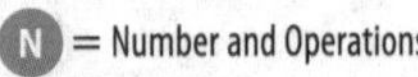 = Proportionality N = Number and Operations 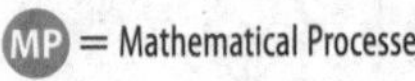 = Mathematical Processes

Hands-On Lab 4-a

Model Circumference

INQUIRY **HOW can I organize ideas to determine how the circumference of a circle is related to its diameter?**

The distance around a flying disc, or its *circumference*, is 37.7 centimeters. The distance across the disc through its center, or its *diameter*, is 12 centimeters. How is the circumference of a circular object, such as a flying disc, related to its diameter?

Texas Essential Knowledge and Skills TEKS

Targeted TEKS

7.8(C) Use models to determine the approximate formulas for the circumference and area of a circle and connect the models to the actual formulas.

Also addresses 7.5(B), 7.9(B).

Mathematical Processes

7.1(C), 7.1(D), 7.1(E), 7.1(F), 7.1(G)

Hands-On Activity

Step 1 Cut a piece of string the length of the circumference of a circular object such as a jar lid. Use a centimeter ruler to measure the length of the string to the nearest tenth of a centimeter. Record this measurement in the table below.

Object	Circumference (C)	Diameter (d)	$\frac{C}{d}$
Disc	37.7 cm	12 cm	

Step 2 Measure and record the diameter of the lid.

Step 3 Use a calculator to determine the ratio of the circumference of the disc to its diameter. Repeat for the circular object you measured in Steps 1 and 2. Round answers to the nearest hundredth.

Step 4 Repeat Steps 1 through 3 for other circular objects.

1. MP **Analyze Relationships** Describe the ratios $\frac{C}{d}$ you found. Identify the number that is closest to the value of each ratio.

____

____

2. **Connect Models to Rules** Write a rule in the form $\frac{C}{d} \approx$ ________, where ________ is the number you identified in Exercise 1. ________________

MP Organize Ideas **Work with a partner. Measure the diameter of two different circular objects. Predict each circumference. Check your predictions by measuring. Then determine each ratio $\frac{C}{d}$. Record your values to the nearest hundredth in the table below.**

	Object	Diameter	Predicted Circumference	Measured Circumference	Ratio $\frac{C}{d}$
3.					
4.					

Analyze and Reflect

Collaborate

5. **MP Analyze Relationships** How do the ratios $\frac{C}{d}$ you found above compare to the ones in the Activity? Identify the number that is closest to the value of all of the ratios.

Create

On Your Own

6. **Connect Models to Rules** Write a formula in the form $\frac{C}{d}$ = ________, that gives the approximate ratio of the circumference C of a circle to its diameter d, where ________ is the number you identified in Exercise 5.

7. **MP Organize Ideas** Multiply both sides of your formula by d to write an equivalent formula in the form C = ________ d that gives the approximate circumference C if you know the diameter d of a circle.

8. **MP Analyze Relationships** The radius of a circle is one half of its diameter. Write a formula that relates the circumference C of a circle to its radius r.

9. **INQUIRY** HOW can I organize ideas to determine how the circumference of a circle is related to its diameter?

Lesson 4

Circumference

Launch the Lesson: Vocabulary

A **circle** is the set of all points in a plane that are the same distance from a point, called the **center**. The **circumference** is the distance around a circle. The **diameter** is the distance across a circle through its center. The **radius** is the distance from the center to any point on the circle.

Fill in each box with one of the following terms: *center, diameter,* and *radius*.

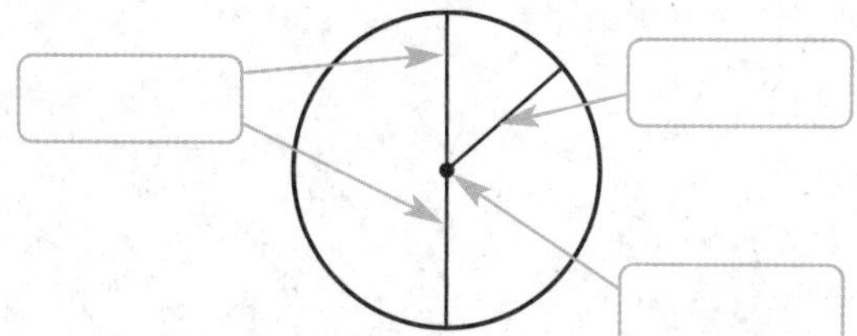

Texas Essential Knowledge and Skills

Targeted TEKS

7.5(B) Describe π as the ratio of the circumference of a circle to its diameter. *Also addresses 7.8(C), 7.9(B).*

Mathematical Processes

7.1(A), 7.1(B), 7.1(D), 7.1(E), 7.1(F)

Vocab

Vocabulary

circle

center

circumference

diameter

radius

pi π

Essential Question

HOW can proportional relationships be applied to geometry?

Real-World Link

Watch

1. The table shows the approximate measurements of two sizes of hula hoops.

Size	Radius (in.)	Diameter (in.)	Circumference (in.)
child	14	28	88
adult	20	40	126

a. Describe the relationship between the diameter and radius of each hula hoop. ______

b. Describe the relationship between the circumference and diameter of each hula hoop. ______

______

Which MP Mathematical Processes did you use? Shade the circle(s) that applies.

Ⓐ Apply Math to the Real World.

Ⓑ Use a Problem-Solving Model.

Ⓒ Select Tools and Techniques.

Ⓓ Use Multiple Representations.

Ⓔ Organize Ideas.

Ⓕ Analyze Relationships.

Ⓖ Justify Arguments.

Key Concept

Radius and Diameter

Words The diameter d of a circle is twice its radius r. The radius r of a circle is half of its diameter d.

Symbols $d = 2r$ $r = \frac{d}{2}$

Work Zone

STOP and Reflect

The diameter of a circle is 36 inches. Circle the radius.

72 in. 18 in.

Tutor

Examples

1. The diameter of a circle is 14 inches. Determine the radius.

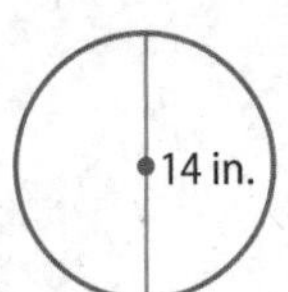

$r = \frac{d}{2}$ Radius of circle

$r = \frac{14}{2}$ Replace d with 14.

$r = 7$ Divide.

The radius is 7 inches.

2. The radius of a circle is 8 feet. Determine the diameter.

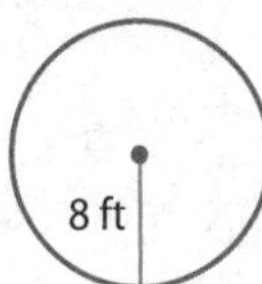

$d = 2r$ Diameter of circle

$d = 2 \cdot 8$ Replace r with 8.

$d = 16$ Multiply.

The diameter is 16 feet.

Got It? Do these problems to find out.

Determine the radius or diameter of each circle with the given dimension.

a. $d = 23$ cm

b. $r = 3$ in.

c. $d = 16$ yd

d. $r = 5.2$

Show your work.

a. ________

b. ________

c. ________

d. ________

Circumference

Key Concept

Words The ratio of the circumference of a circle to its diameter is π. So, the circumference of a circle is equal to π times its diameter or π times twice its radius.

Model

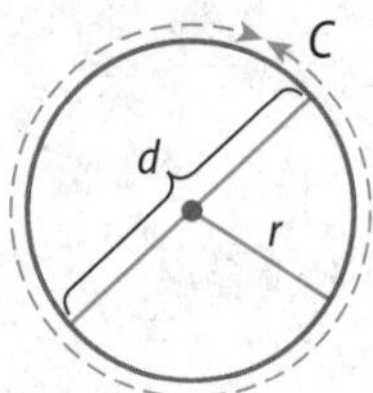

C

d

r

Symbols $\frac{C}{d} = \pi$, so $C = \pi d$ or $C = 2\pi r$

Estimation
To estimate the circumference of a circle, you can use 3 for π since $\pi \approx 3$.

In the Hands-On Lab, you learned that $\frac{C}{d} \approx 3$ or 3.14. The exact ratio of the circumference of a circle to its diameter is represented by the Greek letter **π (pi)**. The value of π is 3.1415926.... The decimal never ends, but it is often approximated as 3.14.

Another approximation for π is $\frac{22}{7}$. Use this value when the radius or diameter is a multiple of 7 or has a multiple of 7 in its numerator if the radius is a fraction.

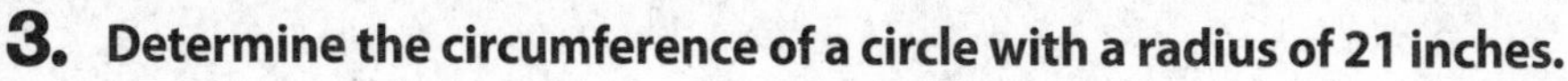

Example

Tutor

3. Determine the circumference of a circle with a radius of 21 inches.

Since 21 is a multiple of 7, use $\frac{22}{7}$ to approximate π.

$C = 2\pi r$ Circumference of a circle

$C \approx 2 \cdot \frac{22}{7} \cdot 21$ Replace π with $\frac{22}{7}$ and r with 21.

$C \approx 2 \cdot \frac{22}{\cancel{7}_1} \cdot \frac{\cancel{21}^3}{1}$ Divide by the GCF, 7.

$C \approx 132$ Simplify.

The circumference of the circle is about 132 inches.

Got It? Do these problems to find out.

Determine the circumference of each circle. Use $\frac{22}{7}$ for π.

e.

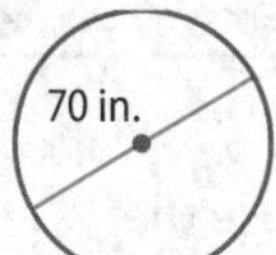

f.

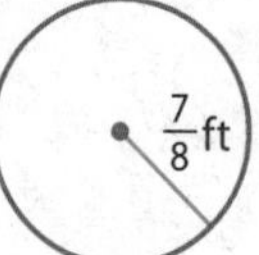

e. ________

f. ________

Example

4. Big Ben is a famous clock tower in London, England. The diameter of the clock face is 23 feet. Determine the circumference of the clock face. Round to the nearest tenth.

$C = \pi d$	Circumference of a circle
$C \approx 3.14(23)$	Replace π with 3.14 and d with 23.
$C \approx 72.2$	Multiply.

So, the distance around the clock is about 72.2 feet.

Got It? Do this problem to find out.

Show your work.

g. A circular fence is being placed to surround a tree. The diameter of the fence is 4 feet. How much fencing is used? Use 3.14 for π. Round to the nearest tenth if necessary.

g. ________

Guided Practice

Determine the radius or diameter of each circle with the given dimension. (Examples 1 and 2)

1. $d = 3$ m ________

2. $r = 14$ ft ________

3. $d = 20$ in. ________

Determine the circumference of each circle. Use 3.14 or $\frac{22}{7}$ for π. Round to the nearest tenth if necessary. (Examples 3 and 4)

4. ________

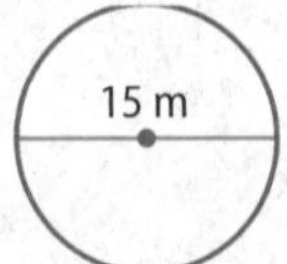

5. ________

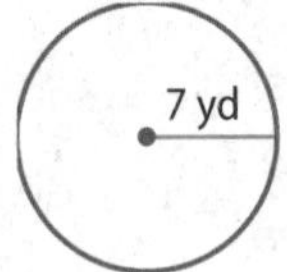

6. **Building on the Essential Question** How can you describe the exact value of the number π using the concept of ratio?

____

____

____

Rate Yourself!

How confident are you about finding the circumference? Check the box that applies.

Find out online. Use the Self-Check Quiz.

Independent Practice

7.5(B), 7.1(E) TEKS

Determine the radius or diameter of each circle with the given dimensions. (Examples 1 and 2)

1. $d = 5$ mm ______

2. $d = 24$ ft ______

3. $r = 17$ cm ______

Determine the circumference of each circle. Use 3.14 or $\frac{22}{7}$ for π. Round to the nearest tenth if necessary. (Example 3)

4. 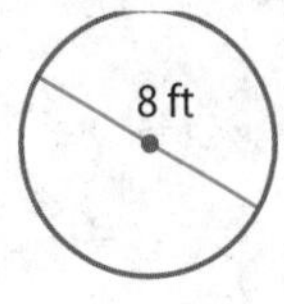

______

5. 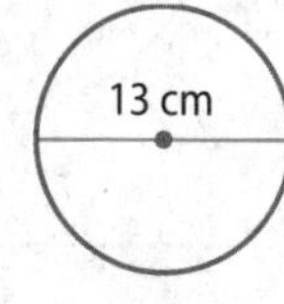

______

6. 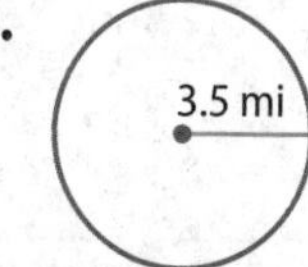

______

7. The largest tree in the world by volume is in Sequoia National Park. The diameter at the base is 36 feet. If a person with outstretched arms can reach 6 feet, how many people would it take to reach around the base of the tree? (Example 4)

______

8. The Belknap shield volcano is located in the Cascade Range in Oregon. The volcano is circular and has a diameter of 5 miles. What is the circumference of this volcano. Round your answer to the nearest tenth. (Example 4)

______

9. MP **Analyze Relationships** Refer to the circle at the right. Determine the circumference of the circle using each estimate of π.

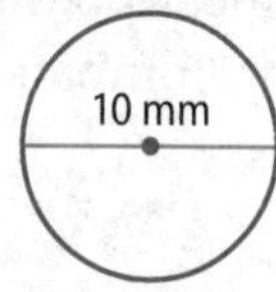

a. $\pi \approx 3$ ______

b. $\pi \approx 3.14$ ______

c. $\pi \approx 3.14159$ ______

d. What do you notice about the estimate used for π and the circumference of the circle?

______

______

10. MP **Use Multiple Representations** The bar diagram shows how the circumference C of a circle relates to its diameter d. How does the bar diagram connect to the formula $C = \pi d$?

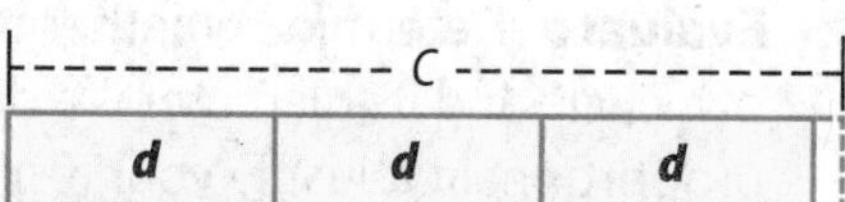

______

______

Copy and Solve **For Exercises 11–15, show your work on a separate piece of paper. Determine the diameter given each circumference. Use 3.14 for π.**

11. a satellite dish with a circumference of 957.7 meters

12. a basketball hoop with a circumference of 56.52 inches

13. a nickel with a circumference of about 65.94 millimeters

Determine the distance around each figure. Use 3.14 for π.

14.

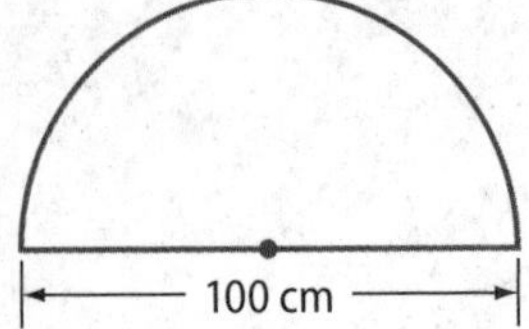

15.

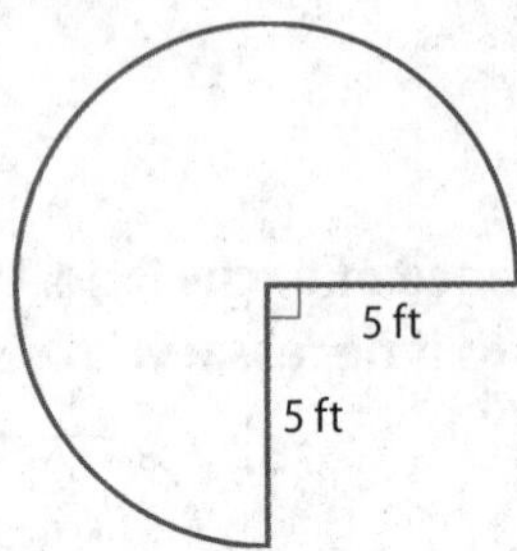

H.O.T. Problems Higher-Order Thinking

16. Evaluate Determine if the circumference of a circle with a radius of 4 feet will be greater or less than 24 feet. Explain.

17. Create Draw and label a circle that has a diameter more than 5 inches, but less than 10 inches. Estimate its circumference and then determine its circumference using a calculator. Compare your results.

18. Analyze Analyze how the circumference of a circle would change if the diameter was doubled. Provide an example to support your explanation.

19. Evaluate Determine whether the relationship between the circumference of a circle and its diameter is a direct variation. If so, identify the constant of proportionality. Justify your response.

Name ____________________

Multi-Step Problem Solving

20. Ramon uses landscape edging to border his circular garden. The diagram at the right represents Ramon's garden. His neighbor has a garden that has a diameter that is 24 inches larger. How much landscape edging does his neighbor need to border their garden? Use 3.14 for π. Round to the nearest tenth. EE P MP

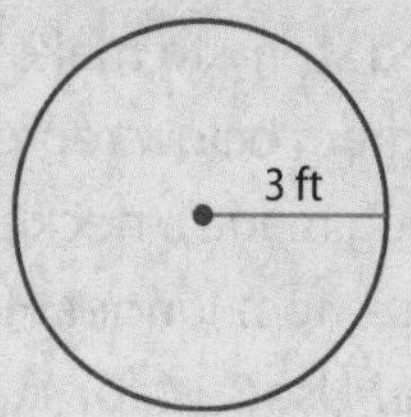

Ⓐ 15.7 feet

Ⓑ 25.1 feet

Ⓒ 26 feet

Ⓓ 31.4 feet

Use a problem-solving model to solve this problem.

1 Analyze

Read the problem. Circle the information you know.
Underline what the problem is asking you to find.

2 Plan

What will you need to do to solve the problem? Write your plan in steps.

Step 1 Determine the ________ of his neighbor's garden.

Step 2 Determine the ____________ of his neighbor's garden.

3 Solve

Use your plan to solve the problem. Show your steps.

Ramon's garden has a diameter of 6 feet. So, his neighbor's garden is 24 inches or ______ feet greater.

6 + ______ = ______

Determine the circumference.

3.14 × 8 = ______

Ramon's neighbor will need ______ feet of landscaping border.

So, the correct answer is ______. Fill in that answer choice.

Read to Succeed!
The diameter of his neighbor's garden is 24 inches larger. Make sure you add this distance to Ramon's diameter, not the radius.

4 Justify and Evaluate

How do you know your solution is accurate?

____

____

____

EE = Expressions, Equations, and Relationships P = Proportionality MP = Mathematical Processes

More Multi-Step Problem Solving

Use a problem-solving model to solve each problem.

21. Bart used string to make this necklace. The diagram below represents the string Bart used. Meg made a necklace with a diameter that was $\frac{1}{2}$ foot longer. How much string did Meg use? Use 3.14 for π. Round to the nearest tenth. N P EE MP

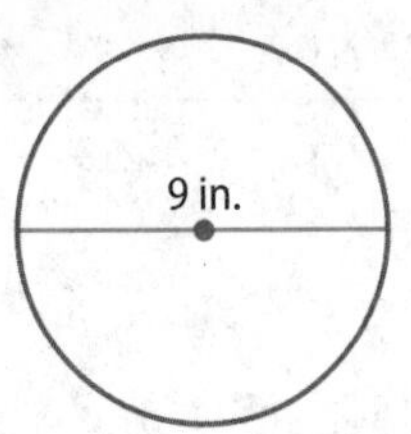

Ⓐ 28.3 inches

Ⓑ 29.8 inches

Ⓒ 40.8 inches

Ⓓ 47.1 inches

22. Diego ran around this track one and one-half times. Then he ran 50 more feet. How far did Diego run? Use 3.14 for π. Round to the nearest tenth. N P EE MP

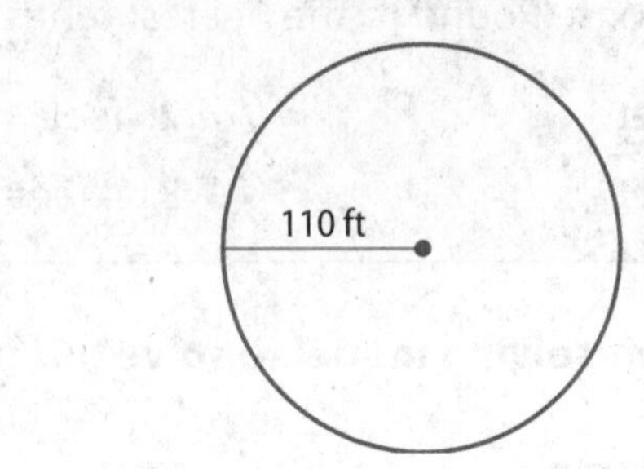

23. The radii for a penny and a nickel are shown. What is the difference in circumferences, in millimeters? Use 3.14 for π. Round to the nearest hundredth. N P EE MP

24. If the radius of a circle is tripled, what would happen to its circumference? Explain and give an example. N P EE MP

N = Number and Operations 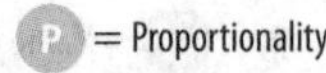 P = Proportionality EE = Expressions, Equations, and Relationships MP = Mathematical Processes

21ST CENTURY CAREER

Roller Coaster Designer

If you have a passion for amusement parks, a great imagination, and enjoy building things, you might want to consider a career in roller coaster design. Roller coaster designers combine creativity, engineering, mathematics, and physics to develop rides that are both exciting and safe. In order to analyze data and make precise calculations, a roller coaster designer must have a solid background in high school math and science.

TEKS

Mathematical Process
7.1(A) Apply mathematics to problems arising in everyday life, society, and the workplace.

Targeted TEKS 7.5(C)

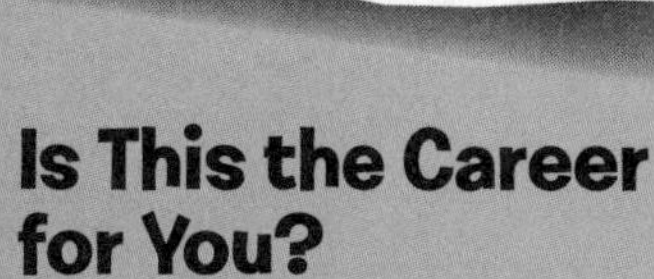

Is This the Career for You?

Are you interested in a career as a roller coaster designer? Take some of the following courses in high school to get started in the right direction.

- Algebra
- Calculus
- Geometry
- Physics
- Trigonometry

Explore college and careers at ccr.mcgraw-hill.com

A Thrilling Ride

Use the information in the table to solve each problem.

1. In a scale drawing of SheiKra, a designer uses a scale of 1 inch = 16 feet. What is the height of the roller coaster in the drawing? ________

2. On a model of Montu, the height of the loop is 13 inches. What is the scale? ________

3. In a scale drawing of Montu, the height of the roller coaster is 10 inches. What is the scale factor? ________

4. SheiKra has a hill that goes through a tunnel. On a model of the roller coaster, the hill is 23 inches tall and the scale is 1 inch = 6 feet. What is the actual height of the tunnel hill?

____

5. An engineer is building a model of SheiKra. She wants the model to be about 32 inches high. Choose an appropriate scale for the model. Then use it to determine the loop height of the model.

____

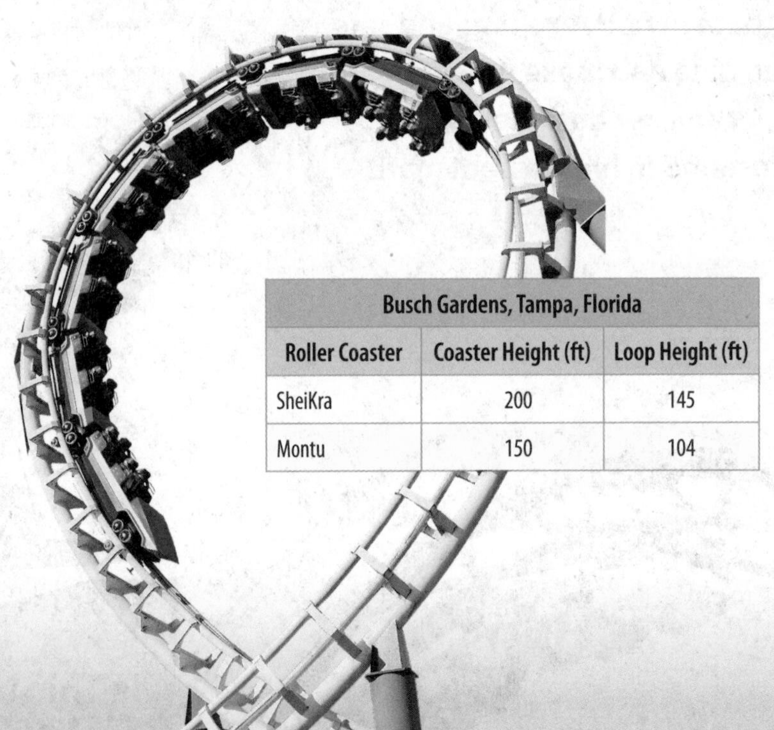

Busch Gardens, Tampa, Florida		
Roller Coaster	**Coaster Height (ft)**	**Loop Height (ft)**
SheiKra	200	145
Montu	150	104

TEKS Career Project

It's time to update your career portfolio! Describe a roller coaster that you, as a roller coaster designer, would create. Include the height and angle of the tallest drop, the total length, maximum speed, number of loops and tunnels, and color scheme. Be sure to include the name of your roller coaster. Then prepare a brief oral presentation to give to your classmates. At the end, ask any clarifying questions.

____

____

____

What problem-solving skills might you use as a roller coaster designer?

- ________
- ________
- ________
- ________
- ________

Chapter Review

Vocabulary Check

Work with a partner to complete each sentence using the vocabulary list at the beginning of the chapter. Then circle the word that completes the sentence in the word search. Take turns reading each sentence aloud while the other student listens carefully.

1. The distance across a circle through its center is called the ________.
2. The ________ is the distance from the center to any point on the circle.
3. A ________ is the set of all points in a plane that are the same distance from a point.
4. The point in a circle from which all other points are equidistant is called the ________.
5. The distance around a circle is the ________.
6. The ratio of circumference to diameter is called ________.
7. A ________ gives the ratio that compares the measurements of the drawing or model to the measurements of the real object.
8. A drawing that is used to represent objects that are too large or too small to be drawn at actual size is called a scale ________ or scale model.
9. A scale written as a ratio without units in simplest form is called the scale ________.
10. Figures that have the same shape but not necessarily the same size are called ________.
11. An ________ is a characteristic of a figure, such as side and angle measures.

J	V	L	E	N	E	F	P	R	H	L	N	B	G	E	D	L	D	M	U	R	R
S	M	G	J	V	S	S	C	I	L	E	C	O	M	E	L	V	T	B	C	U	H
I	X	S	D	Y	K	C	S	I	Z	Z	N	F	J	H	A	S	Z	F	I	V	G
M	S	Y	M	S	C	T	A	Y	X	E	J	J	W	P	T	M	D	Z	R	S	E
I	B	E	B	K	I	E	V	L	S	E	W	D	Z	Q	T	W	D	P	C	C	X
L	Q	P	P	L	R	Z	J	Z	E	M	O	Z	P	D	R	X	I	S	U	A	G
A	O	K	E	Q	C	F	S	C	S	F	O	D	U	N	I	X	A	V	M	L	Y
R	M	U	Y	V	L	V	C	N	E	J	A	T	O	R	B	F	M	P	F	E	W
F	F	P	G	D	E	W	A	R	B	N	L	C	L	P	U	H	E	P	E	D	X
I	M	Q	M	R	L	D	L	O	A	N	T	V	T	I	T	E	T	C	R	R	X
G	Y	V	W	N	A	L	E	Q	W	J	X	E	F	O	E	H	E	U	E	A	Z
U	H	A	I	R	F	D	Y	L	W	C	C	G	R	C	R	B	R	W	N	W	R
R	K	E	G	D	S	F	I	P	X	W	Z	B	S	P	K	F	R	E	C	I	G
E	M	M	N	W	Y	G	B	U	T	U	H	I	P	A	S	M	V	C	E	N	N
S	O	G	L	L	V	G	W	T	S	H	R	X	O	X	U	I	F	Y	W	G	I
H	W	R	M	V	Q	N	K	B	Z	D	P	C	D	J	R	H	A	B	S	P	C

Key Concept Check

Use Your FOLDABLES

Use your Foldable to help review the chapter. Share your Foldable with a partner and take turns summarizing what you learned in this chapter, while the other partner listens carefully. Ask for and give help of any concept if needed. TEKS 7.1(E)

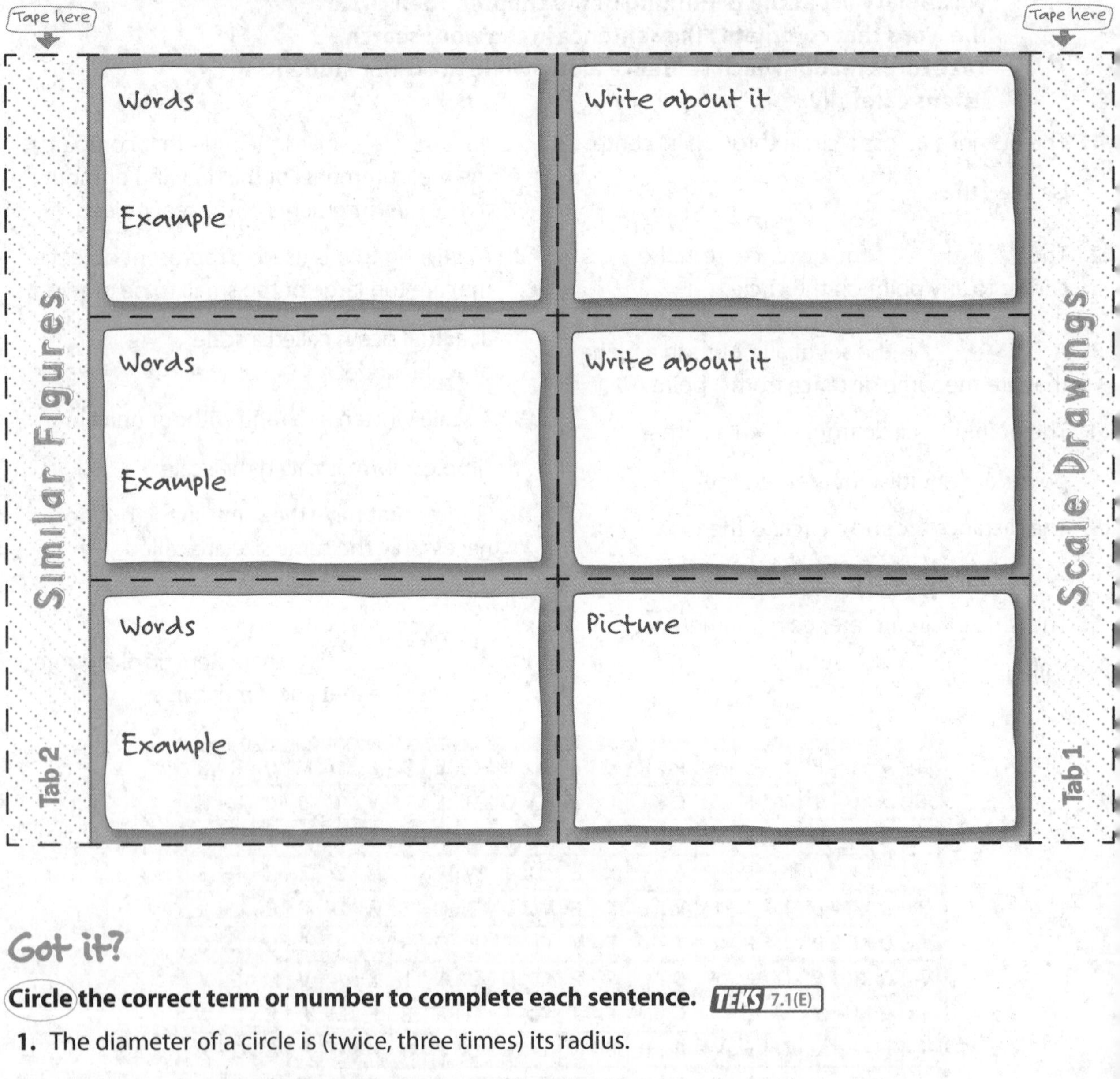

Tape here

Tape here

Tab 2 Similar Figures

Words Example	Write about it
Words Example	Write about it
Words Example	Picture

Tab 1 Scale Drawings

Got it?

Circle the correct term or number to complete each sentence. TEKS 7.1(E)

1. The diameter of a circle is (twice, three times) its radius.

2. The ratios of corresponding sides between similar triangles are (equal, not equal).

3. The angle measures of similar figures is a characteristic or (scale, attribute).

4. A (scale drawing, similar figure) is used to represent objects that are too large or too small to be drawn or built at actual size.

Multi-Step Problem Solving

5. Maria and her sister went on a bike ride. The tires on Maria's bike have a diameter of 24 inches. Her sister's bike tires have a diameter of 18 inches. If one revolution is equal to the circumference, how many feet farther will Maria travel after 25 revolutions? Use 3.14 for π. Round to the nearest tenth. Justify your solution. EE N MP

1 Analyze

2 Plan

3 Solve

4 Justify and Evaluate

Got it?

6. Florencia uses a copy machine to increase the size of her paper. The page she is copying measures $8\frac{1}{2}$ inches in width and 11 inches in length. The setting on the copy machine increases the size of the page by 130%. What is the area of the new page? Round to the nearest tenth. Justify your solution. N P MP

EE = Expressions, Equations, and Relationships N = Number and Operations P = Proportionality MP = Mathematical Processes

Reflect

Answering the Essential Question

Use what you learned about proportionality and geometry to complete the graphic organizer. TEKS 7.1(D), 7.1(F), 7.1(G)

How do scale drawings help us describe real-world objects?

Essential Question

HOW can proportional relationships be applied to geometry?

How do similar figures help us describe real-world objects?

Answer the Essential Question. HOW can proportional relationships be applied to geometry? Verbally share your responses with a partner, asking for and giving help if needed.

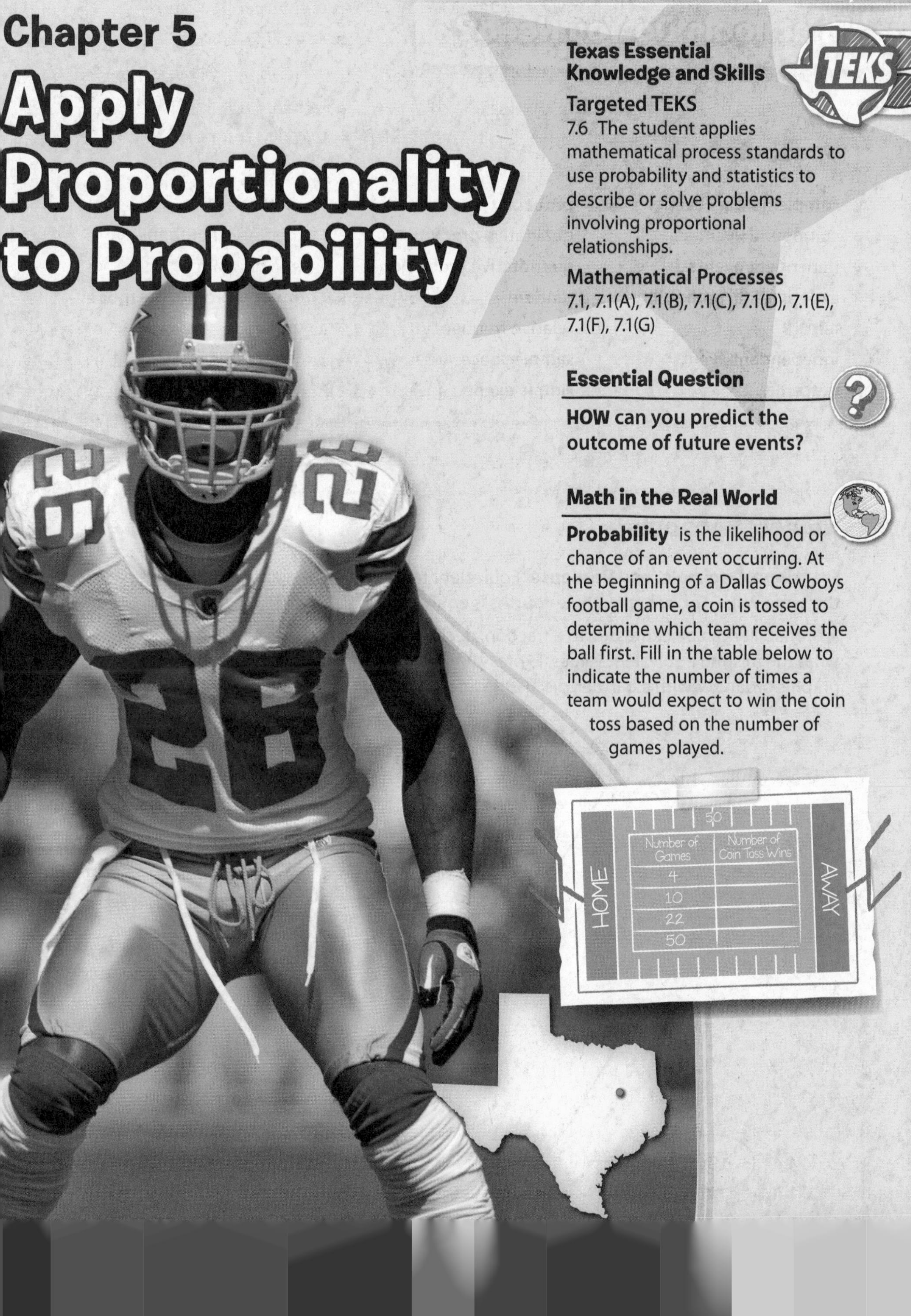

Chapter 5

Apply Proportionality to Probability

Texas Essential Knowledge and Skills

Targeted TEKS

7.6 The student applies mathematical process standards to use probability and statistics to describe or solve problems involving proportional relationships.

Mathematical Processes

7.1, 7.1(A), 7.1(B), 7.1(C), 7.1(D), 7.1(E), 7.1(F), 7.1(G)

Essential Question

HOW can you predict the outcome of future events?

Math in the Real World

Probability is the likelihood or chance of an event occurring. At the beginning of a Dallas Cowboys football game, a coin is tossed to determine which team receives the ball first. Fill in the table below to indicate the number of times a team would expect to win the coin toss based on the number of games played.

Number of Games	Number of Coin Toss Wins
4	
10	
22	
50	

What Tools Do You Need?

Vocabulary

complementary events
compound event
dependent events
experimental probability
fair
independent events
outcome
probability
qualitative predictions
quantitative predictions
random
relative frequency
sample space
simple event
simulation
theoretical probability
tree diagram
uniform probability model
unfair

Review Vocabulary

Fractions, Decimals, and Percents Equivalent rational numbers are numbers that have the same value. For example, three-fourths is equivalent to 0.75 or 75%.

A probability can be expressed as a fraction, decimal, or percent. For each rational number, write the missing equivalent values. Express fractions in simplest form. Then share your graphic organizer with a partner, discussing and comparing any differences.

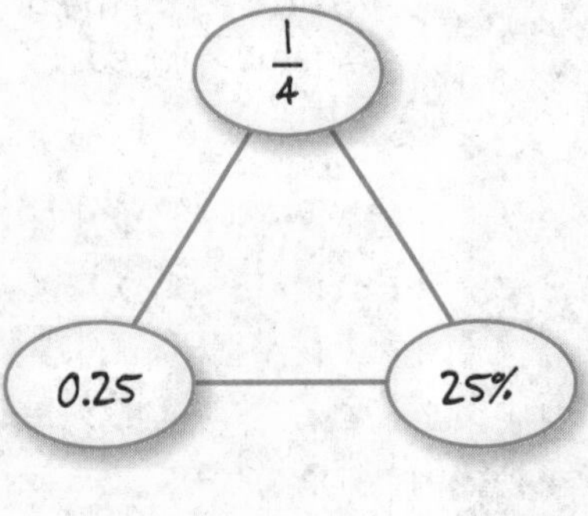

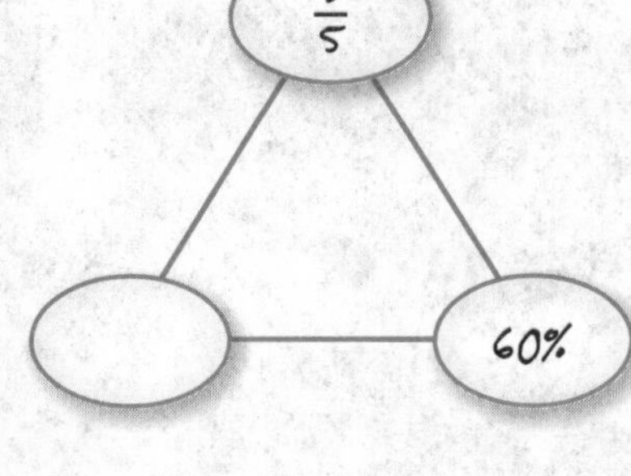

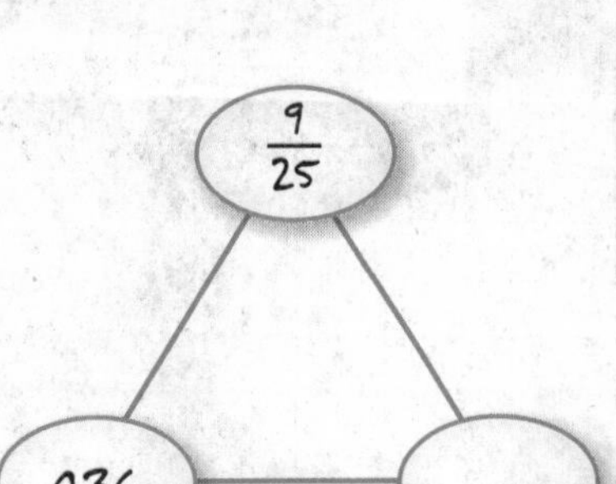

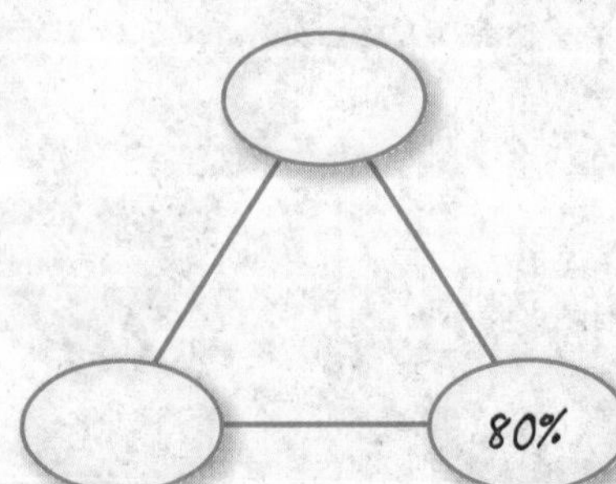

When Will You Use This?

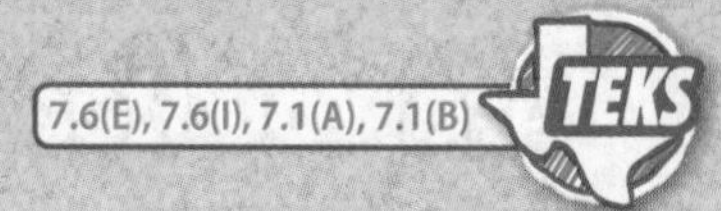

Jamar and Theresa in

Radio Surveys

WGRV FM 92.0

Are you ready for our first task as radio station interns?

I'm ready! It's gonna be fun! What should we do first?

Well, we need to find out what teens want to listen to.

We could make a survey with different kinds of music choices on it.

Good idea! The survey could have the teens rank their favorites from 1 to 5.

How many outcomes will that be?

MALL

We could pass out surveys at the mall to the first 100 teens we see.

We could ask the fans at tonight's football game.

The lunchroom would be a great place to pass out surveys, too.

Are you ready to get to work?

Your Turn! **You will solve this problem in the chapter.**

Are You Ready?

Quick Review

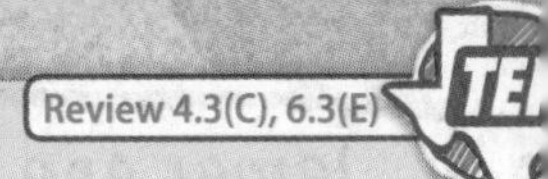

Example 1

Express $\frac{21}{28}$ in simplest form.

$\frac{21}{28} = \frac{3}{4}$ (÷7, ÷7) Divide the numerator and denominator by the GCF, 7.

Example 2

Determine 7 • 6 • 5 • 4.

$7 \cdot 6 \cdot 5 \cdot 4 = 42 \cdot 5 \cdot 4$ Multiply from left to right.

$= 210 \cdot 4$

$= 840$

Quick Check

Fractions **Express each fraction in simplest form.**

1. $\frac{5}{15} =$ ________

Show your work.

2. $\frac{3}{18} =$ ________

3. $\frac{8}{12} =$ ________

4. $\frac{12}{20} =$ ________

Products **Determine each product.**

5. $6 \cdot 5 =$ ________

6. $10 \cdot 9 \cdot 8 =$ ________

7. $4 \cdot 3 \cdot 2 \cdot 1 =$ ________

8. Suppose you listen to 9 songs each hour for 5 hours every day this week. How many songs will you have listened to this week?

____

Which problems did you answer correctly in the Quick Check? Shade those exercise numbers below.

1 2 3 4 5   8

Use the Foldable throughout this chapter to help you learn about probability.

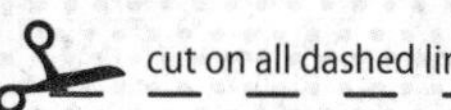 cut on all dashed lines

fold on all solid lines

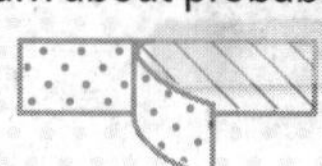 tape to page 430

Probability

simple event

compound event

Use the Foldable throughout this chapter to help you learn about probability.

 cut on all dashed lines — fold on all solid lines 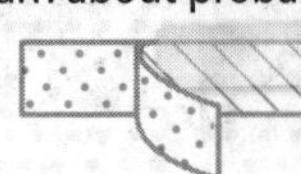 tape to page 430

page 430

Definition

Definition

Hands-On Lab 1-a
Sample Spaces

INQUIRY HOW can I use multiple representations to determine the number of outcomes for an action?

Texas Essential Knowledge and Skills
Targeted TEKS
7.6(A) Represent sample spaces for simple and compound events using lists and tree diagrams.
Mathematical Processes
7.1(C), 7.1(D), 7.1(E), 7.1(F), 7.1(G)

A number cube has six faces. When you roll a number cube, there are six possibilities. An **outcome** is any one of the possible results of an action. The set of all of the possible outcomes is called the **sample space**. The sample space is 1, 2, 3, 4, 5, 6.

Organized lists, tables, and tree diagrams can be used to represent the sample space. A **tree diagram** uses branches to show the total number of outcomes.

Hands-On Activity

Draw a tree diagram to determine the sample space when a coin is tossed and a number cube is rolled.

Step 1 List the outcomes for tossing a coin.

Step 2 For each outcome, list the outcomes for rolling a number cube.

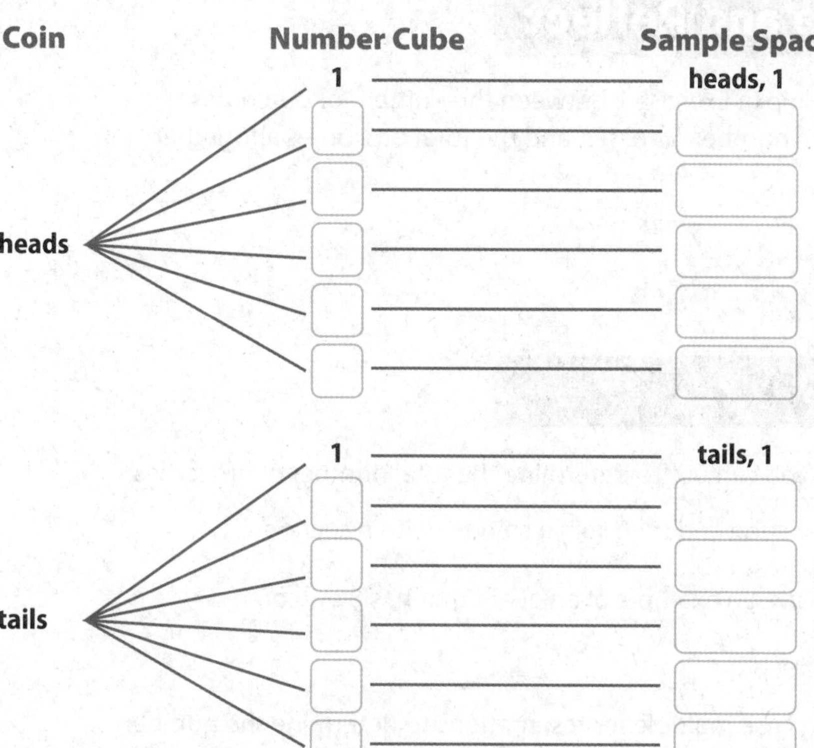

The tree diagram shows that there are _____ possible outcomes.

Investigate

Use a list or tree diagram to show the sample space for each action. Work with a partner.

1.

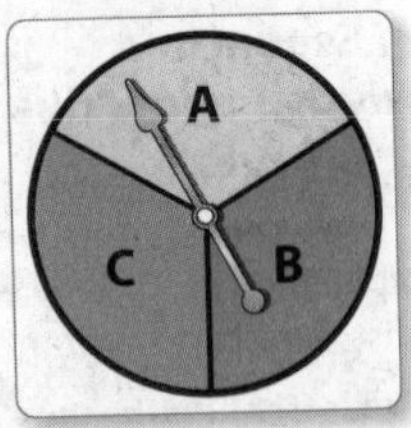

sample space: ______

2. tossing a coin three times

Coin	Coin	Coin	Sample Space

sample space: ______

3.

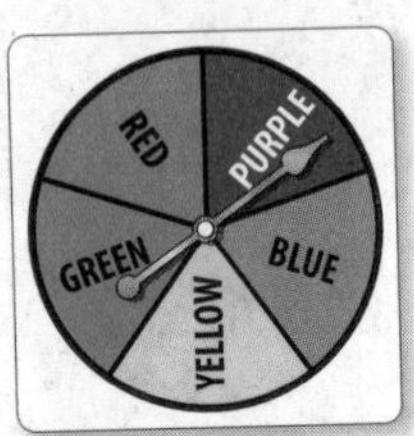

sample space: ______

Collaborate

Analyze and Reflect

4. Analyze the relationship in Exercise 2 between the number of outcomes for each coin toss, the number of tosses, and the total outcomes altogether.

What do you notice? ______

Create

5. Write a formula that you can use to determine the total number of outcomes O if you roll a number cube and then spin a spinner with n sections. ______

6. MP **Organize Ideas** Give an example of an event that has 8 outcomes.

7. INQUIRY HOW can I use multiple representations to determine the number of outcomes for an action?

Lesson 1

Probability of Simple Events

Launch the Lesson: Vocabulary

Probability is the chance that some event will occur. A **simple event** is one outcome or a collection of outcomes. What is an outcome?

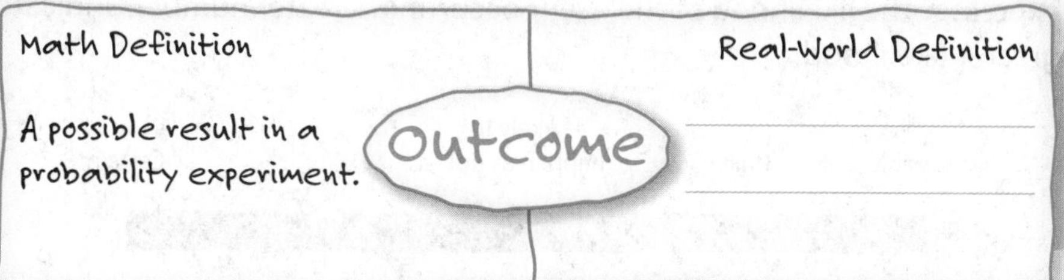

Real-World Link

For a sledding trip, you randomly select one of the four hats shown. Complete the table to show the possible outcomes.

Hat Selection Outcomes			
Outcome 1	green hat	Outcome 3	
Outcome 2		Outcome 4	

1. Write a ratio that compares the number of blue hats to the total number of hats. ______

2. Describe a hat display in which you would have a better chance of selecting a red hat.

______

______

Texas Essential Knowledge and Skills

Targeted TEKS
7.6(E) Find the probabilities of a simple event and its complement and describe the relationship between the two. *Also addresses 7.6(A).*

Mathematical Processes
7.1(A), 7.1(B), 7.1(C), 7.1(F)

Vocab

Vocabulary
probability
simple event
random
complementary events

Essential Question
HOW can you predict the outcome of future events?

Which MP Mathematical Processes did you use? Shade the circle(s) that applies.

Ⓐ Apply Math to the Real World.
Ⓑ Use a Problem-Solving Model.
Ⓒ Select Tools and Techniques.
Ⓓ Use Multiple Representations.
Ⓔ Organize Ideas.
Ⓕ Analyze Relationships.
Ⓖ Justify Arguments.

Key Concept

Probability

Words The probability of an event is a ratio that compares the number of favorable outcomes to the number of possible outcomes. The number of favorable outcomes represents the sample space.

Symbols $P(\text{event}) = \frac{\text{number of favorable outcomes}}{\text{number of possible outcomes}}$

Work Zone

STOP and Reflect

In the space below, describe an example of a simple event that is certain to occur.

The probability of a chance event is a number between 0 and 1 that expresses the likelihood of the event occurring. Greater numbers indicate greater likelihood.

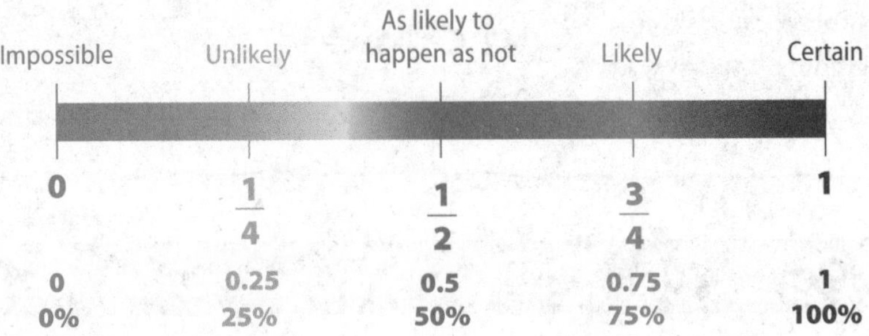

Outcomes occur at **random** if each outcome is equally likely to occur.

Tools Tutor

Example

There are six equally likely outcomes if a number cube with sides labeled 1 through 6 is rolled.

1. Determine $P(6)$ or the probability of rolling a 6. How likely is it to roll a 6?

There is only one 6 on the number cube.

$P(6) = \frac{\text{number of favorable outcomes}}{\text{number of possible outcomes}}$

$= \frac{1}{6}$

Number Cube

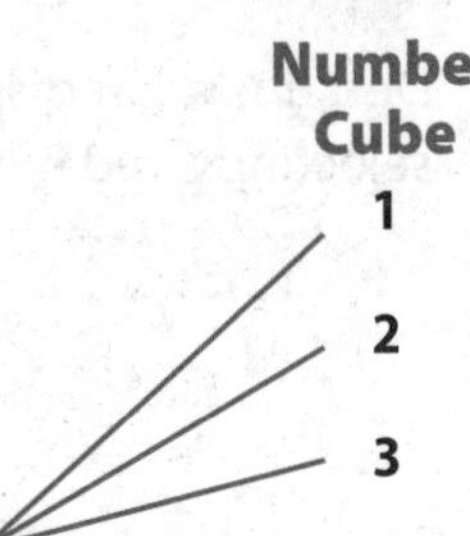

The tree diagram shows that there are 6 possible outcomes. The probability of rolling a 6 is $\frac{1}{6}$, or about 17%, or about 0.17.

Since $\frac{1}{6} \approx \frac{1}{4}$, it is unlikely to roll a 6.

Got It? Do this problem to find out.

a. A coin is tossed. Determine the probability of the coin landing on heads. How likely is it to land on heads?

a. ______

Example

2. Determine the probability of rolling 2, 3, or 4 on a number cube.

The word or indicates that the number of favorable outcomes needs to include the numbers 2, 3, and 4.

$$P(2, 3, \text{or } 4) = \frac{\text{number of favorable outcomes}}{\text{number of possible outcomes}}$$

$$= \frac{3}{6} \text{ or } \frac{1}{2} \quad \text{Simplify.}$$

The probability of rolling a 2, 3, or 4 is $\frac{1}{2}$, 50%, or 0.5.

Got It? Do these problems to find out.

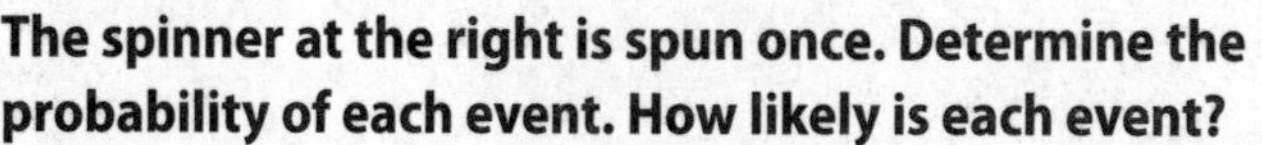

The spinner at the right is spun once. Determine the probability of each event. How likely is each event?

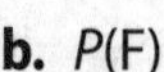

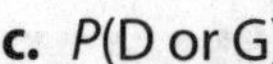

b. $P(F)$ **c.** $P(D \text{ or } G)$ **d.** $P(\text{vowel})$

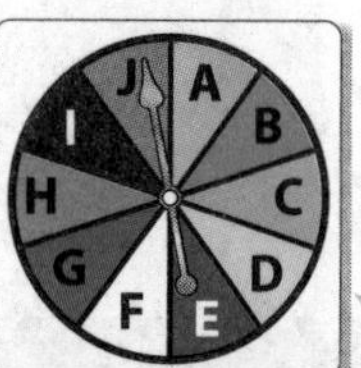

Show your work.

b. ______

c. ______

d. ______

Determine Probability of a Complement

Complementary events are two events in which either one or the other must happen, but they cannot happen at the same time. The sum of the probability of an event and its complement is 1 or 100%.

Complement

In everyday language complement means the quantity required to make something complete. This is similar to the math meaning.

Example

3. Determine the probability of rolling and *not* rolling a 6 in Example 1. Describe the relationship between the two.

The probability of *not* rolling a 6 and the probability of rolling a 6 are complementary. So, the sum of the probabilities is 1.

$P(6) + P(not\ 6) = 1$ — $P(6)$ and $P(not\ 6)$ are complements.

$\frac{1}{6} + P(not\ 6) = 1$ — Replace $P(6)$ with $\frac{1}{6}$.

$\frac{1}{6} + \frac{5}{6} = 1$ — **THINK** $\frac{1}{6}$ plus what number equals 1?

The probability of rolling a 6 is $\frac{1}{6}$ and the probability of *not* rolling a 6 is $\frac{5}{6}$, or about 83% or 0.83. Since the sum of the two probabilities are equal to 1 or 100%, they are complementary events.

Got It? Do this problem to find out.

e. A bag contains 5 blue, 8 red, and 7 green marbles. A marble is selected at random. Determine the probability the marble is red and *not* red. Describe the relationship between the two.

e. ______

Example

4. Mr. Harada surveyed his class and discovered that 30% of his students have blue eyes. Identify the complement of this event. Then determine its probability.

The complement of having blue eyes is *not* having blue eyes. The sum of the probabilities is 100%.

$P(\text{blue eyes}) + P(\textit{not}\text{ blue eyes}) = 100\%$ — *P*(blue eyes) and *P*(*not* blue eyes) are complements.

$30\% + P(\textit{not}\text{ blue eyes}) = 100\%$ — Replace *P*(blue eyes) with 30%.

$30\% + 70\% = 100\%$ — **THINK** 30% plus what number equals 100%?

So, the probability that a student does *not* have blue eyes is 70%, 0.7, or $\frac{7}{10}$.

Guided Practice

A letter tile is chosen randomly. Determine the probability of each event. Express each answer as a fraction, percent, and decimal. (Examples 1 and 2)

1. *P*(D) ______

2. *P*(S, V, or L) ______

3. *P*(*not* D) ______

4. The probability of choosing a "Go Back 1 Space" card in a board game is 25%. Describe the complement of this event and determine its probability. (Example 3)

5. **Building on the Essential Question** Explain the relationship between the probability of an event and its complement. Give an example.

Rate Yourself!

How confident are you about determining the probability of simple events? Shade the ring on the target.

Find out online. Use the Self-Check Quiz.

FOLDABLES Time to update your Foldable!

Independent Practice

The spinner shown is spun once. Determine the probability of each event. How likely is each event? (Examples 1 and 2)

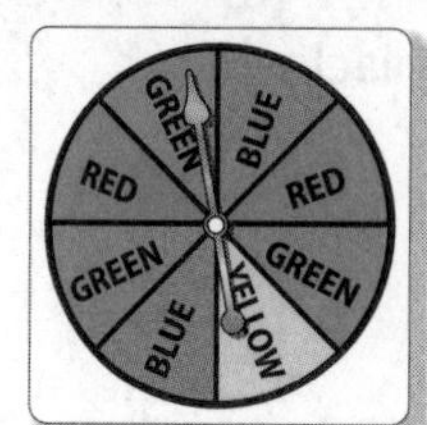

1. P(blue)

2. P(red or yellow)

3. P(*not* brown)

4. P(*not* green)

5. If the probability of landing on a certain color is p, write an expression for the probability of *not* landing on that color or the complement. Suppose the probability of p is $\frac{1}{4}$. Solve the expression and explain their relationship. (Example 3)

6. Refer to the table on air travel. Suppose a flight that arrived at El Centro is selected at random. What is the probability that the flight did *not* arrive on time? Express the answer as a fraction, decimal, and percent. Explain your reasoning. (Example 4)

Air Travel	
Airport	Arrivals (Percent on-time)
El Centro (CA)	80
Baltimore (MD)	82

7. MP **Apply Math to the Real World** Refer to the graphic novel frame below. Jamar and Theresa decide to create a music mix and include an equal number of songs from each genre. What is the probability that any given song would be from the hip-hop genre? ______

One jelly bean is picked, without looking, from the dish. Write a sentence that explains how likely it is for each event to happen.

8. black

9. purple, red, or yellow

H.O.T. Problems Higher-Order Thinking

10. **Analyze** The probability of landing in a certain section on a spinner can be found by considering the size of the angle formed by that section. On the spinner shown, the angle formed by the yellow section is one-fourth of the angle formed by the entire circle. So, $P(\text{yellow}) = \frac{1}{4}$, 0.25, or 25%.

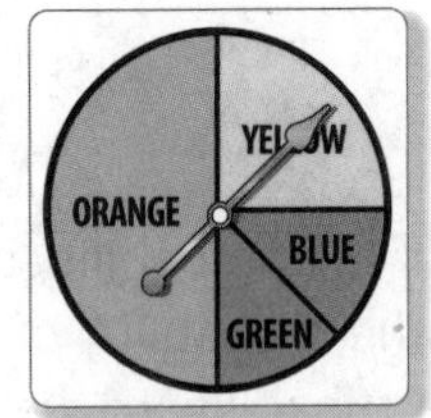

   a. On a separate sheet of paper, draw a tree diagram to show the sample space.

   b. Determine *P*(green) and *P*(orange) for the spinner. Express the probabilities as fractions, decimals, and percents.

   c. Determine *P*(*not* yellow).

11. **Analyze** A bag contains 6 red, 4 blue, and 8 green marbles. How many marbles of each color should be added so that the total number of marbles is 27, but the probability of randomly selecting one marble of each color remains unchanged?

12. **Evaluate** Circle the pair of probabilities that do not represent probabilities of complementary events. Explain your reasoning.

$0.625, \frac{3}{8}$	0.38, 62%	$\frac{7}{8}, 0.125$	$70\%, \frac{1}{3}$

Name ______________________________

Multi-Step Problem Solving

13. The table shows Bobby's number of hits for his entire baseball season. How much greater is the probability that Bobby hit a single or double compared to a triple or homerun? P N MP

Result	Number of Times
Singles	41
Doubles	13
Triples	14
Homeruns	7

Ⓐ $\frac{9}{25}$ Ⓒ $\frac{11}{25}$

Ⓑ $\frac{2}{5}$ Ⓓ $\frac{18}{25}$

Use a problem-solving model to solve this problem.

1 Analyze

Read the problem. Circle the information you know. Underline what the problem is asking you to find.

2 Plan

What will you need to do to solve the problem? Write your plan in steps.

Step 1 Determine the __________ of each event.

Step 2 Combine the probabilities, then determine the __________.

3 Solve

Use your plan to solve the problem. Show your steps.

P(single or double) = ________ *P*(triple or homerun) = ________

Determine the difference between the probabilities.

____ − ____ = ____

The probability of Bobby hitting a single or double is ____ greater than hitting a triple or homerun.

So, the correct answer is ____. Fill in that answer choice.

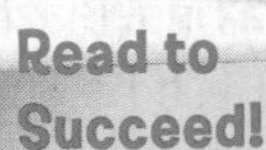

Read to Succeed!

Add the number of favorable outcomes for each type of hit before expressing it as a fraction and determining the probability.

4 Justify and Evaluate

How do you know your solution is accurate?

____

____

____

P = Proportionality N = Number and Operations MP = Mathematical Processes

More Multi-Step Problem Solving

Use a problem-solving model to solve each problem.

14. Suppose you spin the spinner one time. How much greater is the probability that the spinner will land on A compared to C or D? P N MP

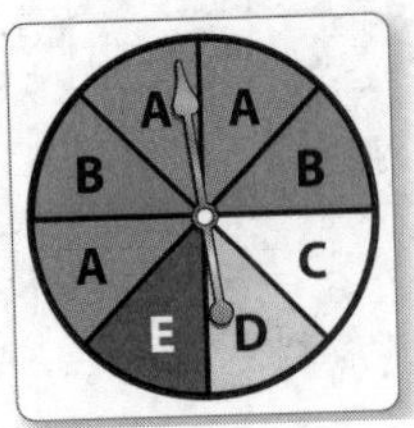

Ⓐ 12.5%

Ⓑ 25%

Ⓒ 37.5%

Ⓓ 50%

15. These six numbered squares are placed in a bag. If you randomly select one square from the bag, how much greater is the probability that you select an even number than an odd number? Express your answer as a fraction, percent, and decimal. P N MP

255	256	260	263	264	270

16. The bar graph shows the number of colored candies in a bag. Blaze's favorite colored candy is blue. If he chooses one candy from the bag without looking, how much greater is the probability that he will choose a green, yellow, or orange candy compared to a red or blue candy? Express your answer as a fraction, percent, and decimal. P N MD MP

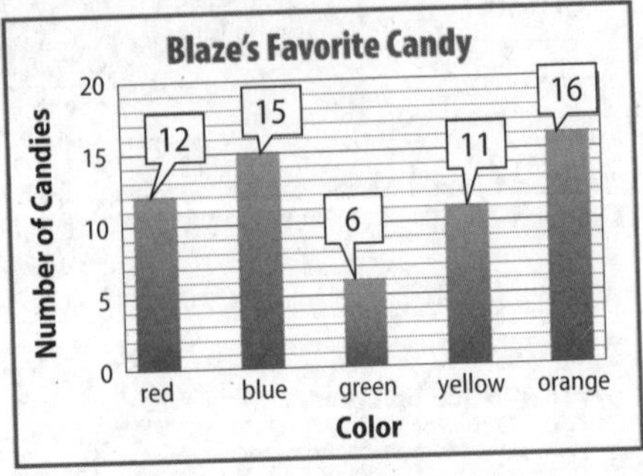

17. What is the probability that a randomly chosen number from 1 to 100 is *not* a multiple of 5? Express your answer as a fraction, percent, and decimal. P N MP

P = Proportionality N = Number and Operations MD = Measurement and Data MP = Mathematical Processes

Hands-On Lab 2-a

Make Predictions

INQUIRY HOW can I analyze relationships to make predictions for probability experiments?

Texas Essential Knowledge and Skills

Targeted TEKS

7.6(H) Solve problems using qualitative and quantitative predictions and comparisons from simple experiments. *Also addresses 7.6(C), 7.6(D).*

Mathematical Processes

7.1(C), 7.1(D), 7.1(E), 7.1(F), 7.1(G)

In a board game, you get an extra turn if you roll doubles or two of the same number. How likely is it that you will roll doubles?

You can conduct an experiment to determine the relative frequency of rolling doubles using two number cubes. **Relative frequency** is the ratio of the number of experimental successes to the number of experimental attempts.

Hands-On Activity 1

Step 1 Complete the table to show the sample space for rolling two number cubes. Shade all of the possible outcomes that are doubles. The probability of rolling doubles is ______

(1, 1)	(2, 1)				
(1, 2)	(2, 2)				
(1, 3)	(2, 3)				
(1, 4)					
(1, 5)					
(1, 6)					

1. How many times would you expect doubles to be rolled if you roll the number cubes 50 times? Explain.

______

______

Step 2 Now, roll two number cubes and record the number of doubles in the table. Repeat the experiment 50 times.

Number of Rolls	50
Number of Doubles	

Step 3 Determine the relative frequency of rolling doubles. Use the ratio $\frac{\text{number of times doubles were rolled}}{\text{number of rolls}}$. ______

2. Compare the ratios in Steps 1 and 3 of Activity 1. What do you notice. Explain.

______

3. How did your prediction compare to the actual number of times you rolled doubles? Explain any difference. ______

You often use predictions when learning about probability. **Quantitative predictions** deal with numerical data or measurable data, while **qualitative predictions** deal with descriptions, observable data, or non-numerical data.

You can use qualitative descriptions like the ones shown to describe how likely it is for an event to occur.

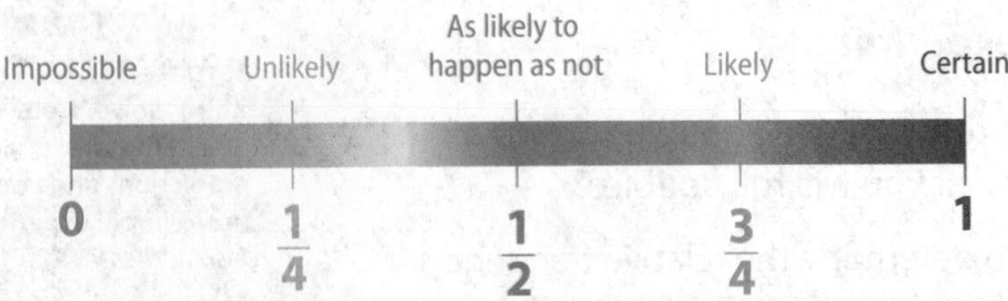

Hands-On Activity 2

Step 1 The table shows all of the possible outcomes for rolling two number cubes. Shade all of the possible outcomes that have a sum of 9. The probability of rolling a sum of 9 is ________

(1, 1)	(2, 1)	(3, 1)	(4, 1)	(5, 1)	(6, 1)
(1, 2)	(2, 2)	(3, 2)	(4, 2)	(5, 2)	(6, 2)
(1, 3)	(2, 3)	(3, 3)	(4, 3)	(5, 3)	(6, 3)
(1, 4)	(2, 4)	(3, 4)	(4, 4)	(5, 4)	(6, 4)
(1, 5)	(2, 5)	(3, 5)	(4, 5)	(5, 5)	(6, 5)
(1, 6)	(2, 6)	(3, 6)	(4, 6)	(5, 6)	(6, 6)

4. Make a qualitative prediction. How likely is it to roll a sum of 9? ________

Step 2 Roll two number cubes and record the number outcomes that have a sum of 9 in the table. Repeat the experiment 50 times.

Number of Rolls	Sum of 9
50	

Step 3 Determine the relative frequency of rolling a sum of 9. Use the ratio $\frac{\text{number of outcomes with sum of 9}}{\text{number of rolls}}$. ________

5. Make a quantitative prediction. How many times would you expect to roll a sum of 9 if you rolled both cubes 50 times? Explain.

____

6. How did your prediction compare to the actual number of times you rolled doubles? Explain any difference. ________

Work with a partner. The spinner shown is spun once. Determine the probability of each event.

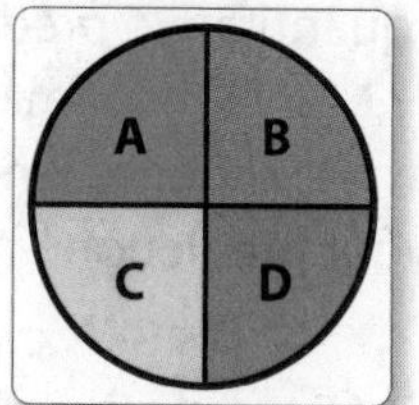

7. *P*(*A*) ______

8. *P*(*not B*) ______

9. MP **Justify Arguments** Make a prediction. How many times would you expect the spinner to land on *A* if the spinner is spun 40 times? Justify your prediction.

____

____

10. Is the prediction you made in Exercise 9 quantitative or qualitative? Explain.

____

11. Place a paperclip around the tip of a pencil. Then place the tip on the center of the spinner. Spin the paperclip 40 times. Record the results in the table below.

Section	A	B	C	D
Frequency				
Relative Frequency				

12. Compare the frequencies from what you expected in Exercise 9 to your results in Exercise 11. What do you notice? Explain.

____

____

13. Would you expect to land on *C* more frequently than landing on *B* if you spin the spinner 50 times? Explain.

____

____

Analyze and Reflect

14. Make a quantitative prediction. If the spinner shown is spun 72 times, how many more times would you expect the spinner to land on green than on blue? Justify your prediction.

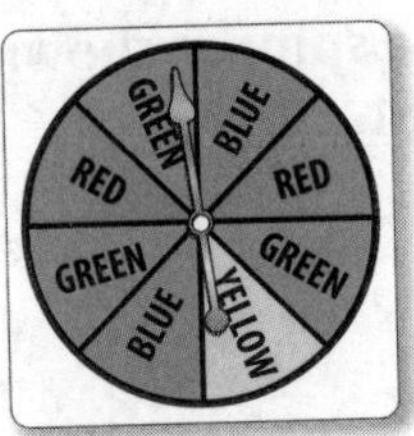

15. Make a qualitative prediction. Based on your results from the spinner above, are the outcomes of red, blue, green, and yellow equally likely? Explain.

16. MP **Organize Ideas** Refer to Exercise 11. What would you expect to happen to the long-run relative frequency of spinning *A* as you increase the number of spins from 40 to 1,000?

Create

17. Two number cubes are rolled *n* times. Write a formula that you can use to make a quantitative prediction for the number of times *D* you would expect to roll doubles.

18. MP **Select Tools and Techniques** Design an experiment in which the probability of an event is unlikely to happen. Perform the experiment and compare the results to your prediction.

19. **INQUIRY** HOW can I analyze relationships to make predictions for probability experiments?

Lesson 2

Theoretical and Experimental Probability

Launch the Lesson: Real World

Watch

The prize wheels for a carnival game are shown. You receive a less expensive prize if you spin and win on wheel A. You receive a more expensive prize if you spin and win on wheel B. Let's investigate the probabilities of winning on either wheel with their respective prize amounts.

Wheel A

Wheel B

In a **uniform probability model**, each outcome has an equal probability of happening.

1. Which wheel has uniform probability? ______
2. Use a paperclip and the tip of your pencil to spin each wheel 4 times. Record your results.

Spin	Wheel A	Wheel B
1		
2		
3		
4		

3. Why do you think winners on wheel A receive a less expensive prize than winners on wheel B?

______

Which MP Mathematical Processes did you use? Shade the circle(s) that applies.

Ⓐ Apply Math to the Real World.
Ⓑ Use a Problem-Solving Model.
Ⓒ Select Tools and Techniques.
Ⓓ Use Multiple Representations.
Ⓔ Organize Ideas.
Ⓕ Analyze Relationships.
Ⓖ Justify Arguments.

Texas Essential Knowledge and Skills

Targeted TEKS

7.6(I) Determine experimental and theoretical probabilities related to simple and compound events using data and sample spaces. *Also addresses 7.6(C), 7.6(D).*

Mathematical Processes

7.1(A), 7.1(B), 7.1(D), 7.1(F)

Vocab

Vocabulary

uniform probability model
theoretical probability
experimental probability

Essential Question

HOW can you predict the outcome of future events?

Work Zone

Experimental and Theoretical Probability

Theoretical probability is based on uniform probability — what *should* happen when conducting a probability experiment. **Experimental probability** is based on relative frequency — what *actually* occurs during such an experiment.

The theoretical probability and the experimental probability of an event may or may not be the same. As the number of attempts increases, the theoretical probability and the experimental probability should become closer in value.

Example

Trials
A trial is one experiment in a series of successive experiments.

1. The graph shows the results of an experiment in which a spinner with 3 equal sections is spun sixty times. Determine the experimental probability of spinning red for this experiment. Predict how many times the spinner will land on red if it is spun 500 times.

Step 1 The spinner landed on red 24 times, blue 15 times, and green 21 times.

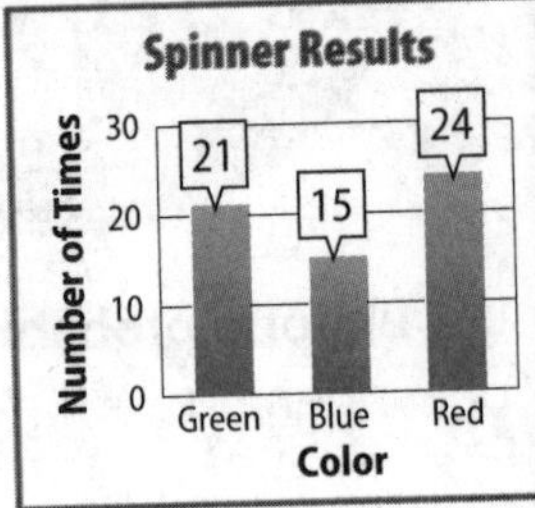

$$P(\text{red}) = \frac{\text{number of times red occurs}}{\text{total number of spins}}$$

$$= \frac{24}{60} \text{ or } \frac{2}{5}$$

The experimental probability of spinning red is $\frac{2}{5}$.

Step 2 Suppose the spinner was spun 500 times. Predict how many times the spinner will land on red.

Use the experimental probability to determine $\frac{2}{5}$ of 500.

$$\frac{2}{5} \times 500 = 200$$

So, the spinner is expected to land on red 200 times.

Got It? Do these problems to find out.

a. Refer to Example 1. If the spinner was spun 3 more times and landed on green each time, determine the experimental probability of spinning green for this experiment.

b. Suppose the experimental probability of spinning blue on a spinner is $\frac{3}{8}$. Predict how many times the spinner will land on blue if it is spun 400 times.

a. ________

b. ________

Examples

2. Two number cubes are rolled together 20 times. A sum of 9 is rolled 8 times. What is the experimental probability of rolling a sum of 9?

$$P(9) = \frac{\text{number of times a sum of 9 occurs}}{\text{total number of rolls}}$$

$$= \frac{8}{20} \text{ or } \frac{2}{5}$$

The experimental probability of rolling a sum of 9 is $\frac{2}{5}$.

3. Compare the experimental probability you found in Example 2 to its theoretical probability. If the probabilities are not close, explain a possible reason for the discrepancy.

When rolling two number cubes, there are 36 possible outcomes. The theoretical probability of rolling a sum of 9 is $\frac{4}{36}$ or $\frac{1}{9}$.

Rolls with Sum of 9	
First Cube	Second Cube
3	6
4	5
5	4
6	3

Since $\frac{1}{9}$ is not close to $\frac{2}{5}$, the experimental probability is *not* close to the theoretical probability. One possible explanation is that there were not enough trials.

Got It? Do these problems to find out.

c. In Example 2, what is the experimental probability of rolling a sum that is *not* 9?

d. Two coins are tossed 10 times. Both coins land on heads 6 times. Compare the experimental probability to the theoretical probability. If the probabilities are not close, explain a possible reason for the discrepancy.

e. Suppose three coins are tossed 10 times. All three coins land on heads 1 time. Compare the experimental probability to the theoretical probability. If the probabilities are not close, explain a possible reason for the discrepancy.

c. ______

d. ______

e. ______

Predict Future Events

Theoretical and experimental probability can be used to make predictions about future events.

Multi-Step Example

4. Last year, a DVD store sold 670 action DVDs, 580 comedy DVDs, 450 drama DVDs, and 300 horror DVDs. If a media buyer expects to sell 5,000 DVDs this year, based on these results, predict how many comedy DVDs she should buy. Explain.

Solving Proportions

The cross products of any proportion are equal.

Step 1 2,000 DVDs were sold and 580 were comedy. So, the experimental probability is $\frac{580}{2,000}$ or $\frac{29}{100}$. Use this to make your prediction.

Step 2

$\frac{29}{100} = \frac{x}{5,000}$ Write a proportion.

$29 \cdot 5,000 = 100 \cdot x$ Determine the cross products.

$145,000 = 100x$ Multiply.

$1,450 = x$ Divide each side by 100.

She should buy about 1,450 comedy DVDs.

Guided Practice

1. A coin is tossed 50 times, and it lands on heads 28 times. Determine the experimental probability and the theoretical probability of the coin landing on heads. Then, compare the experimental and theoretical probabilities. (Examples 1–4)

2. Yesterday, 50 bakery customers bought muffins and 11 of those customers bought banana muffins. If 100 customers buy muffins tomorrow, how many would you expect to buy a banana muffin? (Example 5)

3. **Building on the Essential Question** How are experimental probability and theoretical probability alike?

Rate Yourself!

Are you ready to move on? Shade the section that applies.

Find out online. Use the Self-Check Quiz.

Name ____________________ My Homework ____________________

Independent Practice

7.6(I), 7.6(C),7.6(D), 7.1(D), 7.1(F) TEKS

1. A number cube is rolled 20 times and the graph shows the results. Determine each experimental probability. Then compare the experimental probability to the theoretical probability. (Examples 1–4)

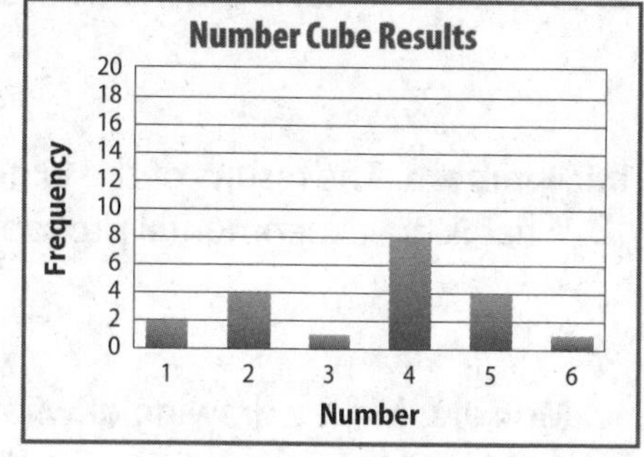

   a. landing on 4

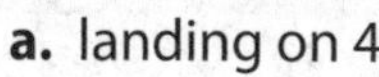

   ____

   ____

   b. *not* landing on 1

   ____

   ____

2. The spinner at the right is spun 12 times. It lands on blue 1 time. (Examples 1–4)

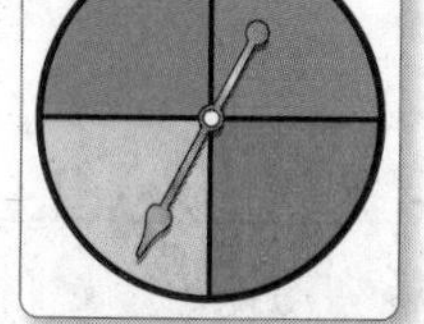

   a. What is the experimental probability of the spinner landing on blue?

   ____

   b. Compare the experimental and theoretical probabilities of the spinner landing on blue. If the probabilities are not close, explain a possible reason for the discrepancy.

   ____

   ____

3. Use the graph of a survey of 70 zoo visitors who were asked to name their favorite animal exhibit. (Example 5)

   a. Suppose 540 people visit the zoo. Predict how many people will choose the monkey exhibit as their favorite. __________

   b. Suppose 720 people visit the zoo. Predict how many people will choose the penguin exhibit as their favorite. __________

What is your Favorite Animal Exhibit?

Exhibit	Tally	Frequency
Bears	𝍸 I	6
Elephants	𝍸 𝍸 𝍸 II	17
Monkeys	𝍸 𝍸 𝍸 𝍸 I	21
Penguins	𝍸 𝍸 III	13
Snakes	𝍸 𝍸 III	13

4. MP **Analyze Relationships** Cross out the part of the concept circle that does *not* belong. Then describe the relationship among the remaining parts.

   ____

   ____

   ____

a coin landing on tails 8 out of 10 times	results based on an experiment
outcomes that should happen	rolling a sum of 9 twice in 5 trials

5. MP **Use Multiple Representations** A spinner with three equal-sized sections marked A, B, and C is spun 100 times.

a. **Numbers** What is the theoretical probability of landing on A?

b. **Numbers** The results of the experiment are shown in the table. What is the experimental probability of landing on A? on C?

Section	Frequency
A	24
B	50
C	26

c. **Models** Make a drawing of what the spinner might look like based on its experimental probabilities. Explain.

Show your work.

H.O.T. Problems Higher Order Thinking

6. **Evaluate** The experimental probability of a coin landing on heads is $\frac{7}{12}$. If the coin landed on tails 30 times, determine the number of tosses.

7. **Evaluate** Twenty sharpened pencils are placed in a box containing an unknown number of unsharpened pencils. Suppose 15 pencils are removed at random and five of the removed pencils are sharpened. Based on this, is it reasonable to assume that the number of unsharpened pencils was 40? Explain your reasoning.

8. **Evaluate** The results of spinning a spinner with six equal sections are shown. Determine the *minimum* number of additional spins needed and their frequency of landing on each color so that the experimental probabilities will be equal to the theoretical probabilities. Explain your answer.

Color	Frequency
Red	8
Orange	12
Yellow	4
Blue	8
Green	6
Purple	10

Name ____________________

Multi-Step Problem Solving

9. Jarvis is playing a board game with his brother. The table shows the results of his number cube rolls throughout the game. If his next roll is an odd number, he will win the game. How much greater is the probability that he will win? P N MP

Number	Number of Occurrences
1	4
2	5
3	7
4	5
5	3
6	1

Ⓐ $\frac{11}{25}$ Ⓒ $\frac{1}{5}$

Ⓑ $\frac{2}{5}$ Ⓓ $\frac{3}{25}$

Use a problem-solving model to solve this problem.

1 Analyze

Read the problem. Circle the information you know.
Underline what the problem is asking you to find.

2 Plan

What will you need to do to solve the problem? Write your plan in steps.

Step 1 Determine the ____________ of each event.

Step 2 Determine the ____________ of the probabilities.

3 Solve

Use your plan to solve the problem. Show your steps.

P(odd) = ______ *P*(even) = ______

Determine the difference between the probabilities.

_____ − _____ = _____

The probability of Jarvis winning is _____ times greater than losing.

So, the correct answer is _____. Fill in that answer choice.

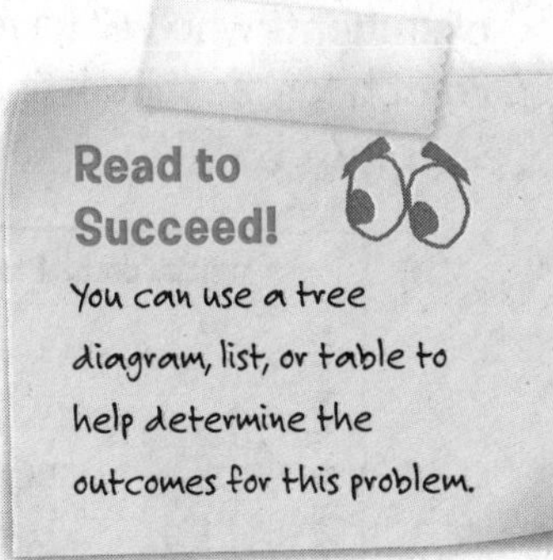

4 Justify and Evaluate

How do you know your solution is accurate?

____

____

____

P = Proportionality N = Number and Operations MP = Mathematical Processes

More Multi-Step Problem Solving

Use a problem-solving model to solve each problem.

10. Mary performed an experiment where she flipped three coins 20 times. The table shows her results. How much greater is the probability that the result will be at least two tails compared to at least two heads? P N MP

Result	Number of Occurrences
3 heads	2
2 heads, 1 tail	6
1 head, 2 tails	11
3 tails	1

Ⓐ $\frac{4}{5}$ Ⓑ $\frac{7}{10}$ Ⓒ $\frac{2}{5}$ Ⓓ $\frac{1}{5}$

11. Yesterday, 75 orchard customers bought apples and 15 of those customers bought gala apples. If 300 customers buy apples tomorrow, predict the number of customers you would expect to buy gala apples. P N MP

12. High school students were asked to report their favorite lunch combo option. The chart shows the survey results. Predict the number of students who will have to purchase a lunch combo for the school to sell 140 bowls of soup? P N MD MP

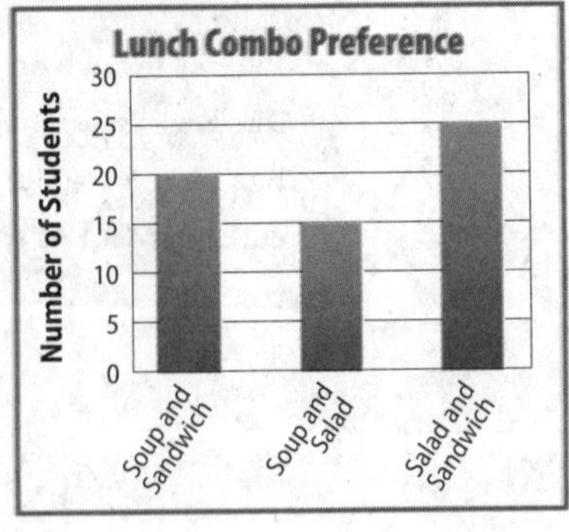

13. The probability of spinning red on a spinner is $\frac{1}{8}$, the probability of blue is $\frac{1}{2}$, and the probability of yellow is $\frac{1}{4}$. There are 3 sections that are green. What is the minimum number of total sections on the spinner? Explain.

P = Proportionality N = Number and Operations MD = Measurement and Data MP = Mathematical Processes

Hands-On Lab 2-b

Experimental Data

INQUIRY **HOW can I select tools and techniques to determine if a game is fair?**

Texas Essential Knowledge and Skills

Targeted TEKS
7.6(C) Make predictions and determine solutions using experimental data for simple and compound events. *Also addresses 7.6(A), 7.6(D), 7.6(H), 7.6(I).*

Mathematical Processes
7.1(C), 7.1(D), 7.1(E), 7.1(F), 7.1(G)

In a counter-toss game, players toss three two-color counters. The winner of each game is determined by how many counters land with either the red or yellow side facing up. Determine if this game is fair or unfair.

Mathematically speaking, a two-player game is **fair** if each player has an equal chance of winning. A game is **unfair** if there is not such a chance.

Hands-On Activity 1

Work in pairs to play the game described above.

Step 1 Player 1 tosses the counters. If 2 or 3 counters land red-side up, Player 1 wins. If 2 or 3 counters land yellow-side up, Player 2 wins. Record the results in the table below. Place a check in the winner's column for each game.

Game	Player 1	Player 2	Game	Player 1	Player 2
1			6		
2			7		
3			8		
4			9		
5			10		

Step 2 Player 2 then tosses the counters and the results are recorded.

Step 3 Continue alternating turns until the counters have been tossed 10 times.

Based on your results, do you think the game is fair or unfair? Circle your response below.

Fair   Unfair

Investigate

MP Organize Ideas Work with a partner.

1. Complete the organized list of all the possible outcomes resulting from one toss of the three counters described in Activity 1.

Counter 1	Counter 2	Counter 3	Outcome
red	red	red	red, red, red

2. In the outcome column of the table above, draw a circle around the outcomes that are a win for Player 1. Draw a box around the outcomes that are a win for Player 2.

3. Calculate the theoretical probability of each player winning. Write each probability as a fraction and as a percent. Is the game fair or unfair?

4. Use your results from Activity 1 to calculate the experimental probability of each player winning.

Analyze and Reflect

5. **MP Justify Arguments** Compare the probabilities you calculated in Exercises 3 and 4. Explain any discrepancies.

6. **MP Analyze Relationships** Quantitatively predict the number of times Player 1 would win if the game were played 100 times. Explain your reasoning.

David and Lyn made up a game using a plastic cup. A cup is tossed. If it lands right-side up or open-end down, David wins. If it lands on its side, Lyn wins. Is this game fair?

Hands-On Activity 2

Work in pairs to play the game and determine if David and Lyn created a fair game.

Step 1 Player 1 tosses the cup. If it lands right-side up or open-end down, Player 1 gets a point. If the cup lands on its side, Player 2 gets a point. Record your results in the table below.

Toss	Player 1	Player 2	Toss	Player 1	Player 2
1			6		
2			7		
3			8		
4			9		
5			10		

Step 2 Player 2 then tosses the cup and the results are recorded.

Step 3 Continue alternating turns until there is a total of 10 tosses.

Based on your results, do you think the game David and Lyn created is fair or unfair? Circle your response below.

Fair   Unfair

There are three possible outcomes when tossing the cup and David wins if two of those outcomes happen. It may appear that David has a better chance of winning, however this is not necessarily true.

7. Explain why Lyn actually has a better chance at winning the game.

8. What was the experimental probability for the cup landing right-side up or open-end down?

Investigate

MP Organize Ideas Work with a partner.

9. A game involves rolling two number cubes. Player 1 wins the game if the total of the numbers rolled is 5 or if a 5 is shown on one or both number cubes. Otherwise, Player 2 wins. Fill in the table for all of the possible outcomes of rolling two number cubes.

	1	2	3	4	5	6
1	1 + 1 = 2	1 + 2 = 3	1 + 3 = 4	1 + 4 = 5	1 + 5 = 6	1 + 6 = 7
2	2 + 1 = 3					
3						
4						
5						
6						

10. Shade in the cells of the table in which Player 1 is a winner.

Analyze and Reflect

11. For the number cube game, calculate the theoretical probability of each player winning. Write each probability as a fraction and as a percent.

12. **MP Justify Arguments** Is the number cube game fair? Explain.

Create

13. **MP Apply Math to the Real World** Design and describe a game in which the outcome is not fair. Then explain how you could change the game to make it fair.

14. **INQUIRY** HOW can I select tools and techniques to determine if a game is fair?

Lesson 3

Probability of Compound Events

Launch the Lesson: Real World

Aimee wants to pack enough items to create 6 different outfits. She packs 1 jacket, 3 shirts, and 2 pairs of jeans. Can Aimee create 6 different outfits from her clothing items?

1. Complete the table below to list the sample space.

Outfit	Clothing Items
1	jacket, shirt 1, jeans 1
2	jacket, shirt 1, jeans 2
3	jacket, shirt 2, jeans 1
4	jacket, shirt 2,
5	jacket, shirt 3,
6	jacket,

2. The table is an example of an organized list. What is another way to show the different outfits that Aimee can create?

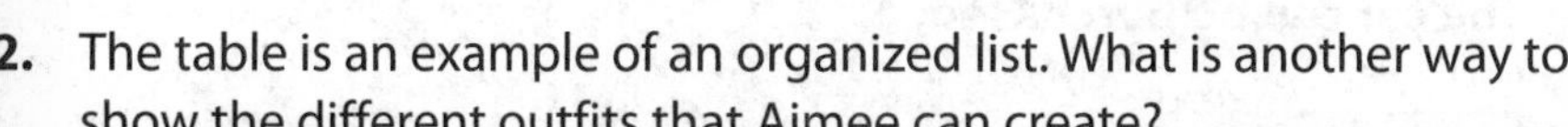

3. Describe another situation for which you might want to list all of the possible outcomes.

Which MP Mathematical Processes did you use? Shade the circle(s) that applies.

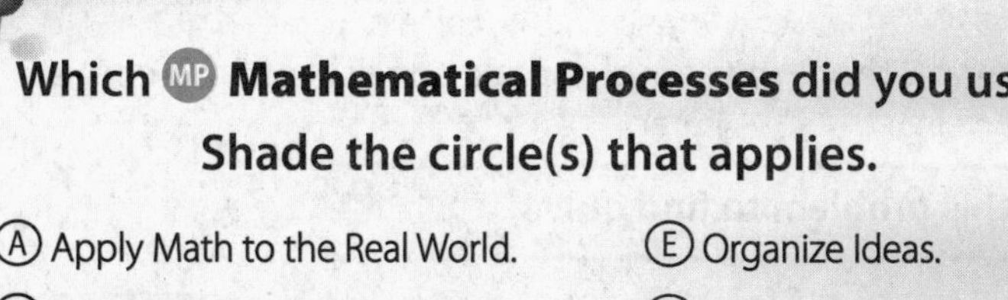

Ⓐ Apply Math to the Real World.
Ⓑ Use a Problem-Solving Model.
Ⓒ Select Tools and Techniques.
Ⓓ Use Multiple Representations.
Ⓔ Organize Ideas.
Ⓕ Analyze Relationships.
Ⓖ Justify Arguments.

Texas Essential Knowledge and Skills

Targeted TEKS
7.6(I) Determine experimental and theoretical probabilities related to simple and compound events using data and sample spaces. *Also addresses 7.6(A), 7.6(D).*

Mathematical Processes
7.1(A), 7.1(B), 7.1(E), 7.1(F)

Vocabulary
compound event

Essential Question
HOW can you predict the outcome of future events?

Work Zone

Represent Sample Spaces

A **compound event** consists of two or more simple events. The sample space of an event is the set of all of the possible outcomes. Organized lists, tables, and tree diagrams can be used to represent sample space.

Tutor

Examples

1. The three students chosen to represent Mr. Balderick's class in a school assembly are shown. All three of them need to sit in a row on the stage. Use a list to determine the sample space for the different ways they can sit in a row.

Students
Adrienne
Carlos
Greg

Use A for Adrienne, C for Carlos, and G for Greg. Use each letter exactly once.

ACG AGC CAG CGA GAC GCA

So, the sample space consists of 6 outcomes.

2. A car can be purchased in blue, silver, red, or purple. It also comes as a convertible or hardtop. Use a table or a tree diagram to determine the sample space for the different styles in which the car can be purchased.

Color	Top
blue	convertible
blue	hardtop
silver	convertible
silver	hardtop
red	convertible
red	hardtop
purple	convertible
purple	hardtop

Color	Top	Sample Space
Blue	Convertible	BC
	Hardtop	BH
Silver	Convertible	SC
	Hardtop	SH
Red	Convertible	RC
	Hardtop	RH
Purple	Convertible	PC
	Hardtop	PH

Using either method, the sample space consists of 8 outcomes.

Got It? Do this problem to find out.

a. The table shows the sandwich choices for a picnic. Determine the sample space using a list, table, or tree diagram for a sandwich consisting of one type of meat and one type of bread.

Meat	Bread
ham turkey	rye sourdough white

a. ________

Determine Probability

The probability of a compound event, just as with simple events, is the fraction of outcomes in the sample space for which the compound event occurs.

Example

3. Suppose you toss a quarter, a dime, and a nickel. Determine the sample space. What is the probability of getting three tails?

Make a tree diagram to show the sample space.

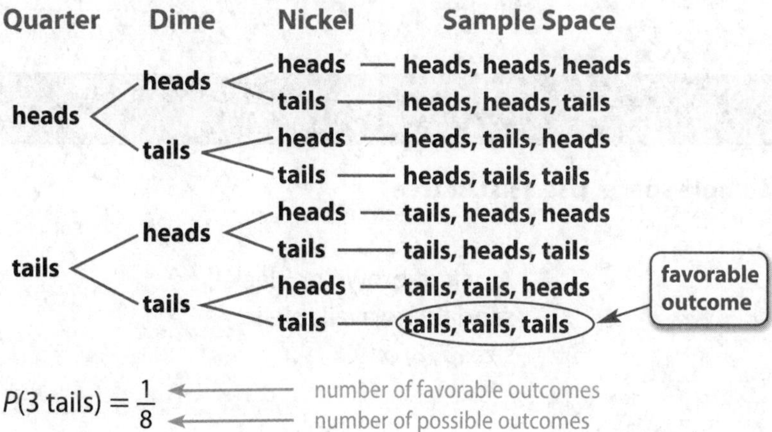

$P(3 \text{ tails}) = \frac{1}{8}$ ← number of favorable outcomes / ← number of possible outcomes

So, the probability of getting three tails is $\frac{1}{8}$.

Got It? Do this problem to find out.

b. The animal shelter has both male and female Labrador Retrievers in yellow, brown, or black. There is an equal number of each kind. What is the probability of choosing a female yellow Labrador Retriever? Show your work in the space below.

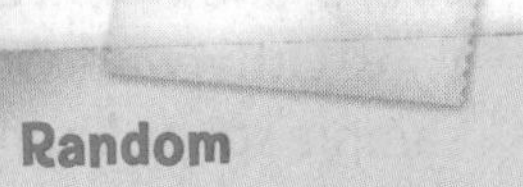

Random
When choosing an outcome, assume that each outcome is chosen randomly.

Example

Tutor

4. To win a carnival prize, you need to choose one of 3 doors labeled 1 through 3. Then you need to choose a red, yellow, or blue box behind each door. What is the probability that the prize is in the blue or yellow box behind door 2?

Outcomes	
door 1	red box
door 1	yellow box
door 1	blue box
door 2	red box
door 2	**yellow box**
door 2	**blue box**
door 3	red box
door 3	yellow box
door 3	blue box

The table shows that there are 9 total outcomes. Two of the outcomes are favorable.

So, the probability that the prize is in a blue or yellow box behind door 2 is $\frac{2}{9}$.

Guided Practice

For each situation, determine the sample space. Use a list or tree diagram. (Examples 1–2)

1. A coin is tossed twice.

2. A pair of brown or black sandals are available in sizes 7, 8, or 9.

3. Gerardo spins a spinner with four equal sections, labeled A, B, C, and D, twice. If letter A is spun at least once, Gerardo wins. Otherwise, Odell wins. Use a list to determine the sample space. Then determine the probability that Odell wins. (Examples 3–4)

4. **Building on the Essential Question** How do tree diagrams, tables, and lists help you determine the probability of a compound event?

Rate Yourself!

☐ I understand how to show a sample space.

Great! You're ready to move on!

☐ I still have questions about showing a sample space.

No problem! Go online to access a Personal Tutor.

Check

FOLDABLES Time to update your Foldable!

Name ______________________ My Homework ______________________

Independent Practice

7.6(I), 7.6(A), 7.6(D), 7.1(B) TEKS

For each situation, determine the sample space. Use a list or tree diagram. (Examples 1–2)

1. tossing a coin and spinning the spinner at the right

2. picking a number from 1 to 5 and choosing the color red, white, or blue

3. choosing a purple, green, black, or silver bike having 10, 18, 21, or 24 speeds

4. choosing a letter from the word SPACE and choosing a consonant from the word MATH

For each game, determine the sample space using a list or tree diagram. Then determine the indicated probability. (Examples 3–4)

5. Alana tosses 2 number cubes. She wins if she rolls double sixes.

   Determine *P*(Alana wins). ______________________

6. Ming rolls a number cube, tosses a coin, and chooses a card from two cards marked A and B. If an even number and heads appears, Ming wins, no matter which card is chosen. Otherwise Lashonda wins. Determine *P*(Ming wins).

   ____

   ____

   ____

7. **MP Use a Problem-Solving Model** The following is a game for two players.
   - Three counters are labeled according to the table at the right.
   - Toss the three counters.
   - If exactly 2 counters match, Player 1 scores a point. Otherwise, Player 2 scores a point.

Counters	Side 1	Side 2
Counter 1	red	blue
Counter 2	red	yellow
Counter 3	blue	yellow

   Determine the probability that each player scores a point.

8. **Find the Error** Caitlyn wants to determine the probability of guessing correctly on two true-false questions on her history test. She draws the tree diagram below using C for correct and I for incorrect. Find her mistake and correct it.

Question 1	Question 2	Sample Space
C	C	CC
	I	CI
I	C	CC
	I	II

H.O.T. Problems Higher-Order Thinking

9. **Analyze** Refer to Exercise 7. Do the two players both have an equal chance of winning? Explain.

10. **Create** Write a real-world problem in which the probability of a compound event occurring is 0.25.

11. **Create** Write an expression that you can use to determine the number of possible outcomes if the spinner at the right is spun x times. Then determine how much greater the probability is to spin an odd number compared to an even number.

Name ______________________________

Multi-Step Problem Solving

12. Morgan rolls a number cube, twice. If the number 1 shows up at least once, Morgan wins. Otherwise, Jaclyn wins. How much greater is the probability that Morgan will win compared to Jaclyn winning? P N MP

Ⓐ $\frac{1}{3}$ Ⓑ $\frac{7}{18}$ Ⓒ $\frac{4}{9}$ Ⓓ $\frac{2}{3}$

Use a problem-solving model to solve this problem.

1 Analyze

Read the problem. Circle the information you know.
Underline what the problem is asking you to find.

2 Plan

What will you need to do to solve the problem? Write your plan in steps.

Step 1 Make a list to determine the ____________.

Step 2 Determine the ____________ for Morgan and Jaclyn. Then ________.

3 Solve

Use your plan to solve the problem. Show your steps.

Use a list.

____

____

Determine the probabilities and then subtract.

P(Morgan wins) = _____ *P*(Jaclyn wins) = _____

_____ − _____ = _______

Read to Succeed!
A number cube has six sides that are numbered 1 through 6. Use this information to help make a list.

The probability of Jaclyn winning is _____ times greater than Morgan winning.

So, the correct answer is _____. Fill in that answer choice.

4 Justify and Evaluate

How do you know your solution is accurate?

____

____

____

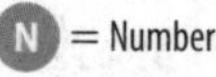

P = Proportionality N = Number and Operations MP = Mathematical Processes

More Multi-Step Problem Solving

Use a problem-solving model to solve each problem.

13. Nicolás tosses a coin three times. If heads appears at least once, he wins. Otherwise, Manny wins. How much greater is the probability that Nicolás will win compared to Manny winning? P N MP

Ⓐ $\frac{1}{8}$

Ⓑ $\frac{1}{2}$

Ⓒ $\frac{3}{4}$

Ⓓ $\frac{7}{8}$

14. The table shows the colors of socks, shoes, and belts that Landon owns. If he randomly selects a pair of socks, a pair of shoes, and a belt, what is the probability that the colors will all match? Write the probability as a decimal rounded to the nearest hundredth.

Socks	Shoes	Belt
Navy	Brown	Brown
Brown stripes	Black	Black leather
Black		Black nylon
Brown dots		
Tan		

15. Jarek randomly selects a card from a pile of 3 unique cards, replaces it, and randomly selects again. What is the probability of selecting any card three times in a row? Write the probability as a percent, rounded to the nearest tenth. P N MP

16. Dakotah was randomly assigned a computer password, where each number can be any digit 0 through 9, but digits will not repeat. The first three digits are shown. If he randomly guesses the last two digits, what is the probability he will guess correctly? Explain. P N MP

7	3	1	?	?

P = Proportionality 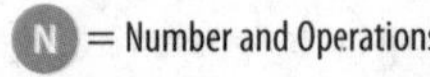 = Number and Operations 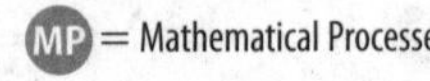 = Mathematical Processes

Focus on Mathematical Processes
Act It Out

Mathematical Process
7.1(B) Use a problem-solving model that incorporates analyzing given information, formulating a plan or strategy, determining a solution, justifying the solution, and evaluating the problem-solving process and the reasonableness of the solution.

Targeted TEKS 7.6(H)

Winning Serves

Edie has been practicing her volleyball serve every day after school. She hits a good serve an average of 3 out of 4 times.

What is the probability that Edie will hit two good serves in a row? Then predict how many good serves she would have out of 120 serves.

Analyze *What are the facts?*

You know that Edie hits a good serve an average of 3 out of 4 times.

Plan

Choose a problem-solving strategy.

I will use the ______________________________ strategy.

Solve

How can you apply the strategy?
Model this problem with a spinner, numbered 1 to 4. Spin it two times. If the spinner lands on 1, 2, or 3, she hits a good serve. If the spinner lands on 4, she does not. Repeat the experiment 10 times.

Possible results are shown. Circle the columns that show two good serves. The first two are done for you.

Trail	1	2	3	4	5	6	7	8	9	10
First Spin	4	1	4	3	1	2	2	1	3	2
Second Spin	2	3	3	2	1	4	1	4	3	3

The circled columns show that six out of 10 trials resulted in two good serves in a row. So, the probability is ☐ %.

Based on this experiment, Edie would have ☐ good serves out of 120 since 60% of 120 = 72.

Justify and Evaluate

How do you know your solution is reasonable?

____

____

Books

James, Rafael, Valery, and Tiana each left one book in the school library. The librarian found the books and randomly returned them to the four students.

What is the probability that Valery received the book she left behind?

Analyze

Read the problem. Circle the information you know. Underline what the problem is asking you to find.

Plan

Choose a problem-solving strategy.

I will use the ______________________________ strategy.

Solve

How can you apply the strategy?

Justify and Evaluate

How do you know your solution is reasonable?

____

____

____

Multi-Step Problem Solving

Work with a small group to solve the following problems. Use any strategy. Show your work on a separate piece of paper.

1. Chess

A chess tournament will be held and 32 students will participate. If a player loses one match, he or she will be eliminated.

How many total games will be played in the tournament?

2. Running

Six runners are entered in a race. Assume there are no ties.

In how many ways can first and second places be awarded?

3. Fair Games

Karla and Jason are playing a game with number cubes. Each number cube is numbered 1 to 6. They roll both number cubes. If the product is a multiple of 3, Jason wins. If the product is a multiple of 4, Karla wins.

Is this game fair or unfair? Justify your response.

4. Algebra

The figure shown at the right is known as Pascal's Triangle.

Make a conjecture for the numbers in the 6th and 7th rows.

Mid-Chapter Check

Vocabulary Check

1. Define *probability*. Give an example of the probability of a simple event. TEKS 7.6(E), 7.1(D)

Key Concept Check

2. Complete the graphic organizer about sample space. Explain three different ways that you can determine sample space. TEKS 7.5(C), 7.1(E)

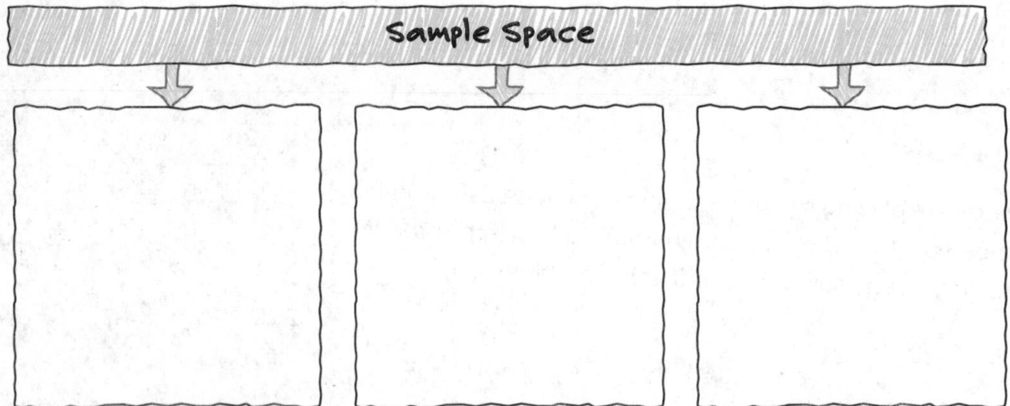

3. For breakfast, a customer can choose two different items from the following list: eggs, pancakes, waffles, oatmeal, bacon, or a muffin. How many different breakfast meals are possible? TEKS 7.6(I), 7.1(A)

Multi-Step Problem Solving

4. Without looking, Santiago grabbed a handful of multi-colored candies from a bag and found that 20% of the candies were yellow and 15% were green. Suppose that there were 480 candies in the bag. Based on Santiago's results, how many more yellow candies would you expect there to be than green candies? N P MP

Ⓐ 24
Ⓑ 72
Ⓒ 96
Ⓓ 168

N = Number and Operations P = Proportionality MP = Mathematical Processes

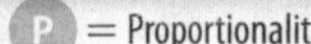

Virtual Manipulative Lab 4-a

Simulate Simple Events

INQUIRY HOW can I select tools and techniques to simulate simple events?

Texas Essential Knowledge and Skills

Targeted TEKS

7.6(B) Select and use different simulations to represent simple and compound events with and without technology.

Mathematical Processes

7.1(C), 7.1(D), 7.1(F), 7.1(G)

Mariko is the point guard on the girls basketball team. She usually makes three out of every four free throws she attempts during a basketball game.

Hands-On Activity

You can use a Virtual Manipulative spinner to *simulate* or act out Mariko shooting free throws.

Since the probability of Mariko making a free throw is 3 out of 4, spinning a spinner with four equal sections is a reasonable activity to simulate this event. The yellow, green, and red sections can represent made free throws and the blue section can represent a missed free throw.

Step 1 Spin the spinner 12 times and record the results in the table below. Write a • for a made free throw and an X for a missed free throw.

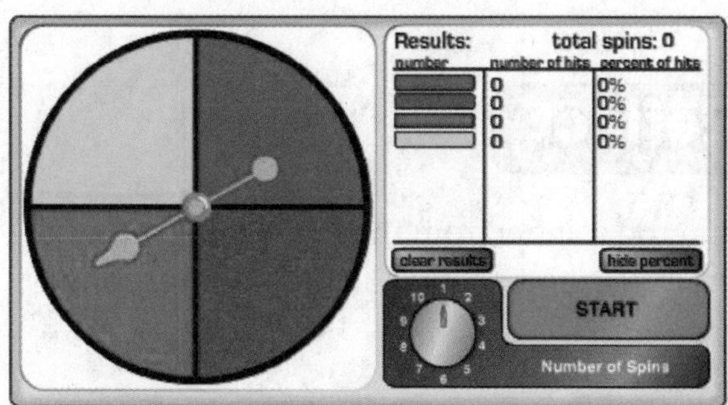

Spin	1	2	3	4	5	6	7	8	9	10	11	12
Simulation 1												
Simulation 2												
Simulation 3												

Step 2 Complete the simulation two more times and record the results in the table above.

Investigate

Work with a partner.

1. Based on your results, how many free throws did Mariko make, out of 12, for each simulation? ____________________

2. What is the experimental probability of making each free throw for each simulation? ____________________

3. Make a graph for spinning 100, 150, 200, 250, 300, 350, 400, and 450 times. Compare the number of spins to the percent made using the graph. What do you notice about the data in the graph?

____

____

Spinner Simulation

Number of Spins: 0, 100, 200, 300, 400, 500

Percent (%): 10 20 30 40 50 60 70 80 90 100

4. **MP Analyze Relationships** How does the experimental probability change as the number of spins increase?

____

____

Analyze and Reflect

Collaborate

5. **MP Justify Arguments** If you spun the spinner from the Activity 500 times, predict how many times the spinner will land on blue. Justify your response.

____

Create

6. **MP Apply Math to the Real World** Design a simulation, using virtual manipulative technology, that could be used to predict the probability of taking a four question multiple-choice test with four answer choices and getting all four questions correct by guessing. Conduct 50 trials of the experiment. Then calculate the experimental probability of getting all four questions correct.

____

7. **INQUIRY** HOW can I select tools and techniques to simulate simple events?

____

____

Lesson 4
Simulations

Launch the Lesson: Real World

A new electronics store is opening at the mall. One out of six new customers will receive a free music download. The winners are chosen at random. On Monday, the store had 50 customers. About how many customers would you expect to receive a free music download?

You can act out or *simulate* 50 random customers by using the random number generator on a graphing calculator.

Type in the following keystrokes to set 1 as the lower bound and 6 as the upper bound for 50 trials.
Keystrokes: MATH ◄ 5 1 , 6 , 50) ENTER

The screen should look similar to the screen shown at the right.

randInt(1,6,50)
{4 5 4 1 3 6 5 ...

A set of 50 numbers ranging from 1 to 6 appears. Use the right arrow key to see the next number in the set.

1. Let the number 3 represent a customer who wins a free download. Write the experimental probability of winning a download.

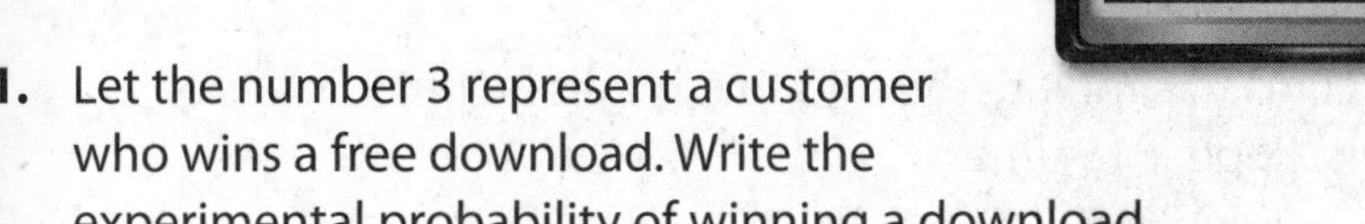

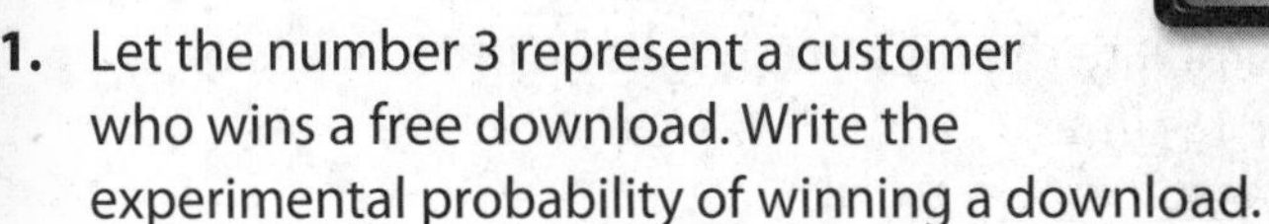

2. Compare the experimental probabilities found in Exercise 1 to the theoretical probability of winning a download.

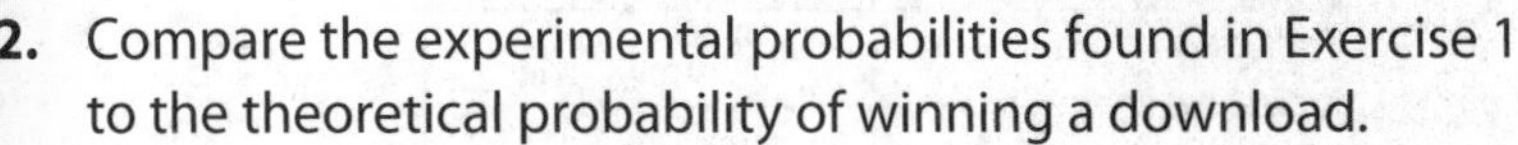

Which MP Mathematical Processes did you use? Shade the circle(s) that applies.

Ⓐ Apply Math to the Real World.
Ⓑ Use a Problem-Solving Model.
Ⓒ Select Tools and Techniques.
Ⓓ Use Multiple Representations.
Ⓔ Organize Ideas.
Ⓕ Analyze Relationships.
Ⓖ Justify Arguments.

Texas Essential Knowledge and Skills

Targeted TEKS
7.6(B) Select and use different simulations to represent simple and compound events with and without technology.

Mathematical Processes
7.1(A), 7.1(B), 7.1(C), 7.1(G)

Vocabulary
simulation

Essential Question
HOW can you predict the outcome of future events?

Work Zone

Model Equally Likely Outcomes

A **simulation** is an experiment that is designed to model the action in a given situation. For example, you used a random number generator to simulate rolling a number cube. Simulations often use models to act out an event that would be impractical to perform.

Example

1. A snack company is placing one of eight different toys in its boxes of crackers. If each toy is equally likely to appear in a box of crackers, describe a model that could be used to simulate the toys you would find in 15 boxes of crackers.

Choose a method that has 8 possible outcomes, such as tossing 3 coins. Let each outcome represent a different card.

For example, the outcome of all three coins landing heads up could simulate finding card 1.

Toss 3 coins to simulate the toys that might be in 15 boxes of crackers. Repeat 15 times.

Coin Toss Simulation			
Outcome	Toy	Outcome	Toy
HHH	1	TTT	5
HHT	2	TTH	6
HTH	3	THT	7
HTT	4	THH	8

Got It? **Do this problem to find out.**

a. __________

a. The sponsors of a music festival are giving away 1 of 5 different CDs with an admission ticket. If the CDs are given out randomly, describe a model that could be used to simulate which CDs would be given with 6 admission tickets.

Example

Tools Tutor

2. Every student who volunteers at the concession stand during basketball games will receive a free school T-shirt. The T-shirts come in 3 different designs.

Design a simulation that could be used to model this situation. Use your simulation to find how many times a student must volunteer in order to get all 3 T-shirts.

Use a spinner divided into 3 equal sections. Assign each section one of the T-shirts. Spin the spinner until you land on each section.

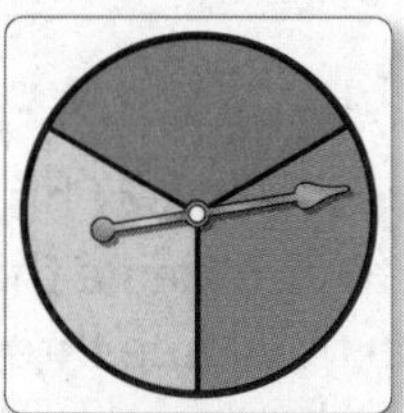

first spin

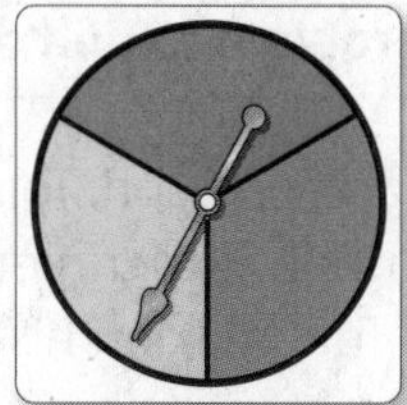

second spin

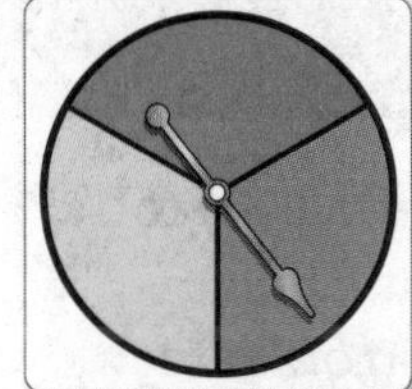

third spin

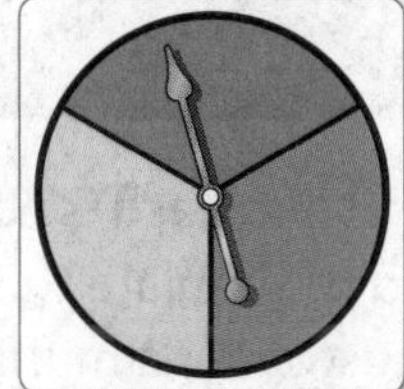

fourth spin

Based on this simulation, a student should volunteer 4 times in order to get all 3 T-shirts.

Got It? Do this problem to find out.

b. Mr. Chen must wear a dress shirt and a tie to work. Each day he picks one of his 6 ties at random. Design a simulation that could be used to model this situation. Use your simulation to determine how many days Mr. Chen must work in order to wear all of his ties.

b. ______________

Model Unequally Likely Outcomes

Simulations can also be used to model events in which the outcomes are not equally likely.

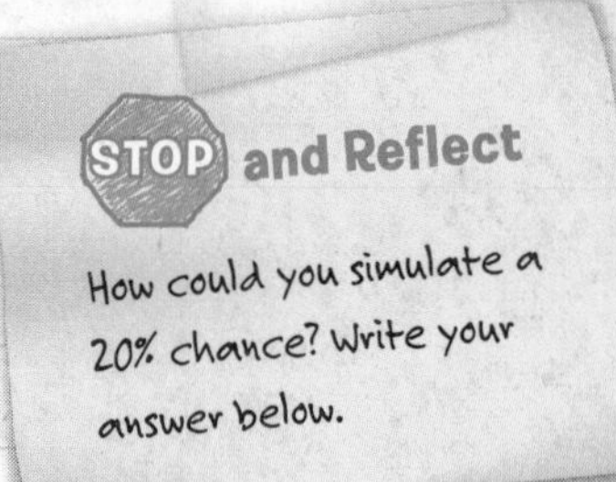

c. ____________

Example

Tutor

3. There is a 40% chance of snow for each of the next two days. Describe a method you could use to determine the experimental probability of having snow on both of the next two days.

Place 2 red and 3 blue marbles in a bag. Let 40% or $\frac{2}{5}$ of them represent snow. Let 60% or $\frac{3}{5}$ of them represent no snow. Randomly pick one marble to simulate the first day. Replace the marble and pick again to simulate the second day. Determine the probability of snow on both days.

Got It? **Do this problem to find out.**

c. During the regular season, Tom made 60% of his free throws. Describe an experiment to determine the experimental probability of Tom making his next two free throws.

Guided Practice

1. A bakery offers chocolate chip or banana nut muffins. Each is equally likely to be chosen. Describe a model that could be used to simulate this situation. Based on your simulation, how many people must order a muffin in order to sell all possible combinations? (Examples 1 and 2)

2. A cellphone company has determined that 45% of its customers buy a smart phone. Describe a model that you could use to determine the experimental probability that the next three customers will buy a smart phone. (Example 3)

3. **Building on the Essential Question** Explain how using a simulation is related to experimental probability.

Rate Yourself!

How well do you understand simulations? Circle the image that applies.

Clear

Somewhat Clear

Not So Clear

Find out online. Use the Self-Check Quiz.

Check

Independent Practice

7.6(B), 7.1(C), 7.1(G) TEKS

1. The questions on a multiple-choice test each have 4 answer choices. Describe a model that you could use to simulate the outcome of guessing the correct answers to a 100-question test. (Example 1)

2. A shopping mall is giving each shopper 1 of 10 different gifts during the holidays. Describe a model that could be used to simulate the selection of the gift. (Example 1)

MP **Select Tools and Techniques Describe a model you could use to simulate each event.**

3. A jar of cookies contains 18 different types of cookies. Each type is equally likely to be chosen. Based on your simulation, how many times must a cookie be chosen in order to get each type? (Example 2)

4. A cooler contains 5 bottles of lemonade, 4 bottles of water, and 3 bottles of juice. Each type is equally likely to be chosen. Based on your simulation, how many times must a drink be chosen in order to get each type? (Example 3)

5. Players at an arcade win about 30% of the time. Based on your simulation, what is the experimental probability that the next four players will win? (Example 3)

6. **Justify Arguments** Barton believes that the coin his teacher uses for an experiment gives an advantage to one team of students. His teacher has students toss the coin 50 times each and record their results. Based on the results in the table, do you think the coin is fair? Explain.

Student	Heads	Tails
1	17	33
2	22	28
3	28	22
4	21	29
5	13	37
6	20	30

H.O.T. Problems Higher-Order Thinking

7. **Create** Describe a situation that could be represented by a simulation. What objects could be used in your simulation?

8. **Analyze** A simulation uses cards numbered 0 through 9 to generate five 2-digit numbers. A card is selected for the tens digit and not replaced. Then a card for the ones digit is drawn and not replaced. The process is repeated until all the cards are used. If the simulation is performed 10 times, about how many times could you expect a 2-digit number to begin with a 5? Explain.

9. **Analyze** Determine whether the following statement is *sometimes, always,* or *never* true. Justify your answer.

A spinner can be used to model equally likely outcomes.

10. **Create** Suppose a mouse is placed in the maze at the right. If each decision about direction is made at random, create a simulation to determine the probability that the mouse will find its way out before coming to a dead end or going out the In opening.

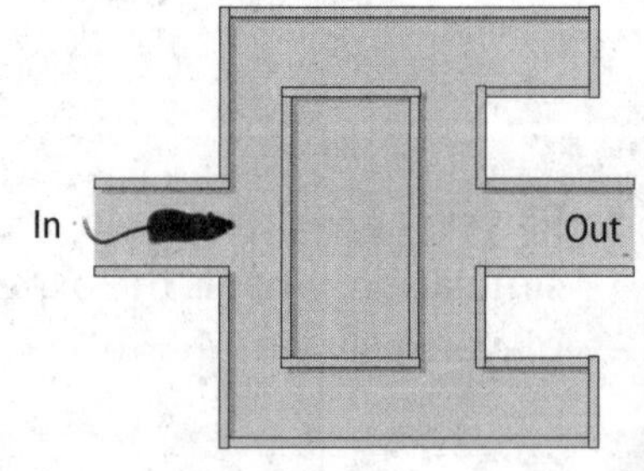

Name ______________________________

Multi-Step Problem Solving

11. Rico conducts a simulation. He spun a spinner with four equal sections labeled A, B, C, and D, twice. The letter D showed up five times, each resulted in a win for Rico. Natasha won all the other games. Based on the simulation, what percent more did Natasha win compared to Rico winning? Write your answer as a percent. P N MP

Use a problem-solving model to solve this problem.

1 Analyze

Read the problem. Circle the information you know.
Underline what the problem is asking you to find.

2 Plan

What will you need to do to solve the problem? Write your plan in steps.

Step 1 Determine the ________.

Step 2 Determine the ________________ for Rico and Natasha. Then ________.

Read to Succeed!
Use a list or tree diagram to help determine the total number of outcomes for the simulation.

3 Solve

Use your plan to solve the problem. Show your steps.

There are a total of ____ outcomes.

Determine the probabilities and then subtract.

P(Rico won) = ____ *P*(Natasha won) = ____

____ − ____ = ________ which is equal to ________

Natasha won ________ more than Rico.

Complete the grid.

					.		
⊕	0	0	0	0		0	0
⊖	1	1	1	1		1	1
	2	2	2	2		2	2
	3	3	3	3		3	3
	4	4	4	4		4	4
	5	5	5	5		5	5
	6	6	6	6		6	6
	7	7	7	7		7	7
	8	8	8	8		8	8
	9	9	9	9		9	9

4 Justify and Evaluate

How do you know your solution is accurate?

____

____

____

P = Proportionality N = Number and Operations MP = Mathematical Processes

More Multi-Step Problem Solving

Use a problem-solving model to solve each problem.

12. Marlene conducts a simulation. She rolled a number cube, twice. The sum of 8 or greater showed up 21 times, each resulted in a win for her. Ashton won all the other games. Based on the simulation, what percent more did Marlene win compared to Ashton winning? Write your answer as a percent rounded to the nearest tenth. P N MP

13. There is a 25% chance of rain every day this week. Sandra set up a spinner to simulate the probability of rain. She spun the spinner below 7 times and her experimental probability was $\frac{2}{7}$. How much greater was the experimental probability compared to the theoretical probability? P MD N MP

14. Rebecca received a $50 check from her grandmother for her birthday. She used the money to buy some new clothes. If she spent $49.75, how many ways could she receive change if no pennies are used? P N MP

15. Juan is playing basketball. During a game, he is fouled 8 times. Each time, he goes to the free-throw line to shoot two shots. A simulation was conducted to determine the experimental probability of making a free-throw shot. Compare the experimental probability, $\frac{3}{8}$, to the theoretical probability, 50%. P N MP

P = Proportionality N = Number and Operations MD = Measurement and Data MP = Mathematical Processes

Hands-On Lab 4-b

Simulate Compound Events

INQUIRY HOW can I select tools to simulate and understand probabilities of compound events?

Texas Essential Knowledge and Skills

Targeted TEKS

7.6(B) Select and use different simulations to represent simple and compound events with and without technology.

Mathematical Processes

7.1(C), 7.1(D), 7.1(F), 7.1(G)

A local shop randomly gives coupons to 3 out of every 8 customers. Use a spinner to determine the probability that a customer will receive a coupon two days in a row.

Hands-On Activity 1

Tools

Step 1 A spinner with eight equal sections can be used to simulate the situation. Label three of the sections with the letter C to represent the people that receive a coupon. Label five of the sections with the letter D to represent the people that do not receive a coupon.

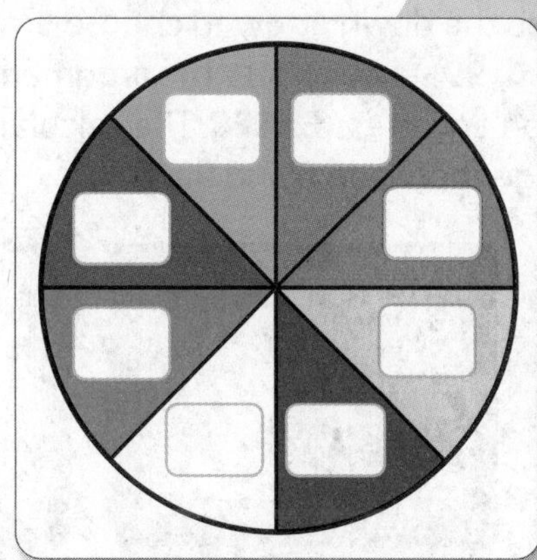

Step 2 Every two spins of the spinner represents one trial. Use a paperclip and the tip of your pencil to spin the spinner twice and record the results in the table. Perform a total of 15 trials.

Trial	Spin 1	Spin 2	Trial	Spin 1	Spin 2	Trial	Spin 1	Spin 2
1			6			11		
2			7			12		
3			8			13		
4			9			14		
5			10			15		

1. **MP Analyze Relationships** Based on your results, what is the experimental probability that a customer will receive a coupon two days in a row?

____

You can also use a graphing calculator to simulate a compound event.

There is a 20% chance of rain on Sunday and a 50% chance on Monday. Use a random number generator to estimate the probability that it will rain both days.

Hands-On Activity 2

Step 1 Set up the simulation. Use a two-digit number to represent the weather on the two days. Assign 0 and 1 in the tens place to represent rain on Sunday and 0, 1, 2, 3, and 4 in the ones place to represent rain on Monday.

Step 2 To access the random number generator of your calculator, press **MATH** and then use the right arrow key to move over to the **PRB** menu. Then use the down arrow to choose **5:randInt(** and press **ENTER**. Key in **0, 99**) to complete the argument of the random integer function and press **ENTER**. The calculator will return a random integer between 0 and 99.

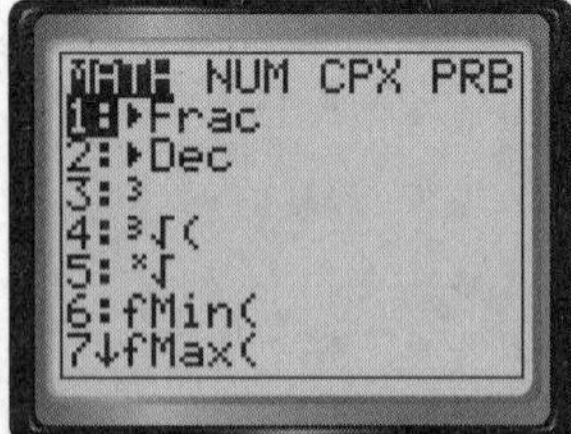

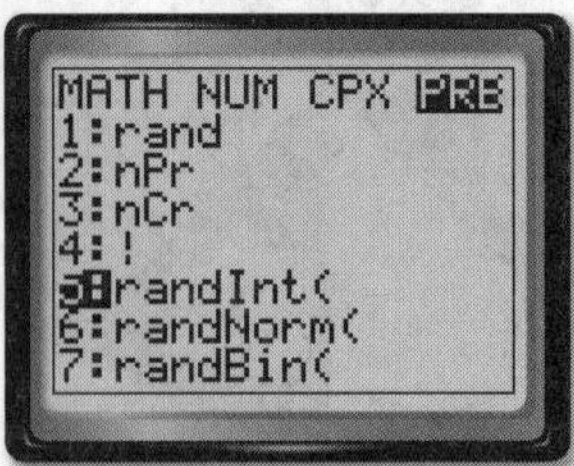

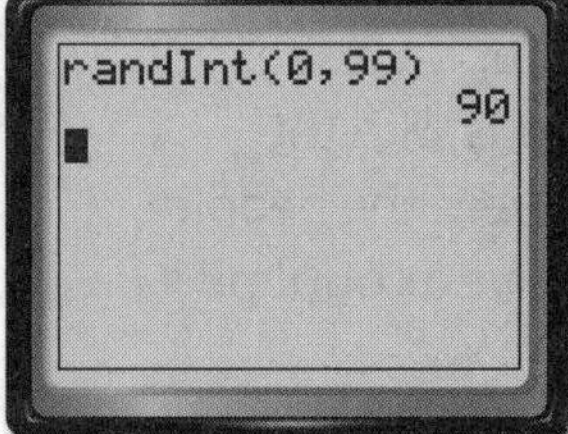

Step 3 Each time you press ENTER, the calculator will return a new random integer between 0 and 99. Record your results in the table below for 20 trials. Then identify the trials in which it rains on both days. Circle the data that represent rain on both days.

Trial	1	2	3	4	5	6	7	8	9	10
Result										

Trial	11	12	13	14	15	16	17	18	19	20
Result										

Step 4 Calculate the experimental probability that it will rain on both days.

$$\frac{\text{number of times it rains on both days}}{\text{total number of trials}} = \_\_\_\_\_$$

So, the probability that it will rain on both days is about ☐.

Work with a partner.

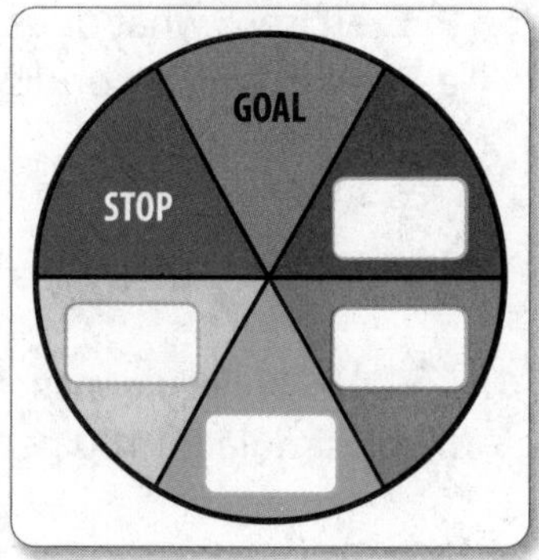

2. Luke plays goalie on his soccer team. He usually stops 2 out of every 6 penalty kicks. Label the sections of the spinner at the right. Then use the spinner to determine the experimental probability that Luke stops 2 penalty kicks in a row.

Trial	Spin 1	Spin 2	Trial	Spin 1	Spin 2	Trial	Spin 1	Spin 2
1			6			11		
2			7			12		
3			8			13		
4			9			14		
5			10			15		

The experimental probability is ______________.

3. Repeat the simulation from Activity 2 and use the table below to keep track of the results. Based on your new simulation, what is the new experimental probability that it will rain on both days? Compare the experimental probability from Activity 2 to this new simulation. Are they close? If not, what are some reasons why?

Trial	1	2	3	4	5	6	7	8	9	10
Result										

Trial	1	2	3	4	5	6	7	8	9	10
Result										

4. The theoretical probability it will rain both days is 10%. Compare the experimental probability you determined in Exercise 3 to the theoretical probability. What do you notice?

Analyze and Reflect

5. In Exercise 2, what does spinning a Stop on your first spin, and spinning a Goal on your second spin represent in this situation?

6. MP **Justify Arguments** Explain how your results might change for Exercise 2 if you simulated 100 penalty kicks.

7. MP **Analyze Relationships** Explain how you could you use the simulation in Activity 2 to estimate each probability.

   a. the probability that it rains on at least one of the two days

   b. the probability that it does not rain on either day

On Your Own

Create

8. MP **Apply Math to the Real World** Describe how you could change the simulation in Activity 2 so that the probability of rain on Sunday is 30% rather than 20%.

9. **INQUIRY** HOW can I select tools to simulate and understand probabilities of compound events?

Hands-On Lab 5-a

Independent and Dependent Events

INQUIRY HOW can I select tools to determine how one event impacts a second event in a probability experiment?

Texas Essential Knowledge and Skills

Targeted TEKS

7.6(B) Select and use different simulations to represent simple and compound events with and without technology. *Also addresses 7.6(A), 7.6(C), 7.6(D), 7.6(H), 7.6(I).*

Mathematical Processes

7.1(C), 7.1(D), 7.1(E), 7.1(F), 7.1(G)

Jeanie wants to go to the movies and Kate wants to go skating. They decide by doing a simulation. They place two red counters in a bag to represent going to the movies and two white counters to represent going skating. If they draw or remove two red counters, they will go to the movies. If they draw two white counters they will go skating. If they draw a red and a white counter, they will stay home.

You can simulate this activity using counters.

Hands-On Activity

Step 1 Place two red counters and two white counters in a paper bag.

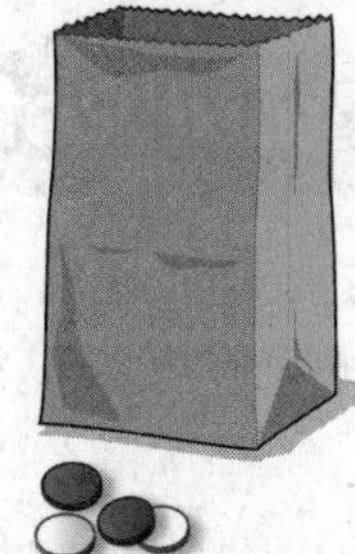

Step 2 Without looking, draw a counter from the bag and record its color in the table below. Place the counter back in the bag.

Step 3 Without looking, draw a second counter and record its color in the table. The two colors are one trial. Place the counter back in the bag.

Step 4 Repeat until you have 18 trials.

Trial	1st Color	2nd Color	Trial	1st Color	2nd Color	Trial	1st Color	2nd Color
1			7			13		
2			8			14		
3			9			15		
4			10			16		
5			11			17		
6			12			18		

1. What is the experimental probability that the girls will go to the movies?

____

Investigate

Work with a partner.

2. Complete the same experiment from the Activity, except do not replace the counter after the first draw for each trial. Record your results.

Trial	1st Color	2nd Color	Trial	1st Color	2nd Color	Trial	1st Color	2nd Color
1			7			13		
2			8			14		
3			9			15		
4			10			16		
5			11			17		
6			12			18		

What is the experimental probability that the girls will go to the movies?

Analyze and Reflect

3. Draw tree diagrams to represent the possible outcomes for the Activity and for Exercise 2 on a separate sheet of paper. Use your diagrams to answer Exercises 4 and 5.

4. What is the theoretical probability of drawing two reds in the Activity?

In Exercise 2? ______

5. MP **Organize Ideas** Is there a better chance that the girls will go to the movies if the counters are replaced after the first draw? Explain.

6. Predict how your results would change if the experiment from the Activity and Exercise 2 were completed over 200 trials.

Create

7. **INQUIRY** HOW can I select tools to determine how one event impacts a second event in a probability experiment?

Lesson 5

Independent and Dependent Events

Launch the Lesson: Vocabulary

When one event does not affect the outcome of the other event, the events are **independent events**. For example, if you toss a coin twice, the first toss has no affect on the second toss. Complete the graphic organizer below.

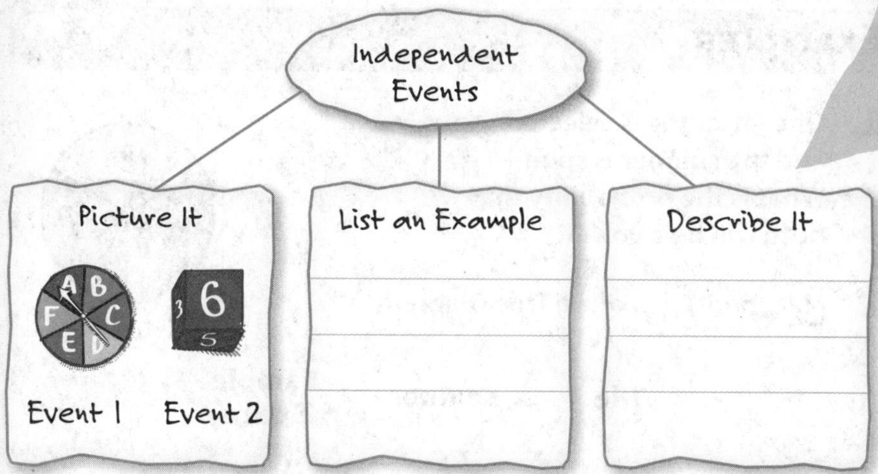

Texas Essential Knowledge and Skills

Targeted TEKS

7.6(D) Make predictions and determine solutions using theoretical probability for simple and compound events.
Also addresses 7.6(A), 7.6(I).

Mathematical Processes

7.1(A), 7.1(B), 7.1(C), 7.1(F), 7.1(G)

Vocab

Vocabulary

independent events
dependent events

Essential Question

HOW can you predict the outcome of future events?

Real-World Link

Independent is a common word in the English language. Use a dictionary to look up its definition. Explain how the dictionary definition can help you remember the mathematical definition of *independent*.

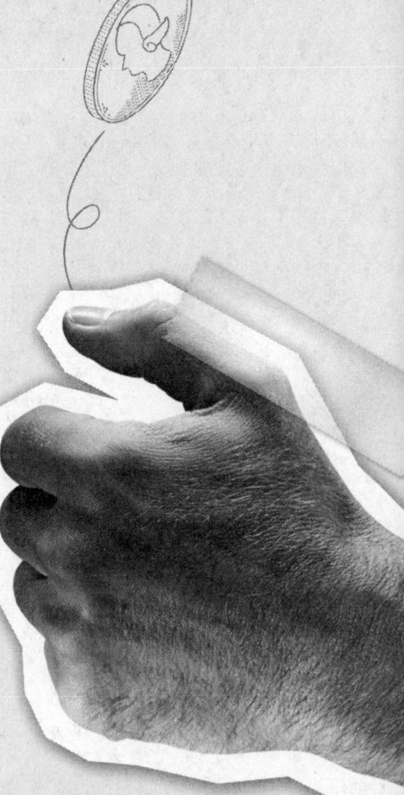

Which MP Mathematical Processes did you use? Shade the circle(s) that applies.

Ⓐ Apply Math to the Real World.
Ⓑ Use a Problem-Solving Model.
Ⓒ Select Tools and Techniques.
Ⓓ Use Multiple Representations.
Ⓔ Organize Ideas.
Ⓕ Analyze Relationships.
Ⓖ Justify Arguments.

Key Concept

Probability of Independent Events

Words The probability of two independent events can be determined by multiplying the probability of the first event by the probability of the second event.

Symbols $P(A \text{ and } B) = P(A) \cdot P(B)$

Work Zone

You can use organized lists, tables, tree diagrams, or multiplication to determine the probability of compound events.

Tools Tutor

Examples

1. One letter tile is selected and the spinner is spun. What is the probability that both will be a vowel?

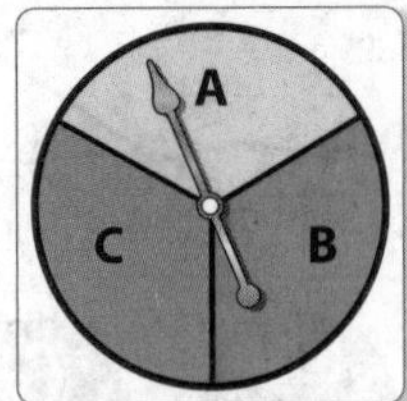

Method 1 **Make a Tree Diagram**

Tile	Spinner	Sample Space
G	A	G, A
	B	G, B
	C	G, C
B	A	B, A
	B	B, B
	C	B, C
E	A	E, A
	B	E, B
	C	E, C
A	A	A, A
	B	A, B
	C	A, C

There are 12 outcomes. Two outcomes contain only vowels. The probability that both will be a vowel is $\frac{2}{12}$ or $\frac{1}{6}$.

Method 2 **Use Multiplication**

$P(\text{selecting a vowel}) = \frac{2}{4}$ or $\frac{1}{2}$. $P(\text{spinning a vowel}) = \frac{1}{3}$.

$P(\text{both vowels}) = \frac{1}{2} \cdot \frac{1}{3}$ or $\frac{1}{6}$. Multiply the probabilities.

So, using either method the probability is $\frac{1}{6}$.

2. **The spinner and number cube shown are used in a game. What is the probability of a player *not* spinning blue and then rolling a 3 or 4?**

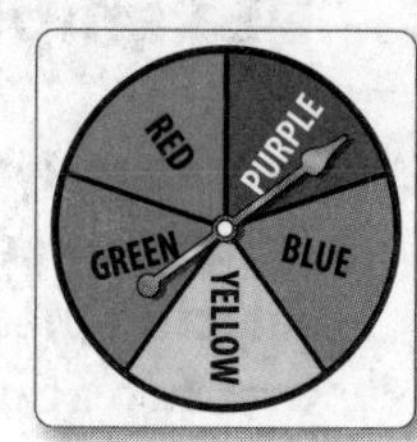

You are asked to determine the probability of the spinner *not* landing on blue and rolling a 3 or 4 on a number cube. The events are independent because spinning the spinner does not affect the outcome of rolling a number cube.

First, determine the probability of each event.

$P(\textit{not}\text{ blue}) = \frac{4}{5}$ ← number of ways not to spin blue / number of possible outcomes

$P(3 \text{ or } 4) = \frac{2}{6} \text{ or } \frac{1}{3}$ ← number of ways to roll 3 or 4 / number of possible outcomes

Then, determine the probability of both events occurring.

$P(\textit{not}\text{ blue and 3 or 4}) = \frac{4}{5} \cdot \frac{1}{3}$ — $P(A \text{ and } B) = P(A) \cdot P(B)$

$= \frac{4}{15}$ — Multiply.

The probability is $\frac{4}{15}$.

Check Make an organized list, table, or a tree diagram to show the sample space.

Got It? **Do this problem to find out.**

a. A game requires players to roll two number cubes to move the game pieces. The faces of the cubes are labeled 1 through 6. What is the probability of rolling a 2 or 4 on the first number cube and then rolling a 5 on the second?

a. ______

Probability of Dependent Events

Key Concept

Words If two events *A* and *B* are dependent, then the probability of both events occurring is the product of the probability of *A* and the probability of *B* after *A* occurs.

Symbols $P(A \text{ and } B) = P(A) \cdot P(B \text{ following } A)$

If the outcome of one event affects the outcome of another event, the events are called **dependent events**. For example, you have a bag with blue and green marbles. You pick one marble, do not replace it, and pick another one.

Example

3. There are 4 oranges, 7 bananas, and 5 apples in a fruit basket. Ignacio selects a piece of fruit at random and then Terrance selects a piece of fruit at random. Determine the probability that two apples are chosen.

Since the first piece of fruit is not replaced, the first event affects the second event. These are dependent events.

$P(\text{first piece is an apple}) = \frac{5}{16}$ ← number of apples / total pieces of fruit

$P(\text{second piece is an apple}) = \frac{4}{15}$ ← number of apples left / total pieces of fruit left

$P(\text{two apples}) = \frac{\overset{1}{\cancel{5}}}{\underset{4}{\cancel{16}}} \cdot \frac{\overset{1}{\cancel{4}}}{\underset{3}{\cancel{15}}} \text{ or } \frac{1}{12}.$

The probability that two apples are chosen is $\frac{1}{12}$.

b. ______

c. ______

Got It? Do these problems to find out.

Refer to the situation above. Determine each probability.

b. P(two bananas)

c. P(orange then apple)

Guided Practice

A penny is tossed and a number cube is rolled. Determine each probability. (Examples 1–2)

1. P(tails and 3) ______

2. P(heads and odd) ______

3. Cards labeled 5, 6, 7, 8, and 9 are in a stack. A card is drawn and not replaced. Then, a second card is drawn at random. Determine the probability of drawing two even numbers.

(Example 3) ______

4. **Building on the Essential Question** Explain the difference between independent events and dependent events.

______

______

______

Rate Yourself!

Are you ready to move on? Shade the section that applies.

I have a few questions. | I'm ready to move on. | I have a lot of questions.

Find out online. Use the Self-Check Quiz.

Name ____________________ My Homework ____________________

Independent Practice

7.6(D), 7.1(A), 7.1(B), 7.1(F) TEKS

A number cube is rolled and a marble is selected at random from the bag at the right. Determine each probability. Show your work. (Example 1)

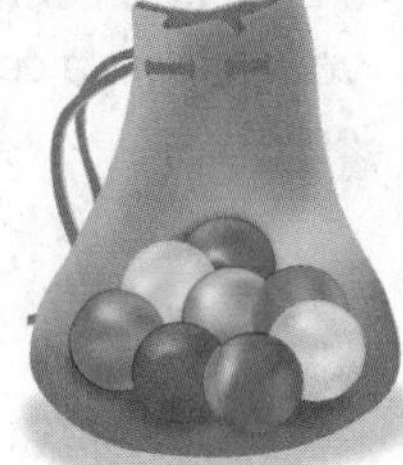

1. P(1 and red) ________

2. P(3 and purple) ________

3. P(even and yellow) ________

4. P(odd and *not* green) ________

5. A carnival game wheel has 12 equal sections. One of the sections contains a star. To win a prize, players must land on the section with the star on two consecutive spins. What is the probability of a player winning? (Example 2)

____

6. A standard set of dominoes contains 28 tiles, with each tile having two sides of dots from 0 to 6. Of these tiles, 7 have the same number of dots on each side. If four players each randomly choose a tile, without replacement, what is the probability that each chooses a tile with the same number of dots on each side? (Example 3) ________

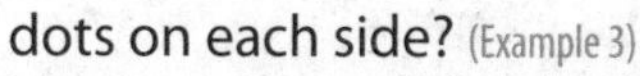

7. **MP Apply Math to the Real World** Refer to the graphic novel frame below. Jamar and Theresa decide to create a new playlist and include a total of ten songs. What is the probability that the first two songs are from the alternative genre if each selection is equally likely?

____

8. **Analyze Relationship** You and a friend plan to see 2 movies over the weekend. You can choose from 6 comedy, 2 drama, 4 romance, 1 science fiction, or 3 action movies. You write the movie titles on pieces of paper, place them in a bag, and each randomly select a movie. What is the probability that neither of you selects a comedy? Is this a dependent or independent event? Explain.

9. **Find the Error** A spinner with equal sections numbered from 1 to 5 is spun twice. Raul is determining the probability that both spins will result in an even number. Find his mistake and correct it.

H.O.T. Problems Higher-Order Thinking

10. **Create** There are 9 marbles representing 3 different colors. Write a problem where 2 marbles are selected at random without replacement and the probability is $\frac{1}{6}$.

11. **Analyze** Determine whether the following statement is true or false. If false, provide a counterexample.
If two events are independent, then the probability of both events is less than 1.

12. **Analyze** A company has determined that 2% of the pudding cups it produces are defective in some way. The pudding cups are sold in packages of two.

a. What is the probability that both pudding cups in a package are defective?

b. The company produces 1,000,000 packages each year. Predict the number of packages in which both cups are defective.

Name ____________________

Multi-Step Problem Solving

13. Wesley exercises about 3% of number of hours in a week. Suppose he is tracking the hours he exercises in a year or 52 weeks. Which prediction could represent the number of hours you would expect Wesley to exercise rounded to the nearest tenth? P N MP

Ⓐ 52.1 hours
Ⓑ 162.1 hours
Ⓒ 252 hours
Ⓓ 262.1 hours

Use a problem-solving model to solve this problem.

Read to Succeed!
You can express 3% as a decimal or a fraction in order to solve this problem.

1 Analyze

Read the problem. Circle the information you know. Underline what the problem is asking you to find.

2 Plan

What will you need to do to solve the problem? Write your plan in steps.

Step 1 Determine the number of ______ he works out each week.

________ the hours he exercises each week by ____ weeks.

3 Solve

Use your plan to solve the problem. Show your steps.

There are 24 hours in a day. Multiply that by 7 to determine the hours in a week.

$24 \times 7 =$ ______

Wesley exercises 3% or ______ of a week. Multiply by the hours in a week.

______ × ______ = ________

Multiply by the number of weeks in a year, 52. ______ × 52 = ______

Wesley would exercise about ______ hours in a year.

So, the correct answer is _____. Fill in that answer choice.

4 Justify and Evaluate

How do you know your solution is accurate?

____

____

____

P = Proportionality N = Number and Operations MP = Mathematical Processes

More Multi-Step Problem Solving

Use a problem-solving model to solve each problem.

14. One letter tile is selected and the spinner is spun. What is the probability that the tile will be a vowel and the spinner will land on a consonant? P N MP

Ⓐ $\frac{1}{4}$

Ⓑ $\frac{1}{3}$

Ⓒ $\frac{1}{6}$

Ⓓ $\frac{1}{12}$

15. Sonya has a bag with 4 green, 7 orange, and 9 blue marbles. She randomly selects one marble and then another. What is the probability that Sonya picks two blue marbles? Express your answer as a percent, rounded to the nearest tenth. P N MP

16. Deepak wants a new video game but is not sure which one to buy. His choices are 5 sports games, 3 role-playing games, and 8 action games. He writes the game titles on pieces of paper and puts them all in a bag. He randomly selects one piece of paper from the bag, does not replace it, and selects another piece of paper. What is the probability that Deepak selects two sports games? Express your answer as a percent, rounded to the nearest hundredth. P N MP

17. Tyrell is rolling two number cubes. He rolls them both at the same time. What is the probability that the sum of the two outcomes will be an even number? P N MP

P = Proportionality N = Number and Operations MP = Mathematical Processes

21ST CENTURY CAREER

Pediatricians

Mathematical Process
7.1(A) Apply mathematics to problems arising in everyday life, society, and the workplace.
Targeted TEKS 7.6(I)

Do you have compassion, a sense of humor, and the ability to analyze data? You might want to consider a career in medicine. Pediatricians care for the health of infants, children, and teenagers. They diagnose illnesses, interpret diagnostic tests, and prescribe and administer treatment.

Is This the Career for You?

Are you interested in a career as a pediatrician? Take some of the following courses in high school.

- Algebra
- Biology
- Calculus
- Chemistry
- Psychology

Explore college and careers at ccr.mcgraw-hill.com

On Call for Kids

Use the information in the table below to solve each problem. Round to the nearest tenth, if necessary. Express each answer as a percent rounded to the nearest whole number.

1. What is the probability that one of the patients tested has strep throat? ______

2. If a patient has strep throat, what is the probability that they have a positive test? ______

3. What is the probability that a patient with the disease has a negative test? ______

4. If a patient does not have the disease, what is the probability that they have a positive test? ______

5. What is the probability that a patient that does *not* have strep throat tested negative for the disease? ______

6. The *positive predictive value*, or *PPV*, is the probability that a patient with a positive test result will have the disease. What is the PPV? ______

7. The *negative predictive value*, or *NPV*, is the probability that a patient with a negative test result will not have the disease. What is the NPV? ______

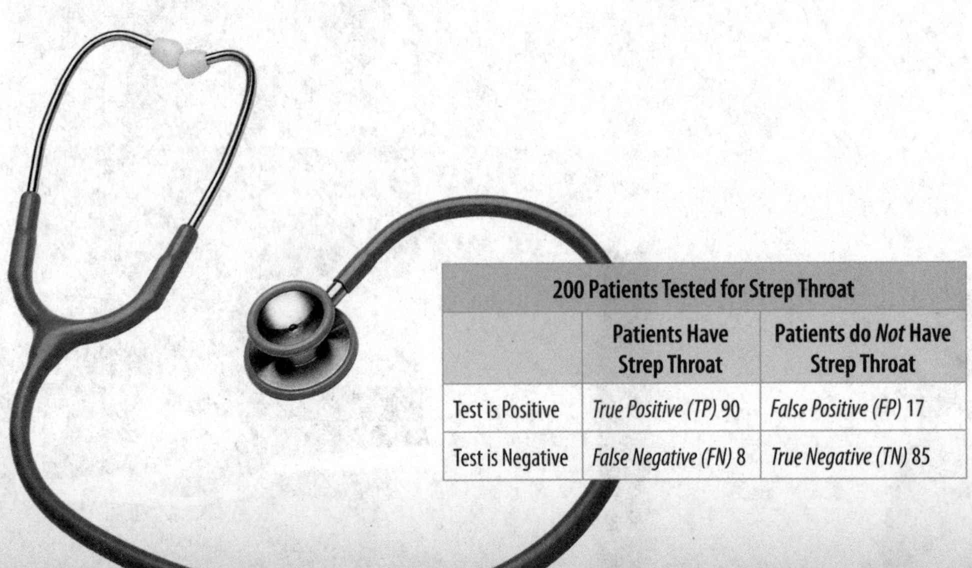

200 Patients Tested for Strep Throat		
	Patients Have Strep Throat	Patients do *Not* Have Strep Throat
Test is Positive	*True Positive (TP)* 90	*False Positive (FP)* 17
Test is Negative	*False Negative (FN)* 8	*True Negative (TN)* 85

Career Project

It's time to update your career portfolio! Interview your pediatrician. Be sure to ask what he or she enjoys most about being a pediatrician and what is most challenging. Then prepare a brief summary of the interview to orally present to your classmates. At the end, ask any clarifying questions.

______

______

______

______

What are some short term goals you need to achieve to become a pediatrician?

- ______
- ______
- ______
- ______
- ______

Chapter Review

TEKS

Vocabulary Check

Work with a partner to unscramble each of the clue words. After unscrambling all of the terms, use the numbered letters to write a phrase associated with probability.

HELATCORTEI

☐☐☐☐☐☐☐☐☐☐☐ (8 under the 8th box, 5 under the 10th box)

ORBITALBYPI

☐☐☐☐☐☐☐☐☐☐☐ (2 under the 3rd box, 1 under the 10th box)

LEAPMS ECPAS

☐☐☐☐☐☐ ☐☐☐☐☐ (4 under the 1st box; 3 under the 1st box and 6 under the 4th box of the second word)

COAPELMERTMYN

☐☐☐☐☐☐☐☐☐☐☐☐☐ (7 under the 2nd box, 9 under the 9th box)

☐☐☐☐ ☐ ☐☐☐☐

1 2 3 4   5   6 7 8 9

Complete each sentence using one or more of the unscrambled words above. Take turns reading each sentence aloud while the other student listens carefully. Ask for and give help if necessary.

1. The ____________________ is the set of all of the possible outcomes of a probability experiment.

2. Two events in which one or the other must happen, but they cannot happen at the same time are ____________________.

3. The ____________________ probability is based on what should happen when conducting a probability experiment.

4. ____________________ is the chance that some event will occur. It is the ratio of the number of favorable outcomes to the number of possible outcomes.

Key Concept Check

Use Your FOLDABLES

Use your Foldable to help review the chapter. Share your Foldable with a partner and take turns summarizing what you learned in this chapter, while the other partner listens carefully. Ask for and give help of any concept if needed. TEKS 7.1(E)

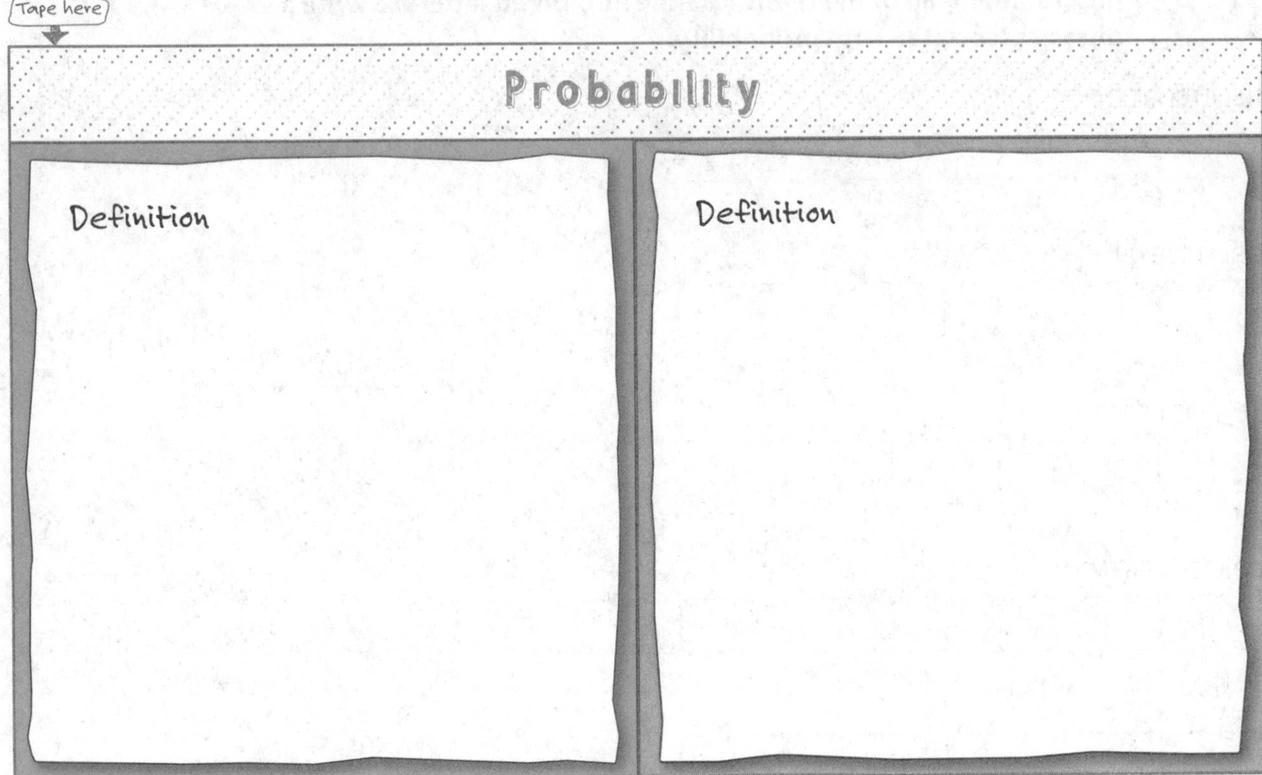

Got it?

Match each term or phrase on the left with the words on the right. TEKS 7.1(D)

1. Based on what actually occurred in a probability experiment
2. The outcome of one event affects the outcome of a separate event
3. Consists of two or more simple events
4. Can be used to determine sample space

a. compound event

b. experimental probability

c. tables

d. dependent event

e. tree diagrams

f. organized lists

Multi-Step Problem Solving

5. Use the graph of a survey of 50 middle school students who were asked to name their favorite NFL team. Suppose 1,200 students were surveyed. Predict how many more students will choose the Texans than the Cowboys as their favorite NFL team. Justify your solution. P MD MP

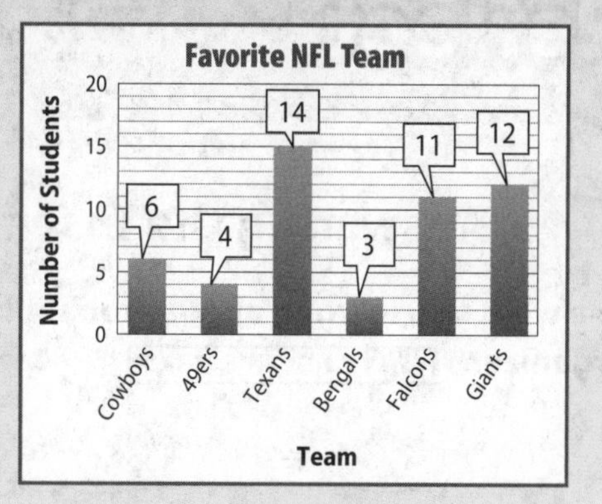

1 Analyze

2 Plan

3 Solve

4 Justify and Evaluate

Got it?

6. A basketball player makes about 75% of her free throws. Suppose she is awarded two free throws a total of 40 times in a season. Predict the number of free throws you would expect her to make. Justify your solution. P N MP

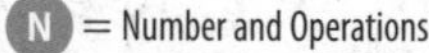 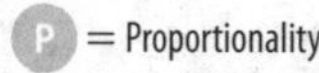 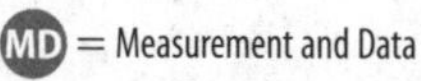 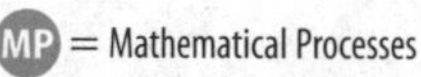

N = Number and Operations P = Proportionality MD = Measurement and Data MP = Mathematical Processes

Reflect

Answering the Essential Question

Use what you learned about probability to complete the graphic organizer. TEKS 7.1(D), 7.1(F), 7.1(G)

Theoretical Probability

Experimental Probability

Essential Question

HOW can you predict the outcome of future events?

Sample Space

Simulation

Answer the Essential Question. HOW can you predict the outcome of future events? Verbally share your responses with a partner, asking for and giving help if needed.

Glossary/Glosario

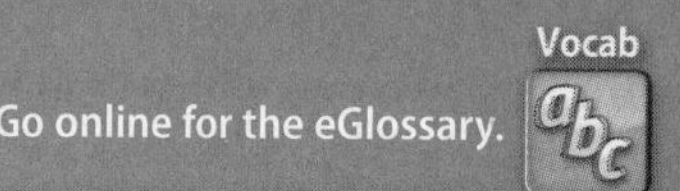

The eGlossary contains words and definitions in the following 13 languages:

Arabic	**Cantonese**	**Hmong**	**Spanish**	**Urdu**
Bengali	**English**	**Korean**	**Tagalog**	**Vietnamese**
Brazilian Portuguese	**Haitian Creole**	**Russian**		

English / Español

Aa

absolute value The distance the number is from zero on a number line.

valor absoluto Distancia a la que se encuentra un número de cero en la recta numérica.

acute angle An angle with a measure greater than 0° and less than 90°.

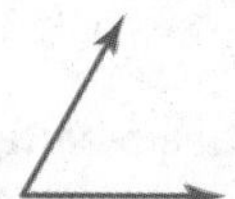

ángulo agudo Ángulo que mide más de 0° y menos de 90°.

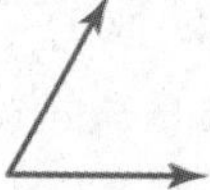

acute triangle A triangle having three acute angles.

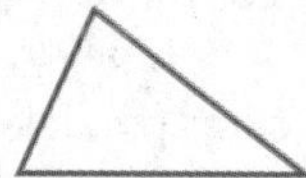

triángulo acutángulo Triángulo con tres ángulos agudos.

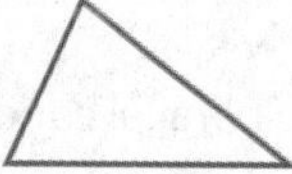

Addition Property of Equality If you add the same number to each side of an equation, the two sides remain equal.

propiedad de adición de la igualdad Si sumas el mismo número a ambos lados de una ecuación, los dos lados permanecen iguales.

Addition Property of Inequality If you add the same number to each side of an inequality, the inequality remains true.

propiedad de desigualdad en la suma Si se suma el mismo número a cada lado de una desigualdad, la desigualdad sigue siendo verdadera.

Additive Identity Property The sum of any number and zero is the number.

propiedad de identidad de la suma La suma de cualquier número y cero es el mismo número.

additive inverse Two integers that are opposites. The sum of an integer and its additive inverse is zero.

inverso aditivo Dos enteros opuestos.

adjacent angles Angles that have the same vertex, share a common side, and do not overlap.

ángulos adyacentes Ángulos que comparten el mismo vértice y un común lado, pero no se sobreponen.

algebra A branch of mathematics that involves expressions with variables.

álgebra Rama de las matemáticas que trata de las expresiones con variables.

algebraic expression A combination of variables, numbers, and at least one operation.

expresión algebraica Combinación de variables, números y por lo menos una operación.

angle Two rays with a common endpoint form an angle. The rays and vertex are used to name the angle.

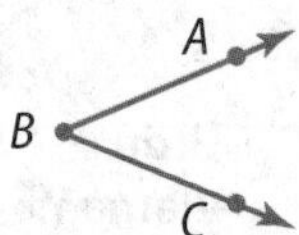

arithmetic sequence A sequence in which the difference between any two consecutive terms is the same.

assets Items that are owned by an individual.

Associative Property The way in which numbers are grouped does not change their sum or product.

attribute A characteristic of a figure.

ángulo Dos rayos con un extremo común forman un ángulo. Los rayos y el vértice se usan para nombrar el ángulo.

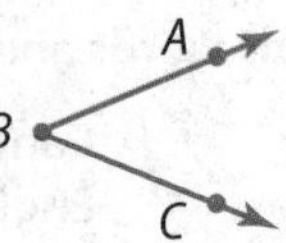

sucesión aritmética Sucesión en la cual la diferencia entre dos términos consecutivos es constante.

activo Bienes que posee una persona.

propiedad asociativa La forma en que se agrupan números al sumarlos o multiplicarlos no altera su suma o producto.

atributo Una característíca de una figura.

Bb

bar notation In repeating decimals, the line or bar placed over the digits that repeat. For example, $2.\overline{63}$ indicates that the digits 63 repeat.

base In a power, the number used as a factor. In 10^3, the base is 10. That is, $10^3 = 10 \times 10 \times 10$.

base One of the two parallel congruent faces of a prism.

biased sample A sample drawn in such a way that one or more parts of the population are favored over others.

box plot A method of visually displaying a distribution of data values by using the median, quartiles, and extremes of the data set. A box shows the middle 50% of the data.

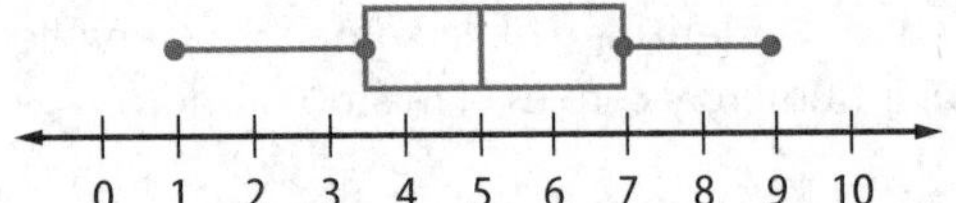

budget A plan for spending.

notación de barra Línea o barra que se coloca sobre los dígitos que se repiten en decimales periódicos. Por ejemplo, $2.\overline{63}$ indica que los dígitos 63 se repiten.

base En una potencia, el número usado como factor. En 10^3, la base es 10. Es decir, $10^3 = 10 \times 10 \times 10$.

base Una de las dos caras paralelas congruentes de un prisma.

muestra sesgada Muestra en que se favorece una o más partes de una población.

diagrama de caja Un método de mostrar visualmente una distribución de valores usando la mediana, cuartiles y extremos del conjunto de datos. Una caja muestra el 50% del medio de los datos.

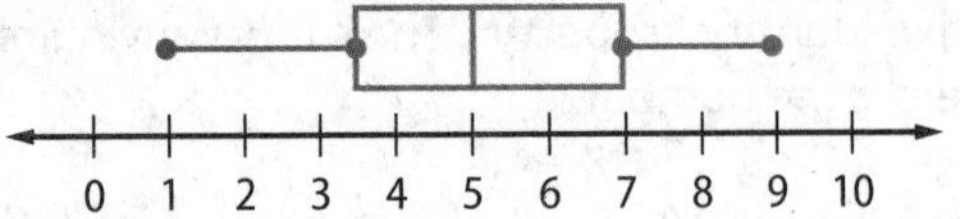

presupuesto Plan de gastos.

Cc

center The point from which all points on circle are the same distance.

circle The set of all points in a plane that are the same distance from a given point called the center.

centro El punto desde el cual todos los puntos en una circunferencia están a la misma distancia.

círculo Conjunto de todos los puntos de un plano que están a la misma distancia de un punto dado denominado "centro".

circle graph A graph that shows data as parts of a whole. In a circle graph, the percents add up to 100.

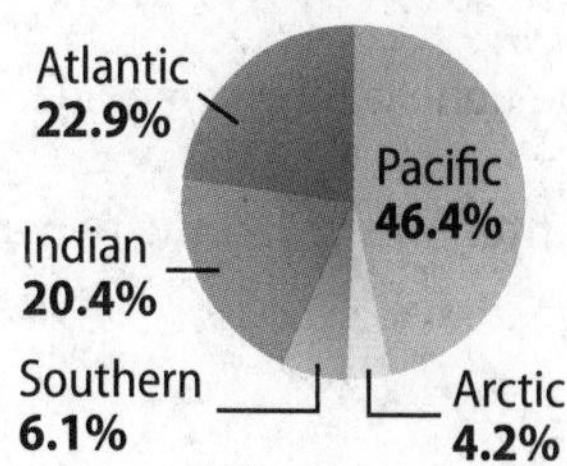

gráfica circular Gráfica que muestra los datos como partes de un todo. En una gráfica circular los porcentajes suman 100.

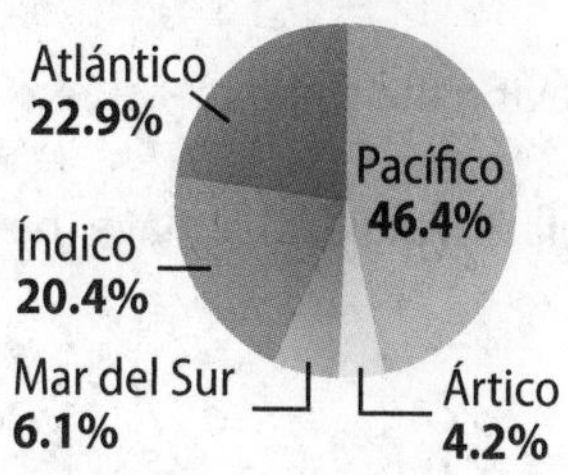

circumference The distance around a circle.

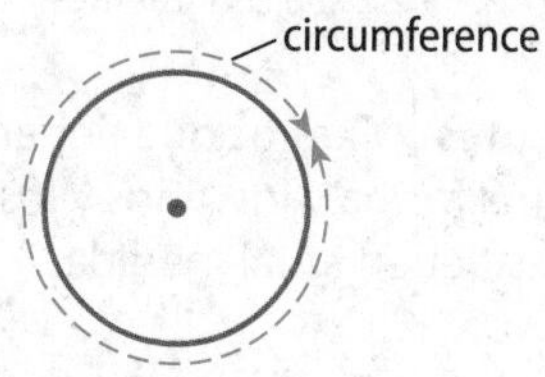

circunferencia Distancia en torno a un círculo.

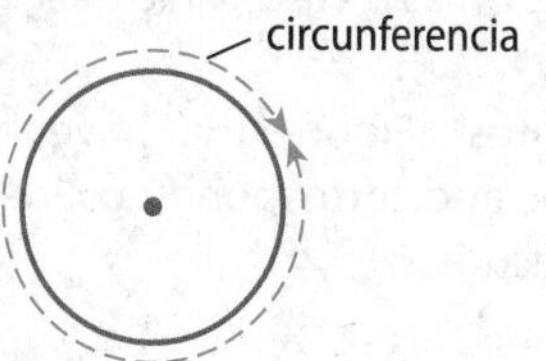

coefficient The numerical factor of a term that contains a variable.

coeficiente El factor numérico de un término que contiene una variable.

common denominator A common multiple of the denominators of two or more fractions. 24 is a common denominator for $\frac{1}{3}$, $\frac{5}{8}$, and $\frac{3}{4}$ because 24 is the LCM of 3, 8, and 4.

común denominador El múltiplo común de los denominadores de dos o más fracciones. 24 es un denominador común para $\frac{1}{3}$, $\frac{5}{8}$ y $\frac{3}{4}$ porque 24 es el mcm de 3, 8 y 4.

Commutative Property The order in which two numbers are added or multiplied does not change their sum or product.

propiedad conmutativa El orden en que se suman o multiplican dos números no altera el resultado.

complementary angles Two angles are complementary if the sum of their measures is 90°.

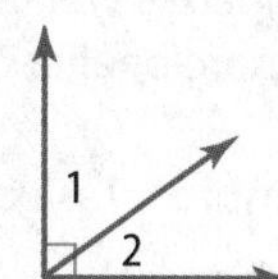

$\angle 1$ and $\angle 2$ are complementary angles.

ángulos complementarios Dos ángulos son complementarios si la suma de sus medidas es 90°.

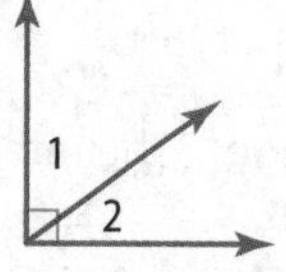

$\angle 1$ y $\angle 2$ son complementarios.

complementary events The events of one outcome happening and that outcome not happening. The sum of the probabilities of an event and its complement is 1 or 100%. In symbols, $P(\text{A}) + P(\textit{not}\ \text{A}) = 1$.

eventos complementarios Los eventos de un resultado que ocurre y ese resultado que no ocurre. La suma de las probabilidades de un evento y su complemento es 1 ó 100. En símbolos $P(\text{A}) + P(\textit{no}\ \text{A}) = 1$.

complex fraction A fraction $\frac{A}{B}$ where *A* or *B* are fractions and *B* does not equal zero.

fracción compleja Una fracción $\frac{A}{B}$ en la cual *A* o *B* son fracciones y *B* no es igual a cero.

composite figure A figure that is made up of two or more three-dimensional figures.

figura compuesta Figura formada por dos o más figuras tridimensionales.

compound event An event consisting of two or more simple events.

evento compuesto Un evento que consiste en dos o más eventos simples.

compound interest Interest paid on the initial principal and on interest earned in the past.

interés compuesto Interés que se paga sobre el capital inicial y los intereses ganados en el pasado.

congruent Having the same measure.

congruente Que tiene la misma medida.

congruent angles Angles that have the same measure.

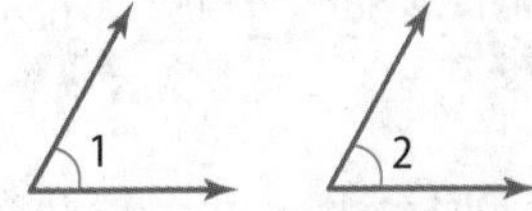

∠1 and ∠2 are congruent angles.

ángulos congruentes Ángulos que tienen la misma medida.

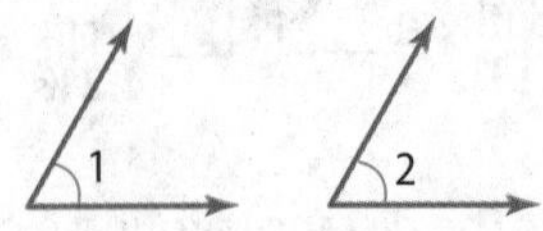

∠1 y ∠2 son congruentes.

congruent figures Figures that have the same size and same shape and corresponding sides and angles with equal measure.

figuras congruentes Figuras que tienen el mismo tamaño y la misma forma y los lados y los ángulos correspondientes tienen igual medida.

congruent segments Sides with the same length.

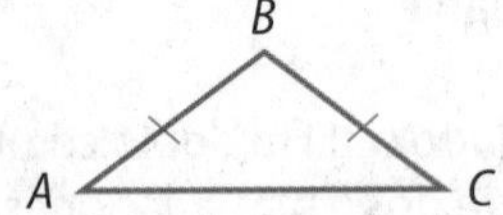

Side $\overline{AB}$ is congruent to side $\overline{BC}$.

segmentos congruentes Lados con la misma longitud.

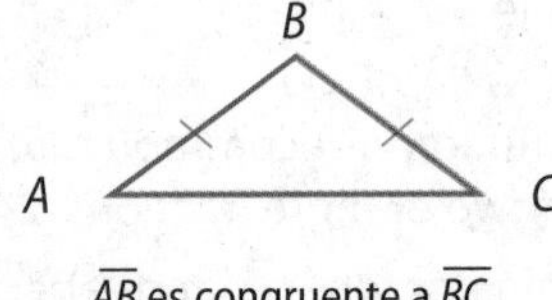

$\overline{AB}$ es congruente a $\overline{BC}$.

constant A term that does not contain a variable.

constante Término que no contiene ninguna variable.

constant of proportionality A constant ratio or unit rate of two variable quantities. It is also called the constant of variation.

constante de proporcionalidad Una razón constante o tasa por unidad de dos cantidades variables. También se llama constante de variación.

constant of variation The constant ratio in a direct variation. It is also called the constant of proportionality.

constante de variación Una razón constante o tasa por unidad de dos cantidades variables. También se llama constante de proporcionalidad.

constant rate of change The rate of change in a linear relationship.

razón constante de cambio Tasa de cambio en una relación lineal.

convenience sample A sample which consists of members of a population that are easily accessed.

muestra de conveniencia Muestra que incluye miembros de una población fácilmente accesibles.

coordinate plane A plane in which a horizontal number line and a vertical number line intersect at their zero points. Also called a coordinate grid.

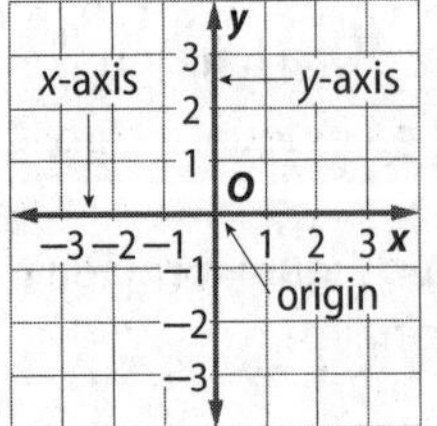

plano de coordenadas Plano en el cual se han trazado dos rectas numéricas, una horizontal y una vertical, que se intersecan en sus puntos cero. También conocido como sistema de coordenadas.

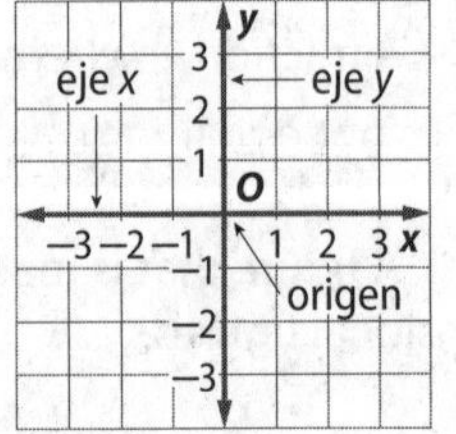

Glossary/Glosario

corresponding angles Angles in the same position on parallel lines in relation to a transversal.

ángulos correspondientes Ángulos que están en la misma posición sobre rectas paralelas en relación con la transversal.

corresponding sides The sides of similar figures that are in the same relative position.

lados correspondientes Lados de figuras semejantes que estan en la misma posición.

counterexample A specific case which proves a statement false.

contraejemplo Caso específico que demuestra la falsedad de un enunciado.

coupon A voucher entitling its user to a cash refund.

cupón Vale que da derecho al usuario a obtener un reembolso en efectivo.

cross product The product of the numerator of one ratio and the denominator of the other ratio. The cross products of any proportion are equal.

producto cruzado Producto del numerador de una razón por el denominador de la otra razón. Los productos cruzados de cualquier proporción son iguales.

cube root One of three equal factors of a number. If $a^3 = b$, then a is the cube root of b. The cube root of 125 is 5 since $5^3 = 125$.

raíz cúbica Uno de tres factores iguales de un número. Si $a^3 = b$, entonces a es la raíz cúbica de b. La raíz cúbica de 125 es 5, dado que $5^3 = 125$.

cubed The product in which a number is a factor three times. Two cubed is 8 because $2 \times 2 \times 2 = 8$.

al cubo El producto de un número por sí mismo, tres veces. Dos al cubo es 8 porque $2 \times 2 \times 2 = 8$.

Dd

decagon A polygon having ten sides.

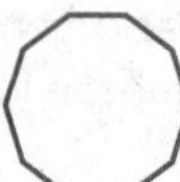

decágono Un polígono con diez lados.

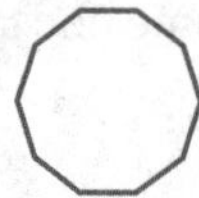

defining a variable Choosing a variable and a quantity for the variable to represent in an expression or equation.

definir una variable El eligir una variable y una cantidad que esté representada por la variable en una expresión o en una ecuacion.

degrees The most common unit of measure for angles. If a circle were divided into 360 equal-sized parts, each part would have an angle measure of 1 degree.

grados La unidad más común para medir ángulos. Si un círculo se divide en 360 partes iguales, cada parte tiene una medida angular de 1 grado.

dependent events Two or more events in which the outcome of one event affects the outcome of the other event(s).

eventos dependientes Dos o más eventos en que el resultado de un evento afecta el resultado de otro u otros eventos.

dependent variable The variable in a relation with a value that depends on the value of the independent variable.

variable dependiente La variable en una relación cuyo valor depende del valor de la variable independiente.

derived unit A unit that is derived from a measurement system base unit, such as length, mass, or time.

unidad derivada Unidad que se deriva de una unidad básica de un sistema de medidas, como la longitud, la masa o el tiempo.

diagonal A line segment that connects two nonconsecutive vertices.

diagonal Segmento de recta que une dos vértices no consecutivos de un polígono.

diameter The distance across a circle through its center.

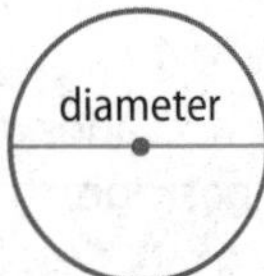

diámetro Segmento que pasa por el centro de un círculo y lo divide en dos partes iguales.

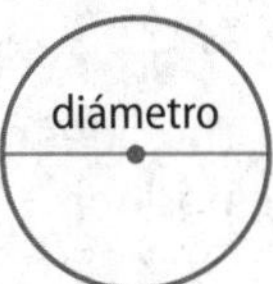

dimensional analysis The process of including units of measurement when you compute.

análisis dimensional Proceso que incluye las unidades de medida al hacer cálculos.

direct variation The relationship between two variable quantities that have a constant ratio.

variación directa Relación entre las cantidades de dos variables que tienen una tasa constante.

discount The amount by which the regular price of an item is reduced.

descuento Cantidad que se le rebaja al precio regular de un artículo.

disjoint events Events that cannot happen at the same time.

eventos disjuntos Eventos que no pueden ocurrir al mismo tiempo.

Distributive Property To multiply a sum by a number, multiply each addend of the sum by the number outside the parentheses. For any numbers a, b, and c, $a(b + c) = ab + ac$ and $a(b - c) = ab - ac$.

Example: $2(5 + 3) = (2 \times 5) + (2 \times 3)$ and $2(5 - 3) = (2 \times 5) - (2 \times 3)$

propiedad distributiva Para multiplicar una suma por un número, multiplíquese cada sumando de la suma por el número que está fuera del paréntesis. Sean cuales fuere los números a, b, y c, $a(b + c) = ab + ac$ y $a(b - c) = ab - ac$.

Ejemplo: $2(5 + 3) = (2 \cdot 5) + (2 \cdot 3)$ y $2(5 - 3) = (2 \cdot 5) - (2 \cdot 3)$

Division Property of Equality If you divide each side of an equation by the same nonzero number, the two sides remain equal.

propiedad de igualdad de la división Si divides ambos lados de una ecuación entre el mismo número no nulo, los lados permanecen iguales.

Division Property of Inequality When you divide each side of an inequality by a negative number, the inequality symbol must be reversed for the inequality to remain true.

propiedad de desigualdad en la división Cuando se divide cada lado de una desigualdad entre un número negativo, el símbolo de desigualdad debe invertirse para que la desigualdad siga siendo verdadera.

double box plot Two box plots graphed on the same number line.

doble diagrama de caja Dos diagramas de caja sobre la misma recta numérica.

double dot plot A method of visually displaying a distribution of two sets of data values where each value is shown as a dot above a number line.

doble diagrama de puntos Un método de mostrar visualmente una distribución de dos conjuntos de valores donde cada valor se muestra como un punto arriba de una recta numérica.

Ee

edge The line segment where two faces of a polyhedron intersect.

borde El segmento de línea donde se cruzan dos caras de un poliedro.

enlargement An image larger than the original.

ampliación Imagen más grande que la original.

equation A mathematical sentence that contains an equals sign, =, stating that two quantities are equal.

ecuación Enunciado matemático que contiene el signo de igualdad = indicando que dos cantidades son iguales.

equiangular In a polygon, all of the angles are congruent.

equilateral In a polygon, all of the sides are congruent.

equilateral triangle A triangle having three congruent sides.

equivalent equations Two or more equations with the same solution.

equivalent expressions Expressions that have the same value.

equivalent ratios Two ratios that have the same value.

evaluate To find the value of an expression.

expenses The cost required to buy an item or service.

experimental probability An estimated probability based on the relative frequency of positive outcomes occurring during an experiment. It is based on what *actually* occurred during such an experiment.

exponent In a power, the number that tells how many times the base is used as a factor. In 5^3, the exponent is 3. That is, $5^3 = 5 \times 5 \times 5$.

exponential form Numbers written with exponents.

equiangular En un polígono, todos los ángulos son congruentes.

equilátero En un polígono, todos los lados son congruentes.

triángulo equilátero Triángulo con tres lados congruentes.

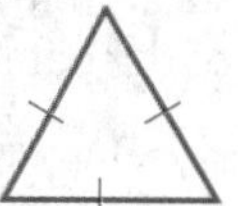

ecuaciones equivalentes Dos o más ecuaciones con la misma solución.

expresiones equivalentes Expresiones que tienen el mismo valor.

razones equivalentes Dos razones que tienen el mismo valor.

evaluar Calcular el valor de una expresión.

gastos Costos necesario para comprar un artículo o un servicio.

probabilidad experimental Probabilidad estimada que se basa en la frecuencia relativa de los resultados positivos que ocurren durante un experimento. Se basa en lo que *en realidad* ocurre durante dicho experimento.

exponente En una potencia, el número que indica las veces que la base se usa como factor. En 5^3, el exponente es 3. Es decir, $5^3 = 5 \times 5 \times 5$.

forma exponencial Números escritos usando exponentes.

face A flat surface of a polyhedron.

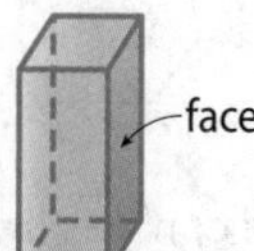

factor To write a number as a product of its factors.

factored form An expression expressed as the product of its factors.

cara Una superficie plana de un poliedro.

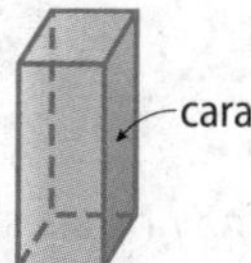

factorizar Escribir un número como el producto de sus factores.

forma factorizada Una expresión expresada como el producto de sus factores.

factors Two or more numbers that are multiplied together to form a product.

factores Dos o más números que se multiplican entre sí para formar un producto.

fair game A game where each player has an equally likely chance of winning.

juego justo Juego donde cada jugador tiene igual posibilidad de ganar.

family budget A family plan for spending.

presupuesto familiar Plan de gastos de una familia.

first quartile For a data set with median *M*, the first quartile is the median of the data values less than *M*.

primer cuartil Para un conjunto de datos con la mediana *M*, el primer cuartil es la mediana de los valores menores que *M*.

fixed expenses Costs that do not change based on the amount that is used.

gastos fijos Costos que no cambian con la cantidad usada.

formula An equation that shows the relationship among certain quantities.

fórmula Ecuación que muestra la relación entre ciertas cantidades.

Fundamental Counting Principle Uses multiplication of the number of ways each event in an experiment can occur to find the number of possible outcomes in a sample space.

Principio Fundamental de Contar Este principio usa la multiplicación del número de veces que puede ocurrir cada evento en un experimento para calcular el número de posibles resultados en un espacio muestral.

Gg

gram A unit of mass in the metric system equivalent to 0.001 kilogram.

gramo Unidad de masa en el sistema métrico que equivale a 0.001 de kilogramo.

graph The process of placing a point on a number line or on a coordinate plane at its proper location.

graficar Proceso de dibujar o trazar un punto en una recta numérica o en un plano de coordenadas en su ubicación correcta.

gratuity Also known as a tip. It is a small amount of money in return for a service.

gratificación También conocida como propina. Es una cantidad pequeña de dinero en retribución por un servicio.

Hh

heptagon A polygon having seven sides.

heptágono Polígono con siete lados.

hexagon A polygon having six sides.

hexágono Polígono con seis lados.

histogram A type of bar graph used to display numerical data that have been organized into equal intervals.

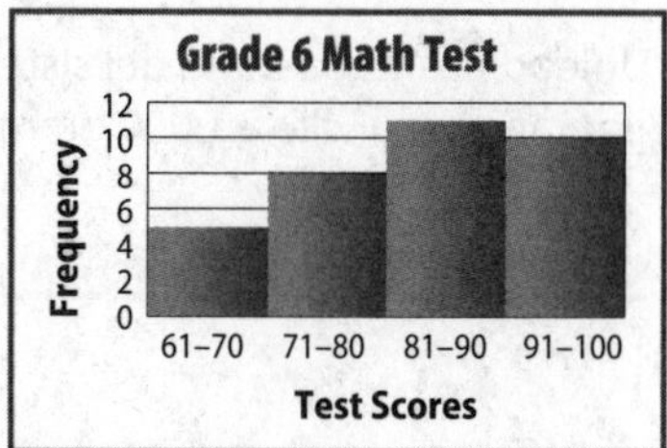

histograma Tipo de gráfica de barras que se usa para exhibir datos que se han organizado en intervalos iguales.

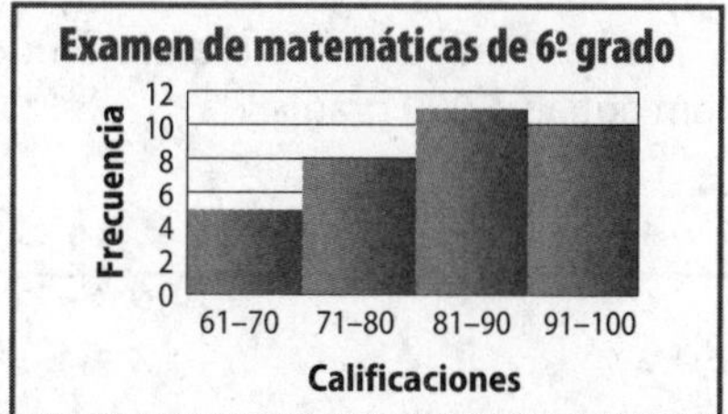

Identity Property of Zero The sum of an addend and zero is the addend. Example: $5 + 0 = 5$

propiedad de identidad del cero La suma de un sumando y cero es igual al sumando. Ejemplo: $5 + 0 = 5$

income A financial gain from capital or labor.

ingreso Ganacia financiera por el capital o el trabajo.

income tax A tax on the net income of an individual or business.

impuesto a los ingresos Impuesto sobre el ingreso neto de una persona o un negocio.

independent events Two or more events in which the outcome of one event does not affect the outcome of the other event(s).

eventos independientes Dos o más eventos en los cuales el resultado de uno de ellos no afecta el resultado de los otros eventos.

independent variable The variable in a function with a value that is subject to choice.

variable independiente Variable en una función cuyo valor está sujeto a elección.

inequality An open sentence that uses $<, >, \neq, \leq,$ or $\geq$ to compare two quantities.

desigualdad Enunciado abierto que usa $<, >, \neq,$ $\leq$ o $\geq$ para comparar dos cantidades.

integer Any number from the set $\{\ldots, -4, -3, -2, -1, 0, 1, 2, 3, 4, \ldots\}$, where … means continues without end.

entero Cualquier número del conjunto $\{\ldots, -4, -3, -2, -1, 0, 1, 2, 3, 4, \ldots\}$, donde … significa que continúa sin fin.

interquartile range A measure of variation in a set of numerical data. It is the distance between first and third quartiles of the data set.

rango intercuartil Una medida de la variación en un conjunto de datos numéricos. Es la distancia entre el primer y el tercer cuartiles del conjunto de datos.

inverse variation A relationship where the product of x and y is a constant k. As x increases in value, y decreases in value, or as y decreases in value, x increases in value.

variación inversa Relación en la cual el producto de x y y es una constante k. A medida que aumenta el valor de x, disminuye el valor de y o a medida que disminuye el valor de y, aumenta el valor de x.

irrational number A number that cannot be expressed as the ratio of two integers.

número irracional Número que no se puede expresar como el razón de dos enteros.

isosceles triangle A triangle having at least two congruent sides.

triángulo isósceles Triángulo que tiene por lo menos dos lados congruentes.

Kk

kilogram The base unit of mass in the metric system. One kilogram equals 1,000 grams.

kilogramo Unidad básica de masa del sistema métrico. Un kilogramo equivale a 1,000 gramos.

Ll

lateral face In a polyhedron, a face that is not a base.

cara lateral En un poliedro, las caras que no forman las bases.

lateral surface area The sum of the areas of all of the lateral faces of a solid.

área de superficie lateral Suma de las áreas de todas las caras de un sólido.

least common denominator (LCD) The least common multiple of the denominators of two or more fractions. You can use the LCD to compare fractions.

mínimo común denominador (mcd) El menor de los múltiplos de los denominadores de dos o más fracciones. Puedes usar el mínimo común denominador para comparar fracciones.

liabilities Debts that are owed by an individual.

pasivo Deudas que tiene una persona.

like fractions Fractions that have the same denominators.

fracciones semejantes Fracciones que tienen los mismos denominadores.

like terms Terms that contain the same variables raised to the same power. Example: $5x$ and $6x$ are like terms.

términos semejante Términos que contienen las mismas variables elevadas a la misma potencia. Ejemplo: $5x$ y $6x$ son *términos semejante*.

line graph A type of statistical graph using lines to show how values change over a period of time.

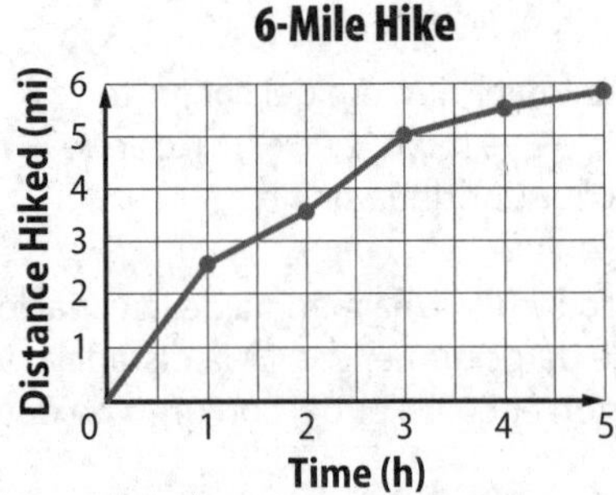

gráfica lineal Tipo de gráfica estadística que usa segmentos de recta para mostrar cómo cambian los valores durante un período de tiempo.

linear equation An equation with a graph that is a straight line.

ecuación lineal Ecuación cuya gráfca es una recta.

linear expression An algebraic expression in which the variable is raised to the first power.

expresión lineal Expresión algebraica en la cual la variable se eleva a la primera potencia.

linear relationship A relationship for which the graph is a straight line.

relación lineal Una relación para la cual la gráfica es una línea recta.

liter The base unit of capacity in the metric system. The amount of dry or liquid material an object can hold.

litro Unidad básica de capacidad del sistema métrico. La cantidad de materia líquida o sólida que puede contener un objeto.

markdown An amount by which the regular price of an item is reduced.

rebaja Una cantidad por la cual el precio regular de un artículo se reduce.

markup The amount the price of an item is increased above the price the store paid for the item.

margen de utilidad Cantidad de aumento en el precio de un artículo por encima del precio que paga la tienda por dicho artículo.

mean The sum of the data divided by the number of items in the data set.

media La suma de los datos dividida entre el número total de artículos en el conjunto de datos.

mean absolute deviation A measure of variation in a set of numerical data, computed by adding the distances between each data value and the mean, then dividing by the number of data values.

desviación media absoluta Una medida de variación en un conjunto de datos numéricos que se calcula sumando las distancias entre el valor de cada dato y la media, y luego dividiendo entre el número de valores.

measures of center Numbers that are used to describe the center of a set of data. These measures include the mean, median, and mode.

medidas del centro Números que se usan para describir el centro de un conjunto de datos. Estas medidas incluyen la media, la mediana y la moda.

measures of variation A measure used to describe the distribution of data.

medidas de variación Medida usada para describir la distribución de los datos.

median A measure of center in a set of numerical data. The median of a list of values is the value appearing at the center of a sorted version of the list—or the mean of the two central values, if the list contains an even number of values.

mediana Una medida del centro en un conjunto de dados númericos. La mediana de una lista de valores es el valor que aparace en el centro de una versíon ordenada de la lista, o la media de dos valores centrales si la lista contiene un número par de valores.

meter The base unit of length in the metric system.

metro Unidad fundamental de longitud del sistema métrico.

metric system A decimal system of measures. The prefixes commonly used in this system are kilo-, centi-, and milli-.

sistema métrico Sistema decimal de medidas. Los prefijos más comunes son kilo-, centi- y mili-.

mode The number or numbers that appear most often in a set of data. If there are two or more numbers that occur most often, all of them are modes.

moda El número o números que aparece con más frecuencia en un conjunto de datos. Si hay dos o más números que ocurren con más frecuencia, todosellos son modas.

monetary incentives Financial reasons, such as sales, rebates, and coupons, to buy a particular item.

incentivos monetarios Razones financieras, como ventas, reembolsos y cupones, para comprar un artículo en particular.

Multiplication Property of Equality If you multiply each side of an equation by the same nonzero number, the two sides remain equal.

propiedad de multiplicación de la igualdad Si multiplicas ambos lados de una ecuación por el mismo número no nulo, lo lados permanecen iguales.

Multiplication Property of Inequality When you multiply each side of an inequality by a negative number, the inequality symbol must be reversed for the inequality to remain true.

propiedad de desigualdad en la multiplicación Cuando se multiplica cada lado de una desigualdad por un número negativo, el símbolo de desigualdad debe invertirse para que la desigualdad siga siendo verdadera.

Multiplicative Identity Property The product of any number and one is the number.

propiedad de identidad de la multiplicación El producto de cualquier número y uno es el mismo número.

Multiplicative Property of Zero The product of any number and zero is zero.

propiedad del cero en la multiplicación El producto de cualquier número y cero es cero.

multiplicative inverse Two numbers with a product of 1. For example, the multiplicative inverse of $\frac{2}{3}$ is $\frac{3}{2}$.

inverso multiplicativo Dos números cuyo producto es 1. Por ejemplo, el inverso multiplicativo de $\frac{2}{3}$ es $\frac{3}{2}$.

Nn

negative exponent Any nonzero number to the negative *n* power. It is the multiplicative inverse of its *n*th power.

exponente negativo Cualquier número que no sea cero a la potencia negative de *n*. Es el inverso multiplicativo de su *enésimo* potencia.

negative integer An integer that is less than zero. Negative integers are written with a − sign.

entero negativo Número menor que cero. Se escriben con el signo −.

net A two-dimensional figure that can be used to build a three-dimensional figure.

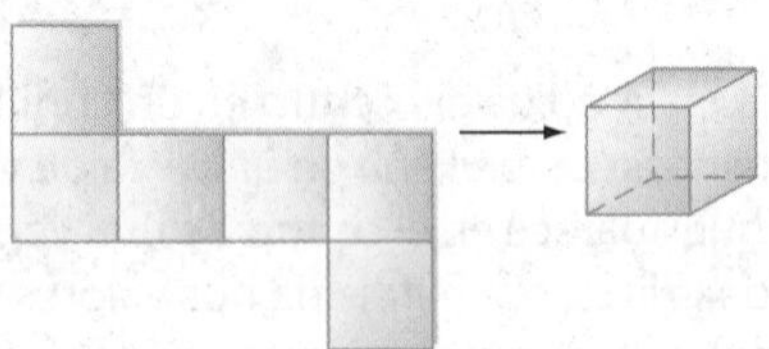

red Figura bidimensional que sirve para hacer una figura tridimensional.

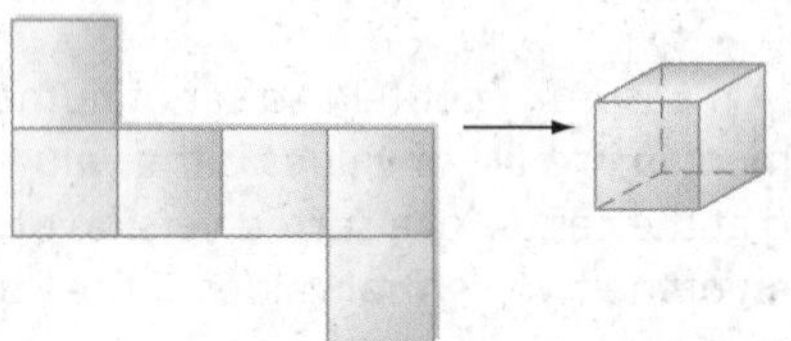

net worth The value of one's assets minus one's liabilities.

patrimonio neto Valor del activo menos el pasivo de una persona.

nonagon A polygon having nine sides.

enágono Polígono que tiene nueve lados.

nonproportional The relationship between two ratios with a rate or ratio that is not constant.

no proporcional Relación entre dos razones cuya tasa o razón no es constante.

numerical expression A combination of numbers and operations.

expresión numérica Combinación de números y operaciones.

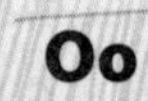

Oo

obtuse angle Any angle that measures greater than 90° but less than 180°.

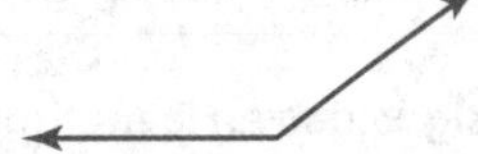

ángulo obtuso Cualquier ángulo que mide más de 90° pero menos de 180°.

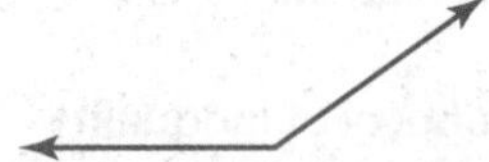

obtuse triangle A triangle having one obtuse angle.

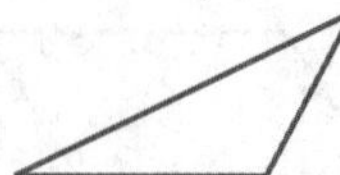

triángulo obtusángulo Triángulo que tiene un ángulo obtuso.

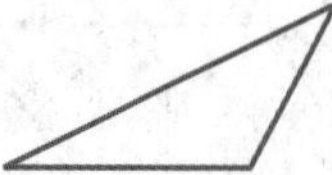

octagon A polygon having eight sides.

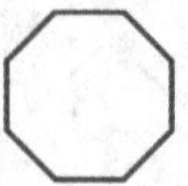

octágono Polígono que tiene ocho lados.

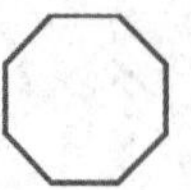

opposites Two integers are opposites if they are represented on the number line by points that are the same distance from zero, but on opposite sides of zero. The sum of two opposites is zero.

opuestos Dos enteros son opuestos si, en la recta numérica, están representados por puntos que equidistan de cero, pero en direcciones opuestas. La suma de dos opuestos es cero.

order of operations The rules to follow when more than one operation is used in a numerical expression.

1. Evaluate the expressions inside grouping symbols.
2. Evaluate all powers.
3. Multiply and divide in order from left to right.
4. Add and subtract in order from left to right.

orden de las operaciones Reglas a seguir cuando se usa más de una operación en una expresión numérica.

1. Primero, evalúa las expresiones dentro de los símbolos de agrupación.
2. Evalúa todas las potencias.
3. Multiplica y divide en orden de izquierda a derecha.
4. Suma y resta en orden de izquierda a derecha.

ordered pair A pair of numbers used to locate a point in the coordinate plane. An ordered pair is written in the form (x-coordinate, y-coordinate).

par ordenado Par de números que se utiliza para ubicar un punto en un plano de coordenadas. Se escribe de la siguiente forma: (coordenada x, coordenada y).

origin The point at which the x-axis and the y-axis intersect in a coordinate plane. The origin is at (0, 0).

origen Punto en que el eje x y el eje y se intersecan en un plano de coordenadas. El origen está ubicado en (0, 0).

outcome Any one of the possible results of an action. For example, 4 is an outcome when a number cube is rolled.

resultado Cualquiera de los resultados posibles de una acción. Por ejemplo, 4 puede ser un resultado al lanzar un cubo numerado.

outlier A data value that is either much *greater* or much *less* than the median.

valor atípico Valor de los datos que es mucho *mayor* o mucho *menor* que la mediana.

Pp

parallel lines Lines in a plane that never intersect.

rectas paralelas Rectas en un plano que nunca se intersecan.

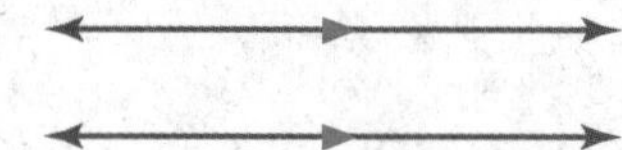

parallelogram A quadrilateral with opposite sides parallel and opposite sides congruent.

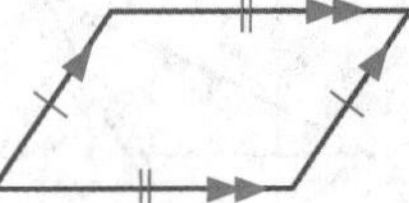

paralelogramo Cuadrilátero cuyos lados opuestos son paralelos y congruentes.

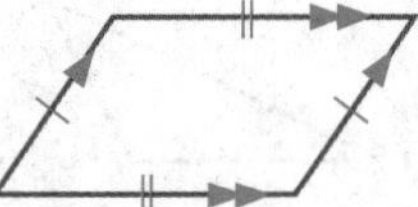

pentagon A polygon having five sides.

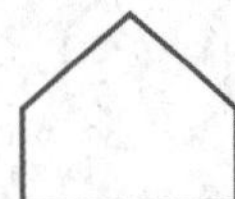

pentágono Polígono que tiene cinco lados.

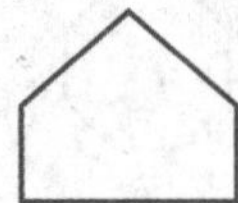

percent equation An equation that describes the relationship between the part, whole, and percent.

part = percent • whole

ecuación porcentual Ecuación que describe la relación entre la parte, el todo y el por ciento.

parte = por ciento • todo

percent error A ratio that compares the inaccuracy of an estimate (amount of error) to the actual amount.

porcentaje de error Una razón que compara la inexactitud de una estimación (cantidad del error) con la cantidad real.

percent of change A ratio that compares the change in a quantity to the original amount.

$$\text{percent of change} = \frac{\text{amount of change}}{\text{original amount}}$$

porcentaje de cambio Razón que compara el cambio en una cantidad a la cantidad original.

$$\text{porcentaje de cambio} = \frac{\text{cantidad del cambio}}{\text{cantidad original}}$$

percent of decrease A negative percent of change.

porcentaje de disminución Porcentaje de cambio negativo.

percent of increase A positive percent of change.

porcentaje de aumento Porcentaje de cambio positivo.

percent proportion One ratio or fraction that compares part of a quantity to the whole quantity. The other ratio is the equivalent percent written as a fraction with a denominator of 100.

$$\frac{\text{part}}{\text{whole}} = \frac{\text{percent}}{100}$$

proporción porcentual Razón o fracción que compara parte de una cantidad a toda la cantidad. La otra razón es el porcentaje equivalente escrito como fracción con 100 de denominador.

$$\frac{\text{parte}}{\text{todo}} = \frac{\text{porcentaje}}{100}$$

perfect squares Numbers with square roots that are whole numbers. 25 is a perfect square because the square root of 25 is 5.

cuadrados perfectos Números cuya raíz cuadrada es un número entero. 25 es un cuadrado perfecto porque la raíz cuadrada de 25 es 5.

perpendicular lines Lines that meet or cross each other to form right angles.

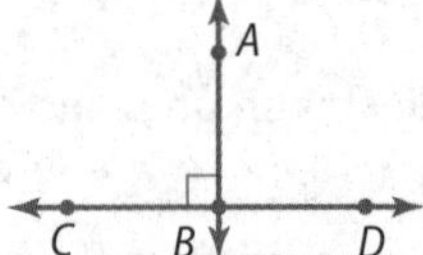

rectas perpendiculares Rectas que al encontrarse o cruzarse forman ángulos rectos.

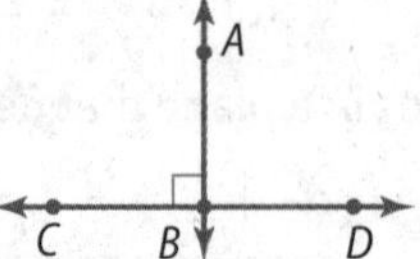

personal budget An individual plan for spending.

presupuesto personal Plan de gastos de una persona.

pi The ratio of the circumference of a circle to its diameter. The Greek letter π represents this number. The value of pi is 3.1415926. . . . Approximations for pi are 3.14 and $\frac{22}{7}$.

pi Relación entre la circunferencia de un círculo y su diámetro. La letra griega π representa este número. El valor de pi es 3.1415926. . . . Las aproximaciones de pi son 3.14 y $\frac{22}{7}$.

plane A two-dimensional flat surface that extends in all directions.

plano Superficie bidimensional que se extiende en todas direcciones.

polygon A simple closed figure formed by three or more straight line segments.

polígono Figura cerrada simple formada por tres o más segmentos de recta.

polyhedron A three-dimensional figure with faces that are polygons.

poliedro Una figura tridimensional con caras que son polígonos.

population The entire group of items or individuals from which the samples under consideration are taken.

población El grupo total de individuos o de artículos del cual se toman las muestras bajo estudio.

positive integer An integer that is greater than zero. They are written with or without a + sign.

entero positivo Entero que es mayor que cero; se escribe con o sin el signo +.

powers Numbers expressed using exponents. The power 3^2 is read three to the *second power*, or *three squared*.

potencias Números que se expresan usando exponentes. La potencia 3^2 se lee *tres a la segunda potencia* o *tres al cuadrado*.

precision The ability of a measurement to be consistently reproduced.

precisión Capacidad que tiene una medición de poder reproducirse consistentemente.

principal The amount of money deposited or borrowed.

capital Cantidad de dinero que se deposita o se toma prestada.

prism A polyhedron with two parallel congruent faces called bases.

prisma Un poliedro con dos caras congruentes paralelas llamadas bases.

probability The chance that some event will happen. It is the ratio of the number of favorable outcomes to the number of possible outcomes.

probabilidad La posibilidad de que suceda un evento. Es la razón del número de resultados favorables al número de resultados posibles.

probability model A model used to assign probabilities to outcomes of a chance process by examining the nature of the process.

modelo de probabilidad Un modelo usado para asignar probabilidades a resultados de un proceso aleatorio examinando la naturaleza del proceso.

properties Statements that are true for any number or variable.

propiedades Enunciados que son verdaderos para cualquier número o variable.

proportion An equation stating that two ratios or rates are equivalent.

proporción Ecuación que indica que dos razones o tasas son equivalentes.

proportional The relationship between two ratios with a constant rate or ratio.

proporcional Relación entre dos razones con una tasa o razón constante.

pyramid A polyhedron with one base that is a polygon and three or more triangular faces that meet at a common vertex.

pirámide Un poliedro con una base que es un polígono y tres o más caras triangulares que se encuentran en un vértice común.

Qq

quadrant One of the four regions into which the two perpendicular number lines of the coordinate plane separate the plane.

cuadrante Una de las cuatro regiones en que dos rectas numéricas perpendiculares dividen el plano de coordenadas.

quadrilateral A closed figure having four sides and four angles.

cuadrilátero Figura cerrada que tiene cuatro lados y cuatro ángulos.

qualitative predictions Predictions that deal with descriptions, observable data, or non-numerical data.

predicciones cualitatives Las predicciones de que tratan los datos numéricos o datos cuantificables.

quantitative predictions Predictions that deal with numerical data or measurable data.

predicciones cuantitatives Las predicciones que tienen que ver con las descripciones, datos observables, o los datos no numéricos.

quarter circle One-fourth of a circle. The formula for the area of a quarter circle is $A = \frac{1}{4}\pi r^2$.

cuarto círculo Un cuarto do un círculo. La fórmula de la superficie de un cuarto círculo es $A = \frac{1}{4}\pi r^2$.

quartile A value that divides the data set into four equal parts.

cuartil Valor que divide el conjunto de datos en cuatro partes iguales.

Rr

radical sign The symbol used to indicate a nonnegative square root, $\sqrt{\ }$.

signo radical Símbolo que se usa para indicar una raíz cuadrada no negativa, $\sqrt{\ }$.

radius The distance from the center of a circle to any point on the circle.

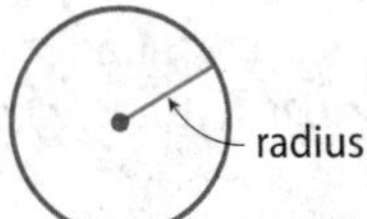

radio Distancia desde el centro de un círculo hasta cualquiera de sus puntos.

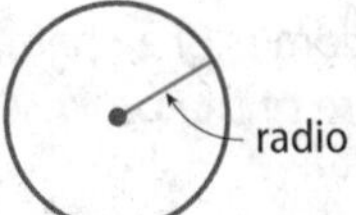

random Outcomes occur at random if each outcome occurs by chance. For example, rolling a number on a number cube occurs at random.

azar Los resultados ocurren aleatoriamente si cada resultado ocurre por casualidad. Por ejemplo, sacar un número en un cubo numerado ocurre al azar.

range The set of output values for a function.

rango Conjunto de valores de salida para una función.

range The difference between the greatest and least data value.

rango La diferencia entre el número mayor y el menor en un conjunto de datos.

rate A ratio that compares two quantities with different kinds of units.

tasa Razón que compara dos cantidades que tienen distintas unidades de medida.

rate of change A rate that describes how one quantity changes in relation to another. A rate of change is usually expressed as a unit rate.

tasa de cambio Tasa que describe cómo cambia una cantidad con respecto a otra. Por lo general, se expresa como tasa unitaria.

rational numbers The set of numbers that can be written in the form $\frac{a}{b}$, where a and b are integers and $b \neq 0$.
Examples: $1 = \frac{1}{1}, \frac{2}{9}, -2.3 = -2\frac{3}{10}$

números racionales Conjunto de números que puede escribirse en la forma $\frac{a}{b}$ donde a y b son números enteros y $b \neq 0$.
Ejemplos: $1 = \frac{1}{1}, \frac{2}{9}, -2.3 = -2\frac{3}{10}$

real numbers A set made up of rational and irrational numbers.

números reales Conjunto de números racionales e irracionales.

rebate A partial return or refund on an amount paid.

reembolso Reintegro o devolución parcial de una cantidad pagada.

reciprocal The multiplicative inverse of a number.

recíproco El inverso multiplicativo de un número.

rectangle A parallelogram having four right angles.

rectángulo Paralelogramo con cuatro ángulos rectos.

rectangular prism A prism that has two parallel congruent bases that are rectangles.

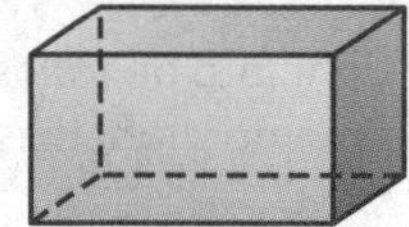

prisma rectangular Un prisma con dos bases paralelas congruentes que son rectángulos.

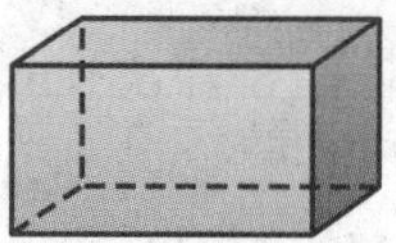

reduction An image smaller than the original.

reducción Imagen más pequeña que la original.

regular polygon A polygon that has all sides congruent and all angles congruent.

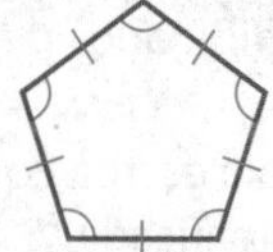

polígono regular Polígono con todos los lados y todos los ángulos congruentes.

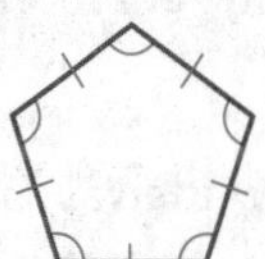

regular pyramid A pyramid whose base is a regular polygon and in which the segment from the vertex to the center of the base is the altitude.

pirámide regular Pirámide cuya base es un polígono regular y en la cual el segmento desde el vértice hasta el centro de la base es la altura.

relative frequency A ratio that compares the frequency of each category to the total.

frecuencia relativa Razón que compara la frecuencia de cada categoría al total.

repeating decimal A decimal whose digits repeat in groups of one or more.

decimal periódico Una decimal cuyos dígitos se repiten en grupos de uno o más.

rhombus A parallelogram having four congruent sides.

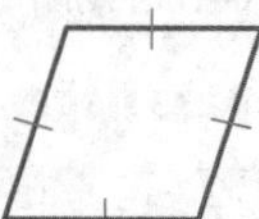

rombo Paralelogramo que tiene cuatro lados congruentes.

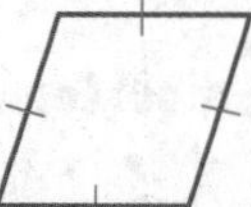

right angle An angle that measures exactly 90°.

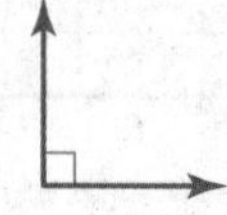

ángulo recto Ángulo que mide exactamente 90°.

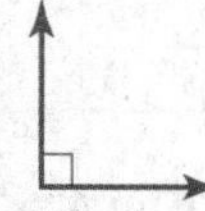

right triangle A triangle having one right angle.

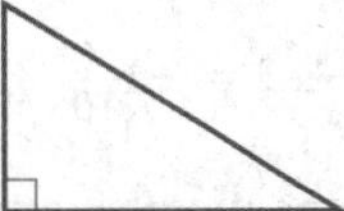

triángulo rectángulo Triángulo que tiene un ángulo recto.

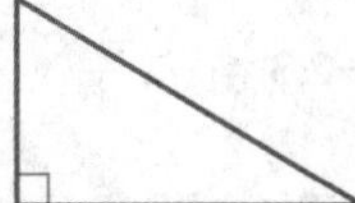

Ss

sales tax An additional amount of money charged on items that people buy.

impuesto sobre las ventas Cantidad adicional de dinero que se cobra sobre los artículos que compra la gente.

sample A randomly selected group chosen for the purpose of collecting data.

muestra Grupo escogido al azar o aleatoriamente que se usa con el propósito de recoger datos.

sample space The set of all possible outcomes of a probability experiment.

espacio muestral Conjunto de todos los resultados posibles de un experimento probabilístico.

scale The scale that gives the ratio that compares the measurements of a drawing or model to the measurements of the real object.

escala Razón que compara las medidas de un dibujo o modelo a las medidas del objeto real.

scale drawing A drawing that is used to represent objects that are too large or too small to be drawn at actual size.

dibujo a escala Dibujo que se usa para representar objetos que son demasiado grandes o demasiado pequeños como para dibujarlos de tamaño natural.

scale factor A scale written as a ratio without units in simplest form.

factor de escala Escala escrita como una razón sin unidades en forma simplificada.

scale model A model used to represent objects that are too large or too small to be built at actual size.

modelo a escala Réplica de un objeto real, el cual es demasiado grande o demasiado pequeño como para construirlo de tamaño natural.

scalene triangle A triangle having no congruent sides.

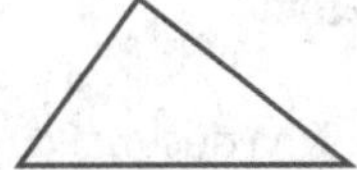

triángulo escaleno Triángulo sin lados congruentes.

scatter plot In a scatter plot, two sets of related data are plotted as ordered pairs on the same graph.

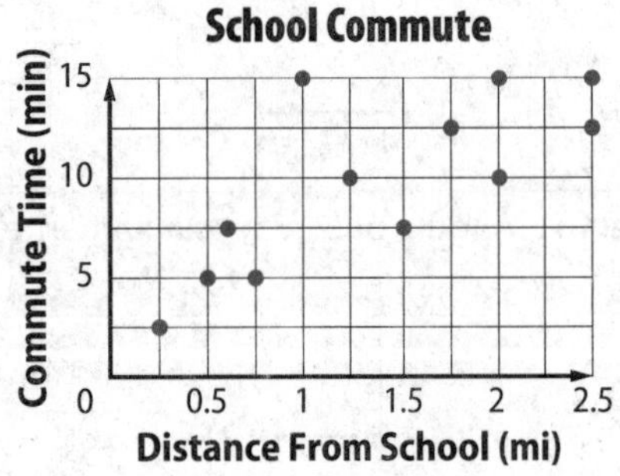

diagrama de dispersión Diagrama en que dos conjuntos de datos relacionados aparecen graficados como pares ordenados en la misma gráfica.

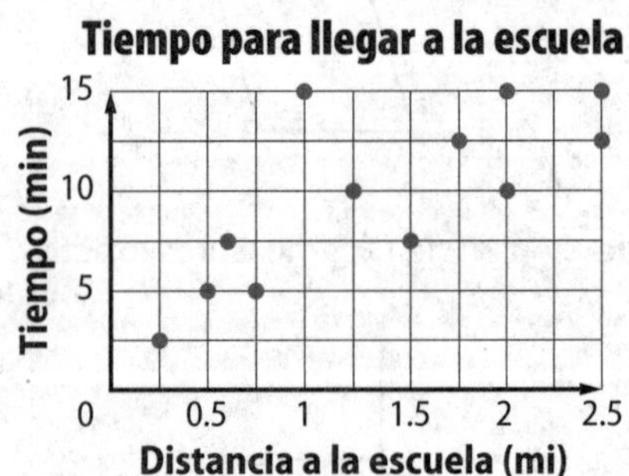

selling price The amount the customer pays for an item.

precio de venta Cantidad de dinero que paga un consumidor por un artículo.

semicircle Half of a circle. The formula for the area of a semicircle is $A = \frac{1}{2}\pi r^2$.

semicírculo Medio círculo La fórmula para el área de un semicírculo es $A = \frac{1}{2}\pi r^2$.

sequence An ordered list of numbers, such as 0, 1, 2, 3 or 2, 4, 6, 8.

sucesión Lista ordenada de números, como 0, 1, 2, 3 ó 2, 4, 6, 8.

similar figures Figures that have the same shape but not necessarily the same size.

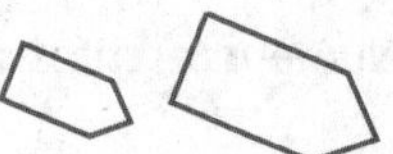

figuras semejantes Figuras que tienen la misma forma, pero no necesariamente el mismo tamaño.

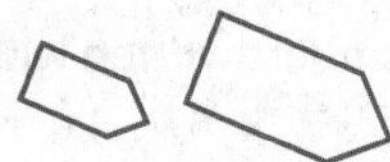

similar solids Solids with the same shape. Their corresponding linear measures are proportional.

sólidos semejantes Sólidos con la misma forma. Sus medidas lineales correspondientes son proporcionales.

simple event One outcome or a collection of outcomes.

eventos simples Un resultado o una colección de resultados.

simple interest The amount paid or earned for the use of money. The formula for simple interest is $I = prt$.

interés simple Cantidad que se paga o que se gana por el uso del dinero. La fórmula para calcular el interés simple es $I = prt$.

simple random sample An unbiased sample where each item or person in the population is as likely to be chosen as any other.

muestra aleatoria simple Muestra de una población que tiene la misma probabilidad de escogerse que cualquier otra.

simplest form An expression is in simplest form when it is replaced by an equivalent expression having no like terms or parentheses.

expresión mínima Expresión en su forma más simple cuando es reemplazada por una expresión equivalente que no tiene términos similares ni paréntesis.

simplify Write an expression in simplest form.

simplificar Escribir una expresión en su forma más simple.

simulation An experiment that is designed to model the action in a given situation.

simulación Un experimento diseñado para modelar la acción en una situación dada.

slant height The height of each lateral face.

altura oblicua Altura de cada cara lateral.

slope The rate of change between any two points on a line. It is the ratio of vertical change to horizontal change. The slope tells how steep the line is.

pendiente Razón de cambio entre cualquier par de puntos en una recta. Es la razón del cambio vertical al cambio horizontal. La pendiente indica el grado de inclinación de la recta.

slope-intercept form An equation written in the form $y = mx + b$, where m is the slope and b is the y-intercept.

forma pendiente intersección Ecuación de la forma $y = mx + b$, donde m es la pendiente y b es la intersección y.

solution A replacement value for the variable in an open sentence. A value for the variable that makes an equation true. Example: The *solution* of $12 = x + 7$ is 5.

solución Valor de reemplazo de la variable en un enunciado abierto. Valor de la variable que hace que una ecuación sea verdadera. Ejemplo: La *solución* de $12 = x + 7$ es 5.

square The product of a number and itself. 36 is the square of 6.

square A parallelogram having four right angles and four congruent sides.

square root The factors multiplied to form perfect squares.

squared The product of a number and itself. 36 is the square of 6.

standard form Numbers written without exponents.

statistics The study of collecting, organizing, and interpreting data.

straight angle An angle that measures exactly 180°.

Subtraction Property of Equality If you subtract the same number from each side of an equation, the two sides remain equal.

Subtraction Property of Inequality If you subtract the same number from each side of an inequality, the inequality remains true.

supplementary angles Two angles are supplementary if the sum of their measures is 180°.

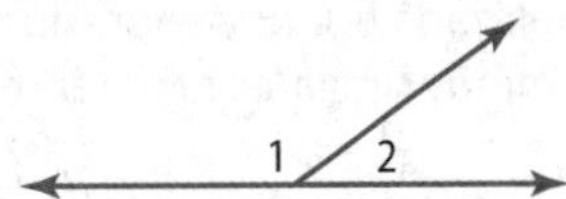

$\angle 1$ and $\angle 2$ are supplementary angles.

surface area The sum of the areas of all the surfaces (faces) of a three-dimensional figure.

survey A question or set of questions designed to collect data about a specific group of people, or population.

systematic random sample A sample where the items or people are selected according to a specific time or item interval.

cuadrado Producto de un número por sí mismo. 36 es el cuadrado de 6.

cuadrado Paralelogramo con cuatro ángulos rectos y cuatro lados congruentes.

al cuadrado Factores multiplicados para formar cuadrados perfectos.

raíz cuadrada El producto de un número por sí mismo. 36 es el cuadrado de 6.

forma estándar Números escritos sin exponentes.

estadística Estudio que consiste en recopilar, organizar e interpretar datos.

ángulo llano Ángulo que mide exactamente 180°.

propiedad de sustracción de la igualdad Si restas el mismo número de ambos lados de una ecuación, los dos lados permanecen iguales.

propiedad de desigualdad en la resta Si se resta el mismo número a cada lado de una desigualdad, la desigualdad sigue siendo verdadera.

ángulos suplementarios Dos ángulos son suplementarios si la suma de sus medidas es 180°.

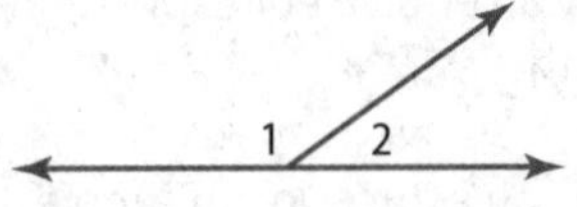

$\angle 1$ y $\angle 2$ son suplementarios.

área de superficie La suma de las áreas de todas las superficies (caras) de una figura tridimensional.

encuesta Pregunta o conjunto de preguntas diseñadas para recoger datos sobre un grupo específico de personas o población.

muestra aleatoria sistemática Muestra en que los elementos o personas se eligen según un intervalo de tiempo o elemento específico.

term Each number in a sequence.

term A number, a variable, or a product or quotient of numbers and variables.

término Cada número en una sucesión.

término Número, variable, producto o cociente de números y de variables.

terminating decimal A repeating decimal which has a repeating digit of 0.

theoretical probability The ratio of the number of ways an event can occur to the number of possible outcomes. It is based on what *should* happen when conducting a probability experiment.

three-dimensional figure A figure with length, width, and height.

third quartile For a data set with median M, the third quartile is the median of the data values greater than M.

tip Also known as a gratuity, it is a small amount of money in return for a service.

transversal The third line formed when two parallel lines are intersected.

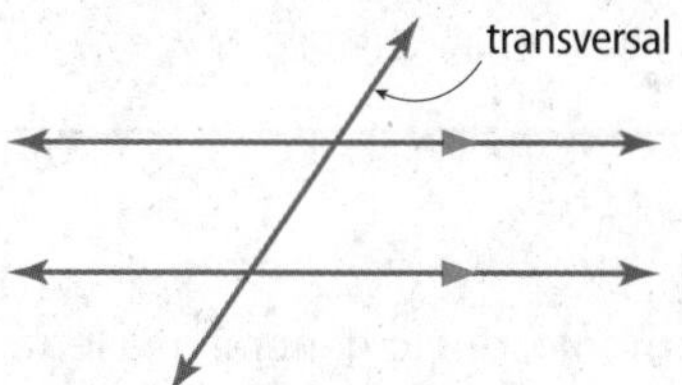

trapezoid A quadrilateral with one pair of parallel sides.

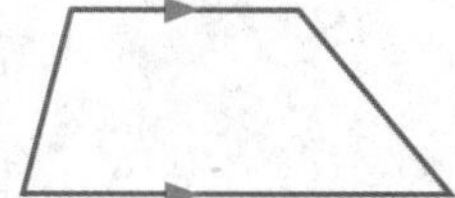

tree diagram A diagram used to show the sample space.

triangle A figure with three sides and three angles.

triangular prism A prism that has two parallel congruent bases that are triangles.

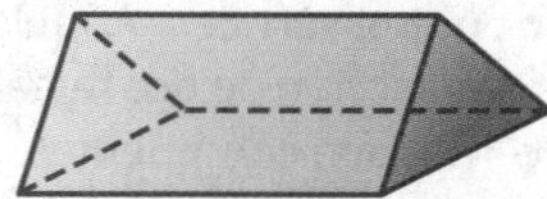

two-step equation An equation having two different operations.

two-step inequality An inequality than contains two operations.

decimal finito Un decimal periódico que tiene un dígito que se repite que es 0.

probabilidad teórica Razón del número de maneras en que puede ocurrir un evento al número de resultados posibles. Se basa en lo que *debería* pasar cuando se conduce un experimento probabilístico.

figura tridimensional Figura que tiene largo, ancho y alto.

tercer cuartil Para un conjunto de datos con la mediana M, el tercer cuartil es la mediana de los valores mayores que M.

propina También conocida como gratificación; es una cantidad pequeña de dinero en recompensa por un servicio.

transversal Tercera recta que se forma cuando se intersecan dos rectas paralelas.

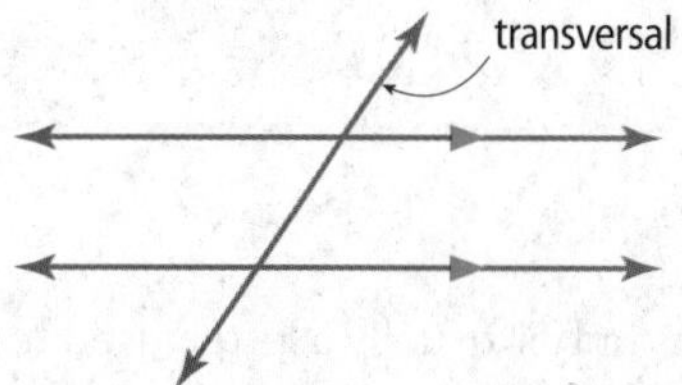

trapecio Cuadrilátero con un único par de lados paralelos.

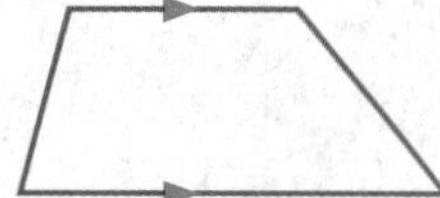

diagrama de árbol Diagrama que se usa para mostrar el espacio muestral.

triángulo Figura con tres lados y tres ángulos.

prisma triangular Un prisma que tiene dos bases congruentes paralelas que triángulos.

ecuación de dos pasos Ecuación que contiene dos operaciones distintas.

desigualdad de dos pasos Desigualdad que contiene dos operaciones.

unbiased sample A sample representative of the entire population.

muestra no sesgada Muestra que se selecciona de modo que se representativa de la población entera.

unfair game A game where there is not a chance of each player being equally likely to win.

juego injusto Juego donde cada jugador no tiene la misma posibilidad de ganar.

uniform probability model A probability model which assigns equal probability to all outcomes.

modelo de probabilidad uniforme Un modelo de probabilidad que asigna igual probabilidad a todos los resultados.

unit rate A rate that is simplified so that it has a denominator of 1 unit.

tasa unitaria Tasa simplificada para que tenga un denominador igual a 1.

unit ratio A unit rate where the denominator is one unit.

razón unitaria Tasa unitaria en que el denominador es la unidad.

unlike fractions Fractions with different denominators.

fracciones con distinto denominador Fracciones cuyos denominadores son diferentes.

variable A symbol, usually a letter, used to represent a number in mathematical expressions or sentences.

variable Símbolo, por lo general una letra, que se usa para representar un número en expresiones o enunciados matemáticos.

variable expenses Costs that do change based on the amount that is used.

gastos variables Costos que cambian con la cantidad usada.

vertex A vertex of an angle is the common endpoint of the rays forming the angle.

vertex

vértice El vértice de un ángulo es el extremo común de los rayos que lo forman.

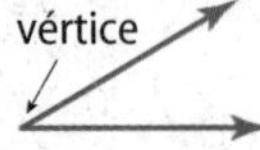

vertex The point where three or more faces of a polyhedron intersect.

vértice El punto donde tres o más caras de un poliedro se cruzan.

vertical angles Opposite angles formed by the intersection of two lines. Vertical angles are congruent.

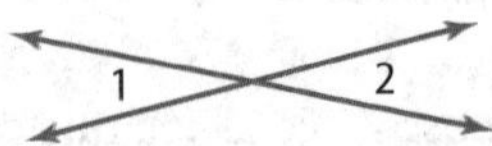

$\angle 1$ and $\angle 2$ are vertical angles.

ángulos opuestos por el vértice Ángulos opuestos formados por la intersección de dos rectas. Los ángulos opuestos por el vértice son congruentes.

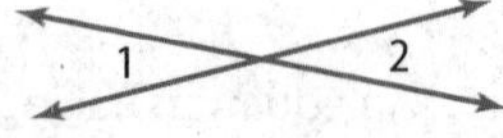

$\angle 1$ y $\angle 2$ son ángulos opuestos por el vértice.

volume The number of cubic units needed to fill the space occupied by a solid.

volumen Número de unidades cúbicas que se requieren para llenar el espacio que ocupa un sólido.

voluntary response sample A sample which involves only those who want to participate in the sampling.

muestra de respuesta voluntaria Muestra que involucra sólo aquellos que quieren participar en el muestreo.

Ww

wages Payments for labor or services.

remuneración Pago por trabajo o servicios.

Xx

***x*-axis** The horizontal number line in a coordinate plane.

eje *x* La recta numérica horizontal en el plano de coordenadas.

***x*-coordinate** The first number of an ordered pair. It corresponds to a number on the *x*-axis.

coordenada *x* El primer número de un par ordenado. Corresponde a un número en el eje *x*.

Yy

***y*-axis** The vertical number line in a coordinate plane.

eje *y* La recta numérica vertical en el plano de coordenadas.

***y*-coordinate** The second number of an ordered pair. It corresponds to a number on the *y*-axis.

coordenada *y* El segundo número de un par ordenado. Corresponde a un número en el eje *y*.

***y*-intercept** The *y*-coordinate of the point where the line crosses the *y*-axis.

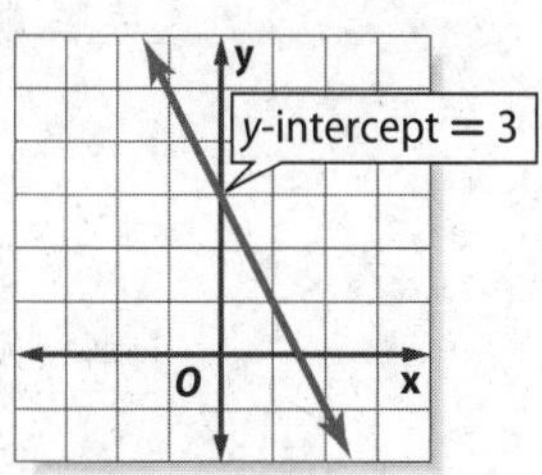

intersección *y* La coordenada *y* del punto donde cruza la gráfica el eje *y*.

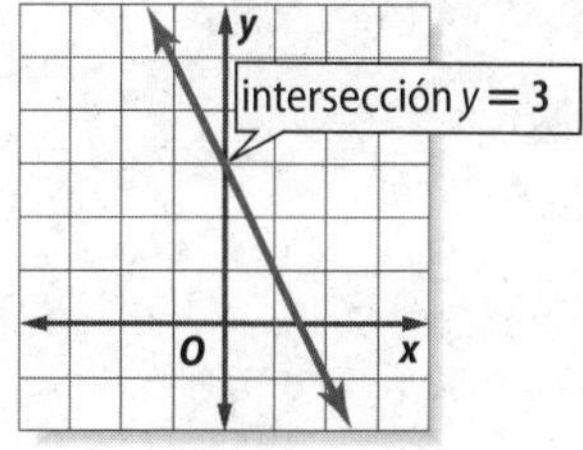

Zz

zero pair The result when one positive counter is paired with one negative counter. The value of a zero pair is 0.

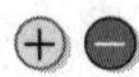

par nulo Resultado de hacer coordinar una ficha positiva con una negativa. El valor de un par nulo es 0.

Chapter 1 Rational Numbers

Page 22 Chapter 1 Are You Ready?

1. $\frac{2}{3}$ **3.** $\frac{8}{11}$

4–7.

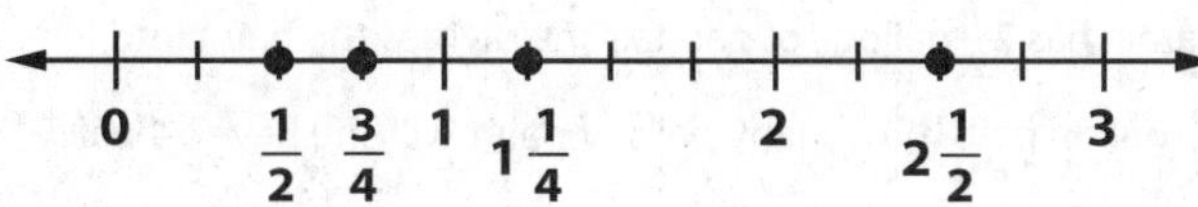

Pages 31–32 Lesson 1-1 Independent Practice

1. 0.5 **3** 0.125 **5.** −0.66 **7.** 5.875 **9.** $-0.\overline{8}$ **11.** $-0.\overline{72}$ **13.** $-\frac{1}{5}$ **15.** $5\frac{24}{25}$ **17** $10\frac{1}{2}$ cm **19.** Sample answer: $\frac{3}{5}$ **21.** Sample answer: $3\frac{1}{7} \approx 3.14286$ and $3\frac{10}{71} \approx 3.14085$; Since 3.1415926... is between $3\frac{1}{7}$ and $3\frac{10}{71}$, Archimedes was correct. **23.** Sample answer: Jason was building a cabin. He cut a board to the length of $8\frac{7}{16}$ feet long.

Page 34 Lesson 1-1 Multi-Step Problem Solving

25. C **27.** 0.125

Pages 41–42 Lesson 1-2 Independent Practice

1. >;

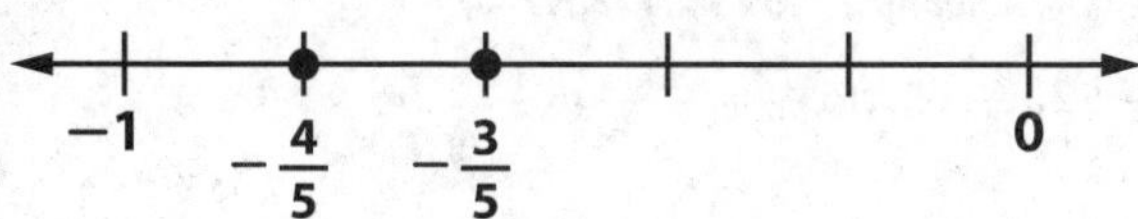

3. > **5** first quiz **7.** $-\frac{5}{8}$, −0.62, −0.615 **9** < **11.** Yes; $69\frac{1}{8} < 69\frac{6}{8}$. **13.** Sample answer: $\frac{63}{32}$ is closest to 2 because the difference of $\frac{63}{32}$ and 2 is the least. **15.** greatest to least; Sample answer: Since the numerators are the same, the values of the fractions decrease as the denominators increase.

Page 44 Lesson 1-2 Multi-Step Problem Solving

17. D **19.** 0.875

Pages 49–50 Lesson 1-3 Independent Practice

1. −11 **3** 14 **5.** −61 **7.** 15 **9.** −9 **11** 224 + (−131) + 67 + (−163); Her final elevation is −3 feet which means she is 3 feet lower than her starting elevation. **13.** Lubbock; 131°F **15.** Sample answer: At midnight the temperature was 0°F. From midnight to 3:00 A.M., the temperature dropped 5°F. From 3:00 A.M. to 6:00 A.M., the temperature rose 4°F. What was the temperature at 6:00 A.M.? **17.** Sample answer: 5 − 15 and −13 − (−3); 5 + (−15) and −13 + 3; To subtract an integer is to add its additive inverse.

Pages 51–52 Lesson 1-3 Multi-Step Problem Solving

19. B **21.** $35 **23.** They each have a final score of +30.

Pages 57–58 Lesson 1-4 Independent Practice

1. 42 **3.** −13 **5.** −5 **7** 72 **9.** −2 **11.** −4,900 ft **13** −8 minutes per mile **15.** [157 + (−85) + (−38) + (−18)] ÷ 4; $4 **17a.** positive; the product of two negative numbers is always a positive number. **17b.** negative; the product of three negative numbers is always a negative number. **17c.** positive; the product of four negative numbers is always a positive number. **17d.** negative; the product of five negative numbers is always a negative number. **19a.** false; 3 − 5 = −2 **19b.** true

Page 60 Lesson 1-4 Multi-Step Problem Solving

21. A **23.** 29.84°F

Page 63 Focus on Mathematical Processes

1. $374.40 **3.** Add 2 to the first term, 3 to the second, 4 to the third, and so on; 15, 21, 28.

Pages 73–74 Lesson 1-5 Independent Practice

1. $1\frac{4}{7}$ **3.** $-\frac{2}{3}$ **5** $-1\frac{1}{2}$ **7** $\frac{3}{14}$ **9a.** $\frac{33}{100}$ **9b.** $\frac{67}{100}$ **9c.** $\frac{41}{100}$ **11.** She needed to add the numerators and write the sum over the denominator. Instead, she also added the denominators. The correct sum is $-\frac{1}{7}$. **13.** $\frac{21}{15} = 1\frac{2}{5}$ **15.** always; $\frac{5}{12} - \left(-\frac{1}{12}\right) = \frac{5}{12} + \frac{1}{12} = \frac{6}{12}$ or $\frac{1}{2}$

Page 76 Lesson 1-5 Multi-Step Problem Solving

17. A **19.** 30 minutes

Pages 81–82 Lesson 1-6 Independent Practice

1 $\frac{13}{24}$ **3.** $1\frac{2}{5}$ **5.** $\frac{4}{9}$ **7.** $-\frac{26}{45}$ **9.** $1\frac{11}{18}$ **11** Subtraction; Sample answer: To determine how much time remained, subtract $\left(\frac{1}{6} + \frac{1}{4}\right)$ from $\frac{2}{3}$; $\frac{1}{4}$ h

13.

Homework	Fraction of Time	
	Pepita	Francisco
Math	$\frac{1}{6}$	$\frac{1}{2}$
English	$\frac{2}{3}$	$\frac{1}{8}$
Science	$\frac{1}{6}$	$\frac{3}{8}$

15. Sample answer: Let $\frac{1}{a}$ and $\frac{1}{b}$ represent the unit fractions, where a and b are not zero. Multiply the first numerator by b and the second numerator by a. Express the product over the denominator ab. Express in simplest form. **17.** $\frac{5}{12}$; Sample answer: $\frac{1}{6}$ of the bucket will be filled with one faucet, while another $\frac{1}{4}$ of the bucket will be filled by the other faucet. Add these fractions to determine the sum.

Page 84 Lesson 1-6 Multi-Step Problem Solving

19. A **21.** 0.5

Pages 89–90 Lesson 1-7 Independent Practice

1. $9\frac{5}{9}$ **3.** $8\frac{3}{5}$ **5** $7\frac{5}{12}$ **7.** $4\frac{14}{15}$ **9.** $4\frac{1}{3}$ **11** Subtraction; the width is shorter than the length; $1\frac{3}{4}$ ft **13.** −5

15. $13\frac{5}{9}$ **17.** Sample answer: A board with a length of $3\frac{7}{8}$ ft needs to be cut from a $5\frac{1}{2}$-foot existing board. How much wood will be left after the cut is made?; $1\frac{5}{8}$ ft

19. Sample answer:

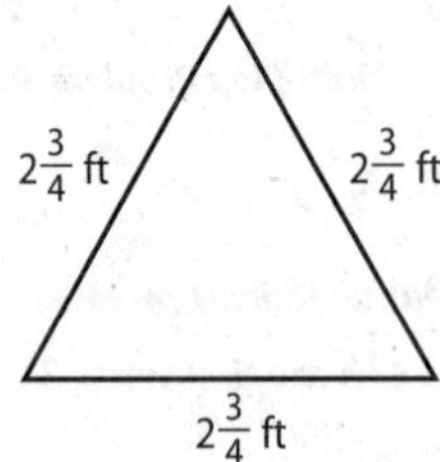

Pages 91–92 Lesson 1-7 Multi-Step Problem Solving

21. B **23.** $52\frac{1}{2}$ inches **25.** $\left(1\frac{1}{3}, -14\frac{1}{6}\right)$; yes. Sample answer: The first point has a negative x-coordinate and a negative y-coordinate, so it lies in Quadrant III. The second point has a positive x-coordinate and a negative y-coordinate, so it lies in Quadrant IV.

Pages 97–98 Lesson 1-8 Independent Practice

1. $\frac{3}{32}$ **3.** $-4\frac{1}{2}$ **5.** $\frac{1}{6}$ **7** $\frac{3}{8}$ **9.** −1 **11** $\frac{1}{16}$

13. $\frac{1}{3} \times \left(\frac{11}{16}\right) = \frac{11}{48}$ **15.** Sample answer: Three fourths of the students at Walnut Middle School were on the honor roll. Of that group, only $\frac{1}{8}$ of them received all As. What fraction of the students received all As? **17.** Sample answer: $\frac{1}{2} \times \frac{2}{3} = \frac{2}{6}$ or $\frac{1}{3}$

Pages 99–100 Lesson 1-8 Multi-Step Problem Solving

19. C **21.** 21,120 yards **23.** $\frac{1}{200}$; Quizzes and Tests; Sample answer: Quizzes and Tests represent $\frac{7}{10}$ of his grade. Quizzes and Homework represent $\frac{6}{10}$ of his grade, and $\frac{7}{10} > \frac{6}{10}$.

Pages 105–106 Lesson 1-9 Independent Practice

1. $\frac{7}{16}$ **3** $\frac{1}{15}$ **5.** $\frac{2}{9}$ **7** 84 movies

9. $1\frac{1}{4}$;

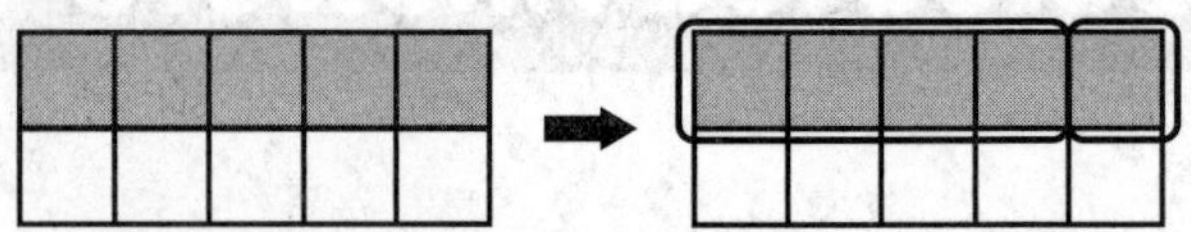

Sample answer: The model above shows that one half of a rectangle with ten sections is five sections. Two fifths of ten sections is four sections. The model on the right shows the five sections divided into $1\frac{1}{4}$ groups of four sections.

11. $\frac{1}{6}$ of a dozen; 2 folders **13.** $\frac{10}{3}$ **15.** Sample answer: Jamie has $2\frac{1}{2}$ gallons of paint. If she divides the paint into $\frac{5}{8}$-gallon pails, how many pails of paint will she have?; 4 pails

Page 108 Lesson 1-9 Multi-Step Problem Solving

17. \$0.48 per pound **19.** 9 bowls

Page 111 Chapter Review Vocabulary Check

1. bar notation **3.** repeating **5.** like fractions

Page 112 Chapter Review Key Concept Check

1. $\frac{3}{5}$ **3.** denominator

Page 113 Chapter Review Multi-Step Problem Solving

5. Trinity

Chapter 2 Proportional Relationships

Page 118 Chapter 2 Are You Ready?

1. $\frac{2}{15}$ **3.** $\frac{1}{51}$ **5.** No; $\frac{12}{20} = \frac{3}{5}, \frac{15}{30} = \frac{1}{2}$

Pages 127–128 Lesson 2-1 Independent Practice

1. 60 mi/h **3** 3.5 m/s **5.** Sample answer: about \$0.50 per pair **7.** 510 words **9** **a.** 20.04 mi/h **b.** about 1.5 h **11.** Sample answer: He should have divided \$5.49 by 10 to get 0.549 or \$0.55 each. **13.** Sometimes; a ratio that compares two measurements with different units is a rate, such as $\frac{2 \text{ miles}}{10 \text{ minutes}}$. **15.** Sample answer: Julie drove 120 miles in 2 hours to visit her friends; 60 miles per hour

Pages 129–130 Lesson 2-1 Multi-Step Problem Solving

17. D **19.** \$4.80 **21.** 25 meters

Pages 135–136 Lesson 2-2 Independent Practice

1. $1\frac{1}{2}$ **3** $\frac{4}{27}$ **5.** $\frac{2}{25}$ **7** \$6 per yard **9.** $\frac{5}{6}$ page per minute **11.** $\frac{39}{250}$ **13.** $\frac{11}{200}$ **15.** $\frac{14}{13}$ or $1\frac{1}{13}$ times larger **17.** Sample answer: $\frac{\frac{1}{32}}{\frac{1}{8}}, \frac{\frac{1}{2}}{\frac{1}{2}}, \frac{\frac{1}{16}}{\frac{1}{4}}$ **19.** $12\frac{1}{2}$ mph

Page 138 Lesson 2-2 Multi-Step Problem Solving

21. C **23.** 105 miles

Pages 143–144 Lesson 2-3 Independent Practice

1 115 mi/h **3** 322,000 m/h **5.** 6.1 mi/h **7.** 7,200 Mb/h
9. more; Sample answer: Since inches are smaller than feet, it will take more inches to make equivalent rates. **11.** 500 ft/min; Sample answer: All of the other rates are equal to 60 miles per hour.

Pages 145–146 Lesson 2-3 Multi-Step Problem Solving

13. 4.35 **15.** 400 **17.** no; Sample answer: The rates are equivalent. If you use dimensional analysis to convert 3,000 grams per week to kilograms per week, you will determine they are equal rates.

Pages 151–152 Lesson 2-4 Independent Practice

1 Yes; the time to water ratios are all equal to $\frac{1}{225}$.

Time (days)	1	2	3	4
Water (L)	225	450	675	900

3. The table for Desmond's Time shows a proportional relationship. The ratio between the time and the number of laps is always 73.

5 **a.** yes; Sample answer:

Side Length (units)	1	2	3	4
Perimeter (units)	4	8	12	16

The side length to perimeter ratio for side lengths of 1, 2, 3 and 4 units is $\frac{1}{4}$, $\frac{2}{8}$ or $\frac{1}{4}$, $\frac{3}{12}$ or $\frac{1}{4}$, $\frac{4}{16}$ or $\frac{1}{4}$. Since these ratios are all equal to $\frac{1}{4}$, the measure of the side length of a square is proportional to the square's perimeter.

5b. no; Sample answer:

Side Length (units)	1	2	3	4
Area (units^2)	1	4	9	16

The side length to area ratio for side lengths of 1, 2, 3 and 4 units is $\frac{1}{1}$ or 1, $\frac{2}{4}$, or $\frac{1}{2}$, $\frac{3}{9}$ or $\frac{1}{3}$, $\frac{4}{16}$ or $\frac{1}{4}$. Since these ratios are not all equal, the measure of the side length of a square is not proportional to the square's area. **7.** It is not proportional because the ratio of laps to time is not consistent; $\ne \frac{6}{2} \ne \frac{8}{3} \ne \frac{10}{4}$. **9.** Sample answer: Store A always has 2 red flowers for every 8 pink flowers in a bouquet. Store B always has 3 more pink flowers than red flowers in a bouquet. The bouquet for Store A is a proportional relationship, while the bouquet for Store B is nonproportional.

Page 154 Lesson 2-4 Multi-Step Problem Solving

1. 10.5 **13.** $8,400

Page 157 Focus on Mathematical Processes

1. $\frac{3}{8}$ pie **3.** $\frac{3}{5}$ mi

Pages 163–164 Lesson 2-5 Independent Practice

1 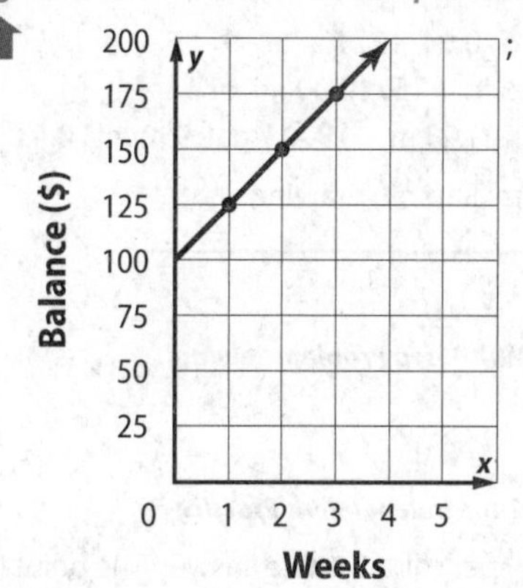

;

Not proportional; The graph does not pass through the origin.
3 Plant B; The graph is a straight line through the origin.
5. Proportional; Sample answer: The ordered pairs would be (0, 0), (1, 35), (2, 70). This would be a straight line through the origin.

7. 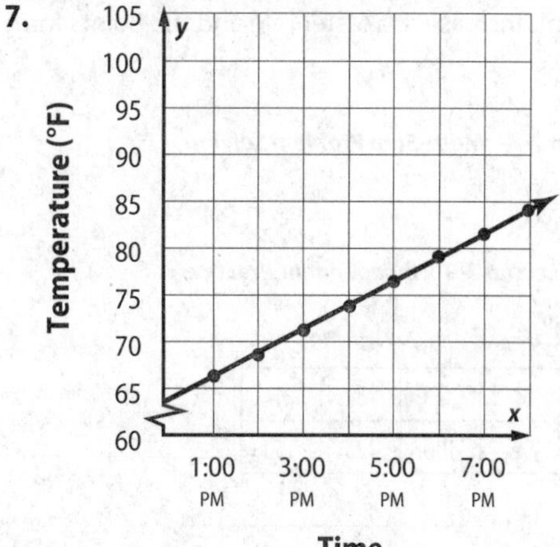

;

Not proportional; The graph does not pass through the origin.

Pages 165–166 Lesson 2-5 Multi-Step Problem Solving

9. D **11.** 120 ft **13.** Gym A; $21; Sample answer: Gym A charges $38 per month, so a year membership would cost $456. Gym B has an annual fee of $15, plus $35 per month, so a year membership would cost $435. So, Gym A costs $21 more per year.

Pages 173–174 Lesson 2-6 Independent Practice

1 40 **3.** 3.5 **5.** $\frac{2}{5} = \frac{x}{20}$; 8 ounces **7** $c = 0.50p$; $4.00
9. $\frac{360}{3} = \frac{n}{7}$; 840 visitors **11.** 22 **13.** 5 **15.** 6 **17.** Sample answer: The product of the length and width is constant. The length is not proportional to the width. The proportions are not equal.

Pages 175–176 Lesson 2-6 Multi-Step Problem Solving

19. B **21.** Car A: 40 km/gal **23.** 20 pencils

Pages 181–182 Lesson 2-7 Independent Practice

1. 12.7 **3.** 128.17 **5.** 0.04 **7.** 15.75 **9.** 1.5 **11.** 887.21 mL **13.** 1.5 lb **15.** 1,000 mL or 1 L **17.** 0.031 m, 0.1 ft, 0.6 in., 1.2 cm **19.** 0.7 gal, 950 mL, 0.4 L, $1\frac{1}{4}$ c **21.** 5.4 cm; 6.7 cm; Sample drawing:

Page 184 Lesson 2-7 Multi-Step Problem Solving

23. A **25.** 1,065 mL

Pages 191–192 Lesson 2-8 Independent Practice

1. 6 m per s **3.** \$9 per shirt; Sample answer: The point (0, 0) represents 0 T-shirts purchased and 0 dollars spent. The point (1, 9) represents 9 dollars spent for 1 T-shirt. **5.** 10 inches per hour **7.** Sample answer:

Feet	3	6	9	12
Inches	18	36	54	72

9. Sample answer: sequence *B*; Since the common difference is greater, its terms increase at a faster rate and the points form a steeper line.

Page 194 Lesson 2-8 Multi-Step Problem Solving

11. D **13.** 355

Pages 199–200 Lesson 2-9 Independent Practice

1. 30 lb per bag

3.

Time (h)	1	2	3	4
Charge (\$)	75	100	125	150

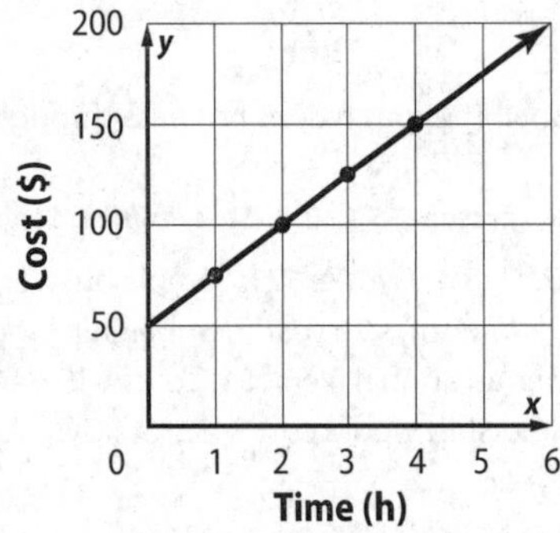

no; sample answer: $\frac{75}{1} \neq \frac{100}{2}$; Because there is no constant ratio and the line does not go through the origin, there is no direct variation. **5.** no **7.** no **9.** $y = \frac{7}{4}x$; 21 **11.** $y = \frac{1}{4}x$; −28 **13.** Sample answer: 9; $5\frac{1}{2}$; 36; 22

15. 19.6 cm;

Page 202 Lesson 2-9 Multi-Step Problem Solving

17. A **19.** 20 cupcakes

Page 205 Chapter Review Vocabulary Check

1. rate **3.** ordered **5.** direct **7.** quadrant **9.** change

Page 206 Chapter Review Key Concept Check

1. denominator **3.** proportional

Page 207 Chapter Review Multi-Step Problem Solving

5. 200 seconds

Chapter 3 Apply Proportionality to Percent

Page 212 Chapter 3 Are You Ready?

1. 48 **3.** \$70 **5.** 72.5% **7.** 92%

Pages 223–234 Lesson 3-1 Independent Practice

1. 120.9 **3.** \$147.20 **5.** 17.5 **7.** 1.3 **9.** 30.1 **11.** \$7.19 at Pirate Bay, \$4.46 at Funtopia, \$9.62 at Zoomland **13.** 4 **15.** 0.61 **17.** 520 **19.** 158 **21.** 0.14 **23.** Sample answer: It is easiest to use a fraction when the denominator of the fraction is a multiple of the number. If this is not the case, a decimal may be easier to use. **25.** Sample answer: saving 15% of my income, tipping 20% at a restaurant

Page 226 Lesson 3-1 Multi-Step Problem Solving

27. B **29.** \$11.15

Pages 231–232 Lesson 3-2 Independent Practice

1. 35; $\frac{1}{2} \cdot 70 = 35$; $0.1 \cdot 70 = 7$ and $5 \cdot 7 = 35$ **3.** 18; $\frac{1}{5} \cdot 90 = 18$; $0.1 \cdot 90 = 9$ and $2 \cdot 9 = 18$ **5.** 168; $\frac{7}{10} \cdot 240 = 168$; $0.1 \cdot 240 = 24$ and $7 \cdot 24 = 168$ **7.** 720; $(2 \cdot 320) + \left(\frac{1}{4} \cdot 320\right) = 720$ **9.** 2; $0.01 \cdot 500 = 5$ and $\frac{2}{5} \cdot 5 =$ **11.** about 96 mi; $0.01 \cdot 12{,}000 = 120$ and $\frac{4}{5} \cdot 120 = 96$

13. 6; $\frac{2}{3} \cdot 9 = 6$ **15.** 24; $\frac{1}{10} \cdot 240 = 24$ **17a.** Sample answer: about 60 cans; $129\% - 100\% = 29\%$; $29\% \approx 30\%$; $0.3 \times 200 = 60$ **17b.** Sample answer: about 390 cans; $260 + 0.5 \times 260 = 390$ **19.** sometimes; Sample answer: one estimate for 37% of 60 is $\frac{2}{5} \cdot 60 = 24$. Since $\frac{2}{5} = 40\%$ and $40\% > 37\%$, 24 is greater than the actual percent.

Pages 233–234 Lesson 3-2 Multi-Step Problem Solving

21. B **23.** Sample answer: \$12 **25.** Sample answer: Melinda made the most shots by about 50 shots.

Pages 241–242 Lesson 3-3 Independent Practice

1. 25% **3** 75 **5.** 36% **7.** \$17 **9.** 80 **11** 0.2% **13a.** about 3.41% **13b.** about 24,795.62 km **13c.** about 6,378.16 km **15.** 20% of 500, 20% of 100, 5% of 100; If the percent is the same but the base is greater, then the part is greater. If the base is the same but the percent is greater, then the part is greater.

Pages 243–244 Lesson 3-3 Multi-Step Problem Solving

17. C **19.** 10% **21.** 15

Pages 249–250 Lesson 3-4 Independent Practice

1 50%; $75 = n \cdot 150$ **3.** 63.7; $p = 0.65 \cdot 98$ **5.** 6; $p = 0.24 \cdot 25$ **7.** 56 books **9** **a.** 63% **9b.** 2% **11.** 0.3; $p = 0.004 \cdot 82.1$ **13.** 115%; $230 = n \cdot 200$ **15.** Sample answer: If the percent is less than 100%, then the part is less than the whole; if the percent equals 100%, then the part equals the whole; if the percent is greater than 100%, then the part is greater than the whole. **17.** Sample answer: It may be easier if the percent and the base are known because after writing the percent as a decimal or fraction, the only step is to multiply. When using the percent proportion, you must first determine the cross products and then divide.

Page 252 Lesson 3-4 Multi-Step Problem Solving

19. 0.25 **21.** 20.2 gallons

Page 255 Focus on Mathematical Processes

1. no; Sample answer: $48\% - 24\% = 24\%$ and 24% of 140 is about 35 **3.** $15 + b = 0.5(36 + b)$; 6 boys; 42 students

Pages 263–264 Lesson 3-5 Independent Practice

1. 20%; increase **3** 25%; decrease **5.** 41%; decrease **7** Performance Plus Sports; It increases by about 12% and All-Sports Gear increased by about 4%. **9.** 13%; increase **11a.** 100% **11b.** 300% **13.** He did not write a ratio comparing the change to the original amount. It should have had a denominator of \$52 and the percent of change would be about 140%. **15.** No; Sample answer: after a 25% increase, the quantity is greater than the original quantity. Decreasing a larger number by the same percent results in a greater change.

Pages 265–266 Lesson 3-5 Multi-Step Problem Solving

17. A **19.** 3.4% **21.** greater than; The amount of change, which is the numerator, is the same in both cases because $|A - B| = |B - A|$. However, the original amount, which is the denominator, is less in the first case because $A < B$. Because a lesser denominator results in a greater quotient, the percent change from A to B is greater.

Pages 271–272 Lesson 3-6 Independent Practice

1. \$69.60 **3** \$1,605 **5** \$35.79 **7.** \$334.80; \$64.80 **9.** \$10.29 **11.** \$1.92; about 27%; Sample answer: Use $7 + 0.0825(7) + t = 9.50$ for the tip t, which is \$1.92. For the percent, use the equation $\$1.92 = p \cdot 7$, where p is the percent, to get about 27% **13.** 7% **15.** \$30

Pages 273–274 Lesson 3-6 Multi-Step Problem Solving

17. 42.12 **19.** \$155.40 **21.** He made $\$7.50 \times 6$, or \$45 on Friday, $\$7.50 \times 15$, or \$112.50 on Saturday, and $\$4.50 \times 22$, or \$99 on Sunday. Umar will make the most money on Saturday.

Pages 279–280 Lesson 3-7 Independent Practice

1. \$51.20 **3** \$6.35 **5** \$4.50 **7a.** \$28.76, \$25.29, \$28.87 **7b.** Funtopia **9.** \$9.00 **11.** Sample answers are given.

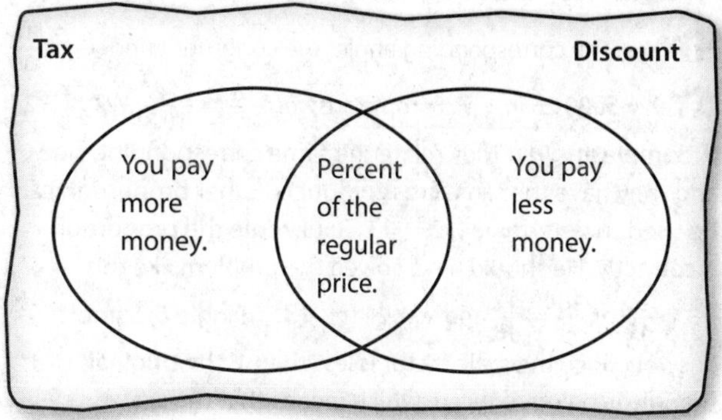

13. \$25

Pages 281–282 Lesson 3-7 Multi-Step Problem Solving

15. C **17.** \$44.63 **19.** \$93

Pages 287–288 Lesson 3-8 Independent Practice

1. \$38.40 **3.** \$5.80 **5** \$1,417.50 **7.** \$75.78 **9** **a.** 5% **9b.** Yes; he would have \$5,208. **11.** Sample answer: If the rate is increased by 1%, then the interest earned is \$60 more. If the time is increased by 1 year, then the interest earned is \$36 more. **13.** Investment A; Sample answer: Investment A has a balance of \$2,850 after 30 years and Investment B has a balance of \$2,512.50 after 15 years.

Page 290 Lesson 3-8 Multi-Step Problem Solving

15. B **17.** 3.36%

Page 295 Chapter Review Vocabulary Check

1. proportion **3.** markup **5.** equation **7.** tip **9.** decrease

Page 296 Chapter Review Key Concept Check

1. 300 **3.** 18 **5.** 12

Page 297 Chapter Review Multi-Step Problem Solving

7. 528 more orders of Tex-Mex than Italian

Chapter 4 Apply Proportionality to Geometry

Page 302 Chapter 4 Are You Ready?

1. 4 **3.** 16 **5.** 25.12 **7.** 34.54

Pages 313–314 Lesson 4-1 Independent Practice

1 200 mi **3** $7\frac{1}{4}$ in.; $\frac{1}{24}$ **5.** 108 ft^2 **9.** Always; sample answer: A scale factor of $\frac{3}{1}$ means that 3 units of the drawing is equal to 1 unit of the object, so the scale drawing or model will be larger than the actual object.

Page 316 Lesson 4-1 Multi-Step Problem Solving

11. A **13.** Sample answer: 52,800 yd

Pages 325–326 Lesson 4-2 Independent Practice

1 Yes; The corresponding angles are congruent and $\frac{6}{12} = \frac{18}{36}$.
3 9 **5.** 20.25 in. **7.** Sample answer: $\frac{18}{WZ} = \frac{27}{10.8}$; $WZ = 7.2$ ft
9. Sample answer: They relate the same corresponding sides and they have the same cross products. Either proportion can be used to determine WZ. **11.** Raul wrote the proportion incorrectly. He should have solved the problem like this: $\frac{16}{12} = \frac{x}{18}$ or $\frac{16}{x} = \frac{12}{18}$ and $x = 24$ ft **13.** Triangle *B*; Sample answer: Since the scale factor is less than 1, the original triangle is being reduced, which means that the scaled triangle will be smaller. The measures of the sides of triangle *A* are less than the measures of the sides of triangle *B*, so triangle *B* must be the original triangle.

Page 328 Lesson 4-2 Multi-Step Problem Solving

15. 22.5 **17.** Rectangle B and Rectangle D

Page 331 Focus on Mathematical Processes

1. 15 tables; 2 people can sit on the ends. Then divide the remaining people by 2. (32 − 2) ÷ 2 = 15. **3.** Faith: Spanish; Sebastián: German; Guadalupe: French

Pages 339–340 Lesson 4-3 Independent Practice

1 The perimeter is 4 times greater. The perimeter of the original figure is 36 cm and the perimeter of the new figure is 144 cm; 144 cm ÷ 36 cm = 4. **3** The area is multiplied by $\frac{1}{3} \cdot \frac{1}{3}$ or $\frac{1}{9}$ the original area. The area of the original figure is 315 yd^2 and the area of the new figure is 35 yd^2; 35 yd^2 ÷ 315 yd^2 = $\frac{1}{9}$. **5.** Use the area and the length to find the width of the queen-size bed. The width of the bed is 4,800 ÷ 80, or 60 inches. So, the width of the dollhouse bed is $60 \cdot \frac{1}{12}$, or 5 inches. The length of the dollhouse bed is $80 \cdot \frac{1}{12}$ or $6\frac{2}{3}$ inches.

7. Sample answer:

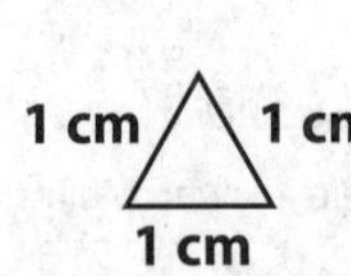

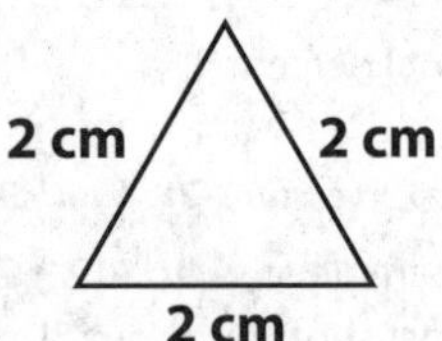

9. larger square: 12 units; smaller square: 6 units; Sample answer: The length of the sides for squares are equal. Divide 48 by 4 to get a side length of 12. The side length of the smaller square is half as big, so 6 units.

Page 342 Lesson 4-3 Multi-Step Problem Solving

11. B **13.** 4 times

Pages 349–350 Lesson 4-4 Independent Practice

1. 2.5 mm **3.** 34 cm **5** 3.14 × 13 = 40.8 cm **7** 19 people **9a.** 30 mm **9b.** 31.4 mm **9c.** 31.4159 mm
9d. Sample answer: The more decimal places of the estimate of π, the more precise the circumference. **11.** 305 m
13. 21 mm **15.** 33.55 ft **17.** Sample answer:

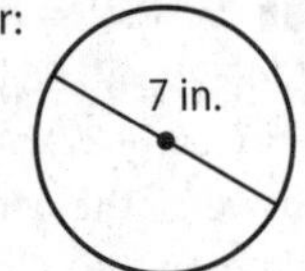

Estimated circumference: 21 in.; using calculator: 22.0. The estimate is close to the value found on the calculator.
19. yes; Sample answer: The formula for the circumference C of a circle related to its diameter d is $C = \pi d$. The two variables C and d have a constant ratio, π. The constant of proportionality is π.

Pages 351–352 Lesson 4-4 Multi-Step Problem Solving

21. D **23.** 6.78 mm

Page 355 Chapter Review Vocabulary Check

1. diameter **3.** circle **5.** circumference **7.** scale
9. factor **11.** attribute

Page 356 Chapter Review Key Concept Check

1. twice **3.** attribute

Page 357 Chapter Review Multi-Step Problem Solving

5. 39.4 feet

Chapter 5 Apply Proportionality to Probability

Page 362 Chapter 5 Are You Ready?

1. $\frac{1}{3}$ **3.** $\frac{2}{3}$ **5.** 30 **7.** 24

Pages 371–372 Lesson 5-1 Independent Practice

1. $\frac{1}{4}$, 25%, or 0.25; unlikely **3** $\frac{1}{1}$, 100%, or 1; certain **5.** $1 - p$; $\frac{3}{4}$; Sample answer: The sum of the probability of an event and its opposite is 1 or 100%. **7** $\frac{1}{5}$ **9.** This is very likely to happen since the probability of picking a purple, red, or yellow jelly bean is 90%, $\frac{9}{10}$, or 0.9. **11.** Sample answer: There are 18 marbles in the bag. Nine marbles should be added. To do so without changing the probability, add 3 red, 2 blue, and 4 green marbles.

Pages 373–374 Lesson 5-1 Multi-Step Problem Solving

13. C **15.** $\frac{1}{3}$, about 33%, or about 0.33 **17.** $\frac{4}{5}$, 80%, or 0.8

Pages 383–384 Lesson 5-2 Independent Practice

1 a. $\frac{2}{5}$; The experimental probability is much greater than the theoretical probability of $\frac{1}{6}$. **1b.** $\frac{9}{10}$; The experimental probability is close to the theoretical probability of $\frac{5}{6}$.
3a. 162 people **3b.** about 134 people **5 a.** $\frac{1}{3}$ **5b.** $\frac{6}{25}$; $\frac{13}{50}$

5c.

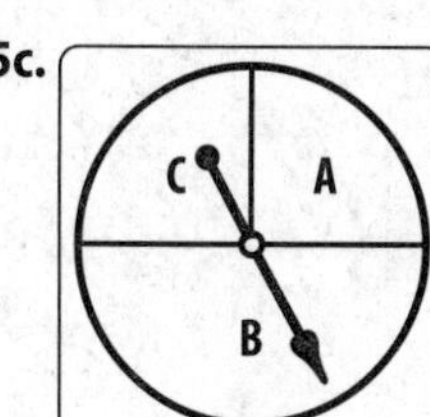

; Sample answer: Section B should be one half of the spinner and sections A and C should each be one fourth of the spinner.

7. Yes; Sample answer: $\frac{5 \text{ sharpened}}{10 \text{ unsharpened}} = \frac{20 \text{ sharpened}}{x \text{ unsharpened}}$. So, $x = 40$.

Pages 385–386 Lesson 5-2 Multi-Step Problem Solving

9. D **11.** 60 customers **13.** 24; Sample answer: The probability of each color is a multiple of the fraction $\frac{1}{8}$.

Pages 395–396 Lesson 5-3 Independent Practice

1. H1, H2, H3, H4, H5, T1, T2, T3, T4, T5 **3** purple 10, purple 18, purple 21, purple 24, green 10, green 18, green 21, green 24, black 10, black 18, black 21, black 24, silver 10, silver 18, silver 21, silver 24

5.

1, 1	1, 2	1, 3	1, 4	1, 5	1, 6
2, 1	2, 2	2, 3	2, 4	2, 5	2, 6
3, 1	3, 2	3, 3	3, 4	3, 5	3, 6
4, 1	4, 2	4, 3	4, 4	4, 5	4, 6
5, 1	5, 2	5, 3	5, 4	5, 5	5, 6
6, 1	6, 2	6, 3	6, 4	6, 5	6, 6

; $\frac{1}{36}$

7 P(Player 1) $= \frac{6}{8}$ or $\frac{3}{4}$; P(Player 2) $= \frac{2}{8}$ or $\frac{1}{4}$ RRB, RYB, RRY, RYY, BRB, BYB, BYY, BRY **9.** Sample answer: No, Player 1 has a better chance of winning because $\frac{3}{4} > \frac{1}{4}$. **11.** 5^x; $\frac{1}{5}$

Page 398 Lesson 5-3 Multi-Step Problem Solving

13. C **15.** 11.1%

Page 401 Focus on Mathematical Processes

1. 31 games **3.** unfair; Sample answer: There are 20 out of 36 outcomes that are multiples of 3 and only 15 that are multiples of 4. Jason has a greater chance of winning.

Pages 409–410 Lesson 5-4 Independent Practice

1 Sample answer: Spin a spinner with 4 equal-size sections 100 times. **3** Sample answer: Spin a spinner divided into 3 equal sections and roll a number cube. Repeat the simulation until all types of cookies are obtained. **5.** Sample answer: Use 3 red marbles to represent winning and 7 blue marbles to represent losing. Draw 1 marble 4 times, replacing the marble each time. **7.** Sample answer: A survey of 100 people voting on whether or not to enact a tax increase, where each person is equally likely to vote yes or no. Toss a coin 100 times.
9. Sample answer: sometimes; The spinner must have equal-sized sections.

Pages 411–412 Lesson 5-4 Multi-Step Problem Solving

11. 37.5 **13.** $\frac{1}{28}$ **15.** Sample answer: The experimental probability is $\frac{1}{8}$ or 12.5% less than the theoretical probability.

Pages 423–424 Lesson 5-5 Independent Practice

1. $\frac{1}{24}$ **3** $\frac{1}{8}$ **5** $\frac{1}{144}$ **7.** $\frac{1}{25}$ **9.** Sample answer: Spinning the spinner twice represents two independent events. The probability of getting an even number is $\frac{2}{5}$ each time; $\frac{2}{5} \cdot \frac{2}{5}$ or $\frac{4}{25}$. **11.** False; sample answer: The probability of tossing heads or tails on a coin and rolling a 6 or less on a number cube.

Pages 425–426 Lesson 5-5 Multi-Step Problem Solving

13. D **15.** 18.9% **17.** $\frac{1}{2}$

Page 429 Chapter Review Vocabulary Check

1. sample space **3.** theoretical

Page 430 Chapter Review Key Concept Check

1. experimental probability **3.** compound event

Page 431 Chapter Review Multi-Step Problem Solving

5. 192 more students prefer the Texans than the Cowboys

Index

21st Century Careers
- biomechnical engineering, 203–204
- fashion designer, 109–110
- landscape architect, 693–694
- market research analyst, 777–778
- pediatricians, 427–428
- roller coaster designer, 353–354
- shark scientist, 491–492
- veterinary technician, 577–578
- video game designer, 293–294

Aa

Acute angle, 589

Acute triangles, 610

Addition
- of integers, 46
- of like fractions, 70–74
- of mixed numbers, 86–92
- of unlike fractions, 77–84
- using models for rational numbers, 65–68

Addition Property of Equality, 512

Addition Property of Inequalities, 558

Adjacent, 598

Adjacent angles, 590

Alternative Method, 125

Analyze, 32, 42, 58, 74, 82, 98, 106, 128, 136, 152, 164, 174, 192, 200, 224, 232, 242, 250, 264, 272, 280, 288, 326, 340, 350, 372, 396, 410, 424, 446, 454, 466, 478, 486, 508, 516, 526, 538, 554, 561, 574, 594, 602, 614, 624, 632, 644, 656, 668, 690, 720, 736, 752, 764, 774

Analyze and Reflect, 68, 122, 168, 186, 218, 258, 292, 306, 308, 320, 334, 344, 366, 378, 388, 390, 416, 418, 440, 470, 472, 490, 520, 532, 548, 568, 608, 618, 648, 662, 684, 714, 742, 756, 758. *See also* Reflect; Stop and Reflect

Angles
- acute, 589
- adjacent, 590
- complementary, 597–604
- determining a missing measure, 591–592, 599–600
- obtuse, 589
- pairs of, 598
- relationships between, 589–596
- right, 589
- straight, 589
- sum of, in triangles, 609–616
- supplementary, 597–604
- in triangles, 605–608
- vertex of, 589
- vertical, 590

Answers, determining reasonable, 253

Answer the Essential Question, 18, 114, 208, 298, 358, 432, 582, 698, 782, 810, 814, 816, 818, 820, 822. *See also* Building on the Essential Question; Essential Question

Area
- changes in, 333–334
- of circles, 619–626
- determining, 620
- modeling, 617–618
- of composite figures, 627–634
- determining, 628–629
- effect of changing dimensions on, 337
- of shaded region
- determining, 629–630

Are You Ready?, 22, 118, 212, 302, 362, 436, 500, 586, 702, 786

Assets, 798–798
- defined, 795
- determining, 796

Attributes, 317
- critical, of similar figures, 321–328

Bb

Bar diagram, 217, 218, 236, 257, 524, 536

Bar graphs, 705–712, 770
- connecting to circle graphs, 713–714
- defined, 706
- double, 770

Bar notation, 27, 29

Base of prisms, 639

Biased samples, 731–738
- defined, 732

Box plots, 770
- double, 758
- shapes of, 758

Budgets
- defined, 791
- family, 791
- personal, 792

Building on the Essential Question, 30, 40, 48, 56, 72, 80, 88, 96, 104, 126, 134, 142, 150, 162, 172, 180, 190, 198, 222, 230, 240, 248, 262, 270, 278, 286, 312, 324, 338, 348, 370, 382, 394, 408, 422, 444, 464, 476, 484, 506, 514, 524, 536, 552, 560, 572, 592, 600, 612, 622, 630, 642, 666, 676, 688, 718, 726, 734, 750, 762, 772. *See also* Answer the Essential Question; Essential Question

Cc

Calculating with π, 621

Career Projects, 110, 204, 294, 354, 428, 492, 578, 694, 778

Career Readiness. *See* 21st Century Careers

Center, 345

Changes in dimension, 335–342
- effect on area, 337
- effect on perimeter, 336

Chapter Review, 111, 205–208, 295–298, 355–358, 429, 493–495, 579–581, 695–697, 779, 807–809

Check for Reasonableness, 79, 229

Choose an Operation, 80, 88

Circle graphs, 715–722, 770
- connecting bar graphs to, 713–714

Circles
- area of, 619–626
  - determining, 620
  - modeling, 617–618
- defined, 345
- formula for area of, 628

Circumference, 347
- defined, 343, 345
- modeling, 343–344

Coefficients, 511

decimal, 522
equations with rational, 551–552
fractions as, 523
modeling and solving equations with rational, 519–520
solving equations with rational, 521–528

Collaborate, 813, 815, 817, 819, 821

College savings, 802

Common denominator, 38
least, 38

Comparisons and equivalents
part-to-part, 707–708, 717
part-to-whole, 706, 716

Complement
defined, 369–370
determining probability of a, 369–370

Complementary angles, 597–604

Complementary events, 369–370

Composite figures, area of, 627–634
determining, 628–629

Compound events
defined, 392
probability of, 391–398
simulating, 413–416

Compound interest, 291–292, 799–802
defined, 291, 799

Congruent segments, 610

Congruent triangles, 629

Connect models to rules, 334, 343, 344, 617, 619, 648, 651

Connect with Health
Health Literacy, 822

Connect with Language Arts
Financial Literacy, 814

Connect with Science
Environmental Literacy, 816, 820

Connect with Social Studies
Civic Literacy, 818

Constant of proportionality, 195–202

Constant of variation, 196

Constant rate of change, 187–194, 189
defined, 187
slope as, 462–464
use a table, 188
use multiple representations, 191

Constant ratio, 195

Convenience sample, 732

Coordinate plane, 159

Coupons, 804

Create, 26, 32, 42, 50, 53, 58, 74, 90, 98, 106, 122, 128, 136, 144, 152, 164, 168, 182, 186, 192, 200, 218, 224, 232, 236, 242, 250, 258, 264, 272, 280, 292, 308, 314, 320, 326, 334, 340, 344, 350, 366, 378, 390, 396, 410, 418, 424, 440, 446, 454, 466, 472, 478, 490, 508, 516, 520, 526, 532, 533, 538, 548, 554, 561, 568, 574, 594, 602, 608, 614, 618, 624, 632, 644, 648, 662, 668, 672, 678, 684, 690, 710, 714, 720, 728, 736, 742, 752, 756, 758, 764, 774

Credit cards, interest on, 285

Cross products, 170

Customary measurement system, 177

Data
collecting, 755–756
describing, 700
experimental, 387–390
multiple samples of, 739–742
visual overlap of distributions, 767–768

Decimal coefficients, 522

Decimals
division with, 522
expressing, as fractions, 30
expressing fractions as, 28–29
percents as, 39
repeating, 27
terminating, 27

Decomposing figures, 640

Denominator
least common, 38

Dependent events, 417–418, 419–426
defined, 421
probability of, 421–422

Diagrams
bar, 217, 218, 236, 257, 524, 536
drawing, 155–156
percent, 215–218
tree, 365, 395
Venn, 36, 64

Diameter, 343, 346
defined, 345

Dimensional analysis, 140, 179

Direct variation, 196–197
determining, 197–198

Discount, 275–282

Display, selecting an appropriate, 769–776

Distance formula, 514

Distributive Property
modeling two-step equations using, 545–548
solving two-step equations using, 549–556

Division
with decimals, 522
of fractions, 102–103
of integers, 55
of mixed numbers, 103–106
of rational numbers, 101–108

Division Property of Equality, 513

Division Property of Inequality, 559

Dot plots, 705–712, 770
defined, 706
double, 758

Double bar graph, 770

Double box plot, 758

Double dot plot, 758

Equations
defined, 503
determining solutions of a two-step, 504
equivalent, 503
of linear relationships, 449–456
graphing, using tables, 450
making predictions about a, 725
modeling, using the Distributive Property, 545–548
modeling and solving two-step, 529–532
with rational coefficients, 551–552
modeling and solving, 519–520
solving, 521–528
solving and writing two-step, 533–540
solving two-step, using the Distributive Property, 549–556
writing, from tables and graphs, 481–488

Equilateral triangles, 610

Equivalent equations, 503

Essential Question, 18, 19, 27, 37, 45, 69, 77, 85, 93, 101, 115, 123, 131, 139, 147, 159, 169, 177, 187, 195, 208

209, 219, 227, 237, 245, 259, 267, 275, 283, 298, 299, 309, 321, 335, 345, 358, 359, 379, 391, 405, 419, 432, 433, 441, 449, 461, 473, 481, 496, 497, 503, 511, 521, 533, 549, 557, 569, 582, 583, 589, 597, 609, 619, 627, 639, 651, 663, 673, 685, 698, 699, 705, 715, 723, 731, 747, 757, 769, 782, 783, 787, 791, 795, 799, 803, 810. *See also* Answer the Essential Question; Building on the Essential Question

Estimation, 347
 percent and, 227–234

Evaluate, 32, 42, 50, 58, 74, 90, 98, 106, 128, 136, 144, 164, 174, 182, 224, 232, 250, 264, 288, 314, 350, 372, 384, 478, 516, 526, 594, 602, 614, 644, 656, 678, 728, 736, 752

Expenses, 791
 fixed, 792
 variable, 792

Experimental data, 387–390

Experimental probability, 379–386
 defined, 380

Family budgets, 791
 building, 794

Family of linear relationships, 489–490

Financial Literacy, 48, 63, 222, 224, 229, 231, 263, 267–274, 271, 283–290, 288, 453, 458, 478, 484, 508, 525, 572

Find the Error, 36, 50, 74, 82, 106, 128, 152, 264, 326, 396, 424, 466, 478, 516, 554, 690, 728, 736

Fixed expenses, 792

Focus on Mathematical Processes. *See also* Mathematical Processes; Mathematical Processes Handbook
 Act it Out, 399–400
 Analyze Relationships, 13–14
 Apply Math to the Real World, 3–4
 Determine Reasonable Answers, 253
 Draw a Diagram, 155–156
 The Four-Step Plan, 61–62
 Justify Arguments, 15–16
 Make a Model, 329–331
 Make a Table, 457–459
 Organize Ideas, 11–12
 Select Tools and Techniques, 7–8
 Solve a Simpler Problem, 635–637
 Use a Graph, 743–745
 Use a Problem-Solving Model, 5–6
 Use Multiple Representations, 9–10
 Work Backward, 541

Foldables® Study Organizers, 23–24, 112, 119–120, 206, 213–214, 296, 303–304, 356, 363–364, 430, 437–438, 494, 501–502, 580, 587–588, 696, 703–704, 780

Formulas
 for area
  of circles, 628
  of parallogram, 628
  of trapezoid, 628
  of triangles, 628
 distance, 514
 for simple interest, 284

Fractions
 as coefficients, 523
 division of, 102–103
 expressing, as decimals, 28–29
 expressing decimals as, 30
 improper, 20, 87
 like, 70–71
 multiplication of, 94, 653
 negative, 70
 unit, 32
 unlike, 77–84

Frequency, relative, 375

Future events, predicting, 382

Geometry Software Lab
 Angles in Triangles, 605–608

Graphing
 linear equations, 475–476
 linear equations using tables, 450
 real-world data, 451–452

Graphing Technology Labs
 Family of Linear Relationships, 489–490
 Nonproportional Linear Relationships, 469–472

Graphs
 bar, 705–712, 770
 circle, 715–722, 770
 connecting bar to circle, 713–714
 double bar, 770
 identifying linear relationships using, 443–444
 line, 770
 misleading, 747–754
 using, 743–745
 writing equations from, 481–488

Greatest common factor (GCF), 94

Guided Practice, 30, 40, 48, 56, 72, 80, 88, 96, 104, 126, 134, 142, 150, 162, 172, 180, 190, 198, 222, 230, 248, 262, 270, 278, 286, 312, 324, 338, 348, 370, 382, 394, 408, 422, 444, 464, 476, 484, 506, 514, 524, 536, 552, 560, 572, 592, 600, 612, 622, 630, 642, 654, 666, 676, 688, 708, 718, 726, 734, 750, 762, 772

Hands-On Labs. *See also* Geometry Software Lab; Graphing Technology Labs; Spreadsheet Lab
 Changes in Perimeter and Area, 333–334
 Collect Data, 755–756
 Connect Bar Graphs to Circle Graphs, 713–714
 Experimental Data, 387–390
 Find Percents, 235–236
 Independent and Dependent Events, 417–418
 Investigate Online Maps and Scale Drawings, 305–308
 Linear Relationships, 439–440
 Make Predictions, 375–378
 Model and Solve Equations with Rational Coefficients, 519–520
 Model and Solve Two-Step Equations, 529–532
 Model and Solve Two-Step Inequalities, 565–568
 Model Area of Circles, 617–618
 Model Circumference, 343–344
 Model Percent of Change, 257–258
 Model Proportional Relationships, 167–168
 Model Rational Numbers, 25–26
 Model Two-Step Equations using the Distributive Property, 545–548
 Multiple Samples of Data, 739–742
 Nets of Rectangular Prisms, 659–662
 Nets of Triangular Prisms, 671–672
 Percent diagrams, 215–218
 Rate of change, 185–186
 Ratio and Rates, 121–122
 Relate surface area and volume, 681–684

Sample Spaces, 365–366
Sets of Rational Numbers, 35–36
Similar Triangles, 317–320
Simulate Compound Events, 413–416
Use Models to Add and Subtract Rational Numbers, 65–68
Visual Overlap of Data Distributions, 767–768
Volume Relationships of Prisms and Pyramids, 647–650

Height
of prisms, 641
of pyramids, 653–654
slant, 685

Histogram, 770

H.O.T. (Higher Order Thinking), 32, 42, 50, 58, 74, 82, 90, 98, 106, 128, 136, 144, 152, 164, 174, 182, 192, 200, 232, 242, 250, 264, 272, 280, 288, 314, 326, 340, 350, 372, 384, 396, 410, 424, 446, 454, 466, 478, 486, 508, 516, 526, 538, 554, 561, 574, 594, 602, 614, 624, 632, 644, 656, 668, 678, 690, 710, 720, 728, 736, 752, 764, 774

Improper fractions, 20, 87

Income, defined, 788

Income tax, 787–790
calculating, 788
defined, 788

Independent events, 417–418, 419–426
defined, 419
probability of, 420–421

Independent Practice, 31, 41, 49–50, 57–58, 73–74, 81–82, 89–90, 97–98, 105, 127–128, 135–136, 143–144, 151–152, 163–164, 173–174, 181–182, 191, 199–200, 223–224, 231–232, 241–242, 249–250, 263–264, 271–272, 279–280, 287–288, 313–314, 325–326, 339–340, 349–350, 371–372, 383–384, 395–396, 409–410, 423–424, 445–446, 453–454, 465–466, 477–478, 485–486, 507–508, 515–516, 525–526, 537–538, 553–554, 561–562, 573–574, 593–594, 601–602, 613–614, 623–624, 631–632, 643–644, 655–656, 667–668, 677–678, 689–690, 709–710, 719–720, 727–728, 735–736, 751–752, 763–764, 773, 789, 793, 797, 801, 805

Inequalities
one-step, solving, 557–564
two-step
determining solutions of, 505–506
modeling and solving, 565–568
solving and writing, 569–576

Inferences, making, about populations, 733–734

Inquiry, 25, 26, 35, 36, 65, 68, 121, 167, 168, 185, 186, 215, 218, 235, 236, 258, 291, 292, 305, 308, 317, 320, 333, 334, 344, 365, 366, 375, 378, 387, 390, 403, 404, 413, 416, 417, 418, 439, 440, 469, 472, 489, 490, 519, 520, 529, 532, 545, 548, 565, 568, 605, 608, 617, 618, 647, 648, 659, 662, 671, 672, 681, 684, 713, 714, 739, 742, 755, 756, 758, 767

Integers, 35
addition of, 46
division of, 55
multiplication of, 54
subtraction of, 46–47, 71

Interest
compound, 291–292, 799–802
simple, 283–290, 799–802

Interquartile range, 759

Investigate, 35, 67, 122, 186, 217, 236, 258, 292, 306, 308, 319, 334, 344, 366, 377, 388, 390, 404, 415, 418, 440, 471, 490, 520, 531, 547, 567, 607, 618, 648, 661, 672, 683, 741, 758. *See also* Real-World Investigation

Investigate and Create, 756

Irrational numbers, 37

Isosceles triangles, 610

Key Concept(s), 54, 55, 70, 78, 94, 102, 170, 196, 238, 246, 260, 284, 322, 323, 336, 337, 346, 347, 368, 420, 474, 512, 513, 558, 559, 590, 598, 610, 611, 620, 640, 641, 652, 664, 674, 686, 770

Key Concept Check, 64, 112, 158, 256, 296, 332, 356, 402, 430, 460, 494, 544, 580, 638, 696, 746, 780, 808

Kilometers, 177

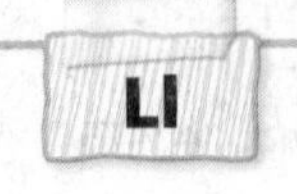

Lateral face, 652

Lateral surface area, 665
determining, 675–676

Launch the Lesson
Real World, 45, 53, 69, 77, 85, 93, 101, 131, 139, 147, 169, 177, 195, 219, 227, 237, 259, 267, 275, 309, 321, 335, 379, 391, 405, 441, 449, 461, 473, 481, 521, 533, 549, 569, 597, 609, 619, 627, 639, 651, 673, 705, 715, 731, 747, 757, 769, 787, 791, 803
Vocabulary, 27, 37, 159, 187, 245, 345, 419, 503, 511, 589, 663, 685, 723, 795

Least common denominator (LCD), 38

Liabilities, 798–798
defined, 795
determining, 796

Like fractions, 70–74
addition of, 70–74
subtraction of, 70–74

Linear equations
defined, 450
graphing, 475–476
graphing, using tables, 450

Linear relationships, 160, 439–440
with constant rate of change, 446
equations of, 449–456
family of, 489–490
identifying, 441–449
using graphs, 443–444
using tables, 442
nonproportional, 469–472
proportional, 440

Line graph, 770

Loans, interest on, 285

Markdown, 276

Markups, 268–269, 270

Math, language of, 584

Mathematical Processes *See also* Focus on Mathematical Processes; Mathematical Processes Handbook
Analyze Relationships, 36, 68, 136, 174, 200, 218, 292, 308, 343, 344, 349, 383, 388, 404, 413, 416, 424, 439, 446, 472, 490, 507, 520, 532, 548, 561, 567, 593, 608, 614, 618, 648, 656, 662, 672, 689, 756, 758

Apply Math to the Real World, 4, 42, 143, 168, 186, 192, 218, 223, 258, 279, 292, 314, 340, 371, 390, 404, 416, 423, 453, 470, 486, 520, 526, 532, 537, 538, 548, 561, 568, 618, 643, 662, 668, 741, 751, 773, 805
Justify Arguments, 127, 136, 152, 217, 287, 339, 388, 390, 404, 410, 416, 525, 532, 602, 607, 624, 667, 684
Organize Ideas, 122, 186, 258, 280, 320, 344, 366, 378, 388, 390, 418, 440, 470, 531, 573, 607, 617, 727, 742
Select Tools and Techniques, 74, 105, 144, 236, 256, 264, 306, 378, 409, 607, 648, 672, 684, 714, 735, 742
Use a Problem-Solving Model, 32, 33, 249, 396, 448, 480, 631
Use Multiple Representations, 191, 199, 308, 349, 466, 472, 490
algebra, 553
diagrams, 515
graphs, 454, 477, 485, 710, 720, 763
models, 347, 384, 553, 655, 678
numbers, 384, 477, 485, 655, 678, 710, 720, 763
symbols, 326, 347, 477, 485, 515, 655
tables, 454
words, 326, 347, 454, 485, 515, 553, 655, 678, 710, 720, 763

Mathematical Processes Handbook, 1–18
Analyze Relationships, 13–14
Apply Math to the Real-World, 3–4
Justify Arguments, 15–16
Organize Ideas, 11–12
Reflect, 18
Review, 17
Select Tools and Techniques, 7–8
Use a Problem-Solving Model, 5–6
Use Multiple Representations, 9–10

Math in the Real World, 19, 115, 209, 299, 359, 433, 497, 583, 699, 783

Measurement systems
converting between, using unit rates, 178–184
customary, 177
metric, 177
using proportion to convert between, 179

Measures, determining missing, 323

Mental math, 269

Metric measurement system, 177

Mid-Chapter Check, 64, 158, 256, 332–334, 402, 460, 544, 638, 746

Mile, 177

Misleading graphs and statistics, 747–754

Mixed numbers
addition of, 86–92
division of, 103–106
multiplication of, 95–100
subtraction of, 86–92

Mode, 749

Models
in adding and subtracting rational numbers, 65–68
connecting to rules, 334, 343, 344, 617, 619, 648, 651
of proportional relationships, 167–168
of rational numbers, 25–26
scale, 310

Monetary incentives
defined, 803
extreme, 806
for shopping, 803–806

Multiplication
of fractions, 94, 653
of integers, 54
meaning of, 96
of mixed numbers, 95–100
of rational numbers, 93–100

Multiplication Property of Equality, 513

Multiplication Property of Inequality, 559

Multi-Step Examples, 56, 125–126, 171–172, 222, 228, 229, 240, 248, 261, 262, 270, 277–278, 312, 382, 451–452, 475–476, 484, 514, 629, 642, 675, 706, 707–708, 716, 717, 788, 804

Multi-Step Problem Solving, 43–44, 51–52, 59–60, 63, 75–76, 83–84, 91–92, 99–100, 107–108, 113, 129–130, 137–138, 145–146, 153–154, 157, 158, 165–166, 175–176, 183–184, 193–194, 201–202, 207, 225–226, 233–234, 243–244, 251–252, 254–255, 256, 265–266, 273–274, 289–290, 297, 315–316, 327–328, 329, 330, 331, 332, 341–342, 351–352, 357, 373–374, 385–386, 397–401, 402, 411–412, 425–426, 431, 447–448, 455–459, 460, 467–468, 479–480, 487–488, 495, 509–510, 517–518, 527–528, 539–543, 544, 555–556, 563–564, 575–576, 581, 595–596, 603–604, 615–616, 625–626, 633–637, 638, 645–646, 657–658, 669–670, 679–680, 691–692, 697, 711–712, 721–722, 729–730, 737–738, 743–745, 746, 753–754, 765–766, 775–776, 781, 790, 794, 798, 802, 806, 809
analyze, 33, 43, 51, 59, 61, 62, 75, 83, 91, 99, 107, 113, 129, 137, 145, 153, 155, 156, 165, 175, 183, 193, 201, 207, 225, 233, 243, 251, 253, 254, 265, 273, 281, 289, 297, 315, 327, 329, 330, 341, 351, 357, 373, 385, 397, 399, 400, 411, 425, 431, 447, 455, 457, 458, 467, 479, 487, 495, 509, 517, 527, 539, 541, 542, 555, 563, 575, 581, 595, 603, 615, 625, 633, 635, 636, 645, 657, 669, 679, 691, 697, 711, 721, 729, 737, 743, 744, 753, 765, 775, 781, 809
justify and evaluate, 33, 43, 51, 59, 61, 62, 75, 83, 91, 99, 107, 113, 129, 137, 145, 153, 155, 156, 165, 175, 183, 193, 201, 207, 225, 233, 243, 251, 253, 254, 265, 273, 281, 289, 297, 315, 327, 329, 330, 341, 351, 357, 373, 385, 397, 399, 400, 411, 425, 431, 447, 455, 457, 458, 467, 479, 487, 495, 509, 517, 527, 539, 541, 542, 555, 563, 575, 581, 595, 603, 615, 625, 633, 635, 636, 645, 657, 669, 679, 691, 697, 711, 721, 729, 737, 743, 744, 753, 765, 775, 781, 809
plan, 33, 43, 51, 59, 61, 62, 75, 83, 91, 99, 107, 113, 129, 137, 145, 153, 155, 156, 165, 175, 183, 193, 201, 207, 225, 233, 243, 251, 253, 254, 265, 273, 281, 289, 297, 315, 327, 329, 330, 341, 351, 357, 373, 385, 397, 399, 400, 411, 425, 431, 447, 455, 457, 458, 467, 479, 487, 495, 509, 517, 527, 539, 541, 542, 555, 563, 575, 581, 595, 603, 615, 625, 633, 635, 636, 645, 657, 669, 679, 691, 697, 711, 721, 729, 737, 743, 744, 753, 765, 775, 781, 809
solve, 33, 43, 51, 59, 61, 62, 75, 83, 91, 99, 129, 137, 145, 153, 155, 156, 165, 175, 183, 193, 201, 207, 225, 233, 243, 251, 253, 254, 265, 273, 281, 289, 297, 315, 327, 329, 330, 341, 351, 357, 373, 385, 397, 399, 400, 411, 425, 431, 447, 455, 457, 458, 467, 479, 487, 495, 509, 517, 527, 539, 541, 542, 555, 563, 575, 581, 595, 603, 615, 625, 633, 635, 636, 645, 657, 669, 679, 691, 697, 711, 721, 729, 737, 743, 744, 753, 765, 775, 781, 809

Negative fractions, 70
Negative in inequalities, 559
Nets, 664
defined, 647
of rectangular prisms, 659–662
of triangular prisms, 671–672
Net worth, 796, 798
defined, 795
determining, 796
Nonproportional linear relationships, 469–472
Notation, bar, 27, 29
Numbers
determining percent of, 220
estimating percent of, 228
irrational, 37
mixed, 20
rational, 35, 37

Obtuse angle, 589
Obtuse triangles, 610
One-step inequalities, solving, 557–564
Online maps, 305
Open and closed dots, 558
Ordered pairs, 159, 189
Order of operations, 534
Orthogonal drawings, 660
Outcomes, 365
model equally likely, 406–407
model unequally likely, 407–408

Parallogram, 628
formula for area of, 628
Part-to-part comparisons and equivalents, 707–708, 717
Part-to-whole comparisons and equivalents, 706, 716
Percent(s), 792
as decimals, 39
determining of a number, 220
estimating, of a number, 228
estimation and, 227–234
finding, 235–236
greater than 100 or less than 1, 229
as a rate, 220
using, greater than 100%, 221
Percent diagrams, 215–218
Percent equation, 245–252, 277
Percent of change, 259–266
defined, 260
modeling, 257–258
Percent of decrease, 260
Percent of increase, 260
Percent proportion
defined, 238
using, 238
Perimeter
changes in, 333–334
effect of changing dimensions on, 336
Personal budgets, 792
Personal Financial Literacy Projects, 790, 794, 798, 802, 806
Pi, 347
Plots
box, 758, 770
double, 758
dot, 705–712, 770
double, 758
Polyhedron, lateral face of, 652
Populations
comparing, 757–766
defined, 723
making inferences about, 733–734
making predictions about a, 723–730
Power notes, 300
Predictions
making, 375–378
making, about equations, 725
making about populations, 7230730
making about ratios, 724
qualitative, 376
quantitative, 376
Price
determining original, 276
determining sale, 276
selling, 268–269
Principal, 283
Prisms
bases of, 639
defined, 639
height of, 641
rectangular, 639
lateral surface area of, 665
nets of, 659–662
surface area of, 663–670
volume of, 640
triangular, 639
lateral surface area of, 675–676
nets of, 671–672
surface area of, 674
volume of, 641
volume of, 639–650
Probability
of compound events, 391–398
defined, 367
of dependent events, 421–422
determining, 393
determining, of a complement, 369–370
of independent events, 420–421
outcome in, 365–366
predicting future events, 382
sample spaces in, 365–366
of simple events, 367–374
theoretical and experimental, 379–386
tree diagram in, 365–366
Problems, solving simpler, 635–637
Problem-Solving Projects
Become a Travel Expert, 813–814
Explore the Ocean Depths, 815–816
Math Genes, 821–822
Stand Up and Be Counted, 817–818
Turn Over a New Leaf, 819–820
Projects. *See* Career Projects; Personal Financial Literacy Projects; Problem-Solving Projects
Properties, 86
of equality, 512–513
Proportionality, 322
Proportional linear relationships, 440
Proportional relationships, 446
graphing, 159–166
identifying, 160–162
modeling, 167–168
solving, 169–176
Proportions
solving, 382
using, to convert between measurement systems, 179
writing and solving, 170
Pyramids
defined, 647
height of, 653–654
surface area of, 685–692
triangular
lateral and total surface area of 687–688

volume of, 651–658
volume relationships of, 647–650

Quadrants, 159
Qualitative predictions, 376
Quantitative predictions, 376
Quarter circle
area of, 621
defined, 621

Radius, 346
defined, 345
Random, 393
Rate of change, 185–186
constant, 187–194
defined, 187
linear relationships with constant, 446
slope as constant, 462–464
Rates, 121–122, 124
percent as a, 220
Rate Yourself!, 30, 40, 48, 56, 72, 80, 88, 96, 104, 126, 134, 142, 150, 162, 172, 180, 190, 198, 222, 230, 240, 248, 262, 270, 278, 286, 312, 324, 338, 348, 370, 382, 394, 408, 422, 444, 464, 476, 484, 506, 514, 524, 536, 552, 560, 572, 592, 600, 612, 622, 630, 642, 654, 666, 676, 688, 708, 718, 726, 734, 750, 762, 772
Rational coefficients
equations with, 551–552
Rational numbers, 35
comparing, 38–39
division of, 101–108
modeling, 25–26
multiplication of, 93–100
ordering, 39
relationships between sets of, 37–44
sets of, 35–36
using models to add and subtract, 65–68
Ratios, 121–122
constant, 195
making predictions about a, 724
Reading Math, 434
identify key information, 498
language of math, 584
Read to Succeed!, 33, 43, 51, 59, 75, 83, 91, 99, 107, 129, 137, 145, 153, 165, 175, 183, 193, 201, 225, 233, 243, 265, 273, 281, 289, 315, 327, 341, 351, 373, 385, 397, 411, 425, 447, 455, 467, 479, 487, 509, 517, 527, 539, 555, 563, 575, 595, 603, 615, 625, 633, 645, 657, 679, 691, 711, 721, 729, 737, 753, 765, 775
Real-world data, graphing, 451–452
Real-World Investigation, 37, 187, 245, 663, 723. *See also* Investigate
Real-World Link, 27, 283, 345, 367, 419, 503, 589, 639, 795
Rebates, 804
Reciprocals, 551
Rectangular prisms, 639
lateral surface area of, 665
nets of, 659–662
surface area of, 663–670
volume of, 640
Reflect, 18, 114, 208, 298, 358, 432, 496, 582, 698, 782, 810, 814, 816, 818, 820, 822. *See also* Analyze and Reflect; Stop and Reflect
Relative frequency, 375
Repeating decimal, 27
Review Vocabulary, 20, 116, 360, 784
Right angle, 589
Right triangles, 610
Rules, connecting models to, 334, 343, 344, 617, 619, 648, 651

Sale price, determining, 276
Sales tax, 268, 787–790
calculating, 788
defined, 787
Samples
defined, 723
multiple, of data, 739–742
unbiased and biased, 731–738
Sample spaces, 365–366
representing, 392
Scale drawings, 305, 309–316
Scale factor, 311
Scale models, using, 310
Scalene triangles, 610
Scales, 310, 311
changing, 748
Selling price, 268–269
Semicircle
area of, 621
defined, 621
Sets of rational numbers, 35–36
Shaded region, area of
determining, 629–630
Share, 814, 816, 818, 820, 822
Shopping: monetary incentives, 803–806
Similar figures
critical attributes of, 321–328
identifying, 322
Similar triangles, 317–320
Simple events
events, 367
probability of, 367–374
simulating, 403–404
Simple interest, 283–290, 799–802
defined, 283, 799
formula for, 284
Simple random sample, 732
Simplifying, 95
Simulations, 405–412
of compound events, 413–416
defined, 406
of simple events, 403–404
Slant height, 685
Slope, 461–468
as constant rate of change, 462–464
defined, 463
Slope-intercept form, 473–480
defined, 474
Solutions, 503
determining, for two-step equations, 504
determining, for two-step inequality, 505–506
Spreadsheet Lab
compound interest, 291–292
Statistics
defined, 723
misleading, 747–754
STEM, 31, 56, 64, 80, 96, 242, 666
Stop and Reflect, 30, 72, 78, 102, 124, 141, 172, 178, 228, 239, 285, 346, 368, 408, 534, 552, 599, 611, 620, 725, 760. *See also* Analyze and Reflect; Reflect
Straight angle, 589
Strip diagram. *See* Bar diagram

Studying Math, 210
power notes, 300

Subtraction
of integers, 46–47, 71
of like fractions, 70–74
of mixed numbers, 86–92
of unlike fractions, 77–84
using models for rational numbers, 65–68

Subtraction Property of Equality, 512

Subtraction Property of Inequalities, 558

Supplementary angles, 597–604

Surface areas
lateral, 665
lateral and total of triangular pyramid, 687–688
of pyramids, 685–692
of rectangular prisms, 663–670
of triangular prisms, 674
volume and, 681–684

Survey, 723

Symbols
angle, 590
congruent to, 590
pi (π), 621

Systematic random sample, 732

Tt

Tables
graphing linear equations using, 450
identifying linear relationships using, 442
making, 457–459
writing equations from, 481–488

Terminating decimal, 27

Texas Essential Knowledge and Skills (TEKS)
Content Standards, 45, 53
Mathematical Processes, 19, 25, 27, 35, 37, 45, 53, 65, 69, 77, 85, 93, 101, 109, 121, 123, 131, 139, 147, 159, 167, 169, 177, 185, 187, 195, 203, 209, 215, 219, 227, 235, 237, 245, 253, 257, 259, 267, 275, 283, 291, 293, 299, 305, 309, 317, 321, 329, 333, 335, 343, 345, 353, 359, 367, 375, 379, 387, 391, 399, 403, 405, 413, 419, 427, 433, 441, 449, 457, 461, 469, 473, 481, 489, 491, 497, 503, 511, 519, 521, 529, 533, 549, 557, 569, 577, 583, 589, 597, 605, 609, 617, 619, 627, 635, 639, 647, 651, 659, 663, 671, 673, 681, 685, 693, 699, 705, 713, 715, 723, 731, 739, 743, 747, 755, 757, 769, 777, 783, 787, 791, 795, 799, 803
Targeted TEKS, 3, 5, 7, 9, 11, 13, 15, 19, 25, 27, 35, 37, 69, 77, 85, 93, 101, 115, 121, 123, 131, 139, 147, 159, 167, 169, 177, 185, 187, 195, 203, 209, 215, 219, 227, 235, 237, 245, 253, 257, 259, 267, 275, 283, 291, 299, 305, 309, 317, 321, 329, 333, 335, 343, 345, 353, 359, 367, 375, 379, 387, 391, 399, 403, 405, 413, 419, 427, 433, 441, 449, 457, 461, 469, 473, 481, 489, 491, 497, 503, 511, 519, 521, 529, 533, 549, 557, 565, 569, 583, 589, 597, 605, 609, 617, 619, 627, 635, 639, 647, 651, 659, 663, 671, 673, 681, 685, 693, 699, 705, 713, 715, 723, 731, 739, 743, 747, 755, 757, 769, 777, 783, 787, 791, 795, 799, 803, 813, 815, 817, 819, 821

Theoretical probability, 379–386

Tips, 268–269

Total purchase amount, calculating, 788

Trapezoid, formula for area of, 628

Tree diagrams, 365, 395

Trials, 380

Triangles
acute, 610
angles in, 605–608, 611
classification of, 610–611
congruent, 629
defined, 610
equilateral, 610
formula for area of, 628
isosceles, 610
obtuse, 610
right, 610
scalene, 610
similar, 317–320
sum of angles in, 609–616

Triangular prisms, 639
lateral surface area of, 675–676
nets of, 671–672
surface area of, 674
volume of, 641

Triangular pyramid, 687
lateral and total surface area of, 687–688

Two-step equations, 534
determining solutions of, 504
modeling, using the distributive property, 545–548
modeling and solving, 529–532
solving, using the Distributive Property, 549–556
solving and writing, 533–540

Two-step inequalities
determining solutions for, 505–506
modeling and solving, 565–568
solving and writing, 569–576

Uu

Unbiased samples, 731–738

Unit fractions, 32

Unit rates, 123–130, 189
calculating, 124, 133–134
converting, 139–146
converting between measurement systems using, 178–184
defined, 124
rate of change and, 185–186
using, 171–174

Unlike fractions
addition of, 77–84
subtraction of, 77–84

Use a graph, 189

Use a table, 188

Vv

Variable expenses, 792

Variables, 503
defined, 450

Venn diagrams, 36, 64

Vertex, 589

Vertical angles, 590

Virtual Manipulative Lab
Simulate Simple Events, 403–404

Visual overlap, 767
of data distributions, 767–768

Vocabulary, 20, 27, 69, 77, 116, 123, 131, 139, 147, 159, 169, 187, 195, 210, 237, 245, 259, 267, 275, 283, 300, 309, 321, 345, 360, 379, 391, 405, 419, 434, 441, 449, 461, 473, 498, 503, 511, 533, 557, 569, 584, 589, 597, 609, 619, 627, 639, 651, 663, 685, 700, 705, 715, 723, 731, 757, 784, 787, 791, 795, 799, 803

See also Launch the Lesson; Review Vocabulary; Vocabulary Check

Vocabulary Check, 25, 64, 111, 158, 256, 332, 355, 402, 429, 460, 493, 544, 579, 638, 695, 746, 779, 807

Volume
- of prisms, 639–646
- rectangular, 640
- triangular, 641
- of pyramids, 651–658
- surface area and, 681–684

Voluntary response sample, 732

Ww

Wages, 788

What Tools Do You Need?, 20, 116, 210, 300, 360, 434, 498, 584, 700, 784

When Will You Use This?, 21, 117, 211, 301, 361, 435, 499, 585, 701, 785

Which One Doesn't Belong?, 508

Work Backward, 541

Work with a partner, 415, 418, 434, 471, 520, 531, 547, 548, 567, 568, 608, 618, 683, 684, 741, 742, 756, 758

Writing an inequality for each sentence, 561

Writing Math
- describe data, 700

Xx

***x*-coordinate,** 159

Yy

***y*-coordinate,** 159

***y*-intercept,** 473

Name ______________________________

Name ______________________________

Name ____________________

0 1 2 3 4 5 6 7 8 9

−11 −10 −9 −8 −7 −6 −5 −4 −3 −2 −1 0 1 2 3 4 5 6 7 8 9 10 11

Name ______________________________

Modeling the Math

Vhat are VKVs® and
low Do I Create Them?

ual Kinethestic Vocabulary Cards® are flashcards that animate words by focusing on ir structure, use, and meaning. The VKVs in this book are used to show cognates, or rds that are similar in Spanish and English.

p 1

:o the back of your book to find the s for the chapter vocabulary you are ently studying. Follow the cutting folding instructions at the top of oage. The vocabulary word on the E background is written in English. Spanish word is on the ORANGE :ground.

2

e are exercises for you to complete on the VKVs. When you understand the concept, you :omplete each exercise. All exercises are written in English and Spanish. You only need ve the answer once.

3

idualize your VKV by writing notes, sketching diagrams, recording examples, and ng plurals (radius: radii or radiuses).

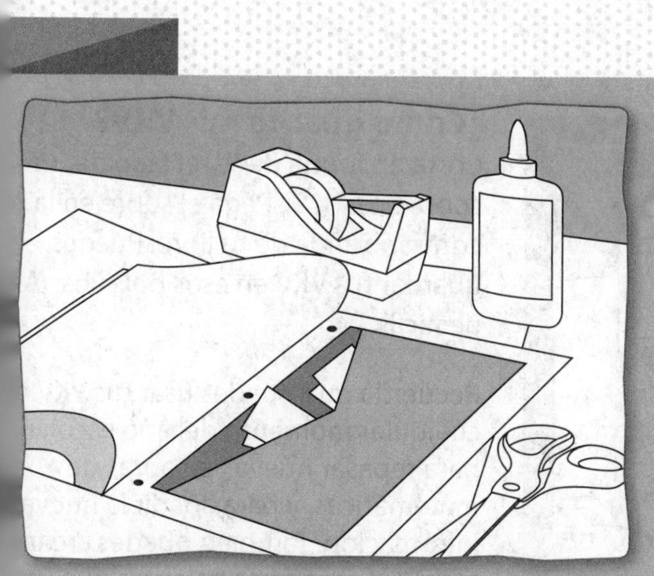

How Do I Store My VKVs?

Take a 6" x 9" envelope and cut away a V on one side only. Glue the envelope into the back cover of your book. Your VKVs can be stored in this pocket!

Remember you can use your VKVs ANY time in the school year to review new words in math, and add new information you learn. Why not create your own VKVs for other words you see and share them with others!

¿Qué son las VKV y cómo se crean?

Las tarjetas de vocabulario visual y cinético (VKV) contienen palabras con animación que está basada en la estructura, uso y significado de las palabras. Las tarjetas de este libro sirven para mostrar cognados, que son palabras similares en español y en inglés.

Paso 1

Busca al final del libro las VKV que tienen el vocabulario del capítulo que estás estudiando. Sigue las instrucciones de cortar y doblar que se muestran al principio. La palabra de vocabulario con fondo AZUL está en inglés. La de español tiene fondo NARANJA.

Paso 2

Hay ejercicios para que completes con las VKV. Cuando entiendas el concepto, puedes completar cada ejercicio. Todos los ejercicios están escritos en inglés y español. Solo tienes que dar la respuesta una vez.

Paso 3

Da tu toque personal a las VKV escribiendo notas, haciendo diagramas, grabando ejemplos y formando plurales (radio: radios).

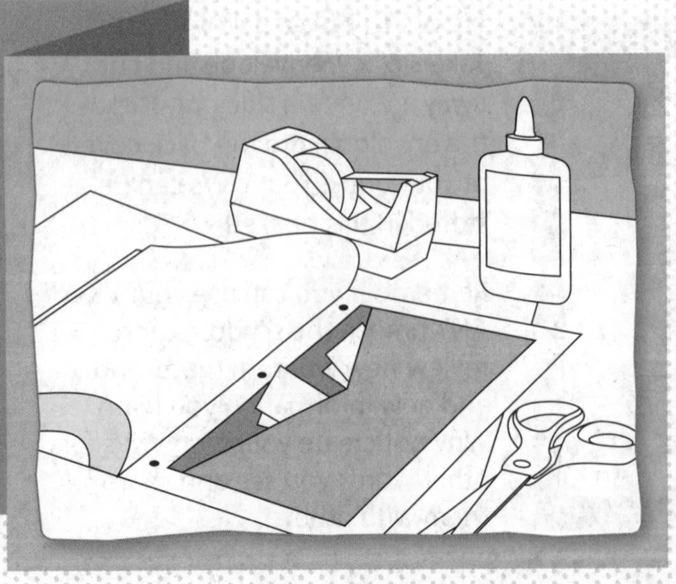

¿Cómo guardo mis VKV?

Corta en forma de "V" el lado de un sobre de 6" X 9". Pega el sobre en la contraportada de tu libro. Puedes guardar tus VKV en esos bolsillos. ¡As de fácil!

Recuerda que puedes usar tus VKV e cualquier momento del año escolar para repasar nuevas palabras de matemáticas, y para añadir la nueva información. También puedes crear más VKV para otras palabras que ve poder compartirlas con los demás.

cut on all dashed lines

fold on all solid lines

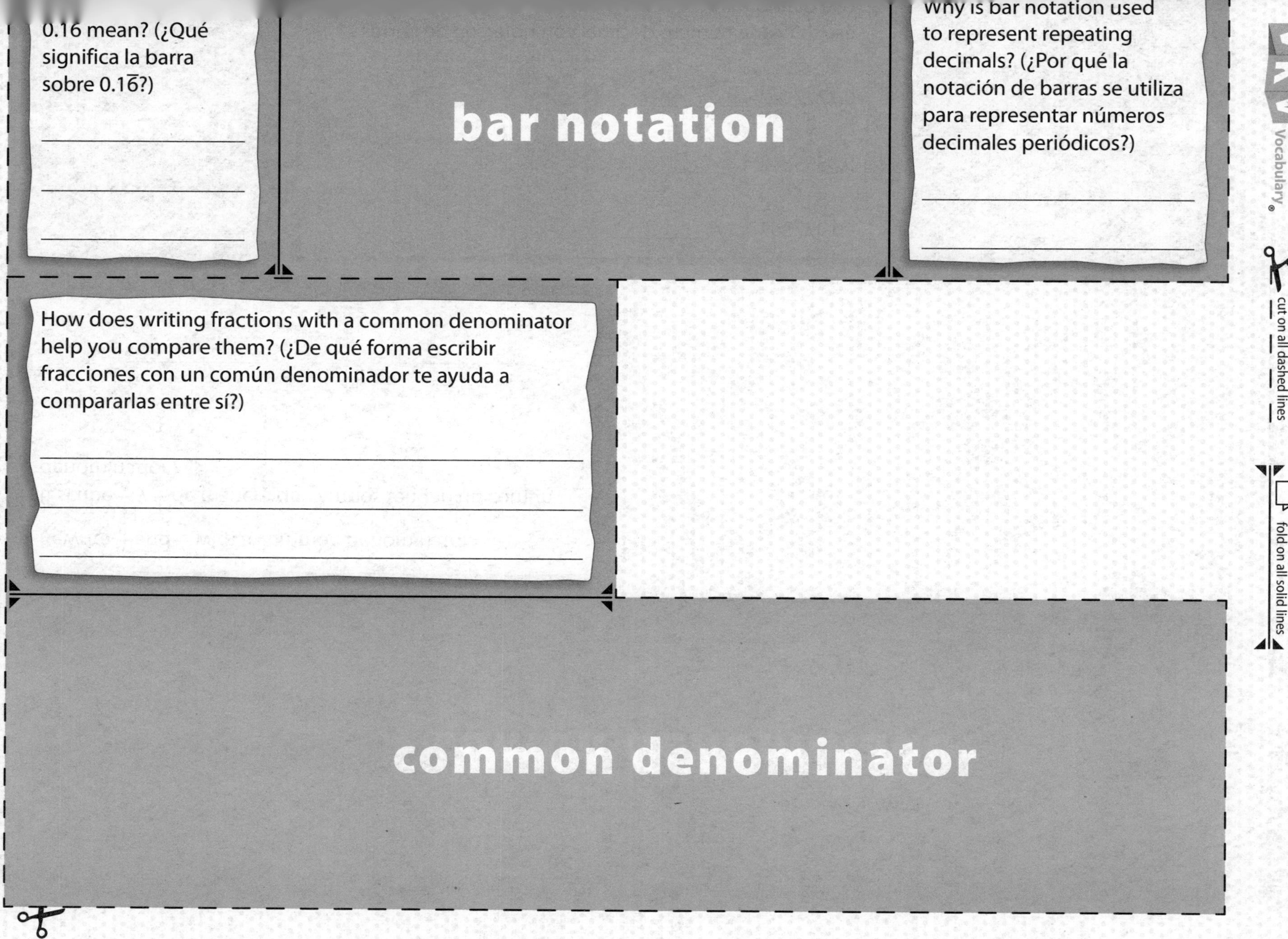

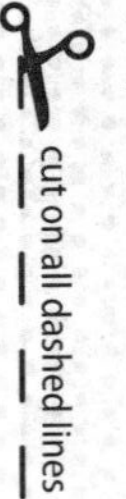

fold on all solid lines

común denominador

Rewrite $\frac{1}{8}$ and $\frac{1}{5}$ with a common denominator.

(Escribe $\frac{1}{8}$ y $\frac{1}{5}$ de manera que ambos tengan un común denominador.)

$\frac{1}{8}$ = ______ $\frac{1}{5}$ = ______

notación de barra

escribir cada número decimal con notación de barras.)

0.7777 . . . = ______

9.3555 . . . = ______

−0.337337 . . . = ______

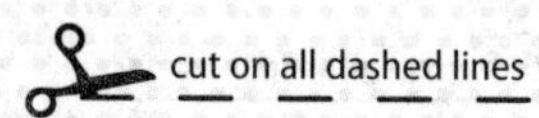
cut on all dashed lines

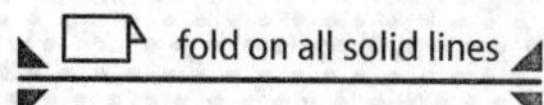
fold on all solid lines

rational number

Define rational number. (Define número racional.)

cut on all dashed lines

fold on all solid lines

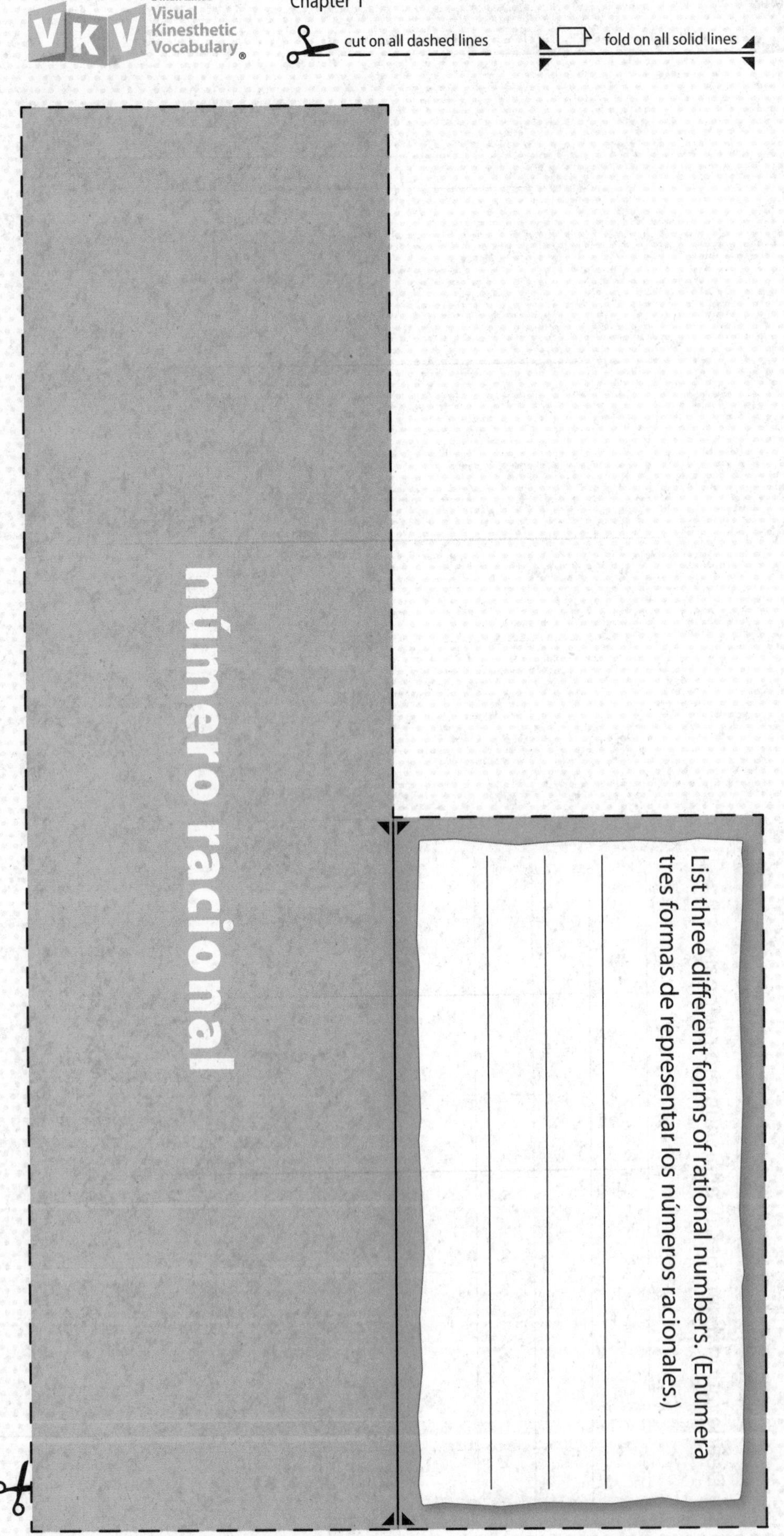

cut on all dashed lines

fold on all solid lines

Solve the proportion. (Resuelve una proporción.)

$\frac{6}{x} = \frac{5}{8}$

proportion

proporción

proportion is an equation stating that (en matemáticas, una proporción es una ecuación que indica que) ________.

direct

variación

Does the graph show a direct variation? Explain. (¿El gráfico muestra una variación directa? Explique.)

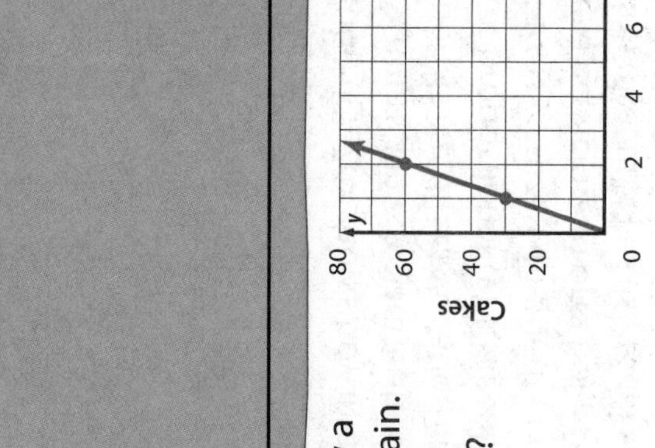

cut on all dashed lines

fold on all solid lines

al

al

Circle the relationships ... en un círculo las relaciones no proporcionales.)

A

x	y
2	4
5	7
7	9

B

x	y
1	6
3	18
5	30

C

x	y
0	3
1	6
2	9

D

x	y
2	4
5	10
8	16

non

no

directa

The equation $y = 70x$ shows how many cars y cross a bridge in x hours. On a separate sheet of paper, graph the equation. Is it a direct variation? If so, what is the constant of proportionality? (La ecuación $y = 70x$ expresa cuántos carros y cruzan un puenta en x horas. Has una gráfica de la ecuación en orta hoja. ¿Es una ecuación de variación directa? Si es así, ¿cuál es la constante de proporcionalidad?)

variation

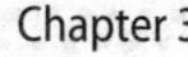

Chapter 3

ecuación

$\frac{\text{part}}{} = \frac{}{100}$

percent proportion

cut on all dashed lines

fold on all solid lines

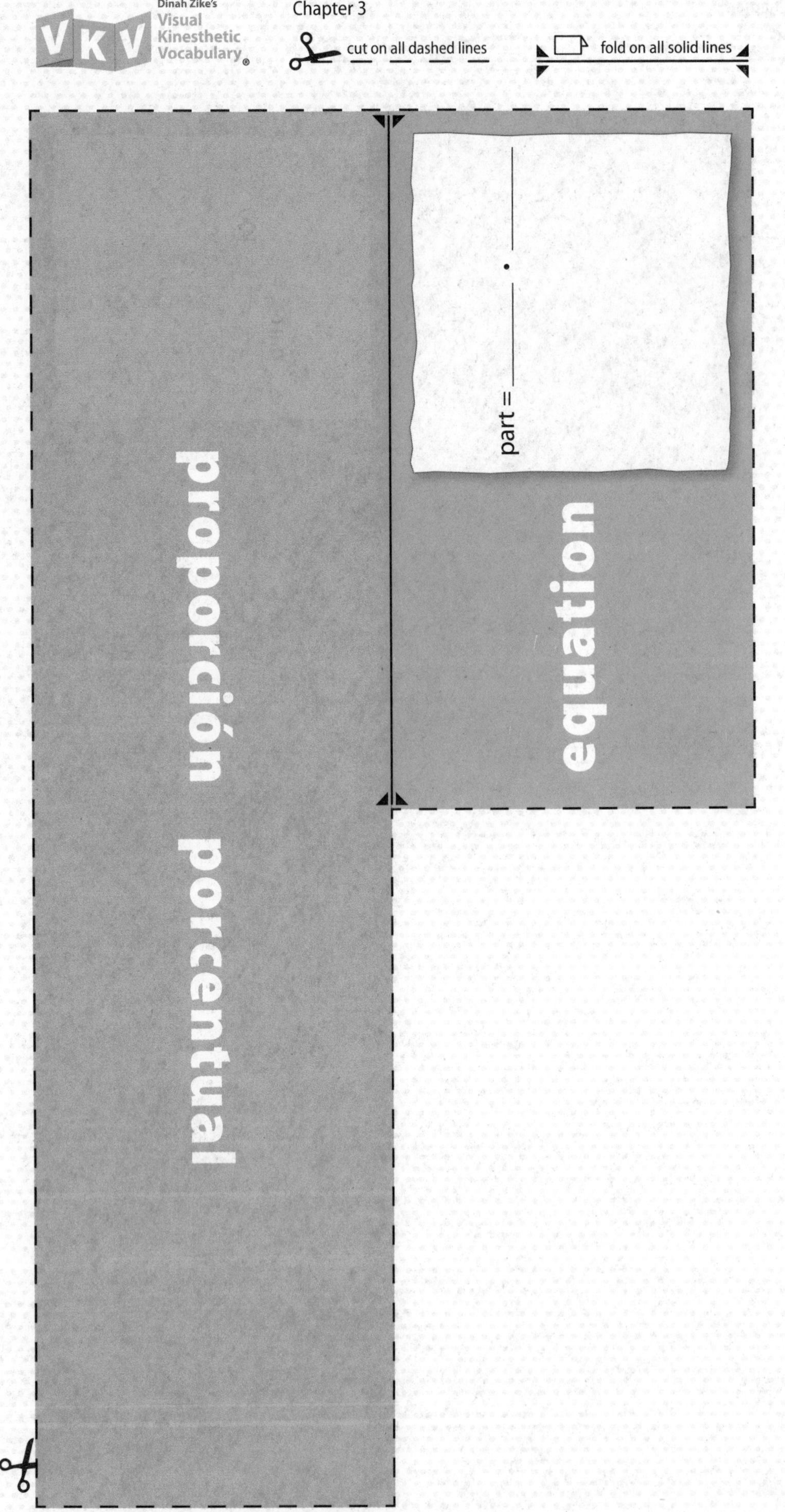

cut on all dashed lines

fold on all solid lines

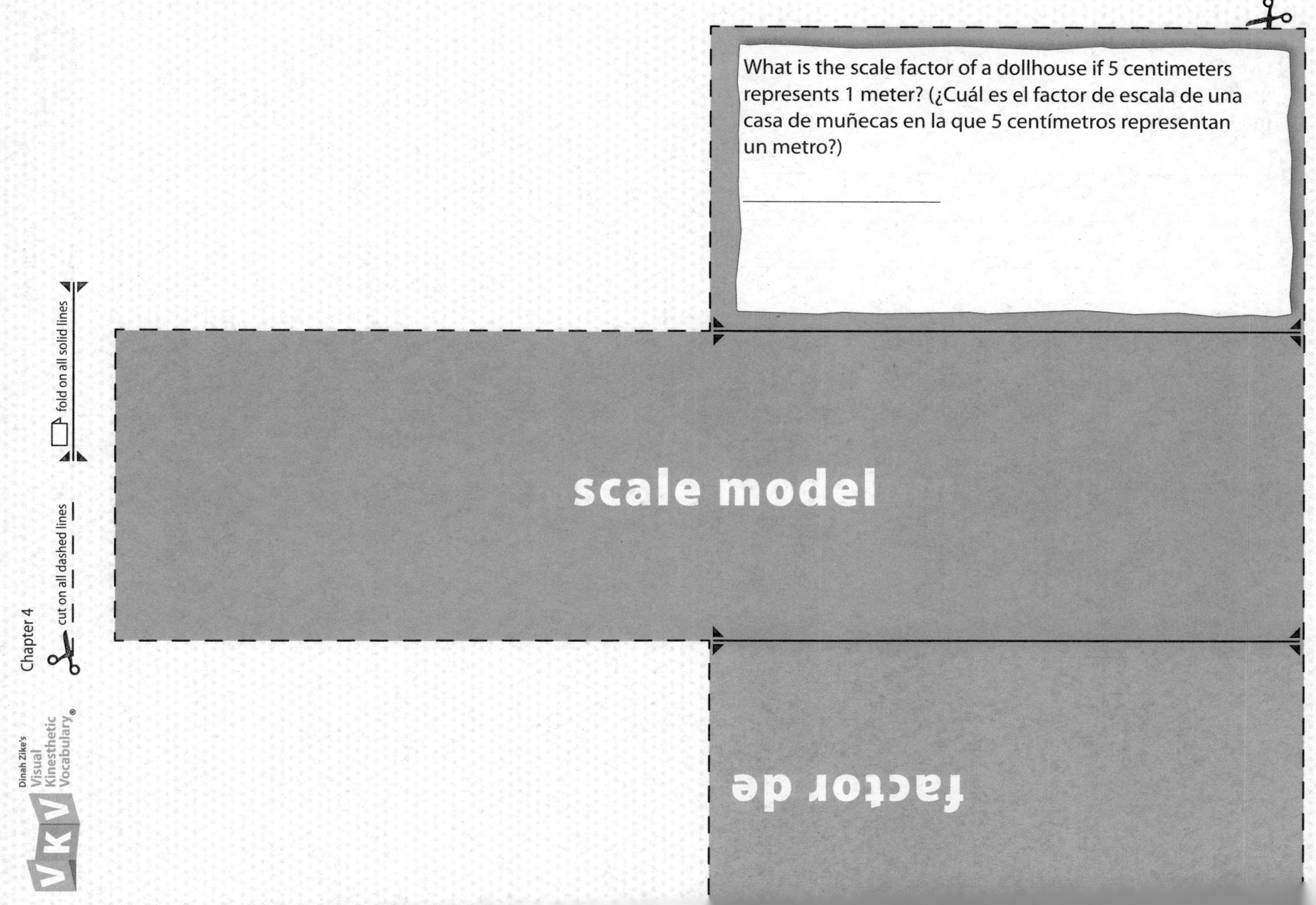

cut on all dashed lines

fold on all solid lines

List three examples where you might find scale models used. (Menciona tres situaciones en las que se utilizan modelos a escala.)

modelo a escala

factor

cut on all dashed lines

fold on all solid lines

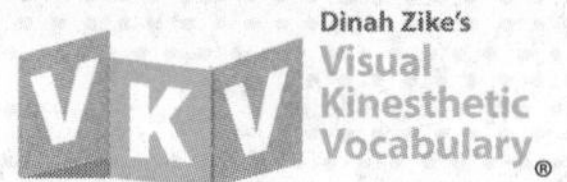

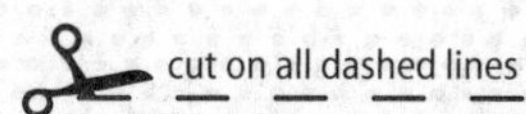

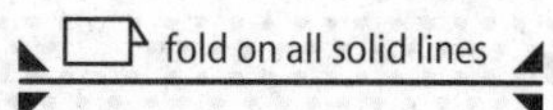

center

nferencia

circle

Define center. (Define centro.)

Define circle. (Define círculo.)

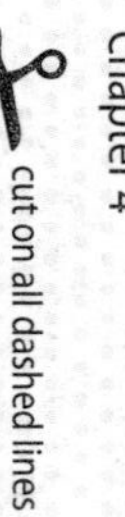

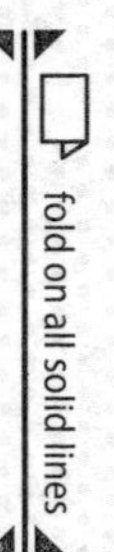

Determine the circumference.
(Halla la circunferencia.)

15 m

circumference

írculo

ro

Use *center* to describe the radius and diameter of a circle. (Utiliza la palabra *centro* para describir el radio y el diámetro de un círculo.)

diameter

A circle's diameter is ______________ the length of the circle's radius. (El diámetro de un círculo es el ______________ de la longitud del radio del círculo.)

radius

If you know the length of a circle's radius, what three other measurements can you find? (¿Cuáles tres medidas puedes calcular con la longitud del radio de un círculo?)

____

____

____

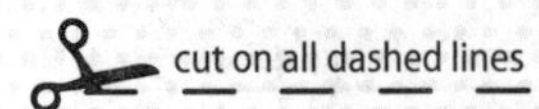

fold on all solid lines

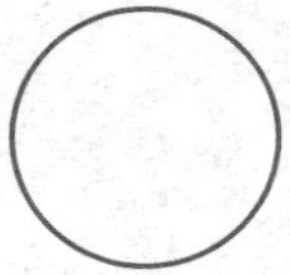

o

ámetro

Draw a radius of the circle. (Dibuja el radio del círculo.)

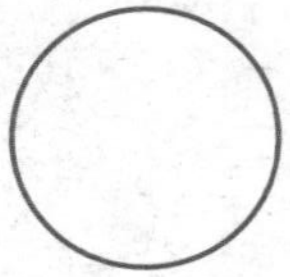

cut on all dashed lines

fold on all solid lines

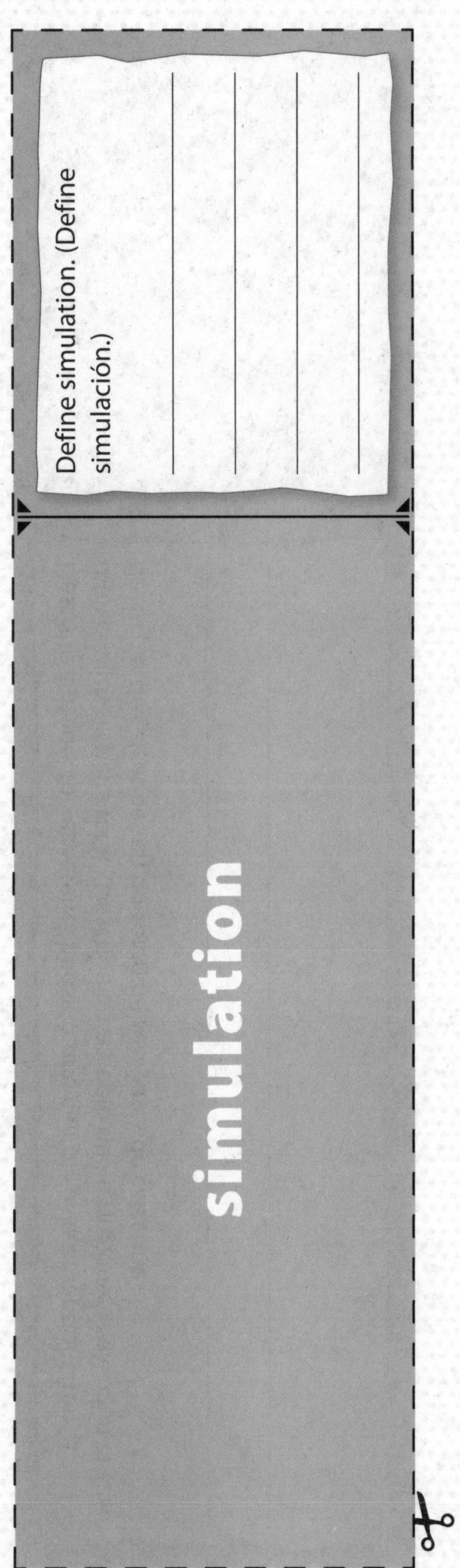
Define simulation. (Define simulación.)
simulation

VKV
Dinah Zike's
Visual
Kinesthetic
Vocabulary®

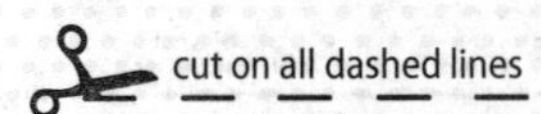
cut on all dashed lines

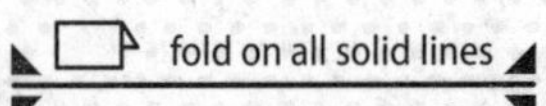
fold on all solid lines

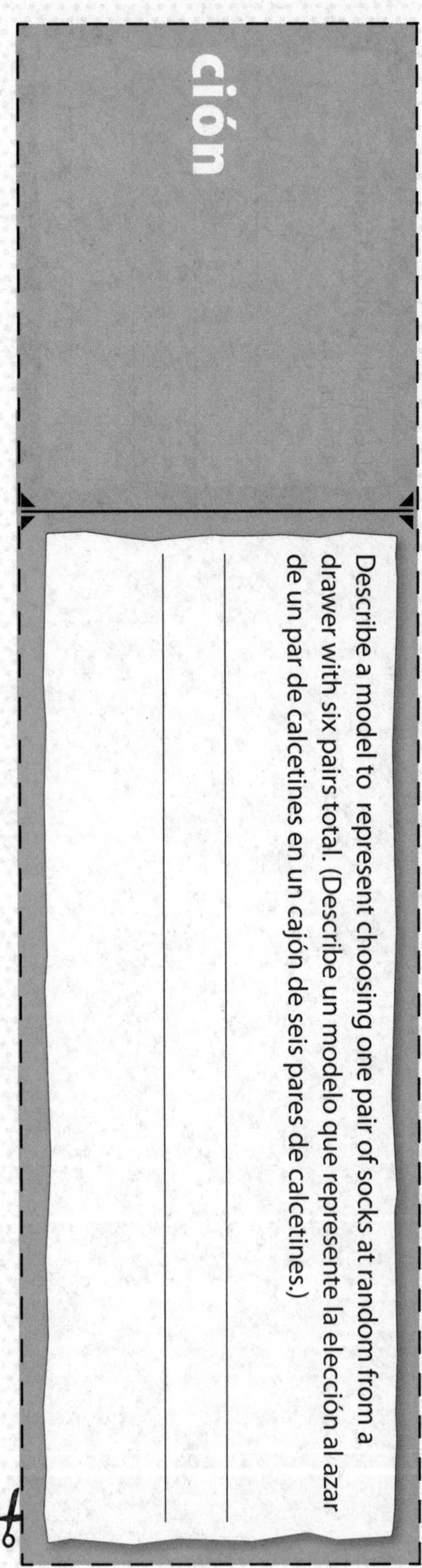
ción
Describe a model to represent choosing one pair of socks at random from a drawer with six pairs total. (Describe un modelo que represente la elección al azar de un par de calcetines en un cajón de seis pares de calcetines.)

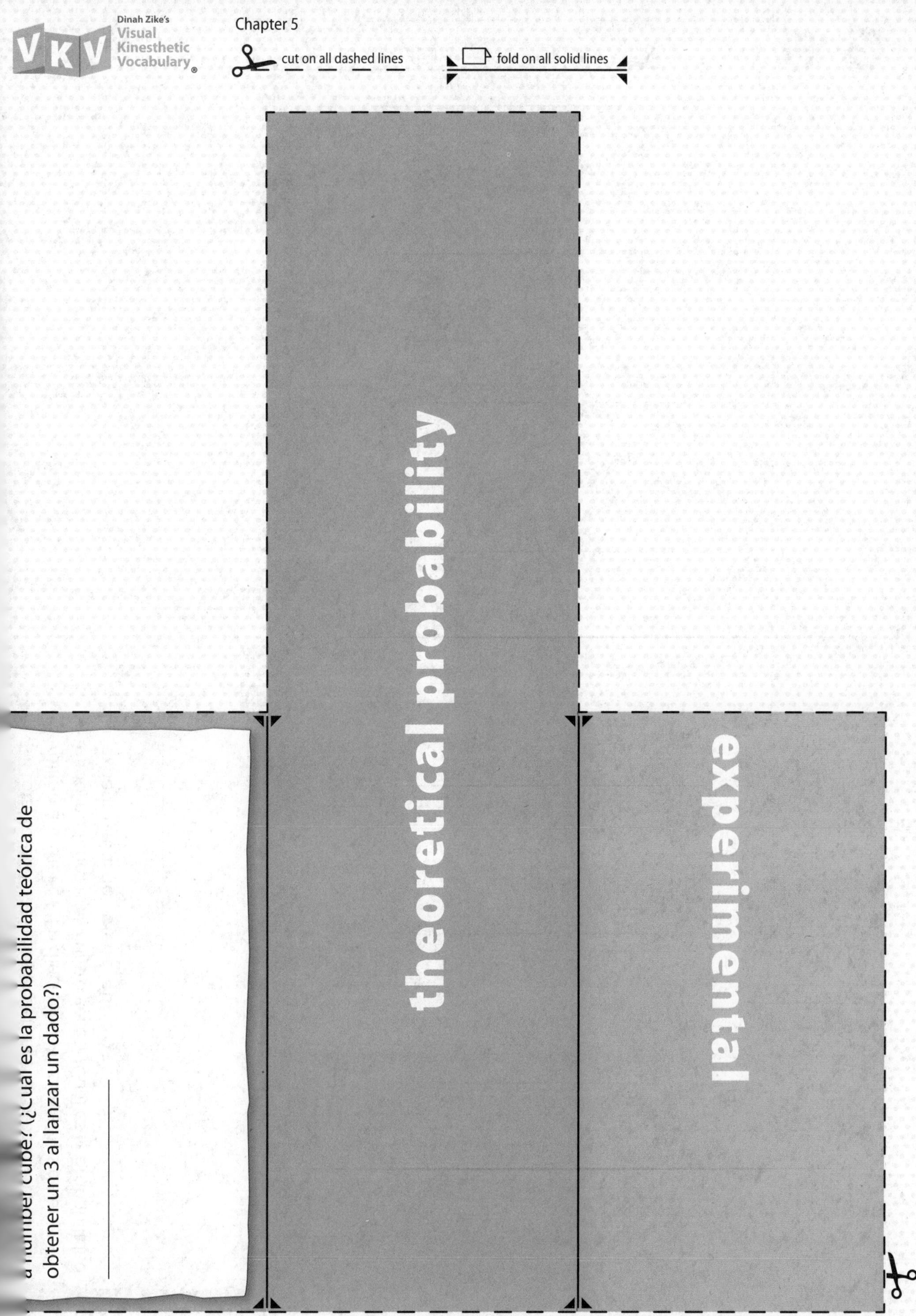
cut on all dashed lines
fold on all solid lines
theoretical probability
experimental
es la probabilidad teórica de
obtener un 3 al lanzar un dado?)

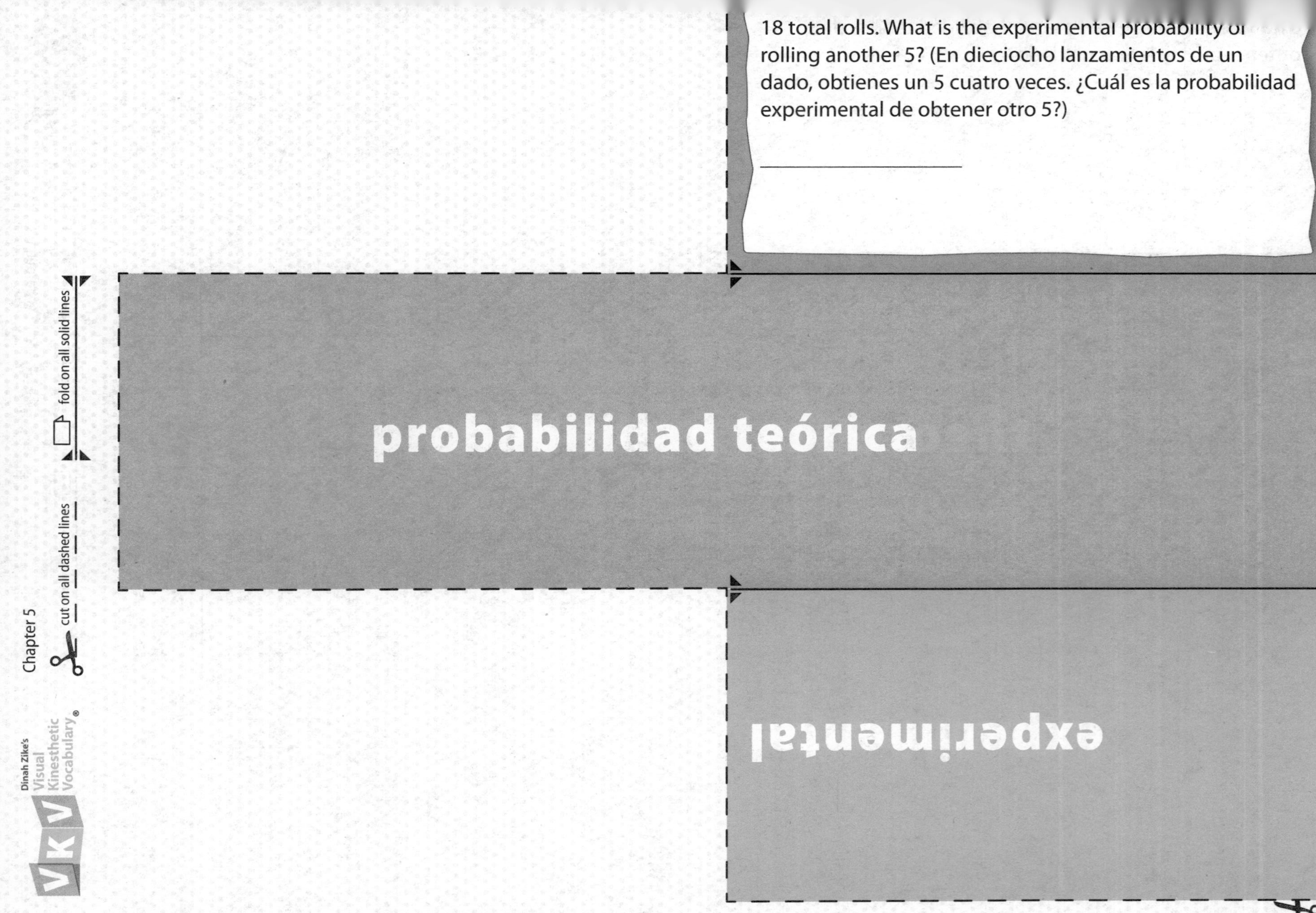
cut on all dashed lines
fold on all solid lines
18 total rolls. What is the experimental probability of
rolling another 5? (En dieciocho lanzamientos de un
dado, obtienes un 5 cuatro veces. ¿Cuál es la probabilidad
experimental de obtener otro 5?)
probabilidad teórica
experimental

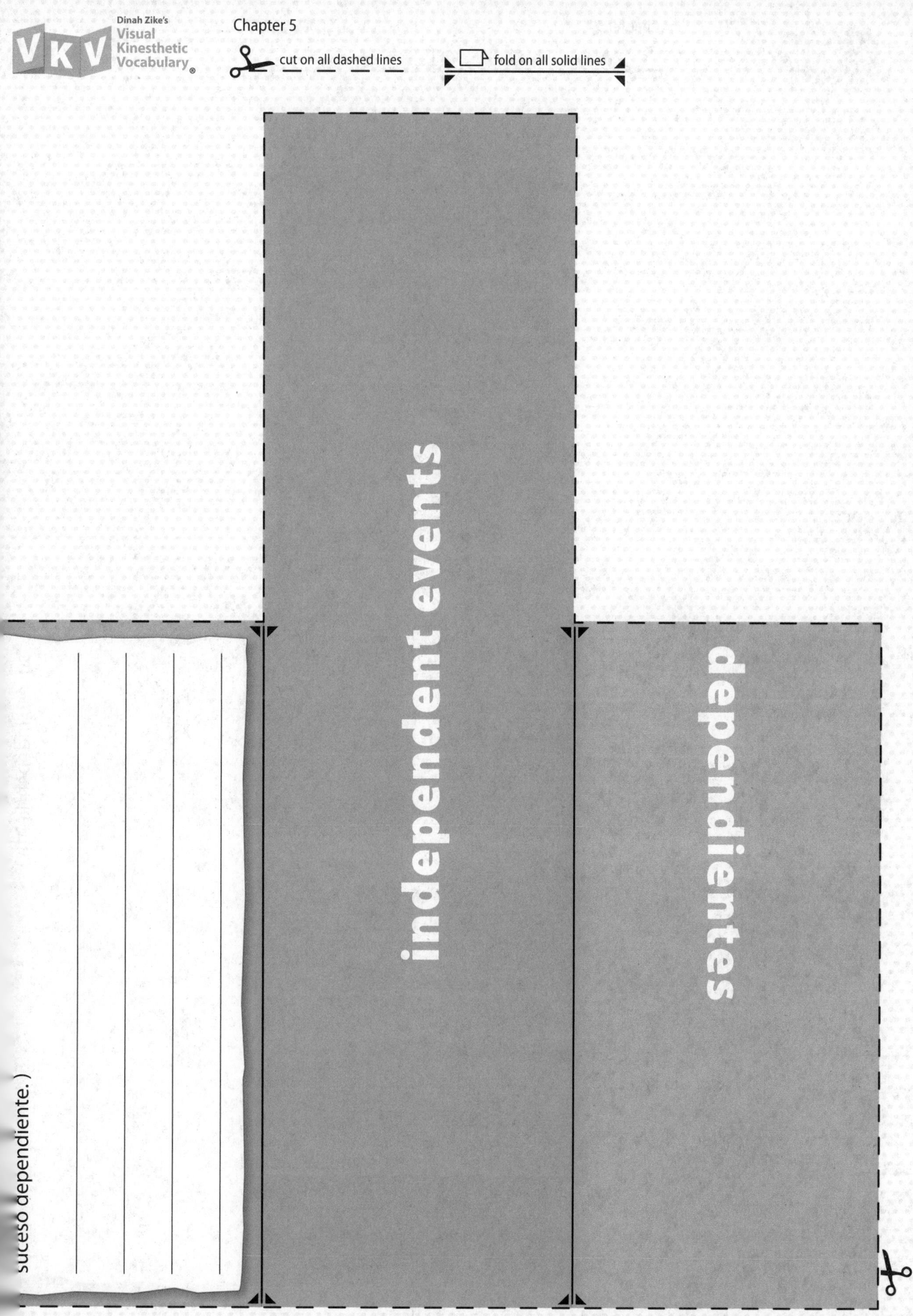
cut on all dashed lines
fold on all solid lines
independent events
dependientes
suceso dependiente.)

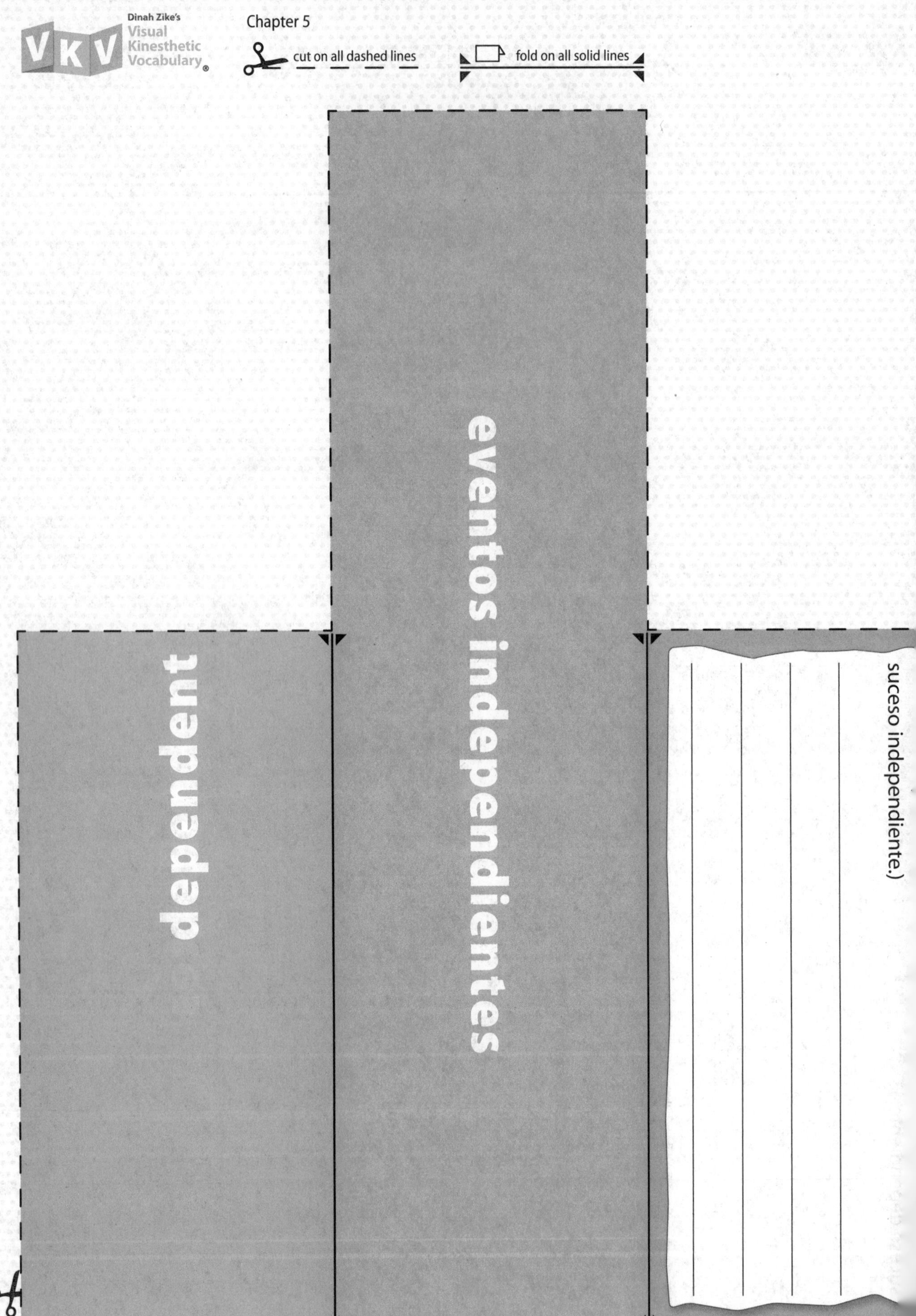
Dinah Zike's
Visual
Kinesthetic
Vocabulary®
VKV
Chapter 5
cut on all dashed lines
fold on all solid lines
eventos independientes
dependent
suceso independiente.)

Grade 7 Mathematics Reference Materials

LENGTH					
	Customary			Metric	
1 mile (mi)	=	1,760 yards (yd)	1 kilometer (km)	=	1,000 meters (m)
1 yard (yd)	=	3 feet (ft)	1 meter (m)	=	100 centimeters (cm)
1 foot (ft)	=	12 inches (in.)	1 centimeter (cm)	=	10 millimeters (mm)

VOLUME AND CAPACITY					
	Customary			Metric	
gallon (gal)	=	4 quarts (qt)	1 liter (L)	=	1,000 milliliters (mL)
quart (qt)	=	2 pints (pt)			
pint (pt)	=	2 cups (c)			
cup (c)	=	8 fluid ounces (fl oz)			

WEIGHT AND MASS					
	Customary			Metric	
ton (T)	=	2,000 pounds (lb)	1 kilogram (kg)	=	1,000 grams (g)
pound (lb)	=	16 ounces (oz)	1 gram (g)	=	1,000 milligrams (mg)

LINEAR EQUATIONS

Slope-intercept Form			$y = mx + b$
Constant of Proportionality			$k = \frac{y}{x}$

CIRCUMFERENCE

Circle	$C = 2\pi r$	or	$C = \pi d$

AREA

Triangle			$A = \frac{1}{2}bh$
Rectangle or Parallelogram			$A = bh$
Trapezoid			$A = \frac{1}{2}(b_1 + b_2)h$
Circle			$A = \pi r^2$

VOLUME

Prism			$V = Bh$
Pyramid			$V = \frac{1}{3}Bh$

ADDITIONAL INFORMATION

Pi	$\pi \approx 3.14$	or	$\pi \approx \frac{22}{7}$
Distance			$d = rt$
Simple Interest			$I = Prt$
Compound Interest			$A = P(1 + r)^t$